NONLINEAR PHYSICAL SCIENCE

NONLINEAR PHYSICAL SCIENCE

Nonlinear Physical Science focuses on recent advances of fundamental theories and principles, analytical and symbolic approaches, as well as computational techniques in nonlinear physical science and nonlinear mathematics with engineering applications.

Topics of interest in *Nonlinear Physical Science* include but are not limited to:

- New findings and discoveries in nonlinear physics and mathematics
- Nonlinearity, complexity and mathematical structures in nonlinear physics
- Nonlinear phenomena and observations in nature and engineering
- Computational methods and theories in complex systems
- Lie group analysis, new theories and principles in mathematical modeling
- Stability, bifurcation, chaos and fractals in physical science and engineering
- Nonlinear chemical and biological physics
- Discontinuity, synchronization and natural complexity in the physical sciences

SERIES EDITORS

INTERNATIONAL ADVISORY BOARD

S.N. Gurbatov
O.V. Rudenko
A.I. Saichev

Waves and Structures in Nonlinear Nondispersive Media

General Theory and Applications to Nonlinear Acoustics

With 181 figures

高等教育出版社
HIGHER EDUCATION PRESS

Springer

Authors

S.N. Gurbatov
Radiophysics Department
Nizhny Novgorod State University
603950 Nizhny Novgorod, Russia
Email: gurb@rf.unn.ru

O.V. Rudenko
Physics Department
Moscow State University
119991 Moscow, Russia
Email: rudenko@acs366.phys.msu.ru

A.I. Saichev
Radiophysics Department
Nizhny Novgorod State University
603950 Nizhny Novgorod, Russia
Email: saichev@hotmail.com

ISSN 1867-8440 e-ISSN 1867-8459
Nonlinear Physical Science

ISBN 978-7-04-031695-7
Higher Education Press, Beijing

ISBN 978-3-642-23616-7 e-ISBN 978-3-642-23617-4
Springer Heidelberg Dordrecht London New York

Library of Congress Control Number: 2011935427

Printed on acid-free paper

Springer is part of Springer Science+Business Media (www.springer.com)

Preface

The book is aimed at natural science undergraduates, as well as at graduate and post-graduate students studying the theory of nonlinear waves of various physical nature. It may also be useful as a handbook for engineers and researchers who encounter the necessity of taking nonlinear wave effects into account in their work.

Evolution of sufficiently intense waves is determined by nonlinear processes, in which the progress is substantially influenced by dispersion (a dependence of the phase velocity on its frequency). Media without dispersion, where the phase velocity does not depend on the frequency, are the simplest ones with respect to their physical properties and are the most common in nature. But nonlinear interactions of the Fourier spectral components in such media are particularly complex and diverse. Here, practically all "virtual" energy-exchange processes between waves of different frequencies become resonant ones and occur with a high efficiency. An avalanche-like increase of the number of spectral components of the field takes place, which, within the space-time representation, corresponds to formation of structures with strongly pronounced nonlinear properties. Examples of such structures are discontinuities of a function describing the wave field or discontinuities of its derivative, steep shock fronts of various types and multidimensional cellular structures.

Nonlinear structures can be stable only in strong fields, under the conditions of competition with effects of absorption, dispersion, etc, which contribute to the decay of such structures. These objects have properties of quasiparticles. For instance, shock fronts undergo inelastic collisions. Thus, in nondispersive media, nonlinearity provides both a possibility of interactions between stable structures and their very existence. Solitons are other well-known objects in nonlinear physics, which are, generally speaking, stable only in idealized conservative systems. At the same time, quasi stability of shock-front structures or sawtooth waves occurs in real dissipative systems.

Structures of different physical nature are described by similar mathematical models. These models are used not only in the wave theory, but also to describe various non-wave objects, *viz.*: forest-fire fronts, density of a flow of non-interacting particles, etc. Because of the universality of such nonlinear models, it is necessary to analyze them on the basis of general principles of mathematical physics, irrespective of the nature of the described phenomena.

On the other hand, nondispersive waves and structures are widely used in science and technology. A review of these applications, from the authors' viewpoint, is what "brightens up" the theory and may be of interest to many readers.

The theory of nonlinear waves and structures is a very extensive and constant developing field of physics (especially radiophysics and mathematical physics). It has many specific applications. Among them there are both the well-known problems of acoustics, electrodynamics and plasma physics (see, e.g., [1–5]), and the less-known problems, such as surface-growth description [6, 7], dynamics of turbulence [8, 9] and development of a gravitational instability of the large-scale distribution of matter in the Universe [10–14]. A wide range of phenomena arising here have led to the development of a variety of mathematical methods, which are effective in addressing various kinds of nonlinear fields and waves (see, e.g., [15–17]). It is clear that within a single monograph, it is not possible to give an exhaustively comprehensive overview of the whole problem. For this reason, the authors limited themselves to a discussion of the "hydrodynamic" type of nonlinear waves in nondispersive medium. First of all, the properties of solutions to such standard nonlinear wave equations in nondispersive media as the simple wave equation, the Burgers equation and the Kardar-Parisi-Zhang equation have been studied in detail. Apart from the importance of these equations for the theory and applications, an analysis of these solutions allows us to trace stages of development of typical nonlinear processes and, above all, nonlinear distortion of profiles, the gradient catastrophe and emergence of shock waves. In order for the theory of nonlinear waves in nondispersive media not to look too abstract, the presentation is based on illustrative geometric interpretations of both the equations themselves and their solutions, as well as on a comprehensive discussion of the physical meaning of these solutions and the methods used to obtain them.

The monograph consists of two parts. The first part is devoted to a detailed description of the concepts and analysis methods of nonlinear waves and structures in nondispersive media. The second part focuses on an in-depth description of the nonlinear theory as applied only to one type of waves — high intensity acoustic waves. This object, on the one hand, is the most straightforward and, on the other hand, has important practical applications.

The authors have attempted to communicate all materialls at the following "two levels" of complexity. The first level is intended to introduce beginning investigators (above all undergraduate, graduate and PhD students) to the concepts and methods of the theory of nonlinear waves and structures in nondispersive media. In order to achieve a deeper understanding of the foundations, it is useful to solve the problems given in the end of the chapters in Part I. The second, higher, level is meant for researchers, who already have experience in this field of study and are interested in the state of the art or in specific results. Naturally, it is impossible to reflect the entire diversity of approaches used to study nonlinear fields and waves in a single monograph. This is why the material is presented at a simple, "physical" level of rigor, where possible. Those, who are interested in a more rigorous mathematical foundation of the problems discussed here, are advised to turn to monographs [15, 17], where mathematical foundations of many topics touched upon in this book are thoroughly discussed. An in-depth review of the methods used to solve nonlinear problems, along with profound results of the nonlinear field theory, can be found in book [16]. In monograph [18], and also in textbook [19], the theory of generalized functions necessary for construction of generalized solutions of nonlinear equations is comprehensively elucidated. We recommend those who intend deeper to delve into the nonlinear field theory, without burying themselves in mathematical subtleties, the following thorough monographs and textbooks: [1, 2, 4, 5], which are written by physicists for physicists. Basic concepts of the nonlinear wave theory, along with illustrative physical examples, can be found in the remarkable textbook [14]. To those who are going professionally to engage themselves in the field of nonlinear acoustics, we recommend monograph [3] and the books of problems [20, 21], where a set of problems aiding in mastering various aspects of nonlinear acoustics is given. If one is interested in statistical properties of nonlinear random waves as applied to nonlinear acoustics, astrophysics and turbulence, he or she can pick up necessary information from monograph [10]. We also advise to turn to monograph [8], which covers the foundations of the theory of strong turbulence and its inherent phenomena, such as intermittency and multifractality.

We are grateful to the renowned scientists, fruitful interactions with whom over the years have formed our vision of the problems and methods of the nonlinear science. First of all, they are: academicians A.V. Gaponov-Grekhov, Ya.B. Zeldovich, R.V. Khokhlov, V.I. Arnold and Ya.G. Sinai; corresponding members of the Russian Academy of Sciences M.I. Rabinovich and D.I. Trubetskov; Professors A.N. Malakhov, L.A. Ostrovsky, S.A. Rybak, S.I. Soluyan, A.P. Sukhorukov, A.S. Chirkin and S.F. Shandarin. We are delighted to remember the years of collaboration with international colleagues, among whom are: D. Crighton, U. Frisch, B. Enflo, D. Blackstock, M. Hamilton, L. Cram, E. Aurell, A. Noullez, W.A. Woyczynski and many others.

We would like also to thank our translators, O. Simdyankina and S. Simdyankin, not only for the speedy production of an English translation of this book, but also for the lucid clarity of their literary representation of the original text.

Nizhny Novgorod, Moscow,
July 2011

Sergey N. Gurbatov
Oleg V. Rudenko
Alexander I. Saichev

References

1. M.J. Lighthill, *Waves in Fluids*, 2nd edn. (Cambridge University Press, 2002)
2. M.I. Rabinovich, D.I. Trubetskov, *Oscillations and Waves in Linear and Nonlinear Systems*. (Springer, Berlin, 1989)
3. O.V. Rudenko, S.I. Soluyan, *Theoretical Foundations of Nonlinear Acoustics* (Plenum, New York, 1977)

4. M.B. Vinogradova, O.V. Rudenko, A.P. Sukhorukov, *Theory of Waves* (Nauka, Moscow, 1979). In Russian
5. G.B. Whitham, *Linear and Nonlinear Waves* (Wiley, New York, 1974)
6. A.L. Barabási, H.E. Stanley, *Fractal Concepts in Surface Growth* (Cambridge University Press, 1995)
7. M. Kardar, G. Parisi, Y.C. Zhang, Dynamical scaling of growing interfaces, Phys. Rev. Lett. **56**, 889–892 (1986)
8. U. Frisch, *Turbulence: The Legacy of A.N. Kolmogorov* (Cambridge University Press, 1995)
9. A.S. Monin, A.M. Yaglom, *Statistical Fluid Mechanics*, vol. 2 (MIT Press, Cambridge, Mass, 1975)
10. S.N. Gurbatov, A.N. Malakhov, A.I. Saichev, *Nonlinear Random Waves and Turbulence in Nondispersive Media: Waves, Rays and Particles.* (Manchester University Press, 1991)
11. P.J.E. Peebles, *Large-Scale Structure of the Universe* (Princeton University Press, 1980)
12. S.F. Shandarin, Y.B. Zeldovich, The large-scale structure of the universe: turbulence, intermittency, structures in a self-gravitating medium, Rev. Mod. Phys. **61**, 185–220 (1989)
13. S. Weinberg, *Gravitation and Cosmology* (Wiley, New York, 1972)
14. Y.B. Zeldovich, *Elements of Mathematical Physics* (Nauka, Moscow, 1973). In Russian
15. V.I. Arnold, *Ordinary Differential Equations* (MIT Press, Cambridge, Mass, 1978)
16. R. Richtmyer, *Principles of Advanced Mathematical Physics*, vol. 1 (Springer, Berlin, 1978)
17. B.L. Rozhdestvenskii, N.N. Yanenko, *Systems of Quasilinear Equations* (Nauka, Moscow, 1978). In Russian
18. A.I. Saichev, W.A. Woyczyński, *Distributions in the Physical and Engineering Sciences* (Birkhäuser, Boston, 1997)
19. S.A. Lapinova, A.I. Saichev, V.A. Filimonov, *Generalized Functions and Asymptotic Methods* (Nizhny Novgorod University Press, 2006). In Russian
20. S.N. Gurbatov, O.V. Rudenko (eds.), *Acoustics in Problems* (Fizmatlit, Moscow, 2009). In Russian
21. O.V. Rudenko, S.N. Gurbatov, C.M. Hedberg, *Nonlinear Acoustics through Problems and Examples* (Trafford, 2010)

Contents

Part I Foundations of the Theory of Waves in Nondispersive Media 1

1 Nonlinear Equations of the First Order ... 3
1.1 Simple wave equation ... 3
1.1.1 The canonical form of the equation ... 3
1.1.2 Particle flow ... 4
1.1.3 Discussion of the Riemann solution ... 5
1.1.4 Compressions and expansions of the particle flow ... 6
1.1.5 Continuity equation ... 8
1.1.6 Construction of the density field ... 9
1.1.7 Momentum-conservation law ... 10
1.1.8 Fourier transforms of density and velocity ... 11
1.2 Line-growth equation ... 13
1.2.1 Forest-fire propagation ... 13
1.2.2 Anisotropic surface growth ... 16
1.2.3 Solution of the surface-growth equation ... 18
1.3 One-dimensional laws of gravitation ... 20
1.3.1 Lagrangian description of one-dimensional gravitation ... 20
1.3.2 Eulerian description of one-dimensional gravitation ... 22
1.3.3 Collapse of a one-dimensional Universe ... 24
1.4 Problems to Chapter 1 ... 25
References ... 36

2 Generalized Solutions of Nonlinear Equations ... 39
2.1 Standard equations ... 39
2.1.1 Particle-flow equations ... 40
2.1.2 Line growth in the small angle approximation ... 40
2.1.3 Nonlinear acoustics equation ... 41
2.2 Multistream solutions ... 42
2.2.1 Interval of single-stream motion ... 42

2.2.2 Appearance of multistreamness 42
2.2.3 Gradient catastrophe 44
2.3 Sum of streams 46
2.3.1 Total particle flow 46
2.3.2 Summation of streams by inverse Fourier transform 47
2.3.3 Algebraic sum of the velocity field 47
2.3.4 Density of a "warm" particle flow 48
2.4 Weak solutions of nonlinear equations of the first order 50
2.4.1 Forest fire 50
2.4.2 The Lax-Oleinik absolute minimum principle 52
2.4.3 Geometric construction of weak solutions 53
2.4.4 Convex hull 54
2.4.5 Maxwell's rule 56
2.5 The E-Rykov-Sinai global principle 59
2.5.1 Flow of inelastically coalescing particles 59
2.5.2 Inelastic collisions of particles 60
2.5.3 Formulation of the global principle 61
2.5.4 Mechanical meaning of the global principle 62
2.5.5 Condition of physical realizability 63
2.5.6 Geometry of the global principle 66
2.5.7 Solutions of the continuity equation 69
2.6 Line-growth geometry 70
2.6.1 Parametric equations of a line 71
2.6.2 Contour in polar coordinates 72
2.6.3 Contour envelopes 74
2.7 Problems to Chapter 2 77
References 82

3 Nonlinear Equations of the Second Order 83
3.1 Regularization of nonlinear equations 83
3.1.1 The Kardar-Parisi-Zhang equation 84
3.1.2 The Burgers equation 85
3.2 Properties of the Burgers equation 86
3.2.1 Galilean invariance 86
3.2.2 Reynolds number 87
3.2.3 Hubble expansion 89
3.2.4 Stationary wave 92
3.2.5 Khokhlov's solution 93
3.2.6 Rudenko's solution 95
3.3 General solution of the Burgers equation 100
3.3.1 The Hopf-Cole substitution 101
3.3.2 General solution of the Burgers equation 102
3.3.3 Averaged Lagrangian coordinate 103
3.3.4 Solution of the Burgers equation with vanishing viscosity 104

3.4 Model equations of gas dynamics . . . 105
3.4.1 One-dimensional model of a polytropic gas . . . 105
3.4.2 Discussion of physical properties of a model gas . . . 108
3.5 Problems to Chapter 3 . . . 111
References . . . 115

4 Field Evolution Within the Framework of the Burgers Equation . . . 117
4.1 Evolution of one-dimensional signals . . . 117
4.1.1 Self-similar solution, once more . . . 117
4.1.2 Approach to the linear stage . . . 119
4.1.3 N-wave and U-wave . . . 120
4.1.4 Sawtooth waves . . . 123
4.1.5 Periodic waves . . . 128
4.2 Evolution of complex signals . . . 131
4.2.1 Quasiperiodic complex signals . . . 132
4.2.2 Evolution of fractal signals . . . 133
4.2.3 Evolution of multi-scale signals — a dynamic turbulence model . . . 135
4.3 Problems to Chapter 4 . . . 147
References . . . 152

5 Evolution of a Noise Field Within the Framework of the Burgers Equation . . . 153
5.1 Burgers turbulence — acoustic turbulence . . . 153
5.2 The Burgers turbulence at the initial stage of evolution . . . 155
5.2.1 One-point probability density of a random Eulerian velocity field . . . 157
5.2.2 Properties of the probability density of a random velocity field . . . 159
5.2.3 Spectra of a velocity field . . . 162
5.3 Turbulence evolution at the stage of developed discontinuities . . . 166
5.3.1 Phenomenology of the Burgers turbulence . . . 167
5.3.2 Evolution of the Burgers turbulence: statistically homogeneous potential and velocity ($n > 1$ and $n < -3$) . . . 171
5.3.3 Exact self-similarity ($n > 2$) . . . 173
5.3.4 Violation of self-similarity ($1 < n < 2$) . . . 176
5.3.5 Evolution of turbulence: statistically inhomogeneous potential ($-3 < n < 1$) . . . 178
5.3.6 Statistically homogeneous velocity and inhomogeneous potential ($-1 < n < 1$) . . . 179
5.3.7 Statistically inhomogeneous velocity and inhomogeneous potential ($-3 < n < -1$) . . . 181
5.3.8 Evolution of intense acoustic noise . . . 182
References . . . 185

6 Multidimensional Nonlinear Equations . . . 189
6.1 Nonlinear equations of the first order . . . 189
6.1.1 Main equations of three-dimensional flows . . . 189
6.1.2 Lagrangian and Eulerian description of a three-dimentional flow . . . 191
6.1.3 Jacobian matrix for the transformation from Lagrangian to Eulerian coordinates . . . 192
6.1.4 Density of a multidimensional flow . . . 193
6.1.5 Weak solution of the surface-growth equation . . . 194
6.1.6 Flows of locally interacting particles and a singular density field . . . 197
6.2 Multidimensional nonlinear equations of the second order . . . 201
6.2.1 The two-dimensional KPZ equation . . . 201
6.2.2 The three-dimensional Burgers equation . . . 202
6.2.3 Model density field . . . 203
6.2.4 Concentration field . . . 204
6.3 Evolution of the main perturbation types in the KPZ equation and in the multidimensional Burgers equation . . . 207
6.3.1 Asymptotic solutions of the multidimensional Burgers equation and local self-similarity . . . 208
6.3.2 Evolution of simple localized perturbations . . . 212
6.3.3 Evolution of periodic structures under infinite Reynolds numbers . . . 214
6.3.4 Evolution of the anisotropic Burgers turbulence . . . 219
6.3.5 Evolution of perturbations with complex internal structure . . . 225
6.3.6 Asymptotic long-time behavior of a localized perturbation . . . 231
6.3.7 Appendix to Section 6.3. Statistical properties of maxima of inhomogeneous random Gaussian fields . . . 233
6.4 Model description of evolution of the large-scale structure of the Universe . . . 236
6.4.1 Gravitational instability in an expanding Universe . . . 236
6.4.2 From the Vlasov-Poisson equation to the Zeldovich approximation and adhesion model . . . 238
References . . . 243

Part II Mathematical Models and Physical Phenomena in Nonlinear Acoustics . . . 245

7 Model Equations and Methods of Finding Their Exact Solutions . . . 247
7.1 Introduction . . . 247
7.1.1 Facts from the linear theory . . . 247
7.1.2 How to add nonlinear terms to simplified equations . . . 253
7.1.3 More general evolution equations . . . 255

7.1.4 Two types of evolution equations 256
7.2 Lie groups and some exact solutions 257
7.2.1 Exact solutions of the Burgers equation 257
7.2.2 Finding exact solutions of the Burgers equation by using the group-theory methods 259
7.2.3 Some methods of finding exact solutions 261
7.3 The *a priori* symmetry method 266
References 268

8 Types of Acoustic Nonlinearities and Methods of Nonlinear Acoustic Diagnostics 271
8.1 Introduction 271
8.1.1 Physical and geometric nonlinearities 271
8.2 Classification of types of acoustic nonlinearity 274
8.2.1 Boundary nonlinearities 275
8.3 Some mechanisms of bulk structural nonlinearity 280
8.3.1 Nonlinearity of media with strongly compressible inclusions 281
8.3.2 Nonlinearity of solid structurally inhomogeneous media 284
8.4 Nonlinear diagnostics 290
8.4.1 Inverse problems of nonlinear diagnostics 292
8.4.2 Peculiarities of nonlinear diagnostics problems 294
8.5 Applications of nonlinear diagnostics methods 297
8.5.1 Detection of bubbles in a liquid and cracks in a solid 297
8.5.2 Measurements based on the use of radiation pressure 299
8.5.3 Nonlinear acoustic diagnostics in construction industry 300
8.6 Non-typical nonlinear phenomena in structurally inhomogeneous media 301
References 304

9 Nonlinear Sawtooth Waves 309
9.1 Sawtooth waves 309
9.2 Field and spectral approaches in the theory of nonlinear waves 312
9.2.1 General remarks 312
9.2.2 Generation of harmonics 313
9.2.3 Degenerate parametric interaction 314
9.3 Diffracting beams of sawtooth waves 318
9.4 Waves in inhomogeneous media and nonlinear geometric acoustics 323
9.5 The focusing of discontinuous waves 328
9.6 Nonlinear absorption and saturation 335
9.7 Kinetics of sawtooth waves 340
9.8 Interaction of waves containing shock fronts 344
References 350

10 Self-action of Spatially Bounded Waves Containing Shock Fronts 357
10.1 Introduction 357
10.2 Self-action of sawtooth ultrasonic wave beams due to the heating of a medium and acoustic wind formation 359
10.3 Self-refraction of weak shock waves in a quardatically nonlinear medium 367
10.4 Non-inertial self-action in a cubically nonlinear medium 373
10.5 Symmetries and conservation laws for an evolution equation describing beam propagation in a nonlinear medium 379
10.6 Conclusions 384
References 385

11 Nonlinear Standing Waves, Resonance Phenomena and Frequency Characteristics of Distributed Systems 389
11.1 Introduction 389
11.2 Methods of evaluation of the characteristics of nonlinear resonators 390
11.3 Standing waves and the Q-factor of a resonator filled with a dissipating medium 395
11.4 Frequency responses of a quadratically nonlinear resonator 400
11.5 Q-factor increase under introduction of losses 408
11.6 Geometric nonlinearity due to boundary motion 412
11.7 Resonator filled with a cubically nonlinear medium 423
References 437

Appendix Fundamental Properties of Generalized Functions 441
A.1 Definition of generalized functions 441
A.2 Fundamental sequences 443
A.3 Derivatives of generalized functions 449
A.4 The Leibniz formula 450
A.5 Derivatives of discontinuous functions 453
A.6 Generalized functions of a composite argument 456
A.7 Multidimensional generalized functions 458
A.8 Continuity equation 463
A.8.1 Singular solution 463
A.8.2 Green's function 464
A.8.3 Lagrangian and Eulerian coordinates 466
A.9 Method of characteristics 466

Index 471

Part I
Foundations of the Theory of Waves in Nondispersive Media

Chapter 1
Nonlinear Equations of the First Order

The basic patterns of nonlinear fields and waves of the hydrodynamic type already can be discerned by the behavior of solutions to the simplest nonlinear partial differential equations of the first order. This chapter discusses solutions of such equations. Those wishing to study the theory of the first-order nonlinear equations more fully are advised to turn to the following literature: [1–4].

1.1 Simple wave equation

The simplest and, at the same time, crucial equation of the nonlinear wave theory of the hydrodynamic type is the *simple wave equation*. In what follows, we will pay tribute to the remarkable mathematician Riemann, who laid the foundations of the nonlinear wave theory, and call this equation the *Riemann equation*. In mathematical literature, this equation is often called the Hopf equation. By using the equation as an example it is most instructive to explain such typically nonlinear effects as the wave steepening and gradient catastrophe.

1.1.1 The canonical form of the equation

The *simple wave (Riemann) equation* is the following first order partial differential equation:

$$\frac{\partial u}{\partial t}+C(u)\frac{\partial u}{\partial x}=0 \tag{1.1}$$

with respect to the function $u(x,t)$ which has different geometric, mechanical, economic, etc. meanings in different applications.

By multiplying Eq. (1.1) by $C'(u)$, it is reduced to the equivalent, but simpler in form, canonical Riemann equation:

$$\frac{\partial v}{\partial t} + v\frac{\partial v}{\partial x} = 0 \tag{1.2}$$

with respect to the new function $v(x,t) = C(u(x,t))$. Thus, without loss of generality, in what follows, we will limit ourselves to a detailed analysis of the Riemann equation (1.2) with an initial condition $v(x,t=0) = v_0(x)$. The following instructive mechanical interpretation of solutions to the Riemann equation helps better familiarize oneself with peculiarities of solutions to this equation.

1.1.2 Particle flow

The easiest way to comprehend properties of solutions to the Riemann equation is by using a flow of particles uniformly moving along the x-axis as an example. Let a particle at the point y at the initial moment of time $t=0$ have the velocity $v_0(y)$. Then the particle's motion is given by the following equations:

$$X(y,t) = y + v_0(y)t, \quad V(y,t) = v_0(y). \tag{1.3}$$

By varying y, we obtain the laws of motion of other particles in the flow. Note that apart from the time t, another argument y, the initial particle position, appears here. Such coordinates, which are rigidly bound to the particles of a flow, are called *Lagrangian coordinates* (a pictorial comparative discussion of flow descriptions in the Lagrangian and Eulerian coordinate systems is given in textbook [4]).

Usually, an observer measures the velocity of a flow at some fixed position with a Cartesian coordinate x. These, more natural for an external observer, coordinates are called *Eulerian*. The mapping from the Lagrangian into Eulerian coordinates is described by the following equation:

$$x = X(y,t). \tag{1.4}$$

In the case of uniformly moving particles, this equation has the following form:

$$x = y + v_0(y)t. \tag{1.5}$$

Let the field $v(x,t)$ of particle velocities in a flow be given as a function of the Eulerian coordinate x and time t. If, in addition to that, the mapping (1.4) of the Lagrangian to Eulerian coordinates is also known, then the dependence of the velocity field on the Lagrangian coordinates is given by the following equation:

$$V(y,t) = v(X(y,t),t). \tag{1.6}$$

In what follows, the fields describing the behavior of particles in the Lagrangian coordinate system will be called the Lagrangian fields, and the fields in the Eulerian coordinate system will be referred to as the Eulerian fields. So $v(x,t)$ is the Eulerian particle-velocity field, and $X(y,t)$ is the Lagrangian field of the Eulerian coordinates of the particles.

From the uniformity of particle motion follows that the velocity $V(y,t)$ of a particle with the Lagrangian coordinate y does not depend on time, i.e. it satisfies the following simplest differential equation:

$$\frac{dV}{dt} = 0, \tag{1.7}$$

and its coordinate obeys a no less obvious equation:

$$\frac{dX}{dt} = V. \tag{1.8}$$

Equations (1.7) and (1.8) are nothing else than *characteristic equations* for the first order partial differential equation (1.2). In order to reconstruct the solution of the Riemann equation from the solutions of the characteristic equation (1.7), (1.8), it is sufficient to find the inverse of function (1.4)

$$y = y(x,t),$$

which maps the Eulerian coordinates to the Lagrangian ones. If this function is known, then, with provision for (1.3) and (1.6), the solution of the Riemann equations takes on the following form:

$$v(x,t) = V(y(x,t),t) = v_0(y(x,t)). \tag{1.9}$$

Let us emphasize that the single-valued inverse function $y(x,t)$ exists, and Eq. (1.9) gives the classical Riemann solution of Eq. (1.2), only if the mapping from the Lagrangian coordinates to the Eulerian ones (1.4), (1.5) is a monotonically increasing function y from $\mathbb{R}$ onto $\mathbb{R}$. In the following chapter we will discuss in detail what happens if this condition is violated. At the moment, let us assume that it is satisfied.

1.1.3 Discussion of the Riemann solution

Let us discuss the characteristic peculiarities of the behavior of the Riemann solution $v(x,t)$ as a function of the x-coordinate and time t. But, before doing that, let us list the main forms of notation for solutions of the Riemann equation. By substituting $y(x,t)$ for y in the equation of uniform motion of a particle (1.5)

$$y(x,t) = x - v_0(y(x,t))t \Rightarrow y(x,t) = x - v(x,t)t \tag{1.10}$$

and by inserting the right-hand side of this expression into Eq. (1.9), we obtain the implicit form of the Riemann solution:

$$v(x,t) = v_0(x - v(x,t)t). \tag{1.11}$$

After elementary computations, an even more direct form of the Riemann solution follows from Eq. (1.10):

$$v(x,t) = \frac{x - y(x,t)}{t}. \tag{1.12}$$

Its meaning is absolutely clear: the velocity v of a uniformly moving particle is equal to the distance $x - y$ travelled by the particle by the moment of time t, divided by the total time of motion. In what follows, a deeper mechanical and geometric meaning of the expression (1.12) will be uncovered.

While constructing a plot of an Eulerian field $v(x,t)$, it is convenient to employ Lagrangian fields and to construct $v(x,t)$ parametrically:

$$x = y + v_0(y)t, \quad v = v_0(y). \tag{1.13}$$

The Riemann solution in Fig. 1.1 is so constructed in the case when the initial profile of the velocity field has a Gaussian form:

$$v_0(x) = V_0 \exp\left(-\frac{x^2}{2\ell^2}\right). \tag{1.14}$$

This figure shows, in the following dimensionless variables

$$z = \frac{x}{\ell}, \quad \tau = \frac{V_0}{\ell}t, \tag{1.15}$$

the velocity field at the moment of time $\tau = 1$. It also depicts (dashed line) the initial velocity $v_0(x)$. Arrows show particle displacements travelled during the time interval τ. It is seen that the greater the velocity of a particle, the greater the displacement travelled by the particle during a time interval. This leads to the steepening of the front of the field $v(x,t)$ on the right-hand-side and to the stretching of the left front.

1.1.4 Compressions and expansions of the particle flow

The steepening of the right part of the velocity-field profile $v(x,t)$ in Fig. 1.1 is accompanied by the thickening of the particle flow. Indeed, particles within the left-hand-side of this interval have a greater velocity than the particles on the right-hand-side. As a result, the faster left particles in time catch up with the slower right particles. On the contrary, the expansion of the left part of the velocity-field profile $v(x,t)$ leads to the rarefaction of the flow. Quantitatively, the measure of rarefaction of different parts of a flow is expressed by a Jacobian, which, in the one-dimensional case, is equal to

$$J(y,t) = \frac{\partial X(y,t)}{\partial y}. \tag{1.16}$$

For uniformly moving particles, whose law of motion is given by Eq. (1.5), the Jacobian is equal to

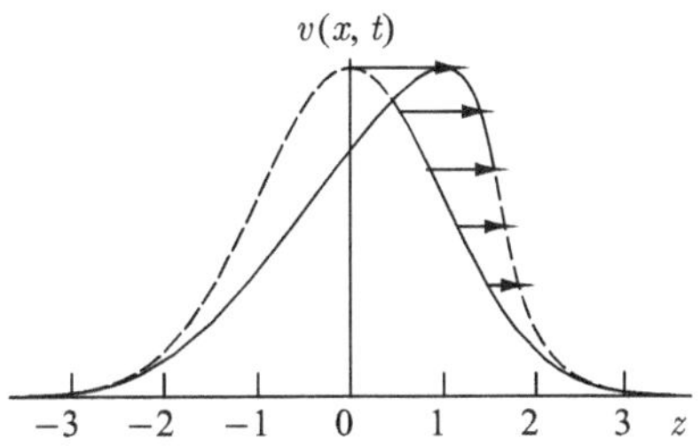

Fig. 1.1 The Riemann solution in the case of a Gaussian initial field.

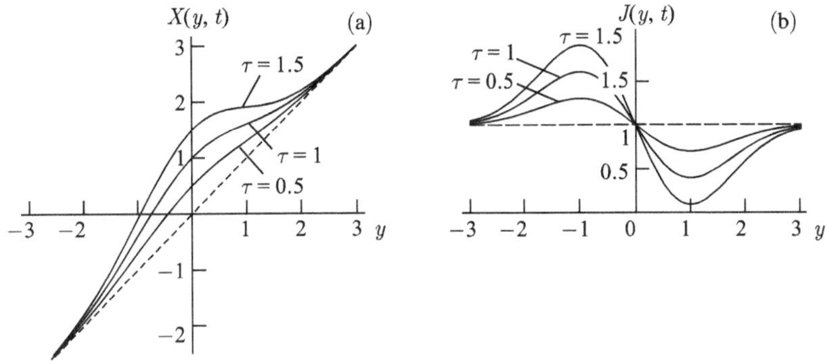

Fig. 1.2 Particle motion pattern $X(y,t)$ (*left*) and the corresponding Lagrangian divergence field $J(y,t)$ (*right*) at different moments of time. It is seen that compressed and expanded parts appear in the flow, where $J(y,t)$ is not equal to unity.

$$J(y,t) = 1 + v_0'(y)t. \tag{1.17}$$

The greater the Jacobian at a given value of y, the more rarefied the flow in a vicinity of the particle with the Lagrangian coordinate y. For this reason, let us call $J(y,t)$ the flow's *divergence*. A plot of the law of motion $X(y,t)$ and the corresponding divergence for uniformly moving particles (whose Eulerian field obeys the Riemann equation (1.2) with the initial condition (1.14)), are depicted in Fig. 1.2.

The field $J(y,t)$ (1.16) is a Lagrangian divergence field. The corresponding Eulerian field is obviously equal to

$$j(x,t) = J(y(x,t),t) \iff J(y,t) = j(X(y,t),t). \tag{1.18}$$

If the rule for transformation of Eulerian coordinates into Lagrangian ones $y(x,t)$ is known, the divergence field can be determined by a more direct method by means of the following geometrically evident expression:

$$\frac{\partial y(x,t)}{\partial x} = \frac{1}{j(x,t)}. \tag{1.19}$$

1.1.5 Continuity equation

A natural question arises in the framework of the mechanical interpretation of the solution to the Riemann equation (1.2) as the velocity field of a flow of uniformly moving particles: how does their density $\rho(x,t)$ change in time and space? It is known that the density obeys the universal *continuity equation*, which describes the law of mass conservation of the particles in a flow. Let us derive this equation by using a method, which allows one better to understand the following analysis of solutions to partial differential nonlinear equations.

Let, for definiteness, the initial particle density of a flow $\rho_0(x)$ be such that the mass of particles to the left of any point x

$$m_0(x) = \int_{-\infty}^{x} \rho_0(z)dz$$

is finite. Let the function $m(x,t)$ describe the variation of the mass of particles to the left of an arbitrary x. Like the velocity field $v(x,t)$, this is an Eulerian field. Knowing the law of particle motion $X(y,t)$, it is easy to make a transformation from the Eulerian left-mass field to the corresponding Lagrangian field:

$$M(y,t) = m(X(y,t),t).$$

The latter is easily obtained from obvious physical considerations. Indeed, if by the current moment of time t the particles have not overtaken each other (have not swapped places), the mass of particles on the left from any point with the Lagrangian coordinate y does not depend on time:

$$M(y,t) = \int_{-\infty}^{y} \rho_0(z)\,dz = m_0(y). \tag{1.20}$$

In other words, the Lagrangian mass field on the left satisfies the following equation:

$$\frac{dM}{dt} = 0.$$

The equivalent to it equation of the Eulerian field is

$$\frac{\partial m}{\partial t} + v\frac{\partial m}{\partial x} = 0. \tag{1.21}$$

Now let us determine the particle density. In the one-dimensional case, the Eulerian density field is equal to the derivative of the mass on the left:

$$\rho(x,t) = \frac{\partial m(x,t)}{\partial x}. \tag{1.22}$$

Hence, by differentiating Eq. (1.21) term by term with respect to x, we arrive at the sought-for one-dimensional variant of the continuity equation:

$$\frac{\partial \rho}{\partial t} + \frac{\partial}{\partial x}(v\rho) = 0. \tag{1.23}$$

Note. Let us note that while deriving the continuity equation, we nowhere used the fact of the uniformity of motion. Therefore, in this derivation, the universality of the continuity equation has been exhibited, which holds for any laws of particle motion.

1.1.6 Construction of the density field

In order to find a solution of the continuity equation (1.23), let us write down the Eulerian mass field on the left. From Eq. (1.20) and the link between Lagrangian and Eulerian fields follows that

$$M(y,t) = m_0(y) \iff m(x,t) = m_0(y(x,t)). \tag{1.24}$$

By differentiating the last equation with respect to x, we obtain

$$\rho(x,t) = \rho_0(y(x,t)) \frac{\partial y(x,t)}{\partial x} \tag{1.25}$$

or, by taking Eq. (1.19) into account,

$$\rho(x,t) = \frac{\rho_0(y(x,t))}{j(x,t)} \iff R(y,t) = \frac{\rho_0(y)}{J(y,t)}. \tag{1.26}$$

These formulas have an apparent geometric meaning: the flow density at any point is equal to the initial density in a vicinity of the particle at this point divided by the degree of compression of particles.

Let us separately discuss the density of a flow of uniformly moving particles, whose velocity field $v(x,t)$ obeys the Riemann equation, and $y(x,t)$ is given by (1.10). Here, as it is seen from (1.25), (1.10), the flow density is expressed via the solution of the Riemann equation in the following way:

$$\rho(x,t) = \rho_0\left(x - v(x,t)t\right)\left(1 - \frac{\partial v(x,t)}{\partial x} t\right). \tag{1.27}$$

In particular, when the initial density is uniform, i.e. if $\rho_0 = const$ does not depend on x, the density is described by the following relation:

$$\rho(x,t) = \rho_0\left(1 - \frac{\partial v(x,t)}{\partial x} t\right), \tag{1.28}$$

which demonstrates a close link between the density of a flow and the steepening of its velocity-field profile.

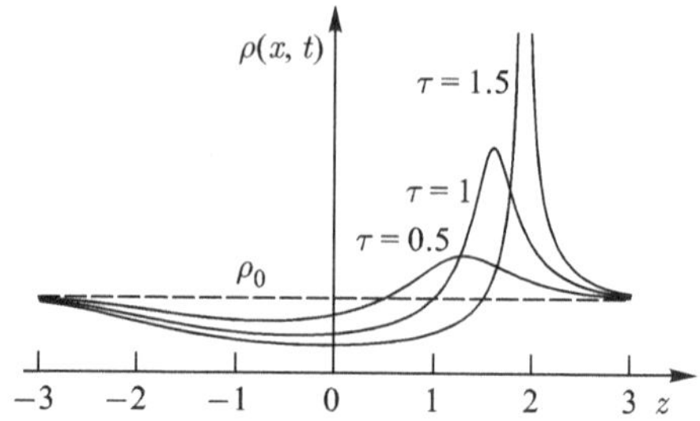

Fig. 1.3 Density of uniformly moving particles with a Gaussian initial velocity field (1.14) and a constant initial density $\rho(x,t=0)=\rho_0$.

As in the case of the velocity field, it is convenient to plot the density of a flow of uniformly moving particles parametrically, by using the fact that the Lagrangian laws of flow evolution are given explicitly:

$$x = y + v_0(y)t, \quad \rho = \frac{\rho_0(y)}{1+v_0'(y)t}. \tag{1.29}$$

The plots of $\rho(x,t)$ in Fig. 1.3 are constructed in this way.

1.1.7 Momentum-conservation law

Apart from the mass conservation law, a flow of uniformly moving particles also possesses an infinite set of invariants (see, e.g., [3, 5]). Most of them do not have any significant physical meaning, while others, for instance the law of conservation of momentum, play a paramount role in physical applications. Here, we discuss this law in more detail.

Let us remind you, that the total momentum of particles to the left of a point x is equal

$$p(x,t) = \int_{-\infty}^{x} v(x,t)\rho(x,t)\,dx.$$

By substituting here Eqs. (1.9) and (1.25) for the velocity and density of a flow, respectively, and then by changing to integration with respect to the Lagrangian coordinate, we reduce the expression for the momentum on the left to the following form:

$$p(x,t) = \int_{-\infty}^{x} v_0(y(x,t))\rho_0(x(y,t))\frac{\partial y(x,t)}{\partial x}dx = \int_{-\infty}^{y(x,t)} v_0(y)\rho_0(y)\,dy.$$

From here, it is seen that, for uniformly moving particles, the Lagrangian field of the momentum on the left does not depend on time:

$$P(y,t) = p_0(y) = \int_{-\infty}^{y} \rho_0(y)v_0(y)\,dy. \tag{1.30}$$

Hence, in analogy with the mass on the left, the corresponding Eulerian field of the momentum on the left obeys the following equation:

$$\frac{\partial p}{\partial t} + v\frac{\partial p}{\partial x} = 0, \tag{1.31}$$

and the momentum density

$$g(x,t) = \rho(x,t)v(x,t) = \frac{\partial p(x,t)}{\partial x}$$

satisfies the continuity equation

$$\frac{\partial g}{\partial t} + \frac{\partial}{\partial x}(vg) = 0. \tag{1.32}$$

Note 1. It is easy to derive this equation as a corollary of the Riemann equation (1.2) and the continuity equation (1.23). But we have deliberately chosen the round-about "integral" method, for it will help, in the following, construct generalized solutions of the equations mentioned here.

Note 2. Since the momentum density obeys the same equation as the simple density $\rho(x,t)$, we obtain expressions for the Eulerian and Lagrangian momentum-density fields "gratis" by substituting the initial momentum for the initial density in (1.26):

$$g(x,t) = \frac{\rho_0(y(x,t))v_0(y(x,t))}{j(x,t)} \iff G(y,t) = \frac{\rho_0(y)v_0(y)}{J(y,t)}. \tag{1.33}$$

1.1.8 Fourier transforms of density and velocity

In applications, it is often important to know not the fields themselves, but their spectra. Therefore we will find expressions for the spatial Fourier transforms of the velocity and density. Let us start with the density

$$\tilde{\rho}(\kappa,t) = \frac{1}{2\pi}\int_{-\infty}^{\infty} e^{-i\kappa x}\rho(x,t)\,dx. \tag{1.34}$$

By substituting the solution of the continuity equation found earlier (1.25) into the integral (1.34), we obtain

$$\tilde{\rho}(\kappa,t) = \frac{1}{2\pi}\int_{-\infty}^{\infty} e^{-i\kappa x}\rho_0(y(x,t))\,dy(x,t).$$

By transforming to integration with respect to the Lagrangian coordinate, we finally obtain

$$\tilde{\rho}(\kappa,t) = \frac{1}{2\pi}\int_{-\infty}^{\infty} e^{-i\kappa X(y,t)}\rho_0(y)\,dy. \tag{1.35}$$

More unwieldy calculations, based on the same idea of transformation to integration with respect to the Lagrangian coordinates in the Fourier integral, give

$$\tilde{v}(\kappa,t) = \frac{i}{2\pi\kappa t}\int_{-\infty}^{\infty}\left[e^{-i\kappa X(y,t)} - e^{-i\kappa y}\right] dy. \tag{1.36}$$

A discussion of this solution can be found in monograph [6].

Example. Generation of harmonics. Formulas (1.35) and (1.36) are remarkable in that they express the Fourier transforms of implicitly given (e.g. by Eq. (1.11)) fields $\rho(x,t)$ and $v(x,t)$ via integrals of explicitly given functions. ▮

Let us use this opportunity to find an explicit expression for the Fourier transform of the density $\rho(x,t)$ in the case of the initial harmonic field and uniform density

$$v_0(x) = a\sin(kx), \quad \rho_0(x) = \rho_0 = const. \tag{1.37}$$

In doing so, we need the following formula from the theory of Bessel functions:

$$e^{iw\sin z} = \sum_{n=-\infty}^{\infty} J_n(w)\, e^{inz}. \tag{1.38}$$

In the case under study, the law of transformation from Lagrangian to Eulerian coordinates is given as

$$x = X(y,t) = y + at\sin(ky). \tag{1.39}$$

By substituting this equality into (1.35), we obtain

$$\tilde{\rho}(\kappa,t) = \frac{\rho_0}{2\pi k}\int_{-\infty}^{\infty} e^{-i\mu z - i\mu\tau\sin z}\, dz.$$

Here we introduced the dimensionless variable of integration $z = ky$, time $\tau = kat$ and spatial frequency $\mu = \kappa/k$. By taking Eq. (1.38) into account we obtain

$$\tilde{\rho}(\kappa,t) = \rho_0 \sum_{n=-\infty}^{\infty} J_n(-\mu\tau)\frac{1}{2\pi k}\int_{-\infty}^{\infty} e^{-i(\mu-n)z}\, dz.$$

According to the theory of generalized functions, the last integral (see, e.g., [7, 8]) has the form:

$$\frac{1}{2\pi k}\int_{-\infty}^{\infty} e^{-i(\mu-n)z}\, dz = \frac{1}{k}\delta(\mu-n) = \delta(\kappa - kn).$$

From this and the previous expression, it follows that the density field investigated here possess the following generalized Fourier transform:

$$\tilde{\rho}(\kappa,t) = \rho_0 \sum_{n=-\infty}^{\infty} J_n(-n\tau)\delta(\kappa - kn).$$

By substituting it into the inverse Fourier integral

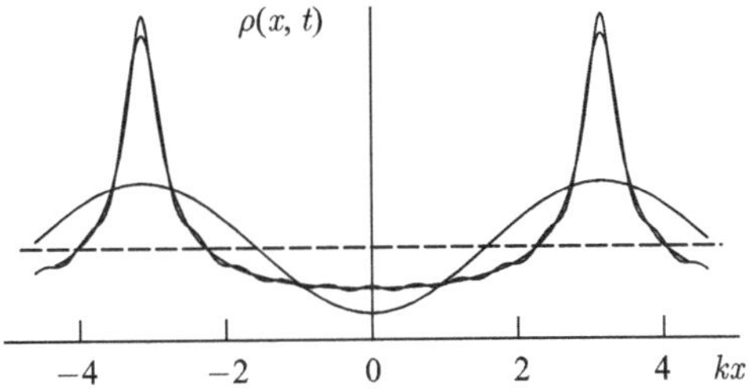

Fig. 1.4 Plot of $\rho(x,t)$ for the initial harmonic velocity field and the uniform density (1.37) at $\tau = akt = 0.7$. Profiles of the first two (one harmonic term) and eleven terms of the Fourier series are also shown. It is seen that the profile of the last sum nearly coincides with the density profile.

$$\rho(x,t) = \int_{-\infty}^{\infty} \tilde{\rho}(\kappa,t)\, e^{i\kappa x}\, d\kappa$$

and taking the symmetry properties of the Bessel function

$$J_{-n}(-w) = J_n(w) \tag{1.40}$$

into account, we arrive at the explicit expression for the density field in the form of a Fourier series:

$$\rho(x,t) = \rho_0 + 2\rho_0 \sum_{n=1}^{\infty} (-1)^n J_n(n\tau)\cos(kx). \tag{1.41}$$

Comparison between the sum of the first terms of this series and the exact density profile constructed parametrically by means of Eqs. (1.29), shows that a few first terms of Fourier series already give a good approximation to the exact solution.

1.2 Line-growth equation

Let us discuss one more of numerous applications of the first order nonlinear partial differential equations: analysis of line and surface growth. It may be: deposited surface of an electronic chip, wave front of a light wave, shock wave of a jet plane and a fire line consuming a forest. All of these surfaces and lines are described by nonlinear partial differential equations (see, e.g., [9–12]). The simplest example of these equations is given below.

1.2.1 Forest-fire propagation

Let a fire move within a forest. In order mathematically to describe the process of fire propagation, we assume that the surface of the forest is flat and introduce within this plane the Cartesian coordinates (x,z). Let us direct the z-axis along the predominant direction of the fire. As a result, it is possible to describe the fire-front

Fig. 1.5 Fire line and its tendency to grow

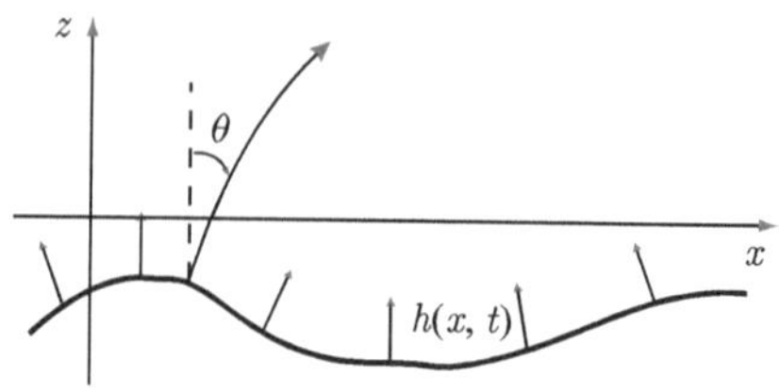

line by a function

$$z = h(x,t). \tag{1.42}$$

It is natural to assume that a fire spreads perpendicularly to the line of fire $h(x,t)$ with a speed c. This means that if one selects a point $\{y, h(y, t = 0)\}$ on the line of fire at the initial moment of time $t = 0$ and traces its motion along the trajectory perpendicular to the lines of fire, as it is seen in Fig. 1.5, then the velocity of the point will be equal to c. Let the coordinates of the specified point change with time according to the laws $\{X(t), Z(t)\}$. Let us call the trajectory of the point's motion a *ray*.

From what has just been said, it is clear that the coordinates of the ray satisfy the equations:

$$\frac{dX}{dt} = c\sin\theta, \quad \frac{dZ}{dt} = c\cos\theta, \tag{1.43}$$

where θ is the angle between the ray and the z-axis. Further we note that the vertical coordinate $Z(t)$ of the ray can be expressed in terms of the fire line (1.42):

$$Z(t) = h(X(t),t). \tag{1.44}$$

By substituting this equality into the second of Eqs. (1.43), we obtain

$$\frac{\partial h}{\partial t} + \frac{dX}{dt}\frac{\partial h}{\partial x} = c\cos\theta$$

or, by taking the first of Eqs. (1.43) into account, we arrive at the partial differential equation for the sought-for line of fire $h(x,t)$:

$$\frac{\partial h}{\partial t} + c\sin\theta\,\frac{\partial h}{\partial x} = c\cos\theta. \tag{1.45}$$

It would seem that the equation is not closed, because it links two functions: the line of fire $h(x,t)$ and the angle $\theta(x,t)$ between the z-axis and the normal to the line of fire. However, it is easy to make it closed by using the obvious geometric relationship between the line $h(x,t)$ and the angle θ:

$$\frac{\partial h}{\partial x} = -\tan\theta. \tag{1.46}$$

In terms of the last result, Eq. (1.45) can be rewritten as

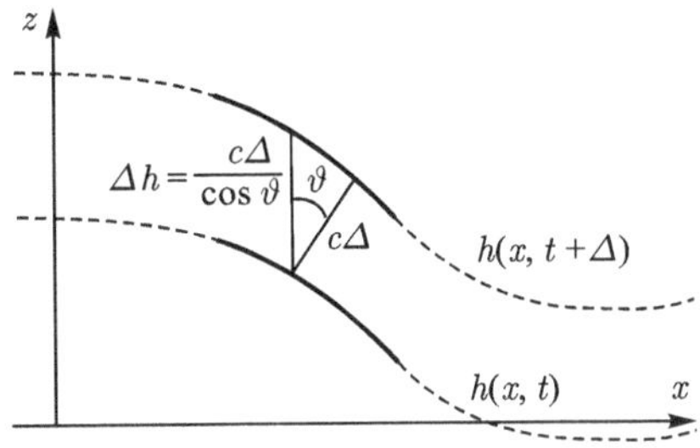

Fig. 1.6 Geometric illustration of the validity of the equation (1.47)

$$\frac{\partial h}{\partial t} = \frac{c}{\cos\theta}. \tag{1.47}$$

Finally, by noting that

$$\cos\theta = \frac{1}{\sqrt{1+\tan^2\theta}},$$

we obtain the final form of the sought-for equation:

$$\frac{\partial h}{\partial t} = c\sqrt{1+\left(\frac{\partial h}{\partial x}\right)^2}. \tag{1.48}$$

Note 1. At first, it seems that the juggling with analytical transformations has led to an absurd from the point of view of the common geometric sense Eq. (1.47). Indeed, one would think, the more the normal to the line $h(x,t)$ deviates from z-axis, i.e. the greater the angle θ between the z-axis and the direction of line growth, the slower the line $h(x,t)$ must grow along the axis z. But the Eq. (1.47) signifies that the greater θ, the faster the growth, and at $\theta = \pi/2$ the growth rate becomes infinite. However, an accurate geometric study convinces one in the validity of Eq. (1.47). Relevant geometrical constructions are given in Fig. 1.6, where fragments of the line $h(x,t)$ are shown at close moments of time t and $t+\Delta$. It is seen that the increment of the line's height at an arbitrary point x

$$\Delta h = h(x,t+\Delta) - h(x,t) \approx \frac{c\Delta}{\cos\theta}$$

is inversely proportional to $\cos\theta$. Perhaps this geometric derivation will convince someone of the correctness of Eqs. (1.47) and (1.48) sooner than the above-stated formal analysis.

Note 2. If the speed in Eq. (1.48) is negative ($c < 0$), we obtain the equation not for growth, but for decay of the line $h(x,t)$. Accordingly, Eq. (1.48) will describe, e.g., the melting of ice in a glass of water or hull corrosion of an oceanic ship.

Note 3. We deliberately called the trajectory $\{X(t), Z(t)\}$ perpendicular to the fire front a ray. This is because the wavefront of an optic wave obeys the above-stated law of propagation perpendicularly to the front with a given speed. The lines, everywhere perpendicular to the wave fronts, by definition, are optic rays. Thus Eq. (1.48) represents a one-dimensional version of the equations describing evolution of wave-fronts of optic waves.

Note 4. Typically, optic waves propagate in a preferential direction — at small angles to it. If the preferential direction of the optic wave is directed along the z-axis, then tilt angles of rays to the z-axis are small, and instead of Eq. (1.48) a simpler, approximate equation is used. That is the following substitutions are used:

$$-\frac{\partial h}{\partial x} = \tan\theta \approx \theta, \quad \sqrt{1+\tan^2\theta} \approx 1 + \frac{1}{2}\left(\frac{\partial h}{\partial x}\right)^2$$

and Eq. (1.48) is rewritten as

$$\frac{\partial h}{\partial t} = c + \frac{c}{2}\left(\frac{\partial h}{\partial x}\right)^2 .$$

For a plane wave propagating exactly along the z-axis, this equation has a simple solution: $h = ct$. If we are interested only in the shape of wavefront, and not in its exact position, then one can exclude the indicated trivial forward motion (translation) by introducing a new function:

$$w(x,t) = h(x,t) - ct. \tag{1.49}$$

The latter satisfies a more elegant equation:

$$\frac{\partial w}{\partial t} = \frac{c}{2}\left(\frac{\partial w}{\partial x}\right)^2 . \tag{1.50}$$

1.2.2 Anisotropic surface growth

Let us introduce the following new notation

$$u(x,t) = -\frac{\partial h(x,t)}{\partial x} . \tag{1.51}$$

Recall that $u = \tan\theta$ characterizes the direction of surface growth. Therefore, $u(x,t)$ came to be called a *tilt-angle field*. Sometimes the surface is growing at different speeds in different directions [9]. For example, during the propagation of an optic wave in an anisotropic medium, or the melting of glaciers, when the melt rate depends on the angle at which a part of the glacier surface is facing the sun. Let us take an anisotropy of growth into account assuming that the speed depends on u and transform from Eq. (1.47) to a more general equation:

$$\frac{\partial h}{\partial t} = \Phi(u), \quad h(x,t=0) = h_0(x), \tag{1.52}$$

where

$$\Phi(u) = c(u)\sqrt{1+u^2}. \tag{1.53}$$

Here are a few examples of anisotropic surfaces.

Example 1. In perfectly calm weather, snow falls vertically on the ground. Therewith a quantity of snow proportional to $\cos\theta\, ds$ falls on an area ds of the snow surface lying at an angle θ to the zenith per unit time. Accordingly, the speed of snow-surface growth in the direction of θ is given by the equation:

$$c(u) = c\cos\theta = \frac{c}{\sqrt{1+u^2}}. \tag{1.54}$$

By substituting this formula into Eq. (1.53), we find that $\Phi = c = const$, and the surface-growth equation (1.52) has a trivial solution:

$$h(x,z) = h_0(x) + ct, \tag{1.55}$$

according to this solution, the snow-surface shape does not change during a snowfall. ∎

Example 2. Let us consider a more general case, when particles are deposited on the surface from different directions. Let $D(\theta)$ be a directivity pattern representing the intensity of a flux of incident particles at an angle θ to the z axis. Then total intensity of particles falling on a surface area titled at an angle θ to the z-axis is

$$c(\theta) = \int_{\theta_-}^{\theta_+} D(\theta')\cos(\theta-\theta')\,d\theta'. \tag{1.56}$$

In particular, the vertically falling snow discussed above corresponds to a singular directivity pattern $D(\theta) = c\delta(\theta)$.

Note that integration limits in (1.56) take into account the effect of shadowing the investigated element of the curve $h(x,t)$ by the rest of the curve and, generally speaking, depend on the relief of the profile $h(x,t)$. For definiteness, let us consider an interval of this line tilted to the z-axis at a positive angle $\theta > 0$. Obviously, in this case

$$\min\theta_- = \theta - \frac{\pi}{2}, \quad \max\theta_+ = \frac{\pi}{2}$$

(see Fig. 1.7). The asymmetry of the minimum and maximum angles in the directivity pattern is connected with the fact that, at a particular geometry ($\theta > 0$) of an interval of the curve $h(x,t)$, the minimum angle $\min\theta_-$ at which particles may get to the surface is limited by the position of the tangent to this interval, and $\max\theta_+$ is limited by the underlying surface $z = const$. For an isotropic flow $D = const$, and ignoring possibility of the shadowing of the line $h(x,t)$ by its remote parts, the growth speed is equal to

$$c(\theta) = D\int_{\theta-\pi/2}^{\pi/2} \cos(\theta'-\theta)\,d\theta' = D(1+\cos\theta). \tag{1.57}$$

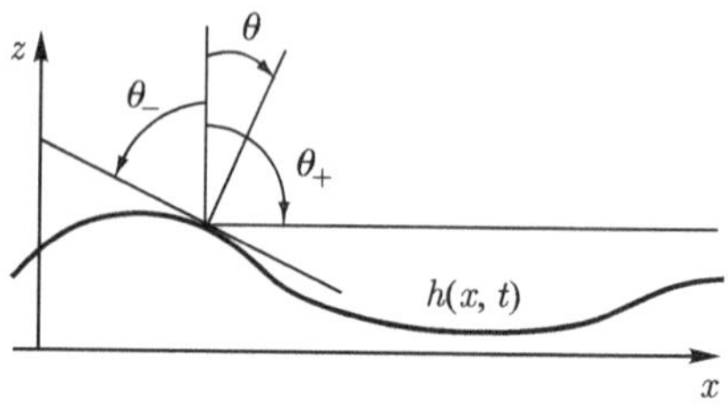

Fig. 1.7 Illustration to the determination of the integration limits (1.56)

The parity of the obtained expression means that it is valid for both $\theta > 0$ (the case considered here) and $\theta < 0$. ∎

1.2.3 Solution of the surface-growth equation

Let us solve Eq. (1.52). By differentiating it with respect to x, we arrive at the equation for the tilt-angle field $u(x,t)$ (1.51):

$$\frac{\partial u}{\partial t} + C(u)\frac{\partial u}{\partial x} = 0. \tag{1.58}$$

Here

$$C(u) = \frac{d\Phi(u)}{du} = \frac{d}{du}\left[c(u)\sqrt{1+u^2}\right]. \tag{1.59}$$

Characteristic equations corresponding to (1.52), (1.58) are

$$\frac{d\tilde{X}}{dt} = C(U), \quad \frac{dU}{dt} = 0, \quad \frac{dH}{dt} = \Lambda(U), \tag{1.60}$$

where the fields along the characteristics are indicated with capital letters. In addition, here the following notation has been used:

$$\Lambda(u) = \Phi(u) - uC(u) = -u^2\frac{d}{du}\left(\frac{\Phi(u)}{u}\right) \tag{1.61}$$

and an auxiliary function $\tilde{X}(y,t)$ has been introduced. The tilde sign is used in order to avoid confusing this function with the function $X(t)$ satisfying the first of Eqs. (1.43):

$$\frac{dX}{dt} = V(u), \quad V(u) = c\sin\theta = \frac{uc(u)}{\sqrt{1+u^2}}, \tag{1.62}$$

and having, in the case of optic wave fronts, a clear geometric meaning of the horizontal coordinate of the trajectory of a ray perpendicular to the wave front. In order to distinguish $X(t)$ from $\tilde{X}(y,t)$, let us call the latter function (together with $\tilde{Z} = h(\tilde{X},t)$) the *trajectory of isoclines* (or *isoclinic line*) of the growing surface $h(x,t)$. The solutions of Eqs. (1.60) have the form:

$$U(y,t) = u_0(y),\ \tilde{X}(y,t) = y + C(u_0(y))t,\ H(y,t) = h_0(y) + \Lambda(u_0(y))t. \quad (1.63)$$

From here it follows, e.g, that the isoclines are always straight unlike the rays which are curved in anisotropic medium. As in the case of the Riemann equation, the sought-for fields $h(x,t)$ and $u(x,t)$ are obtained from Eq. (1.63) by substituting into $H(y,t)$ and $U(y,t)$ the function $y = \tilde{y}(x,t)$ inverse to the function $x = \tilde{X}(y,t)$.

Example 1. Isotropic growth speed. Let the growth speed be independent of the line tilt, i.e. the case $c(u) = c = const$ is realized. This is valid, e.g., for optic waves in an isotropic medium. In such a medium, the velocity of motion along rays and isoclines are the same:

$$C(u) = V(u) = \frac{cu}{\sqrt{1+u^2}} = c\sin\theta,$$

and the rays coincide with the isoclines. Therewith line growth is given parametrically:

$$x = y + \frac{u_0(y)}{\sqrt{1+u_0^2(y)}}ct, \quad h = h_0(y) + \frac{ct}{\sqrt{1+u_0^2(y)}}. \quad (1.64)$$

Let us take the following sinusoid as the initial profile of the curve $h(x,t)$:

$$h_0(x) = h_0 \cos kx \Rightarrow u_0(x) = h_0 k \sin kx.$$

Then the parametric equation of the line $h(x,t)$ has the form:

$$z = \mu + \frac{\varepsilon\tau\sin\mu}{\sqrt{1+\varepsilon^2\sin^2\mu}}, \quad \eta = \varepsilon\cos\mu + \frac{\tau}{\sqrt{1+\varepsilon^2\sin^2\mu}}, \quad (1.65)$$

where we have used the following dimensionless variables:

$$kx = z, \quad ky = \mu, \quad ckt = \tau, \quad kh = \eta, \quad (1.66)$$

and parameter:

$$kh_0 = \varepsilon. \quad (1.67)$$

Constructed on the basis of Eqs. (1.65), lines $h(x,t)$ for various τ and $\varepsilon = 1/2$ are displayed in Fig. 1.8. ∎

Example 2. Let us plot a graph of $h(x,t)$ by using the same parametric Eqs. (1.65) as in the previous example. But let us the speed be negative ($c < 0$). Physically, this corresponds not to growth, but to the melting of the surface. Let us find profiles of the melting surface at progressively larger moments of time, by inverting in Eqs. (1.65) the signs of τ from "+" to "−". These profiles of the melting surface are shown in Fig. 1.9. ∎

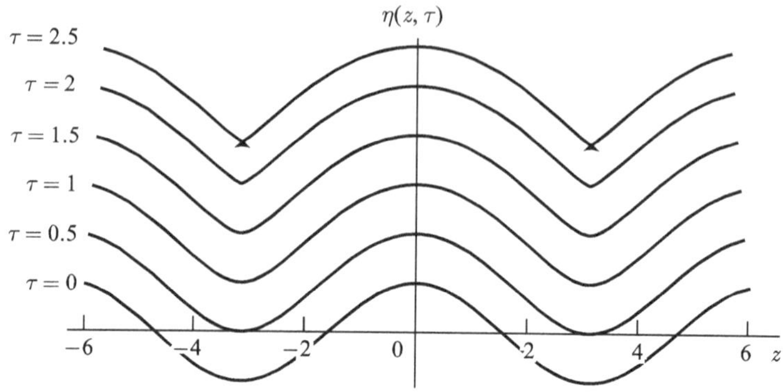

Fig. 1.8 Lines $h(x,t)$ at different moments of time. It is natural to interpret them as graphs of the wave front of an optic wave in an isotropic medium. Over time, the crests of $h(x,t)$ are becoming flatter, and troughs are getting sharper

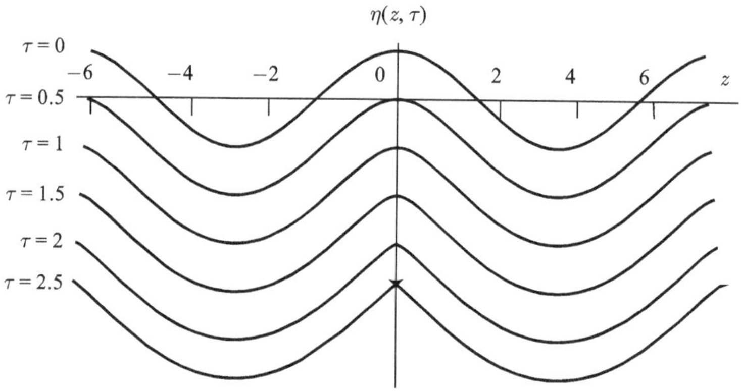

Fig. 1.9 Melting line $h(x,t)$. It is seen, that in contrast to the growth line, the crests are getting sharper with time, and the troughs are becoming flatter. Perhaps everyone has observed something similar by noticing how edges of ice pieces in a drink are getting sharper as the ice melts.

1.3 One-dimensional laws of gravitation

1.3.1 Lagrangian description of one-dimensional gravitation

Let us imagine a one-dimensional World, where the Law of Universal Gravitation is very simple: the force of mutual attraction of two bodies is proportional to their masses and does not depend on the distance between them. Let us formulate this by using a language of equations. Let two bodies be situated on the x-axis directed along the one-dimensional World, one is on the left with a mass M_l, and the other one is on the right with a mass M_r. Let us denote the x-component of the force exerted on the left body by the right one as F_l, and the same for the force acting on the right body as F_r. Since in a one-dimensional World there is no other direction but the direction of the x-axis, let us call these components simply *forces*. According to the Law of Universal Gravitation of the one-dimensional World, the interaction forces between the particles are equal to

$$F_l = -F_r = \gamma M_l M_r .$$

Here γ is a gravitational constant.

Let the initial velocity and density of particles in the one-dimensional World equal $v_0(x)$ and $\rho_0(x)$, respectively. Let also the total mass of the particles be finite and equal

$$M = \int_{-\infty}^{\infty} \rho_0(x)\, dx .$$

Let us find the Lagrangian fields of the velocity and density of a one-dimensional flow of gravitationally interacting particles before they undergo any collision. For this, let us investigate the motion of individual particles of the flow. Let us consider a particle of the flow with an arbitrary Lagrangian coordinate y. As usual, we denote its Eulerian coordinate as $x = X(y,t)$. The particle's motion obeys the second Newton law, which according to the Law of Universal Gravitation has the following form:

$$\frac{d^2X}{dt^2} = \gamma\left[M_r(y,t) - M_l(y,t)\right] .$$

Here $M_r(y,t)$ is the mass of matter in the flow to the right of the chosen particle, and $M_l(y,t)$ is the same to the left of this particle. As long as the particles do not change their sequence order, the masses specified above do not depend on time and are equal to

$$M_l(y) = \int_{-\infty}^{y} \rho_0(y')\, dy, \quad M_r(y) = \int_{y}^{\infty} \rho_0(y')\, dy,$$

and the Newton equation becomes quite simple:

$$\frac{dX(y,t)}{dt} = V(y,t), \qquad \frac{dV(y,t)}{dt} = \gamma\left[M_r(y) - M_l(y)\right] . \tag{1.68}$$

We have separated the Newton equation into two first order equations, in order to explicitly to single out the sought-for Lagrangian field of the velocity of the flow $V(y,t)$.

Equations (1.68) should be supplemented by the initial conditions

$$X(y,t=0) = y, \quad V(y,t=0) = v_0(y).$$

By solving these equations with the given initial conditions, we find the Lagrangian velocity field

$$v = V(y,t) = v_0(y) + \gamma\left[M - 2M(y)\right]t \tag{1.69}$$

and the Lagrangian-to-Eulerian coordinate transformation

$$x = X(y,t) = y + v_0(y)t + \frac{\gamma}{2}[M - 2M(y)]t^2. \tag{1.70}$$

Here it is taken into account that the masses of matter in the flow to the left and to the right of the chosen particle are connected by the identity

$$M_l(y) + M_r(y) \equiv M,$$

and we have dropped the subscript of the mass on the left: $M(y) = M_l(y)$. As a result, the right-hand side of the Newton equation has taken on the following form:

$$M_r(y) - M_l(y) = M - 2M_l(y) = M - 2M(y).$$

The Lagrangian density field, as is known, is described by the following universal relationship:

$$R(y,t) = \frac{\rho_0(y)}{J(y,t)}. \tag{1.71}$$

This equation contains the Jacobian of the Lagrangian-to-Eulerian coordinate transformation, which in our case is equal to

$$J(y,t) = \frac{\partial X}{\partial y} = 1 + v_0'(y)t - \frac{\gamma}{2}\rho_0(y)t^2. \tag{1.72}$$

Note. Let us pay attention to the remarkable peculiarity of the density field (1.71) of gravitationally interacting particles. While the velocity field (1.69) depends on the masses of all matter to the left and to the right of a point with a given Lagrangian coordinate y, the density field *is locally connected with the properties of the flow* — its behavior is determined by the initial velocity and density only at a single point.

1.3.2 Eulerian description of one-dimensional gravitation

In principle, knowing the Lagrangian characteristics of the fields, it is not difficult to reconstruct from them the corresponding fields in the Eulerian representation. For instance, it is easy to plot the Eulerian field of the density field $\rho(x,t)$ of a one-dimensional flow of gravitationally interacting particles parametrically by using the equalities

$$\rho = R(y,t), \quad x = X(y,t),$$

where, in the case of gravitationally interacting particles, the fields $X(y,t)$ and $R(y,t)$ are given by Eqs. (1.70)–(1.72). Nevertheless, there are specific questions, e.g. the character of the steepening of Eulerian fields, which are expedient to discuss precisely in the Eulerian representation. In order to confirm what has just been said, in what follows, we will consider an example of an analysis of Eulerian fields of the density and velocity of a one-dimensional flow of gravitationally interacting particles.

Let the initial density field equal

$$\rho_0(x) = \rho_0 \frac{\ell^2}{x^2 + \ell^2}, \tag{1.73}$$

and the initial velocity field be equal to zero. Let us plot the Eulerian fields of the velocity $v(x,t)$ and density $\rho(x,t)$ of a flow of gravitationally interacting particles at growing values of time and demonstrate by means of these graphs the development of gravitational instability.

First of all, let us calculate the mass of matter to the left of the point with the Lagrangian coordinate y. It is equal to

$$M(y) = \rho_0 \ell^2 \int_{-\infty}^{y} \frac{dz}{z^2 + \ell^2} = \frac{M}{\pi} \left[\arctan\left(\frac{y}{\ell}\right) + \frac{\pi}{2} \right].$$

Here it is taken into account that the total mass of the flow is

$$M = \pi \rho_0 \ell.$$

Let us separately write down the combination of the masses on the left and on the right entering the expression for the Largangian velocity field (1.69) and the Lagrangian-to-Eulerian coordinate transformation (1.70):

$$M - 2M(y) = -2\rho_0 \ell \arctan\left(\frac{y}{\ell}\right).$$

By substituting it into Eqs. (1.69) and (1.70), we obtain the following parametric specification of the Eulerian velocity and density fields:

$$\eta = \zeta - \tau^2 \arctan \zeta, \quad u = -2\tau \arctan \zeta, \quad r = \frac{1}{1 + \zeta^2 - \tau^2}.$$

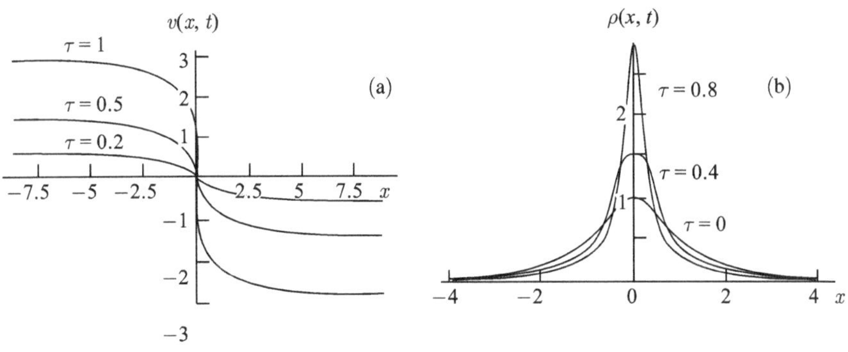

Fig. 1.10 Plots of the dimensionless Eulerian fields of the velocity and density of gravitationally interacting particles at different moments of time. It is seen that the gravitational interaction leads to progressively accelerating tendency of particles towards the center, to growth and compression of the density curve in a vicinity of the center of the one-dimensional World $x = 0$.

Here we introduced dimensionless coordinates, time, velocity and density

$$\eta = \frac{x}{\ell}, \quad \zeta = \frac{y}{\ell}, \quad \tau = \sqrt{\gamma\rho_0}\,t, \quad u = \frac{v}{\sqrt{\gamma\rho_0}\,\ell}, \quad r = \frac{\rho}{\rho_0}.$$

1.3.3 Collapse of a one-dimensional Universe

The equations for the Lagrangian and Eulerian description of a gravitationally interacting one-dimensional flow of particles "work" only if the total mass of the particles is finite. Sometimes it is necessary to study such flows' motion in the case when the total mass of a flow is infinite. Sometimes it can be done by considering a flow with an infinite mass as the limit of a flow with its mass tending to infinity. Let us consider below an example of such calculations.

Let us suppose that we are interested in evolution of an one-dimensional Universe, whose density at the initial moment of time $t = 0$ was uniform:

$$\rho_0(x) = \rho_0 = const.$$

For this, let us introduce an auxiliary initial density field

$$\rho_0(x) = \rho_0 g\left(\frac{x}{\ell}\right), \tag{1.74}$$

where $g(z)$ is a continuous absolutely integrable nonnegative and even function, such that $g(0) = 1$. Then by tending $\ell \to \infty$, we find the sought-for expressions for the Lagrangian fields of the velocity and density of a flow in the limit of a uniform initial density $\rho_0 = const$. Moreover, we will also assume the one-dimensional Universe is initially expanding: $v_0(y) = Hy$, where H is the Hubble constant. Let us find the collapse time of the one-dimensional Universe.

In this case, by using the even parity of the function $g(z)$, the mass combination entering Eqs. (1.69), (1.70) may be written as

$$M - 2M(y) = \int_{-y}^{y} \rho_0(y')\,dy' = \rho_0 \ell \int_{-y/\ell}^{y/\ell} g(z)\,dz,$$

which demonstrates that behavior of the flow velocity essentially depends only on the particle density in the interval $[-y, y]$ and is independent of behavior of the initial density field outside this interval. This opens a possibility easily to trace the limit towards a uniform initial density. Indeed, by tending ℓ to infinity and noting that due to continuity of the function $g(z)$ the last integral converges to $2y/\ell$, we obtain

$$\lim_{\ell \to \infty} [M - 2M(y)] = 2\rho_0 y.$$

By substituting the limiting value into the right-hand sides of Eqs. (1.69), (1.70), we find the velocity field and the law of the Lagrangian-to-Eulerian coordinate transformation for an initially uniform flow of gravitationally interacting particles

$$x = y\left(1 - \gamma\rho_0 t^2\right) + v_0(y)\,t, \quad v = v_0(y) + 2\gamma\rho_0 y t.$$

Accordingly, the Lagrangian density field following from (1.71), (1.70) is equal to

$$R(y,t) = \frac{\rho_0}{1 + v_0'(y)\,t - \gamma\rho_0 t^2}.$$

For a uniformly expanding Universe, when $v_0(y) = Hy$, its density, while remaining uniform, tends to infinity at $\tau \to \tau_n$, where the dimensionless time of collapse is equal to

$$\tau_n = \delta + \sqrt{1+\delta^2}, \quad \tau = \sqrt{\gamma\rho_0}\,t, \quad \delta = \sqrt{H/4\gamma\rho_0}.$$

1.4 Problems to Chapter 1

Problem 1. Prove that, in the single-stream regime, the field $q(x,t)$ of the derivative with respect to x of the solution $v(x,t)$ to the Riemann equation (1.2) satisfies the following inequality

$$q(x,t) < \frac{1}{t}. \tag{1.75}$$

Illustrate the validity of this inequality by plotting $q(x,t)$ as a function of x in the case of the following initial condition:

$$v_0(x) = a\sin(kx). \tag{1.76}$$

Solution. The simplest way to prove the above mentioned inequality is based on the Riemann solution written in the form (1.12). By differentiating both sides of this relation with respect to x, we obtain

$$q(x,t) = \frac{1}{t}\left(1 - \frac{\partial y(x,t)}{\partial x}\right).$$

Since, in the single-stream regime, $y(x,t)$ is everywhere monotonously growing function, its derivative in non-negative, the expression in parentheses is less or equal to unity, and it means that the condition specified in the formulation of the problem is satisfied.

Let us demonstrate the validity of the inequality (1.75) by means of a plot of $q(x,t)$. It is convenient to plot this function by means of a parametric representation of $q(x,t)$, by using the Lagrangian coordinate y as a parameter:

$$x = X(y,t) = y + v_0(y)\,t, \quad q = Q(y,t).$$

We used the notation $Q(y,t)$ adopted in the book for the Lagrangian field corresponding to the Eulerian field $q(x,t)$. Let us find $Q(y,t)$, noticing that there is the following relationship:

$$\left.\frac{\partial y(x,t)}{\partial x}\right|_{x=X(y,t)} = \left(\frac{\partial X(y,t)}{\partial y}\right)^{-1} = \frac{1}{J(y,t)}.$$

Here $J(y,t)$ is the Jacobian of the Lagrangian-to-Eulerian coordinate transformation (1.16). By using the explicit expression of the Jacobian (1.17), we arrive at the following parametric equations of the field $q(x,t)$:

$$x = y + v_0(y)t, \quad q = \frac{v_0'(y)}{1+v_0'(y)t}. \tag{1.77}$$

By substituting here the sinusoidal initial condition (1.76), we finally obtain

$$\eta = \zeta + \tau \sin\zeta, \quad \theta = \frac{\tau\cos\zeta}{1+\tau\cos\zeta}.$$

Here we used the dimensionless variables:

$$\eta = kx, \quad \zeta = ky, \quad \tau = kat, \quad \theta = tq.$$

$q(x,t)$ plotted by using these equations is shown in Fig. 1.11.

Problem 2. Find the interval of possible values of the single-stream field $q(x,t)$ in the case when the initial condition of the Riemann equation $v_0(x)$ obeys the following conditions:

$$-\mu < v_0'(x) < \mu \quad (x \in \mathbb{R},\ \mu > 0).$$

Solution. In order to solve this problem, it is quite unnecessary to analyze Eulerian fields, as it has been done in the previous problem. Indeed, within the interval of single-stream motion (at $t < t_n$), when the Eulerian-to-Lagrangian coordinate transformation $y = y(x,t)$ is strictly monotonous and maps $\mathbb{R}_x$ onto $\mathbb{R}_y$, the following inequalities are equivalent:

$$a(t) \leqslant q(x,t) \leqslant b(t) \quad (x \in \mathbb{R}) \iff a(t) \leqslant Q(y,t) \leqslant b(t) \quad (y \in \mathbb{R}).$$

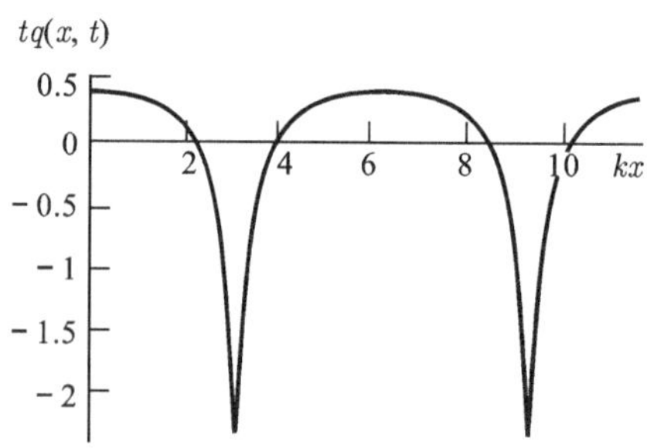

Fig. 1.11 Eulerian field $q(x,t)$ plotted parametrically by means of the Lagrangian fields (1.77).

Therefore it is sufficient to investigate the convenient for analysis Lagrangian field $q = Q(y,t)$. From (1.77) follows that

$$tQ < c(z), \quad c(z) = \frac{z}{1+z}, \quad z = tv_0'. \tag{1.78}$$

Let us further note that $c(z)$ monotonically grows within the interval $z \in (-1,\infty)$. Hence, by substituting the maximum value $z = \mu t$ into, (1.78) we obtain the upper limit for the values of q:

$$tq \leqslant \frac{\mu t}{1+\mu t} < 1. \tag{1.79}$$

In exactly the same way, as long as the inequality

$$\mu t < 1, \tag{1.80}$$

holds, we find the lower limit for the values of q:

$$qt \geqslant -\frac{\mu t}{1-\mu t}. \tag{1.81}$$

For the complete solution of the problem, it remains to note that the inequality (1.80) is equivalent to the condition of single-streamness $t < t_n$. Hence, as long as the solution $v(x,t)$ of the Riemann equation is a single-stream one, both inequalities (1.79) and (1.81) are valid.

Note 1. In the case considered in the previous problem $\mu = ka$, so that the spatial derivative of the field $v(x,t)$ in this case satisfies the inequality

$$-\frac{\tau}{1-\tau} \leqslant tq(x,t) \leqslant \frac{\tau}{1+\tau} \quad (\tau = kax).$$

Note 2. It is important to emphasize that the upper limit of values of the field $q(x,t)$, with time, depends on the initial maximum value of μ increasingly weaker, while asymptotically tending to the universal upper limit $1/t$ established in the previous problem. Such weakening of a dependence, with growing time t, on initial conditions is very characteristic for nonlinear (i.e. satisfying nonlinear equations) fields and waves.

Note 3. On the contrary, the lower limit of values of the field $q(x,t)$ at $t \to t_n$ tends to minus infinity, which inevitably leads to a gradient catastrophe at $t = t_n$.

Problem 3. Let the initial density and velocity of a cluster of uniformly moving particles are equal $\rho_0(x)$ and $v_0(x)$, respectively. The initial mass of the particles and their center of mass are finite:

$$M = \int_{-\infty}^{\infty} \rho_0(y)\, dy < \infty, \quad x_c = \frac{1}{M}\int_{-\infty}^{\infty} y\rho_0(y)\, dy < \infty.$$

Find the law of motion of the cluster's center of mass

$$\bar{x}(t) = \frac{1}{M}\int_{-\infty}^{\infty} x\rho(x,t)\,dx$$

along with the dependence on time of its dispersion

$$D(t) = \frac{1}{M}\int_{-\infty}^{\infty} (x-x_c)^2\rho(x,t)\,dx.$$

Solve the problem by expressing the sought-for characteristics of the cluster's density via its Fourier transform (1.35).

Solution. Let us first calculate the cluster's center of mass. For this, let us multiply both sides of the equality

$$\rho(x,t) = \int_{-\infty}^{\infty} \tilde{\rho}(\varkappa,t)\,e^{i\varkappa x}\,d\varkappa$$

by x and integrate over all x-axis. As a result, after changing the order of integration in the repeated integral on the right-hand side, we obtain:

$$\int_{-\infty}^{\infty} x\rho(x,t)\,dx = \int_{-\infty}^{\infty} d\kappa\tilde{\rho}(\kappa,t)\int_{-\infty}^{\infty} dx\,x\,e^{i\varkappa x}.$$

The latter integral, as we know from Appendix, is equal to the derivative of the delta function:

$$\int_{-\infty}^{\infty} x\,e^{i\varkappa x}\,dx = -2\pi i\frac{\partial}{\partial\kappa}\delta(\kappa).$$

From here and from the previous equation follows the well-known relation

$$\int_{-\infty}^{\infty} x\rho(x,t)\,dx = 2\pi i\frac{\partial}{\partial\kappa}\,\tilde{\rho}(\kappa,t)|_{\kappa=0}\,. \tag{1.82}$$

By substituting here the derivative of the integral (1.35) with respect to κ, we have

$$\bar{x}(t) = \int_{-\infty}^{\infty} X(y,t)\,\rho_0(y)\,dy.$$

Knowing the Lagrangian-to-Eulerian coordinate transformation (1.4), (1.5) for uniformly moving particles, we finally obtain

$$\bar{x}(t) = x_c + \bar{v}_0\,t, \tag{1.83}$$

where

$$\bar{v}_0 = \frac{1}{M}\int_{-\infty}^{\infty} v_0(y)\,\rho_0(y)\,dx.$$

Let us begin with the calculation of the cluster's dispersion. After simple manipulations, it is easy to show that the following relationship holds:

$$D(t) = \overline{x^2}(t) - \bar{x}^2(t), \tag{1.84}$$

where

$$\overline{x^2}(t) = \int_{-\infty}^{\infty} x^2 \rho(x,t)\, dx.$$

Let us evaluate this integral. Similarly to (1.82), we have

$$\int_{-\infty}^{\infty} x^2 \rho(x,t)\, dx = -2\pi \frac{\partial^2}{\partial \kappa^2} \tilde{\rho}(\kappa,t)|_{\kappa=0},$$

and consequently, according to (1.35),

$$\overline{x^2}(t) = \frac{1}{M} \int_{-\infty}^{\infty} X^2(y,t)\, \rho_0(y)\, dy.$$

By substituting here the explicit form of the transformation $X(y,t)$ (1.5) and by using Eqs. (1.83), (1.84), we finally obtain

$$D(t) = D_y + t^2 D_v + 2t \left[\overline{y\, v_0(y)} - \bar{y}\, \overline{v_0(y)}\right].$$

Here we used the following notations:

$$D_y = \overline{y^2} - \bar{y}^2, \quad D_v = \overline{v_0^2(y)} - \overline{v_0(y)}^2,$$

and also introduced an operator of spatial averaging with respect to the initial density of the cluster:

$$\overline{f(y)} = \frac{1}{M} \int_{-\infty}^{\infty} f(y)\, \rho_0(y)\, dy.$$

Problem 4. If particles move in a medium which resists their motion (e.g. in a stationary gas), the particle velocities decrease with time, and the velocity field is described by the following equation:

$$\frac{dV}{dt} + \frac{1}{\tau} V = 0 \quad \Rightarrow \quad \frac{\partial v}{\partial t} + v \frac{\partial v}{\partial x} + \frac{1}{\tau} v = 0, \quad v(x,t=0) = v_0(x),$$

where τ is a characteristic time of velocity dissipation. Find the law of evolution of the velocity field $v(x,t)$ and trace its asymptotic at $t \to \infty$.

Solution. Let us solve this problem by transforming from the original first order partial differential equation to the following characteristic equations:

$$\frac{dX}{dt} = V, \; \frac{dV}{dt} = -\frac{1}{\tau} V, \; X(y,t=0) = y, \; V(y,t=0) = v_0(y).$$

The solutions of these equations are

$$V(y,t) = v_0(y)\, e^{-t/\tau}, \quad X(y,t) = y + v_0(y)\, \theta.$$

Here we introduced an auxiliary "time"

$$\theta = \tau(1 - e^{-t/\tau}).$$

By comparing the obtained expressions with the solution of the standard Riemann equation (1.2), it is easy to figure out that

$$v(x,t) = e^{-t/\tau}\, u(x,\theta),$$

where $u(x,\theta)$ satisfies the Riemann equation

$$\frac{\partial u}{\partial \theta} + u\frac{\partial u}{\partial x} = 0, \quad u(x,\theta = 0) = v_0(x). \tag{1.85}$$

At $t \to \infty$, the auxiliary time $\theta \to \tau$. In fact, this means that due to velocity dissipation nonlinear effects weaken with time, and the shape of the velocity field gets "frozen", i.e. remains such as if the time elapsed since the starting moment of uniform motion did not exceed τ.

Problem 5. For physicists and engineers, the main sign of nonlinearity is generation of higher harmonics of an originally harmonic signal. Investigate the process of generation of harmonics in the field $v(x,t)$ satisfying the Riemann equation (1.2), if the field has initially been purely harmonic: $v_0(x) = a\sin(kx)$.

Solution. It is required to obtain the Fourier series of the Riemann solution $v(x,t)$. Let us first find the generalized Fourier transform of the field $v(x,t)$. It is given by Eq. (1.36), which, in this case, has the following form:

$$\tilde{v}(\kappa,t) = \frac{i}{2\pi\kappa k t}\int_{-\infty}^{\infty} e^{-i\mu z}\left[e^{-i\mu\tau\sin z} - 1\right] dz.$$

Here we used already familiar dimensionless variables

$$\mu = \kappa/k, \quad z = ky, \quad \tau = kat.$$

By using Eq. (1.38) and substituting delta function for integrals appearing in the expression, let us write the Fourier transform as a series:

$$\tilde{v}(\kappa,t) = \frac{ia}{k}\left\{\left[J_0\left(\frac{\kappa\tau}{k}\right) - 1\right]\delta(\kappa) \right.$$
$$\left. + \frac{k}{\kappa\tau}\sum_{n=1}^{\infty}\left[J_n\left(-\frac{\kappa\tau}{k}\right)\delta(\kappa - kn) + J_{-n}\left(-\frac{\kappa\tau}{k}\right)\delta(\kappa + kn)\right]\right\}.$$

By using the sifting (probing) property of the delta function, the fact that $J_0(0) = 1$ and also the symmetry (1.40) the Bessel functions, we obtain

$$\tilde{v}(\kappa,t) = ia\sum_{n=1}^{\infty}(-1)^n\frac{J_n(n\tau)}{n\tau}\left[\delta(\kappa - kn) - \delta(\kappa + kn)\right].$$

By computing the inverse Fourier transform, we find the sought-for expansion of the Riemann solution in terms of harmonics:

$$v(x,t) = 2a \sum_{n=1}^{\infty} (-1)^{n+1} \frac{J_n(n\tau)}{n\tau} \sin(nkx). \tag{1.86}$$

Problem 6. One-dimensional motion of cold plasma is described by equations for the velocity of electrons $v(x,t)$, their density $\rho(x,t)$

$$\begin{gathered} \frac{\partial v}{\partial t} + v\frac{\partial v}{\partial x} = -\frac{e}{m}E, \quad \frac{\partial \rho}{\partial t} + \frac{\partial}{\partial x}(v\rho) = 0, \\ v(x,t=0) = v_0(x), \quad \rho(x,t=0) = \rho_0(x), \end{gathered} \tag{1.87}$$

and longitudinal electric field $E(x,t)$

$$\frac{\partial E}{\partial x} = -4\pi e(\rho - \rho_0).$$

Here e and m are the electron charge and mass, respectively, ρ_0 is the density of immobile ions. Solve the equations by means of the method of characteristics. Discuss the case of $\rho(x,t=0) = \rho_0$ in detail. Assume that at $x \to -\infty$, the electron velocity and balance of the mass on the left of electrons and ions

$$m(x,t) = \int_{-\infty}^{x} [\rho(x',t) - \rho_0]\, dx'.$$

tend to zero.

Hint. Use the following relationship:

$$E(x,t) = -4\pi e m(x,t).$$

Solution. It follows from the continuity equation that the balance of the mass on the left obeys the equation

$$\frac{\partial m}{\partial t} + v\frac{\partial m}{\partial x} + \rho_0 v = 0.$$

By multiplying it by $-4\pi e$, we obtain the following equation for the electric field:

$$\frac{\partial E}{\partial t} + v\frac{\partial E}{\partial x} = 4\pi e\rho_0 v.$$

Let us solve the last equation, along with the first equation (1.87), by the method of characteristics by going over to the following characteristic equations:

$$\frac{dX}{dt} = V, \quad \frac{dV}{dt} = -\frac{e}{m}E, \quad \frac{dE}{dt} = 4\pi e\rho_0 V.$$

Let the initial electric field be equal to $E_0(x)$. Then the solutions of the above characteristic equations have the form:

$$
\begin{aligned}
V(y,t) &= v_0(y)\cos\omega t - E_0(y)\frac{1}{\gamma}\sin\omega t,\\
E(y,t) &= E_0(y)\cos\omega t + v_0(y)\gamma\sin\omega t,\\
X(y,t) &= y + \frac{E_0(y)}{\gamma\omega} + \frac{1}{\gamma\omega}\left[v_0(y)\gamma\sin\omega t + E_0(y)\cos\omega t\right].
\end{aligned}
\tag{1.88}
$$

Here we used the notation for the plasma frequency ω and parameter γ:

$$
\omega = \sqrt{\frac{4\pi e^2\rho_0}{m}}, \qquad \gamma = \frac{m}{e}\omega.
$$

From the expressions (1.88) for the Lagrangian fields, it is seen that electrons of cold plasma harmonically oscillate, and along with them the electric field in a vicinity of any electron of cold plasma changes harmonically. But the corresponding Eulerian fields do not change in time and space harmonically. Let us verify this by discussing the case when, at the initial moment of time, electrons and ions are everywhere balanced. Because of the tight link between variations of the density and electric field, the above assumption means that $E_0(y) \equiv 0$, and the Lagrangian fields (1.79) simplify significantly:

$$
V(y,t) = v_0(y)\cos\omega t, \quad E(y,t) = \gamma v_0(y)\sin\omega t,
$$
$$
X(y,t) = y + \frac{v_0(y)}{\omega}\sin\omega t.
$$

Comparison of these Lagrangian fields with the Lagrangian fields of the velocity and coordinate for the Riemann equation shows that the Eulerian fields of the velocity and electric field of cold plasma may be represented as:

$$
v(x,t) = u(x,\theta)\cos\omega t, \quad E(x,t) = u(x,\theta)\gamma\sin\omega t,
$$

where

$$
\theta = \omega^{-1}\sin\omega t,
$$

and $u(x,\theta)$ is the Riemann solution (1.75).

Problem 7. Let a snowfall be accompanied by wind and snow fall at an angle $\theta_0 \neq 0$ to the zenith. Let also the initial snow profile $h_0(x)$ be such that its tilt angles θ everywhere satisfy the following inequality:

$$
|\theta - \theta_0| < \frac{\pi}{2}. \tag{1.89}
$$

How will $h(x,t)$ be changing with time?

Solution. In this case, the directivity pattern is equal to $D(\theta') = c\delta(\theta' - \theta_0)$. The condition (1.89) guaranties that for all points of the initial line $h_0(x)$ the delta function does not "fall out of" the limits of integration. Hence the speed at which falling snow is attached to a piece of surface whose normal vector is at an angle θ to the z-axis is equal to

$$c(\theta) = c\cos(\theta - \theta_0) = \cos\theta\cos\theta_0 + \sin\theta\sin\theta_0.$$

By substituting this expression into (1.56), transforming from θ to u and introducing the notations $c_\perp = c\cos\theta_0$, $c_\parallel = c\sin\theta_0$, we arrive at the following equation for $h(x,t)$:

$$\frac{\partial h}{\partial t} = c_\perp + c_\parallel u,$$

or

$$\frac{\partial h}{\partial t} - c_\parallel \frac{\partial h}{\partial x} = c_\perp, \quad h(x,t=0) = h_0(x).$$

This is a purely linear equation, which has an obvious solution:

$$h(x,t) = h_0(x - c_\parallel t) + c_\perp t. \tag{1.90}$$

From this solution, it is seen, that snow hills do not change shape, and only move towards the wind like plants stretching towards the sun.

Problem 8. Generalize the solution of the previous problem to the case of a directivity pattern $D(\theta')$, which is equal to zero outside the interval $[\theta_1, \theta_2]$, and an initial line $h_0(x)$, such that everywhere the following inequalities hold:

$$\{\theta - \theta_1, \theta_2 - \theta\} < \frac{\pi}{2}.$$

Solution. It is not difficult to show that in this case growth of the line $h(x,t)$ is also described by Eq. (1.90), where now

$$c_\perp = \int_{-\pi/2}^{\pi/2} D(\theta')\cos\theta'\, d\theta', \quad c_\parallel = \int_{-\pi/2}^{\pi/2} D(\theta')\sin\theta'\, d\theta'.$$

Problem 9. Let the directivity pattern be equal to $D(\theta) = c\cos^2\theta$. Investigate growth of the line $h(x,t)$. While constructing its equation, use the small angle approximation assuming that $|\theta| \ll 1$, $|u| \ll 1$. Discuss the case of the following initial line: $h_0(x) = h\cos(kx)$ $(kh \gg 1)$.

Solution. First, let us compute the speed of surface growth at an angle θ by using Eq. (1.56):

$$c(\theta) = c\int_{-\theta-\pi/2}^{\pi/2} \cos^2\theta' \cos(\theta' - \theta)\, d\theta' = \frac{1}{3}(1 + \cos\theta)^2.$$

By transforming from θ to u and by substituting this expression into (1.53), we have

$$\Phi(u) = \frac{1}{3}\left(1 + \frac{1}{\sqrt{1+u^2}}\right)^2 \sqrt{1+u^2}.$$

Since we are going to solve the problem in the small angle approximation, let us expand the function $\Phi(u)$ into the Taylor series in powers of u and let us retain only the first term with a nonzero power of u:

$$\Phi(u) \approx \frac{4}{3}c + \frac{c}{12}u^4.$$

By substituting this expression into Eq. (1.52) and by dropping the trivial constant term, we find that, in the small angle approximation, the shape of the line $h(x,t)$ obeys the following equation:

$$\frac{\partial h}{\partial t} = \frac{c}{12}\left(\frac{\partial h}{\partial x}\right)^4.$$

The functions entering the characteristic equations (1.60) are equal to

$$\Phi(u) = \frac{c}{12}u^4 \quad \Rightarrow \quad C(u) = \frac{c}{3}u^3, \quad \Lambda(u) = -\frac{c}{4}u^4.$$

By substituting them into Eqs. (1.63) describing shape change of the line $h(x,t)$, we arrive at the parametric equations of the line $h(x,t)$:

$$x = y + \frac{c}{3}(u_0(y))^3 t, \quad h = h_0(y) - \frac{c}{4}(u_0(y))^4 t.$$

For the sinusoidal initial line, we have

$$kx = \mu + \frac{\tau}{3}\varepsilon^3 \sin^3\mu, \quad kh = \varepsilon\cos\mu - \frac{\tau}{4}\varepsilon^4 \sin^4\mu.$$

Here dimensionless variables $\mu = ky$, $\varepsilon = kh$, $\tau = ckt$ are introduced. Plots of the shape of the line $h(x,t)$ for different values of τ are shown in Fig. 1.12.

Problem 10. Investigate line growth in the case when $c(\theta) = c\cos^2\theta$. Use the small angle approximation. Plot the solution at different moments of time t in the case of the initial line shape

$$h_0(x) = -h\cos(kx) \quad (h > 0). \tag{1.91}$$

Solution. The line-growth equation (1.52) here has the following form:

$$\frac{\partial h}{\partial t} = \frac{c}{\sqrt{1+u^2}}.$$

The equation in the small angle approximation, after the average growth ct has been removed, is

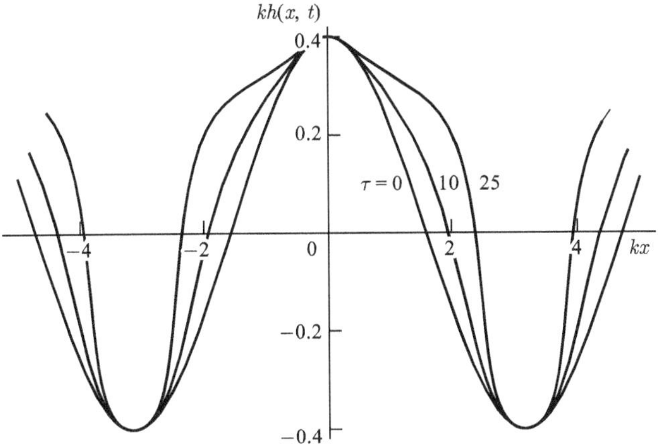

Fig. 1.12 Lines $h(x,t)$ for $\varepsilon = 0.4$, at the moments of time $\tau = 0$, 10 and 25.

$$\frac{\partial h}{\partial t} + \frac{c}{2}\left(\frac{\partial h}{\partial x}\right)^2 = 0.$$

The auxiliary functions entering Eq. (1.63) are equal to

$$\Phi(u) = -\frac{c}{2}u^2 \Rightarrow C(u) = -cu, \quad \Lambda(u) = \frac{c}{2}u^2.$$

Consequently, the line $h(x,t)$ is given by the following parametric equations:

$$x = y - cu_0(y)\,t, \quad h = h_0(y) + \frac{c}{2}u_0^2(y)\,t.$$

For the sinusoidal shape of the initial line (1.91) we obtain

$$kx = \mu + \varepsilon\tau \sin\mu, \; kh = -\varepsilon\cos\mu + \frac{\tau}{2}\varepsilon^2 \sin^2\mu, \; \varepsilon = kh, \; \mu = ky, \; \tau = kct.$$

Plots of $h(x,t)$ are shown in Fig. 1.13. For the feature of evolution of the shape of $h(x,t)$ to be more clearly seen, the plots are slightly elevated towards growth. Here the line shape evolves according to the "corrosion" scenario It is characterized by the sharpening of the crests and by the flattening of the throughs.

Problem 11. Let $v(x,t)$ and $y(x,t)$ be sufficiently smooth functions of x, and such that $v(x,t)$ sufficiently rapidly drops to zero as $x \to \pm\infty$, and $y(x,t)$ is a strictly monotonously growing function, which maps the x-axis onto the entire y-axis. Prove Eq. (1.36) for the Fourier transform of the Riemann solution.

Solution. By substituting the Riemann solution (1.9) into the Fourier integral, we obtain

$$\tilde{v}(\kappa,t) = \frac{1}{2\pi}\int_{-\infty}^{\infty} v_0(y(x,t))\, e^{-i\kappa x}\, dx.$$

Let us transform to integration with respect to the Lagrangian coordinate:

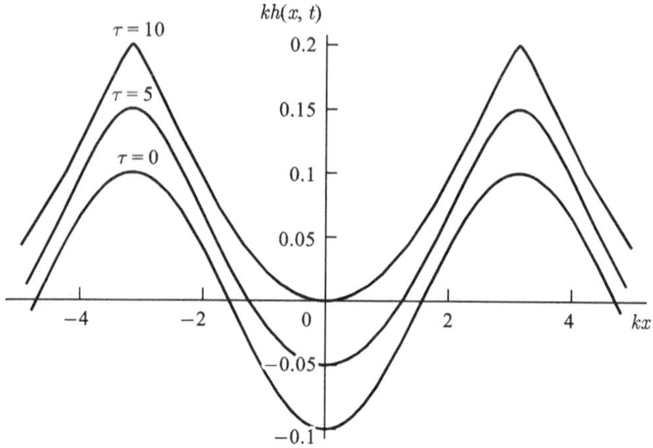

Fig. 1.13 Lines $h(x,t)$ for $\varepsilon = 0.4$ and $\tau = 0, 5, 10.$

$$\tilde{v}(\kappa,t) = \frac{1}{2\pi}\int_{-\infty}^{\infty} v_0(y)\, e^{-i\kappa X(y,t)}\,\frac{\partial X}{\partial y}\,dy.$$

By transforming the last integral by integration by parts, we arrive at the expression

$$\tilde{v}(\kappa,t) = -\frac{i}{2\pi\kappa}\int_{-\infty}^{\infty} e^{-i\kappa X(y,t)}\,v_0'(y)\,dy.$$

By substituting here the explicit expression (1.5) for the function $X(y,t)$, we find that

$$\tilde{v}(\kappa,t) = -\frac{i}{2\pi\kappa}\int_{-\infty}^{\infty} e^{-i\kappa y}\,v_0'(y)\,e^{-i\kappa v_0(y)}\,dy.$$

The form of the integrand as if forces us to rewrite the integral as

$$\tilde{v}(\kappa,t) = \frac{1}{2\pi\kappa^2 t}\int_{-\infty}^{\infty} e^{-i\kappa y}\,d\left[e^{-i\kappa v_0(y)t} - 1\right]$$

and apply integration by parts once more. As a result, we arrive at the sought-for formula (1.36).

References

1. V.I. Arnold, *Ordinary differential equations* (MIT Press, Cambridge, Mass, 1978)
2. M.I. Rabinovich, D.I. Trubetskov, *Oscillations and Waves in Linear and Nonlinear Systems.* (Springer, Berlin, 1989)
3. G.B. Whitham, *Linear and Nonlinear Waves* (Wiley, New York, 1974)
4. Y.B. Zeldovich, *Elements of Mathematical Physics* (Nauka, Moscow, 1973). In Russian
5. V.I. Karpman, *Non-linear Waves in Dispersive Media* (Pergamon Press, Oxford, 1974)

6. O.V. Rudenko, S.I. Soluyan, *Theoretical Foundations of Nonlinear Acoustics* (Plenum, New York, 1977)
7. S.A. Lapinova, A.I. Saichev, V.A. Filimonov, *Generalized Functions and Asymptotic Methods* (Nizhny Novgorod University Press, 2006). In Russian
8. A.I. Saichev, W.A. Woyczyński, *Distributions in the Physical and Engineering Sciences* (Birkhäuser, Boston, 1997)
9. A.L. Barabási, H.E. Stanley, *Fractal Concepts in Surface Growth* (Cambridge University Press, 1995)
10. M. Kardar, G. Parisi, Y.C. Zhang, Dynamical scaling of growing interfaces, Phys. Rev. Lett. **56**, 889–892 (1986)
11. M. Schwartz, S.F. Edwards, Nonlinear deposition: a new approach, Europhys. Lett. **20**, 301–305 (1992)
12. W.A. Woyczynski, *Burgers-KPZ Turbulence. Gottingen Lectures* (Springer, Berlin, 1998)

Chapter 2
Generalized Solutions of Nonlinear Equations

Equations of mathematical physics and, in particular, nonlinear partial differential equations of the first order appear as a result of certain idealizations. This allows one to achieve elegance of mathematical models, a possibility to use them in order to predict, in an adequately quantitative way, important aspects of various real world phenomena. But any idealizations come at a cost. Factors unaccounted for by these idealizations gradually, and sometimes abruptly, begin to dominate, while the initial models cease to be able to describe what actually happens.

A natural remedy against such situations is to use a more complex, but also more adequate model of the phenomenon under study. Often, however, it is possible to achieve the desired goal by constructing *generalized solutions* of the original equations. In fact, differential equations, as a rule, are corollaries of more general *integral equations*. If a generalized solution is consistent with integral equations, it can correctly describe the phenomena of interest even when the classical solutions of differential equations no longer exist. Basic principles of constructing the generalized solutions of partial differential equations of the first order are discussed below. Additional useful information on generalized solutions of first-order partial differential equations can be found in [1–3].

2.1 Standard equations

In order to concentrate on the construction of generalized solutions, without digressing into important in certain applications, but non-fundamental details, let us discuss generalized solutions of the most simple, but at the same time key partial differential equations of the first order.

2.1.1 Particle-flow equations

First of all, this is the Riemann equation for the velocity field $v(x,t)$ of a one-dimensional flow of uniformly moving particles

$$\frac{\partial v}{\partial t}+v\frac{\partial v}{\partial x}=0,\quad v(x,t=0)=v_0(x), \tag{2.1}$$

and the continuity equation

$$\frac{\partial \rho}{\partial t}+\frac{\partial}{\partial x}(v\rho)=0,\quad \rho(x,t=0)=\rho_0(x) \tag{2.2}$$

for the flow density $\rho(x,t)$. In addition, the equation for the potential

$$s(x,t)=\int^x v(x',t)\,dx' \tag{2.3}$$

of the velocity field will play a key role in our presentation. Here we have deliberately omitted a constant lower limit, symbolizing the presence of an arbitrary constant, up to which any physical potential is defined. The potential of the velocity field satisfies the nonlinear equation

$$\frac{\partial s}{\partial t}+\frac{1}{2}\left(\frac{\partial s}{\partial x}\right)^2=0,\quad s(x,t=0)=s_0(x). \tag{2.4}$$

It is easy to check the validity of this equation by differentiating it with respect to x and going back to the Riemann equation (2.1) for the velocity field.

2.1.2 Line growth in the small angle approximation

Construction of generalized solutions for the velocity field and its potential are geometrically more comprehensible if they are compared with the generalized solutions of the line-growth equation written in the small angle approximation. Recall that if $h(x,t)$ is the line of fire or of a one-dimensional wave front and propagates at a speed c perpendicularly to $h(x,t)$, then, in the small angle approximation, $h(x,t)$ satisfies the following equation:

$$\frac{\partial h}{\partial t}=\frac{c}{2}\left(\frac{\partial h}{\partial x}\right)^2,\quad h(x,t=0)=h_0(x), \tag{2.5}$$

and tilts of the wave front

$$u(x,t)=-\frac{\partial h}{\partial x} \tag{2.6}$$

obey the equation

$$\frac{\partial u}{\partial t}+cu\frac{\partial u}{\partial x}=0, \quad u(x,t=0)=u_0(x), \tag{2.7}$$

which is related to the Riemann equation. Moreover, the equations of particle flow and surface growth exactly coincide, if we make the following substitutions:

$$v=cu, \quad s=-chap. \tag{2.8}$$

2.1.3 Nonlinear acoustics equation

Let us consider an example of nonlinear acoustic waves, which is closer to practical applications. Let $P(r,t)$ be a deviation from the atmospheric pressure caused by the presence of acoustic waves. It can be shown that distribution of intense acoustic waves, such as the sound of a jet engine, obeys the equation (see, e.g., [4, 5])

$$\frac{\partial P}{\partial r}-\frac{1}{c}\frac{\partial P}{\partial t}-\beta P\frac{\partial P}{\partial t}+\frac{n}{2r}P=0. \tag{2.9}$$

It describes the propagation of a spherical ($n=2$), cylindrical ($n=1$) or plane ($n=0$) intense acoustic wave. Here c is the linear speed of sound and β is a nonlinearity parameter of the medium.

Equation (2.9) is reduced to a more convenient form by introducing a local time

$$\theta=t-\frac{r}{c}$$

retarded by the time the wave propagates from the origin $r=0$ to the observation point r. Thereby we eliminate one term of Eq. (2.9):

$$\frac{\partial P}{\partial r}-\beta P\frac{\partial P}{\partial \theta}+\frac{n}{2r}P=0.$$

The last term, which takes into account wave attenuation due to geometric divergence, can be eliminated by a suitable substitution of new variables. For example, for a spherical wave ($n=2$), the new variables are

$$p=\frac{r}{r_0}\beta P, \quad z=r_0\ln\left(\frac{r}{r_0}\right).$$

As a result, the equation of nonlinear acoustic wave transforms into the canonical Riemann equation for the field $p(z,\theta)$:

$$\frac{\partial p}{\partial z}+p\frac{\partial p}{\partial \theta}=0. \tag{2.10}$$

2.2 Multistream solutions

Let us start a discussion of generalized solutions of nonlinear partial differential equations of the first order with an analysis of *multistream solutions.*

2.2.1 Interval of single-stream motion

From here on, construction of generalized solutions will be substantially based on the relationship between the Lagrangian y and Eulerian x coordinates:

$$x = X(y,t) = y + v_0(y)t. \tag{2.11}$$

We assume that $v_0(x)$ is a differentiable function and its derivative is bounded from below by the value $-u_{\min}$:

$$v_0'(x) \geqslant -u_{\min}. \tag{2.12}$$

Then within the time interval

$$0 < t < t_n, \quad \text{where} \quad t_n = 1/u_{\min}, \tag{2.13}$$

there exists a function

$$y = y(x,t), \tag{2.14}$$

which is the inverse of (2.11). Thereby the Riemann solution (2.11) can be written as

$$v(x,t) = \frac{x - y(x,t)}{t}, \tag{2.15}$$

which means that the velocity of a flow at the current moment of time t, at the point x is equal to the velocity of a uniformly moving particle placed at this point.

2.2.2 Appearance of multistreamness

The moment of time t_n is called a *wave-overturning time.* For $t > t_n$, the Lagrangian-to-Eulerian coordinate transformation (2.11) ceases to be an everywhere monotonically increasing mapping. In terms of the particle flow, this means that some particles overtake others and some particles with different Lagrangian (initial) coordinates y find themselves within the same intervals of the x-axis. In other words, intervals of *multistream motion* form on the x-axis.

Appearance of the multistreamness can be conveniently traced on the plot of the Lagrangian-to-Eulerian coordinate transformation $x = X(y,t)$ (2.11) (see Fig. 2.1). It was plotted for the Gaussian initial velocity field

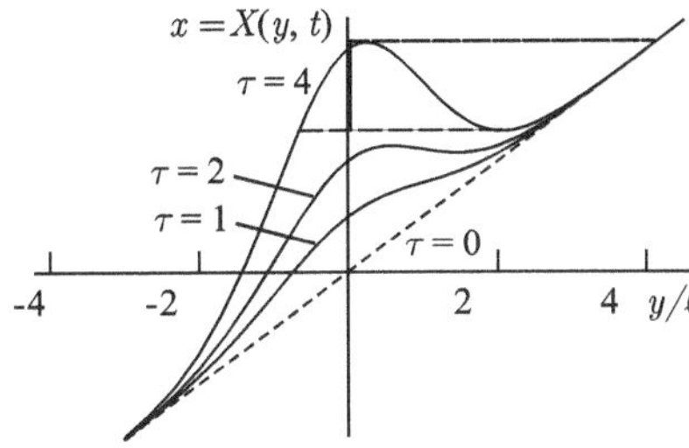

Fig. 2.1 Lagrangian-to-Eulerian coordinate transformation of a flow of uniformly moving particles for the following values of the dimensionless time: $\tau = 1, 2, 4$. Multistreamness interval on the x-axis is shown by the bold line segment for $\tau = 4$.

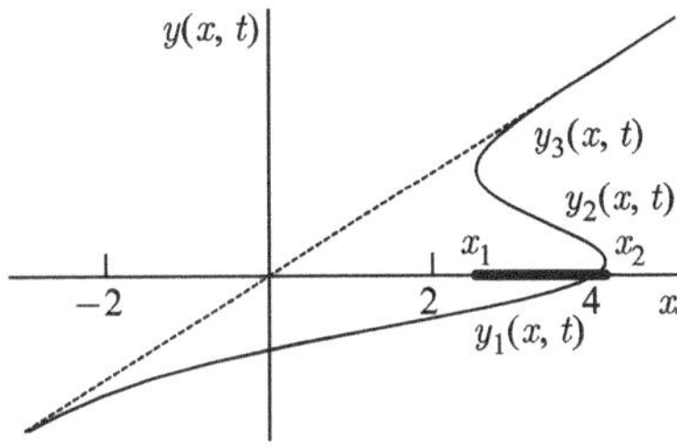

Fig. 2.2 Multivalued mapping from the Eulerian into Lagrangian coordinates at a time of $\tau = 4$. Bold line segment on the x-axis highlights the interval of multistreamness, and the three branches of the function $y(x,t)$ are marked.

$$v_0(x) = V_0 \exp\left(-\frac{x^2}{2\ell^2}\right) \tag{2.16}$$

at different values of the dimensionless time $\tau = V_0 t/\ell$. For the initial field (2.16), multistreamness is takes place, if $\tau_n \geqslant \sqrt{e} \approx 1.65$.

Nonmonotonicity of the mapping $x = X(y,t)$ at $t > t_n$ causes a multivaluedness of the inverse function $x = y(x,t)$. In other words, at $t > t_n$, on the x-axis, there are intervals, where $y(x,t)$ has not one, but n values at once:

$$\{y_1(x,t), y_2(x,t), \ldots, y_n(x,t)\}.$$

Figure 2.2 shows the profile of $y(x,t)$ for the initial field (2.16) and the moment of time $\tau = 4$. It is seen that there is an interval on the x-axis, whose each point is, at once, the destination of three ($n = 3$) particles with different Lagrangian coordinates.

Let $x \in [x_1, x_2]$ be an interval of multivaluedness of the mapping $y(x,t)$. By substituting the different branches of the multivalued in the range $[x_1, x_2]$ function $y(x,t)$ into the expression for the velocity field (2.15), we obtain the multistream field $v(x,t)$, which assumes n values within the interval of multivaluedness:

$$v(x,t) = \{v_1(x,t), v_2(x,t), \ldots, v_n(x,t)\}, \quad v_i(x,t) = \frac{x - y_i(x,t)}{t}. \tag{2.17}$$

The multivalued field $v(x,t)$ found in such way is plotted in Fig. 2.3.

In addition to the velocity field at $t > t_n$, the density field also becomes a multistream one, each branch of which

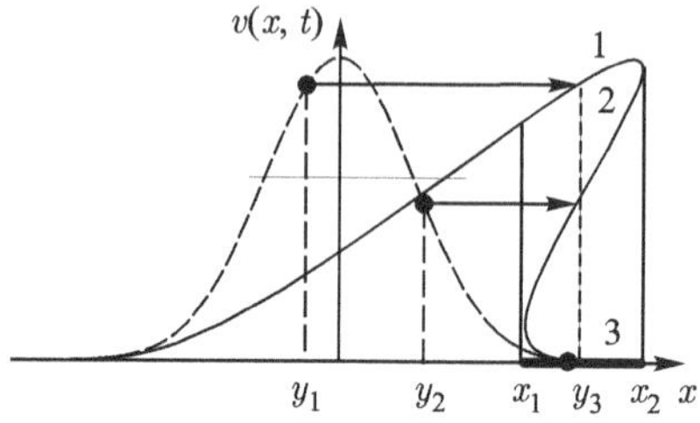

Fig. 2.3 Field $v(x,t)$ at the moment of time $\tau = 4$. The dashed line shows the initial field (2.16). On its profile, three particles meeting at the same point at $\tau = 4$ are shown and their Lagrangian coordinates are marked. It is seen that the particles with greater velocities are catching up with the nearly stationary particle with the coordinate y_3.

$$\rho_i(x,t) = (-1)^{i-1}\rho_0(y_i(x,t))\frac{\partial y_i(x,t)}{\partial x} \quad (i = 1,2,\dots,n) \tag{2.18}$$

specifies the density of particles of the corresponding stream. The factor $(-1)^{i-1}$ takes into account alternation of signs of the derivative $\partial y_i(x,t)/\partial x$ in the streams, caused by a change of the particle-sequence order, and makes sure that the physical requirement of non-negativity of the stream densities holds.

2.2.3 Gradient catastrophe

Multistream solutions are natural as applied to flows of non-interacting particles and optic waves. But, from the standpoint of classical mathematics, they cannot be solutions of differential equations because multistreamness is preceded by a *gradient catastrophe*, i.e. singular behavior of the spatial derivative

$$q(x,t) = \frac{\partial v(x,t)}{\partial x} \tag{2.19}$$

of the Riemann solutions at $t \to t_n$. Let us trace the beginning of the gradient catastrophe. From Eq. (2.15), it follows that this derivative is equal to

$$q(x,t) = \frac{1}{t}\left(1 - \frac{\partial y(x,t)}{\partial x}\right). \tag{2.20}$$

This expression includes the derivative of the mapping $y = y(x,t)$. The best way to study its peculiarities is to examine "more decent", everywhere differentiable inverse function $x = X(y,t)$ (2.11) and its derivative with respect to y

$$J(y,t) = \frac{\partial X(y,t)}{\partial y} = 1 + v_0'(y)t. \tag{2.21}$$

At the time of overturning t_n, the mapping $X(y,t)$ ceases to be strictly monotonous, and the minimum value of its derivative (2.21) attained at some point y_* becomes equal to zero: $J(y_*,t_n) = 1 + v_0'(y_*)\,t_n = 0$. Since the point y_* is, at the same time, the point of a minimum of the function $J(y,t_n)$, then, at this point, not only $J(y,t_n)$, but also its derivative become equal to zero:

$$\left.\frac{\partial J(y,t)}{\partial y}\right|_{y=y_*} = v_0''(y_*)\,t_n = 0 \Rightarrow v_0''(y_*) = 0.$$

Hence the mapping (2.11) $X(y,t)$ itself has a cubic asymptotic in the neighborhood of the point y_*:

$$x = X(y,t) \sim x_* + b(y-y_*)^3, \quad b = -\frac{v_0'''(y_*)}{v_0'(y_*)}. \tag{2.22}$$

This expression includes the *point of overturning* x_*, which is the Eulerian coordinate of the point y_*.

According to (2.22), in the neighborhood of the point of overturning x_*, the inverse to $X(y,t)$ function $y(x,t)$, and along with it the velocity field $v(x,t)$ (2.15), obey the following asymptotic law:

$$y(x,t) \sim y_* + \sqrt[3]{\frac{|x-x_*|}{b}}\ \mathrm{sgn}(x-x_*) \Rightarrow$$

$$v(x,t) \sim v_* - \sqrt[3]{\frac{|x-x_*|}{d}}\ \mathrm{sgn}(x-x_*),$$

$$v_* = \frac{x-x_*}{t}. \quad d = \frac{v_0'''(y_*)}{\left[v_0'(y_*)\right]^4}.$$

Accordingly, at the time of overturning, the derivative $q(x,t)$ of the field $v(x,t)$ at the point of overturning has an infinite singularity of the following type:

$$q(x,t) \sim -\frac{1}{3\sqrt[3]{d}}\,\frac{1}{|x-x_*|^{2/3}}.$$

Mathematically, this asymptotic formula expresses a gradient catastrophe. It means that, at the time of overturning, the field $v(x,t)$ becomes non-differentiable at least at one point and can no longer be a solution to the differential equation.

Recall that the density field $\rho(x,t)$ (2.18) is proportional to the derivative of the mapping $y(x,t)$ with respect to x. Precisely this derivative determines the character of a gradient catastrophe. Thus, in terms of a particle flow, a gradient catastrophe is accompanied by an infinite compression of the flow at the point of overturning, and the density at this point (at $\rho_0(y_*) \neq 0$) becomes infinite.

In conclusion. Because of the gradient catastrophe, the classical, everywhere differentiable Riemann solution exists only within the interval of single-streamness $t \in (0,t_n)$. However, a multistream solution, constructed on the basis of the nonmonotonic mapping (2.11) for $t > t_n$, sometimes has a physical meaning, and therefore has a right to exist. Therefore it is natural to interpret the multivalued Riemann solution described above as a variety of generalized solutions of this equation.

2.3 Sum of streams

Let us emphasize: the same first-order nonlinear partial differential equation, with the same initial and boundary conditions, can have different generalized solutions. Therefore it is necessary to impose a certain set of additional conditions upon the sought-for solution. This may narrow down the class of possible generalized solutions, or even make a generalized solution unique.

The most common condition of this kind, which is consistent with the requirements of most applications, e.g., in nonlinear acoustic, consists in that the solution must be *single-valued*. If we accept it, we need discard the multistream solutions discussed above. Yet, we retain the right to attempt to use different streams as construction material for building generalized single-valued solutions, and test their compliance with certain applications.

First of all, let us discuss the properties of single-valued fields obtained as an algebraic sum of the streams of multistream fields described above.

2.3.1 *Total particle flow*

Let us start with the multistream density field. The first thing that comes to mind is to construct a single-valued density field as the sum of the densities (2.18) of all streams present at a given point x and moment of time t:

$$\rho(x,t) = \sum_{i=1}^{n} \rho_i(x,t) = \sum_{i=1}^{n} (-1)^{i-1} \rho_0(y_i(x,t)) \frac{\partial y_i(x,t)}{\partial x}. \tag{2.23}$$

In order to justify this construction, the following physical argument is used: the density of gas particles within a physically infinitesimal interval Δx is single-valued and equal to the total number of particles arrived in the given interval divided by its length. Mathematical formulation of this statement as applied to the single-valued particles streams, whose motion is described by the nonmonotonic mapping $x = X(y,t)$, leads to the expression (2.23). Note that there is a more compact way to write the density field (2.23) by means of a delta function:

$$\rho(x,t) = \int_{-\infty}^{\infty} \rho_0(y)\delta\left(X(y,t) - x\right) dy. \tag{2.24}$$

By using the properties of a delta function of a complex argument, it easy to prove the equivalence of Eqs. (2.23) and (2.24).

2.3.2 Summation of streams by inverse Fourier transform

Fourier transform of the total density (2.23)

$$\tilde{\rho}(\kappa,t) = \frac{1}{2\pi}\int_{-\infty}^{\infty} \rho(x,t)e^{-i\kappa x}\,dx$$

will help us to study its properties. According to (2.24), the Fourier transform of the density field is equal to

$$\tilde{\rho}(\kappa,t) = \frac{1}{2\pi}\int_{-\infty}^{\infty} e^{-i\kappa X(y,t)}\rho_0(y)\,dy. \qquad (2.25)$$

Note, the right-hand side of this expression exists also for a nonmonotonic mapping $x = X(y,t)$. The inverse Fourier integral of (2.25)

$$\rho(x,t) = \int_{-\infty}^{\infty} \tilde{\rho}(\kappa,t)e^{i\kappa x}\,d\kappa \qquad (2.26)$$

is a single-valued function which can be interpreted as a generalized solution of the continuity equation (2.2). By closely tracing the transformation from the Eulerian integration variable x to the Lagrangian y in the integral (2.25), it easy to see that the inverse Fourier integral (2.25) is equal to the density sum (2.23) of a flow of uniformly moving particles.

2.3.3 Algebraic sum of the velocity field

Similarly, by using the inverse Fourier transform, we can construct a certain single-valued field $v_{\pm}(x,t)$. It can easily be shown that the field defined in this way is an alternating-sign sum of stream velocities of the multistream Riemann solution:

$$v_{\pm}(x,t) = \sum_{i=1}^{n}(-1)^{i-1}v_i(x,t) = \sum_{i=1}^{n}(-1)^{i-1}v_0(y_i(x,t)). \qquad (2.27)$$

In contrast to the total density (2.23), (2.26), physical meaning of this function is unclear. But perhaps it will find its biological, economic or other area of application. Figure. 2.4 shows the field (2.27) for a sinusoidal initial condition, constructed by partial summation of the series

$$v_{\pm}(x,t) = 2a\sum_{n=1}^{\infty}(-1)^{n+1}\frac{J_n(n\tau)}{n\tau}\sin(nkx). \qquad (2.28)$$

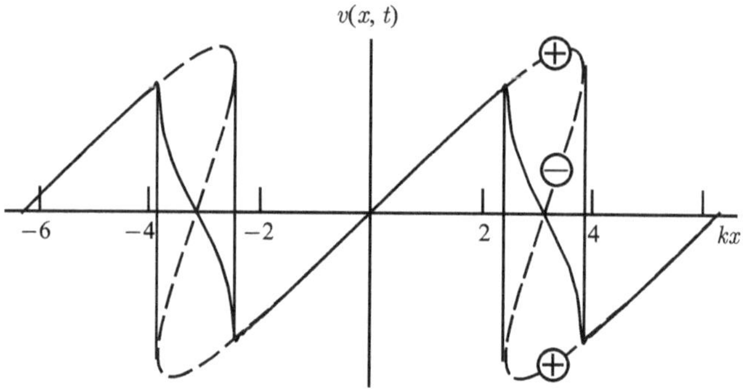

Fig. 2.4 Field $v_{\pm}(x,t)$ found by summing 50 terms of the series (2.28) at $\tau = kat = 2$. The dashed line shows the multistream velocity field of uniformly moving particles. Pluses and minuses indicate the sign, with which each stream is added to the total sum. Characteristically pointed peaks at the boundaries of the intervals of multistreamness are due to non-differentiability of the velocity field at these points.

2.3.4 Density of a "warm" particle flow

Let us discuss the behavior of total density (2.23) of uniformly moving particles at $t > t_n$. In order to avoid a density singularity at points where particles overtake one another, let us take the effect of *thermal smoothing* into account. To do this, we recall that molecules of a real gas, in addition to the collective velocity v, also have a chaotic component u due to by thermal motion. The thermal component of uniformly moving particles is taken into account by substituting $v_0(y) + u$ for $v_0(y)$ in the mapping (2.11)

$$x = X(y,u,t) = y + [v_0(y) + u]\,t = X(y,t) + ut.$$

Here $X(y,t)$ describes the "hydrodynamic component" of the particles' law of motion given by the expression (2.11).

Let us describe the contribution of particles with different u to the total flow by using initial density $\rho_0(x,u)$, which depends not only on x, but also on u. The dependence on u takes the distribution of particles according to their velocities into account. Thereby the density $\rho_0(x,u)$ must satisfy the condition of consistency:

$$\int_{-\infty}^{\infty} \rho_0(x,u)\,du = \rho_0(x),$$

where $\rho_0(x)$ is the regular initial density of particles in the neighborhood of the point x.

Obvious generalization of the density field (2.24) to the case of a warm flow has the following form:

$$\rho(x,t) = \iint \rho_0(y,u)\,\delta\left(X(y,u,t) - x\right) du\,dy. \tag{2.29}$$

Let us consider a more illustrative special case, when

$$\rho_0(y,u) = \rho_0(y)\, f(u), \tag{2.30}$$

where $f(u)$ is the distribution of the thermal component of the velocity of particles of a "uniformly heated" flow. Let it be the Maxwell distribution

$$f(u) = \frac{1}{\sqrt{2\pi\varepsilon}} \exp\left(-\frac{u^2}{2\varepsilon}\right), \tag{2.31}$$

where ε is the "temperature" of the flow. By substituting (2.31) and (2.30) into (2.29), we obtain the following "transparent" formula:

$$\rho_\varepsilon(x,t) = \int_{-\infty}^{\infty} \rho(x-ut,t)\, f(u)\, du. \tag{2.32}$$

Here $\rho(x-ut,t)$ is the density field (2.24) translated along the x-axis by a distance ut without thermal spreading of particles. The subscript ε in (2.32) shows that $\rho_\varepsilon(x,t)$ is the density of a "warm" flow with a "temperature" ε. Equation (2.32) means that the thermal spreading of particle velocities leads to a spatial averaging of the hydrodynamic density field $\rho(x,t)$. Such averaging smoothes density features. Let us verify this by working out the density for the homogeneous initial density and sinusoidal initial velocity field (1.37). By substituting the expression for $\rho(x,t)$ in the form of the Fourier series (1.41) into (2.32), we find

$$\rho(x,t) = \rho_0 + 2\rho_0 \sum_{n=1}^{\infty} (-1)^n J_n(n\tau)\varphi_n(x,t), \tag{2.33}$$

where

$$\varphi_n(x,t) = \int_{-\infty}^{\infty} \cos(knx - kunt)\, f(u)\, du.$$

From here, in the case of the Maxwell distribution (2.31), we obtain

$$\varphi_n(x,t) = \exp\left[-\frac{\varepsilon}{2}(knt)^2\right] \cos(nkx).$$

By substituting this expression into (2.33), we finally find

$$\rho(x,t) = \rho_0 + 2\rho_0 \sum_{n=1}^{\infty} (-1)^n J_n(n\tau) \cos(nkx) \exp\left(-\frac{\delta}{2}\tau^2 n^2\right). \tag{2.34}$$

Here and in (2.33), we used the dimensionless time $\tau = kat$ and parameter $\delta = \varepsilon/a^2$. This parameter characterizes the relative contribution of the thermal spread of particle velocities into the behavior of the flow. At small δ, the field $\rho(x,t)$ is, for a long time, formed by hydrodynamic compression and rarefaction of the flow. At large δ, thermal dissolution of density inhomogeneities proceeds rapidly during the time period $\tau_* = \sqrt{2/\delta}$. Residual variations of the density are described by the first two terms of the series (2.34)

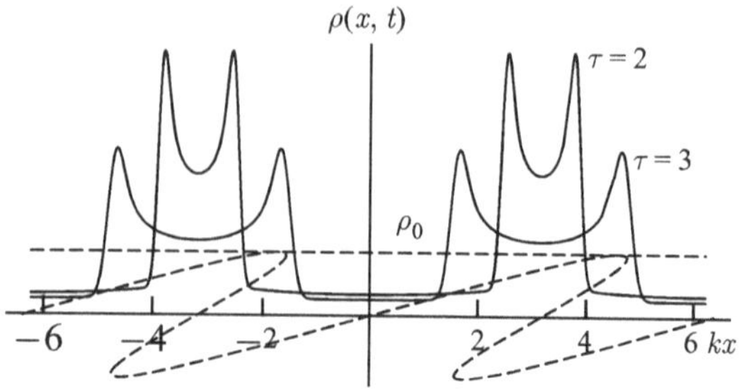

Fig. 2.5 Density (2.34) for $\delta = 0.002$ at $\tau = 2$ and 3. The dashed line shows the multistream velocity for $\tau = 3$. All elements of the structure of the density field of the hydrodynamic flow are clearly seen.

$$\rho(x,t) \sim \rho_0 \left[1 - 2J_1(\tau)\, e^{-\delta\tau^2/2} \cos(kx)\right].$$

The density (2.34) for $\delta = 0.002$ is plotted in Fig. 2.5.

2.4 Weak solutions of nonlinear equations of the first order

Weak solutions of nonlinear partial differential equations of the first order are functions satisfying the equations, wherever derivatives of the given functions exist, and having discontinuities (of the functions themselves or of their derivatives) along some curves $\{x^*(t)\}$ in the plane (x,t). The shape and position of the curves $\{x^*(t)\}$ can be found on the basis of integral conservation laws and other requirements imposed on the fields of interest (see, e.g., [2, 6]). Sometimes, in order to determine the only needed weak solution of the problem at hand, it happens to be sufficient to invoke illustrative geometrical arguments. We start our discussion of weak solutions with an example of such kind.

2.4.1 Forest fire

Let us return to the problem of forest-fire. If the fire propagates predominantly along z-axis, the small angle approximation is valid, and the fire line $h(x,t)$ obeys Eq. (2.5). In order to kill two birds with one stone, i.e. to make the following analysis be also useful for particle-flow studies, let us use the substitution (2.8). It expresses the fire front $h(x,t)$ and its tilt angles $u(x,t)$ through the fields $s(x,t)$ and $v(x,t)$. The latter have a natural interpretation in terms of flows of uniformly moving particles. With regard to forest fires, the transformation from h to s means that the fire propagates against the z-axis. In other words, by the time t, everything above the line $s(x,t)$ has been burned.

Recall that there are at least three known physical meanings of the function $s(x,t)$. This may be the potential of the velocity (2.3), line of fire or optic wave front. In this section, we address the latter two interpretations. Let us find the line

$s(x,t)$ of a propagating downwards fire by solving Eqs. (2.1), (2.4) by the method of characteristics. These equations can be rewritten in a more mutually consistent form:

$$\begin{aligned} &\frac{\partial s}{\partial t}+v\frac{\partial s}{\partial x}=\frac{1}{2}v^2, \qquad s(x,t=0)=s_0(x),\\ &\frac{\partial v}{\partial t}+v\frac{\partial v}{\partial x}=0, \qquad v(x,t=0)=v_0(x). \end{aligned} \tag{2.35}$$

The corresponding characteristic equations have the following form:

$$\frac{dX}{dt}=V, \quad \frac{dV}{dt}=0, \quad \frac{dS}{dt}=\frac{1}{2}V^2.$$

Let us write down the already well-known solutions of the above listed equations:

$$X(y,t)=y+v_0(y)t,\ V(y,t)=v_0(y),\ S(y,t)=s_0(y)+\frac{1}{2}v_0^2(y)t. \tag{2.36}$$

The corresponding Eulerian fields $s(x,t)$ and $v(x,t)$ are conveniently expressed via the mapping $y(x,t)$, which is the inverse of the mapping $x=X(y,t)$:

$$s(x,t)=s_0(y(x,t))+\frac{(y(x,t)-x)^2}{2t}, \quad v(x,t)=\frac{x-y(x,t)}{t}. \tag{2.37}$$

A typical plot of a forest-fire line $s(x,t)$ constructed parametrically with the use of Lagrangian fields:

$$x=X(y,t)=y+v_0(y)t, \quad s=S(y,t)=s_0(y)+\frac{1}{2}v_0^2(y)t, \tag{2.38}$$

is shown in Fig. 2.6. The line $s(x,t)$ is shown at the moment, when the function $s(x,t)$ is already multivalued. As far as optic wave fronts are concerned, multivaluedness of $s(x,t)$ does not contradict anything. It only means that there are parts of the wave front, which are left behind and move in the region already passed by the other parts of the front. In another physical situation, where $s(x,t)$ is a forest-fire line, it must be single-valued. Indeed, a fire burns any part of a forest only once, and there cannot be any lines of fire left behind. There simply is no any combustible material left for them. Therefore, if we intend to find the actual fire front by solving Eq. (2.4), we must determine a generalized (week) solution of this equation by using the following formula:

$$s_w(x,t)=\min_i\left\{s_0(y_i(x,t))+\frac{(y_i(x,t)-x)^2}{2t}\right\}, \tag{2.39}$$

where the minimum is sought within the set of all values of the multivalued mapping $y(x,t)$ at a given point x and moment of time t.

The corresponding discontinuous weak Riemann solution can be found from

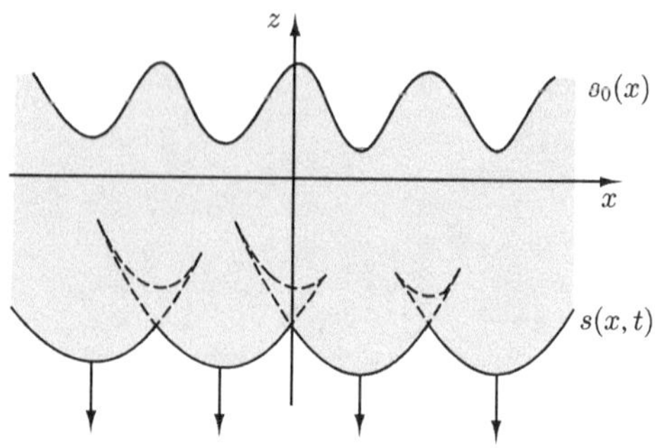

Fig. 2.6 Initial line of fire $s_0(x)$ (above) and fire front $s(x,t)$ (below) at the current moment of time. Shaded area between the initial and current lines of fire is scorched earth. In order to obtain the generalized weak solution of the fire-line equation, the top segments of the multivalued line $s(x,t)$ need to be removed.

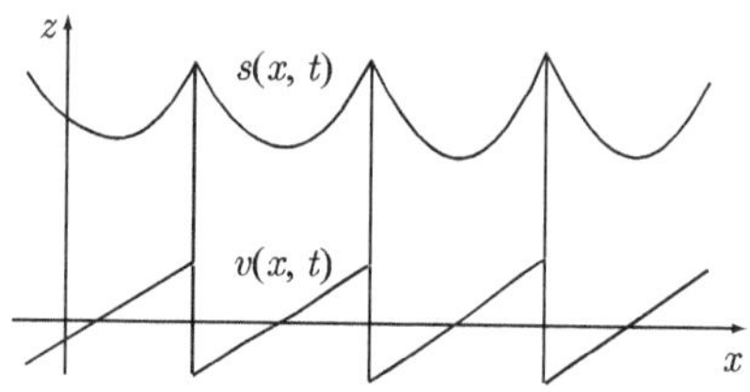

Fig. 2.7 Sawtooth weak solution (2.40) of the Riemann equation (bottom) and piecewise smooth weak solution (2.39) of Eq. (2.4) (top).

$$v_w(x,t) = \frac{x - y_w(x,t)}{t}, \tag{2.40}$$

where $y_w(x,t)$ is the value of the multivalued function $y(x,t)$, at which the function $s(x,t)$ (2.37) assumes the minimum value. Typical weak solutions $s(x,t)$ and $v(x,t)$ are shown in Fig. 2.7.

2.4.2 The Lax-Oleinik absolute minimum principle

While the weak solutions $s_w(x,t)$ and $v_w(x,t)$, described above, completely suit a fireman, they have, from a mathematician's point of view, a significant flaw: they force one to manipulate a multivalued function $y(x,t)$. That is why we now set out in search of another, equivalent to the one described above, procedure for constructing weak solutions $v_w(x,t)$ and $s_w(x,t)$, which deals with a single-valued functions. To achieve the desired goal, we extend the number of arguments of functions under study. Namely, let us take the mapping $x = y + v_0(y)t$, depending on two arguments y, t; and construct, on its basis, the following function of three arguments:

$$\mathscr{R}(y;x,t) = X(y,t) - x = v_0(y)t + (y - x). \tag{2.41}$$

The graph of this function as a function of y, for fixed x and t, passes through zero at the points $\{y_i(x,t)\}$, which are values of the multivalued (in a general case) Eulerian-to-Lagrangian coordinate transformation

$$y = y(x,t). \tag{2.42}$$

Let us introduce another auxiliary function

$$\mathscr{G}(y;x,t) = \int^{y} \mathscr{R}(z,x,t)\,dz = \int^{y} [X(z,t) - x]\,dz, \tag{2.43}$$

which is, up to an arbitrary constant, equal to

$$\mathscr{G}(y;x,t) = s_0(y)\,t + \frac{1}{2}(y-x)^2, \tag{2.44}$$

where $s_0(x)$ is the initial potential (2.3) of the field $v(x,t)$.

We further assume that $\mathscr{G}(y;x,t)$ is a continuous function of y, depending on x and t as parameters. Note a remarkable property of the function $\mathscr{G}(y;x,t)$, built-in by construction; which means that the coordinate $y_i(x,t)$ of each extremum, including the absolute minimum, coincides with one of the values of the mapping (2.42). As is seen from the comparison of Eq. (2.44) with (2.39), the absolute minimum value $\mathscr{G}(y;x,t)$ is equal to the actual fire-line (2.39). Having realized this, we arrive at the following algorithm for constructing the weak solutions $v_w(x,t)$ and $s_w(x,t)$: they are determined by following formulas:

$$s_w(x,t) = \frac{1}{t}\mathscr{G}(y_w(x,t),x,t) = s_0(y_w(x,t)) + \frac{(y_w(x,t)-x)^2}{2t}, \tag{2.45}$$

$$v_w(x,t) = \frac{1}{t}\left[x - y_w(x,t)\right], \tag{2.46}$$

where $y_w(x,t)$ is the coordinate of the absolute minimum of the function (2.44).

This is the *Lax-Oleinik absolute minimum principle* mentioned in the title of this section. It defines the discontinuous Eulerian-to-Lagrangian coordinate transformation $y = y_w(x,t)$, whose substitution into the right-hand side of Eqs. (2.45), (2.46) gives the sought-for weak solutions.

2.4.3 Geometric construction of weak solutions

The principle of absolute minimum is visual: according to it, in order to find the coordinate $y_w(x,t)$ of the absolute minimum of the function $\mathscr{G}(y;x,t)$ we must shift the parabola

$$\mathscr{P}(y;x,t) = -\frac{(y-x)^2}{2t} + H \tag{2.47}$$

upwards by increasing H from $-\infty$ until the first contact with profile of the initial potential $s_0(y)$. The coordinate $y_w(x,t)$ of the first point of tangency is the sought-for coordinate of the absolute minimum of the function $\mathscr{G}(y;x,t)$ (2.44); and the fields (2.45), (2.46), found with the help of this coordinate, are the sought-for weak solutions. The geometric procedure described above is shown in Fig. 2.8.

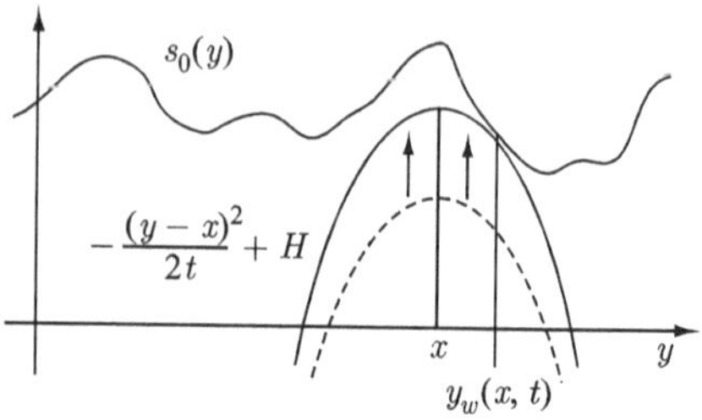

Fig. 2.8 Determination of the absolute minimum coordinate of the function $\mathscr{G}(y;x,t)$. By shifting the parabola $\mathscr{P}$ with the center at the point x upwards, we find the coordinate $y_w(x,t)$ of the first contact point with profile of the initial potential $s_0(y)$.

Note that the center of parabola (2.47) is an Eulerian coordinate x, and the point of tangency of the parabola with the initial potential $s_0(y)$ gives the corresponding Lagrangian coordinate $y_w(x,t)$. Thus the pair of these points $\{x, y_w(x,t)\}$ geometrically illustrates the relationship between the Lagrangian and Eulerian coordinates.

We further note that it is enough to shift the parabola (2.47) upwards until the first contact with the initial potential only once, and then by varying x we can slide along the profile $s_0(y)$ while tracking the motion of the tangent point $y_w(x,t)$.

The way the parabola slides along the initial potential is qualitatively different for different values of t. As long as $0 < t < t_n$, the branches of the parabola steeply go down, and the parabola itself has, at all x, only a single point of contact with the profile of $s_0(y)$. With growing t, the parabola is getting more shallow (flatter). As a result, at $t > t_n$, there exist such $x = x_k^*$, where the parabola is tangent to the curve $s_0(y)$ simultaneously at two points with the coordinates $y_k{}^-(x,t)$ and $y_k{}^+(x,t)$ $(y_k{}^+ > y_k{}^-)$. Small movement of x from $x_k^* - 0$ to $x_k^* + 0$ leads to a jump of the function $y_w(x,t)$. Following $y_w(x,t)$, the field $v_w(x,t)$ (2.46) also goes through a jump. Thus the point of double tangency of the parabola $\mathscr{P}$ (2.47) and the initial potential $s_0(y)$ specifies the location of the discontinuity of the weak Riemann solution $v_w(x,t)$, and distance between the coordinates of double tangency is equal to the magnitude of the discontinuous jump

$$V_k = v_w(x_k^* - 0, t) - v_w(x_k^* + 0, t) = \frac{y_k^+ - y_k^-}{t}. \tag{2.48}$$

An example of *critical parabolas*, establishing all parameters of the discontinuities of a weak Riemann solution, is shown in Fig. 2.9.

2.4.4 Convex hull

Above we have described the principle of absolute minimum, which determines the Eulerian-to-Lagrangian coordinate transformation $y = y_w(x,t)$. In a general case, this is a discontinuous function. Sometimes, it is more convenient to work with the continuous inverse function $X_w(y,t)$. The latter can be found by means of a beautiful geometric procedure. In order to describe this procedure, we again turn to the function $\mathscr{G}(y;x,t)$ (2.44):

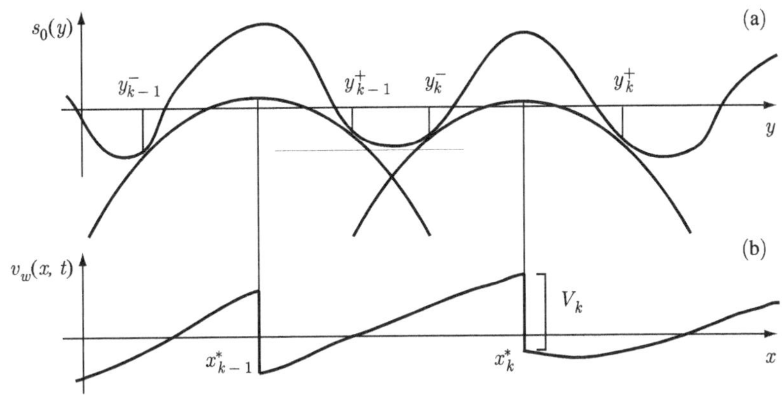

Fig. 2.9 (a) Initial potential $s_0(y)$ and two critical parabolas . **(b)** The respective weak Riemann solution, whose coordinates of discontinuities (shocks) coincide with the centers of critical parabolas.

$$\mathcal{G}(y;x,t) = s_0(y)t + \frac{y^2}{2} - xy + \frac{x^2}{2}. \tag{2.49}$$

While looking for the coordinate of the absolute minimum of $\mathcal{G}(y;x,t)$ as a function of y, note that the last term in (2.49) plays the role of a constant component, which does not have an effect on the sought-for coordinate. Therefore this term can be harmlessly disregarded. While at it, let us introduce the following notation:

$$\varphi(y,t) = \frac{y^2}{2} + s_0(y)t. \tag{2.50}$$

As a result, the problem is reduced to finding the coordinates of the absolute minimum of the function

$$\varphi(y,t) - xy. \tag{2.51}$$

In order to find it, we bring, from below, the straight line

$$xy + h, \tag{2.52}$$

in contact with the graph of the function $\varphi(y,t)$ (2.50) by selecting the magnitude of h in a suitable way. The coordinate of the point of tangency between the straight line(2.52) and function $\varphi(y,t)$ (2.50) is precisely the sought-for mapping $y_w(x,t)$. By varying the slope x of the straight line (2.52), we find $y_w(x,t)$ for all values of x.

Note that the result of the shown geometric construction would remain unchanged if we replaced $\varphi(y,t)$ by its *convex hull* $\bar{\varphi}(y,t)$, and would look for the coordinate of the absolute minimum not of (2.51), but of the function

$$\bar{\varphi}(y,t) - xy. \tag{2.53}$$

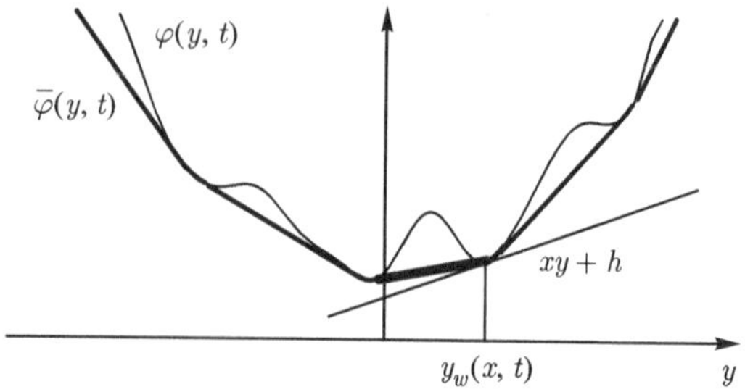

Fig. 2.10 A function $\varphi(y,t)$ and its convex hull $\bar{\varphi}(y,t)$. It is seen that, at each point of the profile of $\bar{\varphi}(y,t)$, we can draw a tangent straight line lying under the convex hull. Here the coordinate of the point of tangency at which the tangent line touches the convex hull is also shown.

Recall the notion of convex hull. Figuratively speaking, the convex hull of any function $\varphi(y)$, which sufficiently rapidly tends to infinity at $y \to \pm\infty$, has the shape of an elastic thread taut over the curve $\varphi(y)$ from below. An example of a function $\varphi(y,t)$ and its convex hull $\bar{\varphi}(y,t)$ are plotted in Fig. 2.10.

The advantage of convex hulls $\bar{\varphi}$, in comparison with the original functions φ, is that each point of the convex hull has a tangent line, above which lies the entire convex hull. Therefore, by constructing a convex hull of the function $\varphi(y,t)$, we can find coordinates of the minimum of the function (2.51), (2.53) in a new way: not by bringing from below the straight line (2.52) directly to the curve $\varphi(y,t)$, but by *selecting the gradient of the tangent line* to the convex hull $\bar{\varphi}(y,t)$ at a given point y. Obviously, the gradient of the line is equal to $x = X_w(y,t)$ which is the value of the Lagrangian-to-Eulerian coordinate transformation for a given y. In other words, the inverse to $y = y_w(x,t)$ mapping $x = X_w(y,t)$ is given by:

$$X_w(y,t) = \frac{\partial \bar{\varphi}(y,t)}{\partial y}. \tag{2.54}$$

The method, described above for constructing the mapping $X_w(y,t)$, shows that it is a continuous, in general, piecewise-constant function of y. The values of the inverse mapping $y = y_w(x,t)$ on both sides of the discontinuity (jump), mentioned in the previous section, serve as the boundaries of constant pieces of $X_w(y,t)$.

2.4.5 *Maxwell's rule*

So far we have found a weak solution $v_w(x,t)$ of the Riemann equation as a function of tilt angles to the real line of fire $s_w(x,t)$. However, in many applications, such as nonlinear acoustics, the Riemann equation and its generalized solutions have their own independent significance. Therefore, let us determine a weak solution of the Riemann equation once more. The Riemann equation in differential form expresses an integral conservation law. Let us verify this statement by rewriting the Riemann equation (2.1) in the divergence form:

$$\frac{\partial v}{\partial t} + \frac{\partial}{\partial x}\left(\frac{v^2}{2}\right) = 0.$$

By integrating this equation with respect to x over infinite limits and assuming that $v(x,t)$ tends to zero as $x \to \pm\infty$, we arrive at the equality

$$\frac{d}{dt}\int_{-\infty}^{\infty} v(x,t)\,dx = 0.$$

From here it follows that there exists the following invariant:

$$\mathscr{I} = \int_{-\infty}^{\infty} v(x,t)\,dx = \int_{-\infty}^{\infty} v_0(x)\,dx = const. \tag{2.55}$$

Precisely this invariant must be obeyed by $v_w(x,t)$, in order for the weak solution of the Riemann equation to have an acoustic meaning.

Let us construct a weak solution of the Riemann equation satisfying the invariant (2.55). In order to do so, let us substitute the second relation of (2.37) into (2.55):

$$\mathscr{I} = \frac{1}{t}\int_{-\infty}^{\infty} [x - y(x,t)]\,dx. \tag{2.56}$$

Geometric considerations indicate that this invariant may be expressed via the mapping $x = X(y,t)$, which is the inverse of $y = y(x,t)$:

$$\mathscr{I} = \frac{1}{t}\int_{-\infty}^{\infty} [X(y,t) - y]\,dy. \tag{2.57}$$

The last integral also exists in the case of a multistream velocity field $v(x,t)$ of uniformly moving particles, and the right-hand side of (2.57) is equal to the area enclosed between the multivalued curve $v(x,t)$ and the x-axis, as it is Seen on Fig. 2.11.

A weak, satisfying the invariant (2.55), solution of the Riemann equation, is constructed in the following way: within the interval of multivaluedness of the multistream field $v(x,t)$, vertical line segments are drawn. Their position is chosen so that, on both sides, the segment clips equal areas of the multivalued field $v(x,t)$ (see Fig. 2.12).

From the representation of the invariant (2.55) in the form of the integral (2.57), it is seen that this rule of equal areas is satisfied, if we apply the well-known Maxwell rule in mechanics. According to this rule, it is necessary to replace the non-monotonous mapping $X(y,t) = y + v_0(y)t$ with a piecewise-constant mapping $X_w(y,t)$, by placing horizontal line segments so that the clipped pieces of nonmonotonicity at the top and bottom had the same areas. Then by substituting the inverse mapping $y_w(x,t)$ into (2.46), we obtain the required weak solution of the Riemann equation satisfying the invariant (2.55).

Analytically, the Maxwell rule, i.e. the condition of clipping the pieces of non-monotonicity of the mapping $X(y,t)$ by the horizontal line segment $x = x_k^*$, is written as:

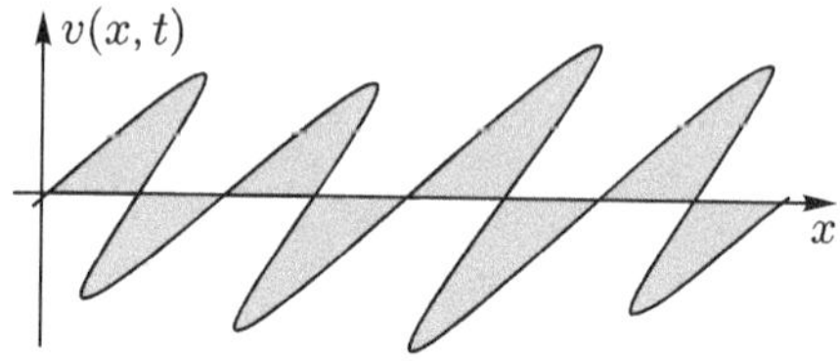

Fig. 2.11 Illustration of the geometric meaning of the invariant (2.55), (2.57) in the case of a multistream field $v(x,t)$. The algebraic sum of the shared areas must be equal to $\mathscr{I}$.

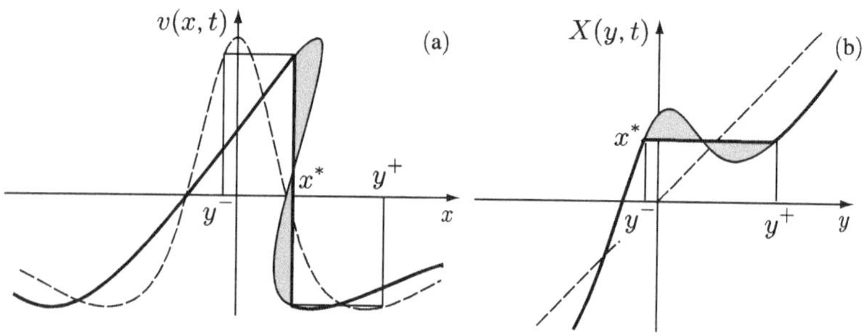

Fig. 2.12 Illustration of the equal area rule (left) and of the Maxwell rule equivalent to it (right). The former shows where to clip the branches of the multivalued field $v(x,t)$ in order to find the discontinuous solution of the Riemann equation (thick line). The latter helps to eliminate the intervals of nonmonotonicity of the Lagrangian-to-Eulerian coordinate transformation $x = y + v_0(y)t$. The shaded areas in each panel are equal. The dashed lines, in both panels, show the curves at the moment of time $t = 0$.

$$\int_{y_k^-}^{y_k^+} [X(z,t) - x_k^*]\, dy = 0, \tag{2.58}$$

where $[y_k^-, y_k^+]$ is the interval of the y, where the clipping segment is projected.

Let us establish the equivalence of the Maxwell rule and the Lax-Oleinik absolute-minimum principle. To do so, we note that if, in going from the left-hand side to the right of the point x_k^*, the mapping discontinuously jumps from y_k^- to y_k^+, then at $x = x_k^*$ the function $\mathscr{G}(y;x_k^*,t)$ has two identical absolute minima in these points. In other words, in all points x_k^* of discontinuities of the weak solution of the Riemann equation, the following equality holds:

$$\mathscr{G}(y_k^-, x_k^*, t) = \mathscr{G}(y_k^+, x_k^*, t). \tag{2.59}$$

According to the definition (2.43) of the function $\mathscr{G}(y;x_k^*,t)$, this condition of the equality of the absolute minima can be written in the form

$$\mathscr{G}(y_k^+, x_k^*, t) - \mathscr{G}(y_k^-, x_k^*, t) = \int_{y_k^-}^{y_k^+} [X(z,t) - x_k^*]\, dy = 0,$$

equivalent to the Maxwell rule (2.58).

2.5 The E-Rykov-Sinai global principle

Let us discuss another, different from the one analyzed above, class of weak solutions of the Riemann equation, suggested and investigated in detail by E, Rykov and Sinai [7]. Namely, let us construct a discontinuous velocity field of a flow of inelastically colliding particles.

2.5.1 Flow of inelastically coalescing particles

In order to clarify the topic of the discussion, let us recall a high-school problem: Let n point masses uniformly move along the x-axis, whose initial (at the moment $t=0$) coordinates, velocities and masses are equal to $\{x_k, v_k, m_k\}$ $(k=1,\dots,n)$. While colliding, the particles coalesce according to the law of absolutely inelastic collisions. This means that the total mass and momentum of the coalesced particles are conserved. Then let it be known that, during the time interval T, the particles coalesce into one macroparticle. It is required to find its coordinate and velocity at an arbitrary moment of time $t>T$.

Solution of this problem is trivial and based on the well-known fact that, in the absence of external forces, the particles' center of mass, denoted as $x^*(t)$, moves uniformly and rectilinearly:

$$x^*(t) = x_c + v^* t. \tag{2.60}$$

Here x_c is the initial center of mass equal to

$$x_c = \frac{1}{m^*}\sum_{k=1}^{n} m_k x_k, \tag{2.61}$$

and v^* is the velocity determined from the law of conservation of momentum:

$$v^* = \frac{p^*}{m^*}. \tag{2.62}$$

Here enter the total mass of the particles and their total momentum

$$m^* = \sum_{k=1}^{n} m_k, \quad p^* = \sum_{k=1}^{n} m_k v_k. \tag{2.63}$$

Obviously, if all particles merge into one, its position will coincide with the center of mass, and the particle itself will move according to the law (2.60). Let us pay attention to a remarkable peculiarity of the answer to the school problem. It order to obtain this answer, one does not need to trace the history of particles' motion. For example, to find out where and when particular particles coalesced.

Let us formulate a more serious problem. Let us take a flow of particles uniformly moving along the x-axis. The dependence of the initial velocity of the particles on the coordinate x is given by the function $v_0(x)$, and the initial density is equal to $\rho_0(x)$. Find the velocity $v(x,t)$ and density $\rho(x,t)$ fields of the particles at an arbitrary moment of time $t > 0$, under the condition that the microparticles inelastically coalesce at collisions with their total momentum being conserved.

The problem of finding the velocity and density fields of a one-dimensional flow of inelastically coalescing particles has a beautiful solution expressed by the *global principle* (*the E-Rykov-Sinai principle*). This solution has something in common with the solution of the above mentioned high-school problem in the sense that for finding the fields $v(x,t)$ and $\rho(x,t)$ at any moment of time $t > 0$, one is not required to know the previous history of particles' motion of the flows during the time interval $[0,t]$. A discussion of the global principle is given below.

2.5.2 Inelastic collisions of particles

Let us start with an analysis of the velocity field of a one-dimensional flow of inelastically coalescing particles. As long as there are no collisions, i.e. until the moment of time t_n (2.13), the velocity and density fields of the flow satisfy the Riemann equation (2.1) and the continuity equation (2.2) in the classical sense, and the motion of particles is described by the mapping (2.11). At $t > t_n$, in the mapping $x = X(y,t)$, there appear regions of nonmonotonicity meaning that some particles swapped places. Such overtaking is allowed, if the role of particles is played by automobiles moving in different lanes along the x-axis showing the direction of the road. But if the particles move in the same line, instead of overtaking, they collide. When the particles are inelastic, at collisions they coalesce, and then move together with the total momentum being conserved.

Coalescence of particles is taken into account in a similar way as it has been done for a fire line or nonlinear acoustic wave, *viz.* the regions of nonmonotonicity of the mapping (2.11) are clipped by horizontal line segments. Here these segments have a transparent physical meaning: all particles initially situated inside the interval $[y^-(t), y^+(t)]$, whose boundaries are the projections of the ends of the clipping segment onto the y-axis, coalesce into a single macroparticle in the point with the coordinate $x^*(t)$, which is the projection of the segment onto the x-axis (see Fig. 2.13). Thereby the velocity field consists of smooth (at a smooth initial condition $v_0(x)$) pieces, describing uniform motion of not-yet-coalesced particles, and points of discontinuities, which are the positions of macroparticles.

The only, but key problem here is determining the law of motion $x^*(t)$ of the macroparticles arising from collisions. Recall that we already have a recipe for placing segments clipping the regions of nonmonotonicity, which is based on the absolute minimum principle, and on the Maxwell rule equivalent to it. While these recipes duly serve for describing fires and nonlinear acoustic waves, they are, however, obviously flawed from the standpoint of physics of particle flows — they place the discontinuities regardless of the distribution of the density of the particle flow. But in the situation of interest here, the initial density must influence the motion

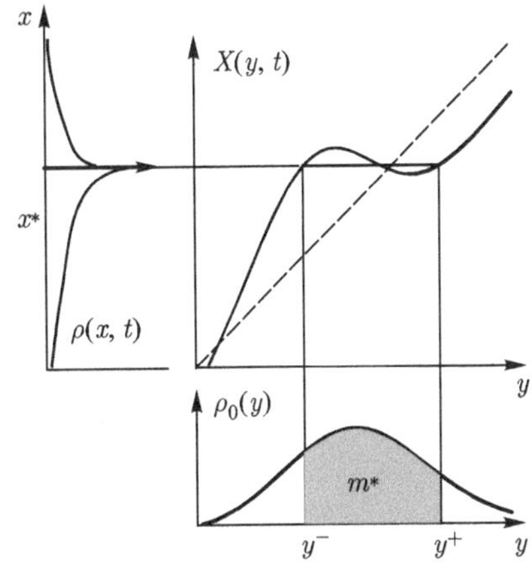

Fig. 2.13 Lagrangian-to-Eulerian coordinate transformation $X(y,t)$, and the initial and current densities of a flow of inelastically colliding particles. The area of the shaded region is equal to the mass m^* of the macroparticle situated at x^*. Its singular density is depicted by the bold arrow.

of macroparticles. Indeed, according to the law of conservation of momentum, the velocity of motion of a macroparticle

$$v^*(t) = \frac{dx^*(t)}{dt} \tag{2.64}$$

is equal to

$$v^*(t) = \frac{p^*(t)}{m^*(t)}, \tag{2.65}$$

where

$$m^*(t) = \int_{y^-(t)}^{y^+(t)} \rho_0(y)\, dy \tag{2.66}$$

is the mass of the macroparticle, and

$$p^*(t) = \int_{y^-(t)}^{y^+(t)} \rho_0(y)\, v_0(y)\, dy \tag{2.67}$$

is its momentum. By varying the initial density $\rho_0(x)$ of the flow, we inevitably change the velocity of the macroparticle, and hence its position on the x-axis.

Nevertheless, it turns out that there is a global principle akin to the absolute minimum principle, which allows us, also in this case, by means of simple geometric constructions, to determine the positions of macroparticles, and along with them also the generalized velocity $v(x,t)$ and density $\rho(x,t)$ fields, at an arbitrary moment of time $t > 0$.

2.5.3 Formulation of the global principle

Similarly to the absolute minimum principle, the global principle consists in finding the coordinate of the absolute minimum of a function of the argument y, depending on x and t as parameters:

$$\mathscr{S}(y;x,t) = \int_{y_0}^{y} [X(z,t) - x]\, \rho_0(z)\, dz. \tag{2.68}$$

Here $X(y,t)$ is the Lagrangian-to-Eulerian coordinate transformation (2.11) of a flow of non-interacting uniformly moving particles, and y_0 is an arbitrary constant. While discussing the physical meaning of the global principle, we assign it to be equal to $y_0 = -\infty$. Apart from this, we assume that $\mathscr{S}(y;x,t)$ is a continuous function of all arguments.

Note that the only, but fundamental difference between $\mathscr{S}(y;x,t)$ and the function $\mathscr{G}(y;x,t)$ (2.43), appearing in the absolute minimum principle, consists in the presence of the initial density $\rho_0(x)$ in the integrand of (2.68). But the main common property of both functions consists in that the coordinates of their extrema are equal to the Lagrangian coordinates $y_i(x,t)$ of noninteracting particles occurring at the point x at the point of time t.

Let us formulate the global principle. The coordinate of the absolute minimum of the function $\mathscr{S}(y;x,t)$ (2.68) with respect to y is taken as the value of $y_w(x,t)$, the mapping determining the weak solution of the Riemann equation

$$v_w(x,t) = \frac{x - y_w(x,t)}{t}. \tag{2.69}$$

2.5.4 Mechanical meaning of the global principle

Let us uncover the mechanical meaning of the global principle on the basis of physical concepts and arguments. In order to specify these concepts and arguments, we substitute the mapping (2.11) into the integral (2.68), open the parentheses in the integrand and rewrite the function $\mathscr{S}(y;x,t)$ in the form, which reveals its close connection with the mechanical properties of a flow of particles:

$$\mathscr{S}(y;x,t) = P(y)\,t - x\,M(y) + x_c(y)\,M(y). \tag{2.70}$$

Here $M(y)$ is the initial mass of all particles to the left of the point y:

$$M(y) = \int_{-\infty}^{y} \rho_0(y)\, dy. \tag{2.71}$$

Equation (2.70) also contains the momentum on the left

$$P(y) = \int_{-\infty}^{y} \rho_0(y)\, v_0(y)\, dy, \tag{2.72}$$

and the initial center of mass of the particles situated to the left of the point y:

$$x_c(y) = \frac{N(y)}{M(y)}, \quad N(y) = \int_{-\infty}^{y} z\rho_0(z)\,dz.$$

Let us further note that if, at an arbitrary fixed t and varying parameter x from $x^*(t)-0$ to $x^*(t)+0$, the coordinate $y(x,t)$ of the absolute minimum of the function $\mathscr{S}(y;x,t)$ (2.68) discontinuously jumps from $y^-(t)$ to $y^+(t)$, then $\mathscr{S}(y;x^*,t)$ has, by virtue of continuity with respect to x, two identical absolute minima situated at the points $y^-(t)$ and $y^+(t)$. This, in its turn, means that the following equality holds:

$$\mathscr{S}(y^+;x^*,t) - \mathscr{S}(y^-;x^*,t) = \int_{y^-(t)}^{y^+(t)} [x^*(t) - y - v_0(y)t]\rho_0(y)\,dy = 0. \qquad (2.73)$$

By opening the parentheses in the integrand and integrating term-by-term, we have

$$x^*(t) = x_c(t) + v^*(t)\,t. \qquad (2.74)$$

Here $v^*(t)$ is described by the expression (2.65), where

$$p^*(t) = P(y^+(t)) - P(y^-(t)), \;\; m^*(t) = M(y^+(t)) - M(y^-(t)) \qquad (2.75)$$

are the momentum and mass, respectively, of the particles, which, at the initial moment of time $t=0$, have been in the interval $y \in [y^-(t), y^+(t)]$, and their center of mass is

$$x_c(t) = \frac{1}{m^*(t)} \int_{y^-(t)}^{y^+(t)} y\rho_0(y)\,dy. \qquad (2.76)$$

The relation (2.74) has almost the same transparent mechanical meaning as the solution (2.60) of the above mentioned high-school problem. It gives motion of the center of mass of the particles, which initially (at $t=0$) have been in the interval $[y^-(t), y^+(t)]$. If, by the moment of time t, these particles merged into a single macroparticle, the equality (2.74) simultaneously describes the motion of this macroparticle. Thus the global principle removes nonmonotonicity of the mapping $X(y,t)$ and places discontinuities (shocks) into the velocity field (2.69) in such a way that they move according to the law of inelastically coalesced particles.

2.5.5 Condition of physical realizability

In order finally to ascertain that the global principle indeed describes inelastic adhesion and real motion of macroparticles, it is necessary to verify the validity of two requirements following from mechanics of inelastic collisions.

Let us first show that the law of motion (2.74) of a macroparticle, following from the global principle, is not contradictory. In other words, let us confirm that the velocity $v^*(t)$ (2.65) of motion of the macroparticle, entering Eq. (2.74), is connected with its coordinate $x^*(t)$ (2.74) by the relation (2.64). Let us show this by differentiating the condition of discontinuity (2.73) with respect to t. As a result, we obtain

$$\frac{d}{dt}\int_{y^-(t)}^{y^+(t)} [x^*(t) - y - v_0(y)t]\,\rho_0(y)\,dy = 0. \tag{2.77}$$

Note further that the derivatives with respect to the limits of integration disappear by virtue of the obvious equalities

$$x^* = X(y^+,t) = y^+ + v_0(y^+)t, \quad x^* = X(y^-,t) = y^- + v_0(y^-)t, \tag{2.78}$$

meaning that, at the boundaries of the interval of integration, the integrand in (2.77) is equal to zero. Thus, differentiating the integrand leads to the required relation:

$$v^*(t) = \frac{d}{dt}x^*(t) = \frac{p^*(t)}{m^*(t)},$$

where $p^*(t)$ and $m^*(t)$ are given by Eqs. (2.75).

The second requirement, let us call it *the rule of absorption*, consists in that macroparticles must *absorb* the surrounding microparticles without releasing those already "captured".

Since such requirements play a special role in the theory of weak solutions, let us make a little digression: these requirements are applied to most weak solutions and they are called *conditions of physical realizability*. They reflect physical or another underlying nature of the applied problem of interest. So, as applied to the fire line $h(x,t)$, any fireman knows that those who ended up in the back of the fire line (see Fig. 2.6), once left behind, already cease to exist in nature and cannot re-emerge at the front, thus forming the real line of fire. In all above mentioned applications of weak solutions of the Riemann equation, *viz.*: lines of fire, nonlinear acoustic waves and flows of inelastically coalescing particles, the condition of physical realizability is expressed by the following inequalities:

$$v^-(t) \geqslant v^*(t) \geqslant v^+(t), \tag{2.79}$$

where

$$v^-(t) = v_0(y^-) = v(x^* - 0,t), \quad v^+(t) = v_0(y^+) = v(x^* + 0,t)$$

are the values of the field $v_w(x,t)$ immediately to the left and to the right of the shock.

When the condition (2.79) expresses the rule of absorption, it has a clear mechanical meaning: microparticles will adhere to a macroparticle, but not detach from it, only if the velocity v^- on the left is greater than v^*, and the velocity v^+ on the right is less than the velocity of the macroparticle.

Let us prove that the global principle gives the weak solution of the Riemann equation satisfying the condition (2.79). In order to do so, let us subtract the first equality in (2.78) from the second one. After elementary manipulations, we find the half-difference of the values of the velocity field $v_w(x,t)$

$$V = \frac{v^- - v^+}{2} = \frac{y^+ - y^-}{2t} > 0 \tag{2.80}$$

to the left and to the right of the shock. From here, it is seen that, firstly, the velocity to the left of the shock v^- is always greater the velocity on the right v^+. Secondly, the magnitude of the discontinuity is expressed through the Lagrangian coordinates of microparticles adhering to the macroparticle at the current moment of time t.

It remains to prove that the velocity of motion of the shock (of the macroparticle) lies within the interval $v^* \in [v^+, v^-]$. To this end, let us add up both parts of the equalities (2.78). As a result, we obtain:

$$2x^* = y^+ + y^- + (v^+ + v^-)t.$$

By substituting here x^* (2.74) and isolating the velocity of the macroparticle from the resultant relation, we have

$$v^* = U + W, \tag{2.81}$$

where

$$U = \frac{v^+ + v^-}{2} \tag{2.82}$$

is the half-sum of the velocities of the microparticles advancing towards the shock, and

$$W = \frac{1}{t}\left[\frac{y^+ + y^-}{2} - x_c\right] \tag{2.83}$$

is the difference between U and the velocity of motion of the shock. Let us prove that v^* (2.81) obeys the inequalities (2.79). For this purpose, we estimate the quantity x_c entering the right-hand side of (2.83). By using the definition (2.76), mathematicians can rigorously prove that

$$y^- \leqslant x_c \leqslant y^+. \tag{2.84}$$

But physicists will refer to physical obviousness of this inequality, following from the fact that the center of mass x_c of matter enclosed within the interval $[y^-, y^+]$, necessarily lies inside it. Both of them, based on the inequality (2.84) end expression for the magnitude of the discontinuity (2.80), will show that

$$-\frac{V}{2} \leqslant W \leqslant \frac{V}{2} \Rightarrow v^+ < U + W < v^-,$$

and, consequently, the velocity of the macroparticle (2.81) satisfies the condition of physical realizability (2.79). All velocities relevant for the motion of the shock are shown in Fig. 2.14.

Note 1. The global principle transforms into the absolute minimum principle, if the initial density is everywhere constant: $\rho_0(x) \equiv \rho_0$. Thus the weak solution of the Riemann equation constructed by means of the Lax-Oleinik principle, can be

Fig. 2.14 Discontinuous velocity field $v_w(x,t)$ and all velocities used in the proof that the global principle gives the weak solution of the Riemann equation satisfying the condition of physical realizability.

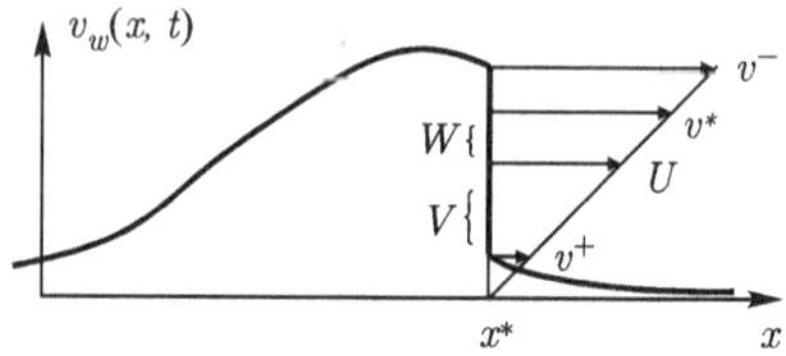

interpreted as the velocity field of an initially homogeneous flow of inelastically coalescing particles.

Note 2. The Lax-Oleinik principle gives a beautiful formula for the velocity of motion of the shock, which is worth presenting on its own. By substituting $\rho_0 = const$ into (2.66), (2.76), we obtain

$$x_c = \frac{y^+ + y^-}{2}.$$

Hence W (2.83) is equal to zero, and the shock moves with the velocity U (2.82), which is equal to the arithmetic mean of the values of the velocity before and after the shock.

2.5.6 Geometry of the global principle

All previously described geometric procedures of constructing the weak solution of the Riemann equation, based on absolute minimum principle, are easily generalizable to the case of the global principle.

Let us give two such generalizations. By using the fact that the function $\mathscr{S}(y;x,t)$ (2.68), (2.70) is defined up to an arbitrary constant, we rewrite it in the form analogous to (2.51):

$$\phi(y,t) - xM(y), \tag{2.85}$$

where

$$\phi(y,t) = P(y)t + N(y). \tag{2.86}$$

The following function entered here:

$$M(y) = \int_0^y \rho_0(z)dz,\ P(y) = \int_0^y \rho_0(z)v_0(z)dz,\ N(y) = \int_0^y y\rho_0(z)dz. \tag{2.87}$$

The mapping $y_w(x,t)$, which gives the solution (2.69), is equal to the coordinate of the absolute minimum of the function (2.85). In order to find it, it is necessary, while increasing h from $-\infty$, to bring the curve

$$M(y)x + h \tag{2.88}$$

in contact with the graph of $\phi(y,t)$ (2.65) from below.

Example. Particle carried by a flow. Let a homogeneous flow uniformly move along the x-axis. Its velocity is equal to v and density is ρ. At the moment of time $t=0$, an immobile particle of a mass m is immersed at the point $x=0$. Find the law of motion of this particle.

Let us first write down the explicit expressions of the functions (2.87):

$$M(y)=\rho y+m\Theta(y),\quad P(y)=\rho vy,\quad N(y)=\frac{\rho}{2}y^2.$$

Here $\Theta(z)$ is the Heaviside function, which is equal to 1 at $z>0$ and to zero otherwise. Note also that the particle does not affect the initial momentum $P(y)$, since its momentum is equal to zero.

Let us continue solving the problem by doing a habitual task for physicists: dimensional analysis of the parameters involved in the problem. With these parameters, the only combinations having the dimensions of length and time are $\ell=m/\rho$, $\theta=m/v\rho$. Their uniqueness means that ℓ and θ are the characteristic spatial and time intervals, where the most dramatic events for the particles immersed in the flow unfold. There we transform to the following dimensionless arguments:

$$\eta=\frac{x}{\ell},\quad \zeta=\frac{y}{\ell},\quad \tau=\frac{t}{\theta},$$

measuring the coordinate and time at the scales peculiar to the particle. By multiplying then Eqs. (2.65) and (2.88) by ρ/m^2, we replace $\phi(y,t)$ and $M(y)x$ with the following dimensionless functions:

$$\psi(\zeta,\tau)=\frac{\rho}{m^2}\phi(y,t)\quad\text{and}\quad \mu(\zeta,\eta)=\frac{\rho}{m^2}M(y)x=\eta[\zeta+\Theta(\zeta)].$$

As $\psi(\zeta,\tau)$, it is convenient to take the function

$$\psi(\zeta,\tau)=\frac{(\zeta+\tau)^2}{2}. \tag{2.89}$$

Determining the law of motion of the particle is equivalent to finding such a value of $\eta=\eta^*(\tau)$, at which the piecewise-linear curve $\mu(\zeta,\eta)$ is tangent to the parabola (2.89) simultaneously at two points. Geometric constructions in Fig. 2.15 lead to the following quadratic equation for η^*:

$$(\eta^*-\tau)^2=2\eta^*\Rightarrow\eta^*=\tau+1-\sqrt{2\tau+1}.$$

The obtained law of motion of the macroparticle has the following asymptotics:

$$\eta^*\sim\frac{\tau^2}{2}\quad(\tau\to 0);\quad \eta^*\sim\tau\quad(\tau\to\infty).$$

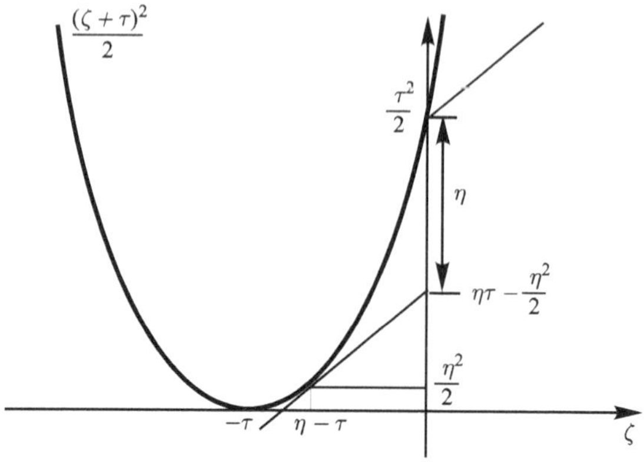

Fig. 2.15 Illustration to the motion of a particle in a homogeneous flow. The zigzag consisting of two rays ($\zeta-\tau$ at $\zeta<0$ and $\zeta-\tau+\eta$ at $\zeta>0$) is brought in contact with the parabola (2.89). The gap between the parabola and lower ray at the point $\zeta=0$ is equal to $(\eta-\tau)^2/2$. If it is compensated by the jump η, there are two points of contact of the parabola with the zigzag.

It is seen from here that, in the beginning, the particle uniformly accelerates. When, while pressing from the left, the mass of the flow greater than the initial mass of the particle "adheres" to the particle, the velocity of the particle tends to the velocity of the flow. ∎

The constructions of the mapping $y=y_w(x,t)$ described above remind of the procedure which, in Sect. 2.4.4, have led to the idea of convex hull. The latter allows us to find the inverse mapping $x=X_w(y,t)$. Let us generalize the concept of convex hull to the case of the global principle. To do so, we introduce a new coordinate:

$$m=M(y)=\int_0^y \rho_0(z)\,dz. \tag{2.90}$$

If the initial density $\rho_0(x)$ is everywhere greater than zero, there exists a continuous, monotonous inverse function $y=\mathscr{Y}(m)$. By substituting it into (2.85)-(2.88), we arrive at the following procedure for constructing the weak solution of the Riemann equation: it is given by the previous formula (2.69), where now

$$y_w(x,t)=\mathscr{Y}(m(x,t)), \tag{2.91}$$

and $m(x,t)$ is the "coordinate" of the lower tangent point of the line

$$xm+h \tag{2.92}$$

and the curve

$$\varphi(m,t)=\mathscr{P}(m)t+\mathscr{N}(m). \tag{2.93}$$

Here

$$\mathscr{P}(m)=P(\mathscr{Y}(m)), \quad \mathscr{N}(m)=N(\mathscr{Y}(m)). \tag{2.94}$$

Construction of the weak solution within the framework of the global principle produces the same result, if $\varphi(m,t)$ is replaced with the convex hull $\bar{\varphi}(m,t)$. By differentiating it with respect to m, let us find the mapping

$$x = X(m,t) = \frac{\partial}{\partial m}\bar{\varphi}(m,t),$$

which is the inverse of $m(x,t)$.

If we are interested only in the dynamics of macroparticles formed due to adhesion, it is sufficient to know only the function $x = X(m,t)$. In reality, the position of the macroparticle $x^*(t)$ coincides with the height of the "plateau" — the horizontal part of the mapping $x = X(m,t)$, and the mass of the macroparticle is equal to the length of the plateau $m^*(t) = m^+ - m^-$, where $[m^+, m^-]$ is the segment of the m-axis, onto which the plateau is projected.

2.5.7 Solutions of the continuity equation

Having said 'a', i.e. having investigated the discontinuous density field of a one-dimensional flow of inelastically colliding particles; we should also say 'b', i.e. show the corresponding generalized solutions of the continuity equation for the particle density of the flow. Since, while constructing the generalized density, we will use integral conservation laws, it is appropriate to analyze not the density, but its integral characteristic, *viz.* the mass of particles to the left of an arbitrary point with the Eulerian coordinate x:

$$m(x,t) = \int_{-\infty}^{x} \rho(x',t)dx'. \tag{2.95}$$

Within the time interval $t \in (0,t_n)$, while the motion is still single-streamed, the Lagrangian field $M(y,t)$ does not depend on time and is given by the expression (2.90). This means that the Eulerian field $m(x,t)$ obeys the equation

$$\frac{\partial m}{\partial t} + v\frac{\partial m}{\partial x} = 0, \quad m(x,t=0) = \int_{-\infty}^{x} \rho_0(x')\,dx = M(x). \tag{2.96}$$

By substituting the mapping $y_w(x,t)$, found by means of the global principle, for y in (2.90); we arrive at the generalized solution of Eq. (2.96):

$$m(x,t) = M(y_w(x,t)). \tag{2.97}$$

It is completely consistent with the laws of physics. In particular, during the transition across the point of discontinuity x^* of the mapping $y_w(x,t)$, the mass on the left is abruptly incremented by the mass of the macroparticle situated at this point

$$m^* = \int_{y^-}^{y^+} \rho_0(z)\,dz, \tag{2.98}$$

and at $x \to \infty$, when $y_w(x,t) \to \infty$, the generalized mass on the left $m(x,t)$ (2.97) tends to the total mass of the particles of the flow.

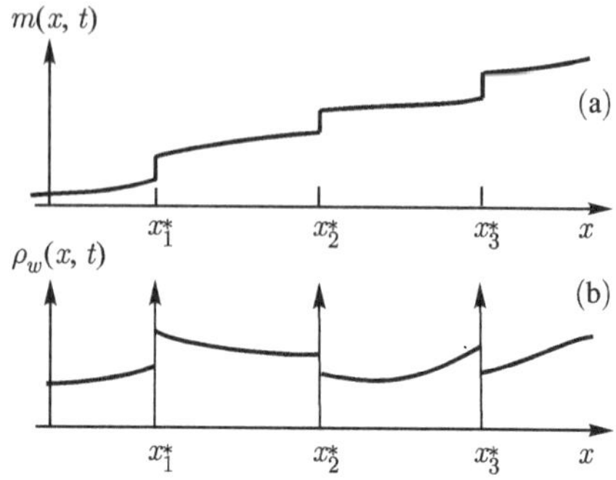

Fig. 2.16 Generalized mass on the left (top) and density of a flow of inelastically coalescing particles. The bold arrows at the bottom represent the delta functions describing the singular density of macroparticles.

In order to obtain the sought-for generalized solution of the continuity equation, it remains to differentiate the mass on the left (2.87) with respect to x. This derivative does not exist in the classical sense. Nevertheless, as a generalized function, it exists and is equal to

$$\rho_w(x,t) = \sum_k m_k^*(t)\,\delta(x_k^*(t) - x) + \rho_c(x,t), \tag{2.99}$$

where the summation is over all points $\{x_k^*\}$ of the discontinuities of the mapping $y_w(x,t)$, the factors in front of the delta functions $\{m_k^*\}$ are equal to the masses of the corresponding macroparticles, and the last term describes the continuous density of uniformly moving microparticles within the intervals between the macroparticles. Fig. 2.16 schematically shows the generalized density field of a flow of inelastically colliding particles.

2.6 Line-growth geometry

Above, during the analysis of line growth, we have preferred to deal with the analytically expedient, approximate Eq. (2.5). However, constructions of the solution of the exact line-growth equation are geometrically more illustrative. Indeed, let a line grows at a speed c, and at the initial moment of time $t = 0$, its shape is given by the function $z = h_0(x)$. Then, in order to find the shape of the line a moment of time $t > 0$, one needs to roll a circle of the radius ct along the curve $z = h_0(x)$. Thereby the centers of the circles describe the sought-for line $h(x,t)$. If the radius of the circle is so large that the circle does not reach for all points of the initial line, the centers of the circles automatically draw a graph of the weak solution $h_w(x,t)$ (see Fig. 2.17). This geometric procedure is also valuable in that it relieves us of worrying whether the initial condition $h_0(x)$ and the current solution $h(x,t)$ are single-valued. Indeed, rolling a circle along any curve preserves the obvious geometric connection with line growth in the direction perpendicular to the line, regardless of the fact whether it is single-valued or not in an artificially chosen Cartesian coordinate system. Below, we consider a few examples of geometric constructions of growing lines.

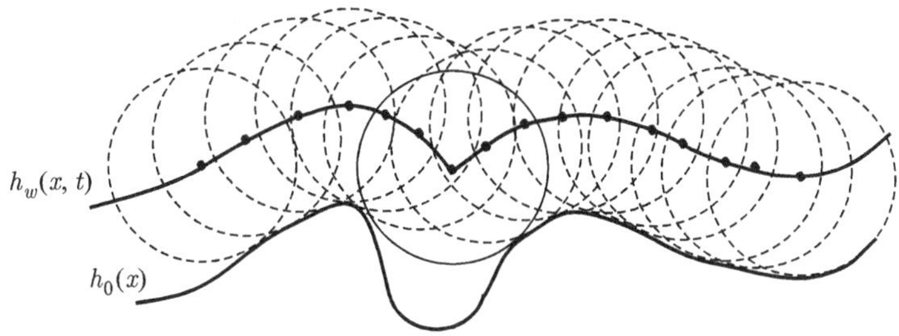

Fig. 2.17 Initial line $h_0(x)$ and, rolling along it, circle (dashed lines) of a radius ct. The centers are connected by the line $h_w(x,t)$. Since the circle cannot roll into the narrow hollow at the center of the figure, the profile of $h_w(x,t)$ has a singularity (break point) characteristic of weak solutions of Eqs. (2.5).

2.6.1 Parametric equations of a line

Let the initial line be given parametrically:

$$x = \zeta(s), \quad z = \eta(s), \quad s \in [a,b].$$

Let us find the parametric equation of the line growing in the (x,z)-plane at a speed c. Let us write the equation of the initial line in the vector form $\mathbf{r} = \mathbf{r}_0(s)$, where $\mathbf{r}_0(s) = \mathbf{l}\,\zeta(s) + \mathbf{m}\,\eta(s)$, and $\{\mathbf{l}, \mathbf{m}\}$ are the unit vectors of the x- and z-axes, respectively. As is well-known, the normal vector to the initial line is equal to

$$\mathbf{n} = \frac{\mathbf{l}\,\dot{\eta} - \mathbf{m}\,\dot{\zeta}}{\sqrt{\dot{\zeta}^2 + \dot{\eta}^2}}.$$

Here the dot symbolizes differentiation with respect to the parameter s. Evidently, the vector equation of the growing line has the following form:

$$\mathbf{r} = \mathbf{r}_0(s) + ct\,\mathbf{n}. \tag{2.100}$$

By substituting here the normal vector and transforming to the coordinate notation, we obtain the sought-for parametric equation of the growing line:

$$x = \zeta(s) + \frac{ct\,\dot{\eta}(s)}{\sqrt{\dot{\zeta}^2 + \dot{\eta}^2}}, \quad z = \eta(s) - \frac{ct\,\dot{\zeta}(s)}{\sqrt{\dot{\zeta}^2 + \dot{\eta}^2}}.$$

Let now the initial condition be given explicitly: $z = h_0(x)$. Then the initial parametric equation assume the following form: $x = s$, $z = h_0(s)$. Hence, in order to obtain the solution with an explicitly given initial condition, it is sufficient to substitute $\zeta(s) = s$, $\eta(s) = h_0(s)$ in the above-derived expressions. As a result, we have

$$x = s + \frac{ct\dot{h}_0(s)}{\sqrt{1+\dot{h}_0^2(s)}}, \quad z = h_0(s) - \frac{ct}{\sqrt{1+\dot{h}_0^2(s)}}.$$

Here $\dot{h}_0(x)$ is the tangent of the angle between the normal to the line $h_0(x)$ and the z-axis. If this gradient is small, $|\dot{h}_0(x)| \ll 1$, it is possible, without introducing a significant error, to Taylor expand the right-hand sides of the equalities in powers of $\dot{h}_0$ and retain only the first terms of non-zero power of $\dot{h}_0$. As a result, we obtain

$$x = s + ct\,\dot{h}_0(s), \quad z = h_0(s) + \frac{ct}{2}\,\dot{h}_0^2(s).$$

It is easy to verify that these equalities give the exact solution of the approximate equation (2.5), given in the parametric form.

2.6.2 Contour in polar coordinates

Let the contour $\mathscr{L}_0$ be given in the polar coordinate system (r, φ) by the equation $r = \rho_0(\varphi)$. Here $\rho_0(\varphi)$ is a smooth positive function satisfying the condition of periodicity $\rho_0(0) = \rho_0(2\pi)$. Let us study growth of the contour by using the polar coordinate system. Let us introduce the unit vectors of the polar coordinate system $(\mathbf{e}_r, \mathbf{e}_\varphi)$ and write the equation of the initial contour in the vector form

$$\mathbf{r} = \rho_0(\varphi)\,\mathbf{e}_r. \tag{2.101}$$

In order to write a similar vector equation $\mathbf{r} = \rho(\varphi, t)\,\mathbf{e}_r$ of the growing contour $\mathscr{L}_t$, we need to add the term $ct\,\mathbf{n}$ to the right-hand side of (2.101), where $\mathbf{n}$ is the unit vector normal to the contour. Let us find this vector by rotating the unit vector tangent to the contour by 90°. The latter is equal

$$\tau = \frac{\mathbf{r}'}{|\mathbf{r}'|},$$

where the prime means differentiation with respect to the angle φ. By differentiating Eq. (2.101) with respect to φ and keeping in mind that $\mathbf{e}_r' = \mathbf{e}_\varphi$, we have

$$\tau = \frac{\rho_0'\,\mathbf{e}_r + \rho_0\,\mathbf{e}_\varphi}{\sqrt{\rho_0^2 + \rho_0'^2}} \Rightarrow \mathbf{n} = \frac{\rho_0\,\mathbf{e}_r - \rho_0'\,\mathbf{e}_\varphi}{\sqrt{\rho_0^2 + \rho_0'^2}}.$$

From Fig. 2.18, it is seen that at the mapping of points of the initial contour into respective points of the growing contour, the angular coordinate varies: the points of the growing line not only move away from the origin of the polar coordinate system, but also participate in rotary motion. Therefore, similarly to Lagrangian and Eulerian coordinates, it is convenient to introduce the initial "Lagrangian" ψ

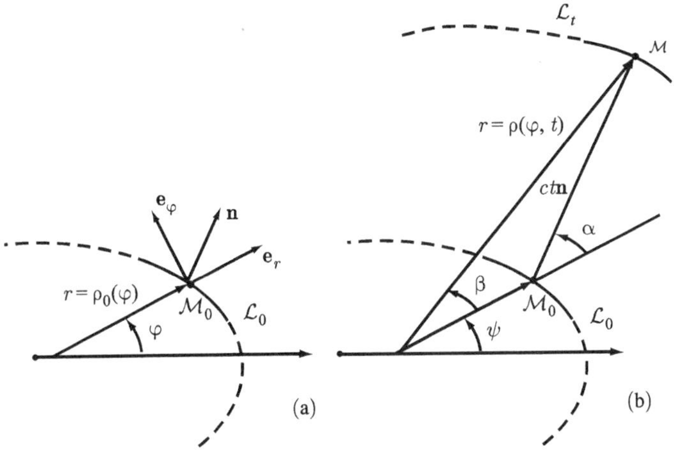

Fig. 2.18 Construction of contour growth in polar coordinates. On the left-hand side, A fragment of the initial contour, its radius vector, local unit vectors of the polar coordinates and normal to a point $\mathscr{M}_0$ on the contour **(a)**. Fragments of the growing contour at the initial $t = 0$ and current $t > 0$ moments of time **(b)**. Also shown are the radius vectors of the point $\mathscr{M}_0$ on the initial contour and its image $\mathscr{M}$ on the contour $\mathscr{L}_t$; and the vector $ct\mathbf{n}$ connecting these points.

and current "Eulerian" φ angles (see Fig. 2.18, b). From the figure, it is seen that these angles are connected by the equality

$$\varphi = \psi + \beta(\psi).$$

Here β is the angle between the angular coordinates of the initial line and the corresponding point on the growing line. It is expressed through the angle α between the normal vector $\mathbf{n}$ and the unit vector $\mathbf{e}_r$ of the polar coordinate system. From the geometry of the vectors $\mathbf{n}$ and $\mathbf{e}_r$, it follows that

$$\sin\beta = \frac{ct}{\rho}\sin\alpha \Rightarrow \beta = \arcsin\left(\frac{ct}{\rho}\sin\alpha\right).$$

Here

$$\rho = \rho(\varphi, t) = \sqrt{(\mathbf{r}\cdot\mathbf{r})} = \sqrt{c^2t^2 + 2ct\rho_0\cos\alpha + \rho_0^2}$$

is the distance from the origin to a point on the growing contour. By noting also that

$$\tan\alpha = -\frac{\rho_0'}{\rho_0}, \quad \sin\alpha = -\frac{\rho_0'}{\sqrt{\rho^2 + \rho_0'^2}}, \quad \cos\alpha = \frac{\rho_0}{\sqrt{\rho^2 + \rho_0'^2}},$$

we finally obtain

$$\begin{cases} \rho = \rho(\psi,t) = \sqrt{c^2t^2 + 2ct\rho_0(\psi)\cos\alpha(\psi) + \rho_0^2(\psi)}, \\ \varphi = \varphi(\psi,t) + \arcsin\left(\dfrac{ct\sin\alpha(\psi)}{\rho(\psi,t)}\right), \\ \alpha(\psi) = -\arctan\left(\dfrac{\rho_0'(\psi)}{\rho_0(\psi)}\right). \end{cases} \tag{2.102}$$

By using the equation of contour in polar coordinates (2.102), let us study its asymptotic form at $t \to \infty$. As an illustration, we take the following initial contour:

$$r = 1 + \varepsilon\cos(4\varphi), \quad \varphi \in [0, 2\pi] \quad (0 < \varepsilon < 1). \tag{2.103}$$

Equations (2.102) are unwieldy and nontransparent. These drawbacks of theirs are partly atoned for by the asymptotic analysis at $ct \to \infty$ based on (2.102). Thereby there appears a small parameter $\mu = \rho_0/ct$. By expanding the right-hand sides of Eqs. (2.102) in this parameter and retaining the terms of the first and second power of μ, we obtain:

$$\rho = ct + \rho_0(\psi)\cos\alpha(\psi), \quad \varphi = \psi + \alpha(\psi). \tag{2.104}$$

Geometric meaning of these equalities is clear: at $ct \gg \rho_0$, any point $\mathscr{M}_0$ of the initial contour is mapped to a point $\mathscr{M}$ of the growing contour, situated practically in the direction of the normal vector, and the distance from $\mathscr{M}$ to the origin is equal to the sum of the length of the vector $ct\mathbf{n}$ and the projection $\rho_0(\psi)\mathbf{e}_r$ onto this vector. Note that if we remove the first term in the first equality in (2.104), which does not affect the line shape; we obtain the time-independent equation of the contour:

$$\rho = \rho_\infty(\rho) = \frac{\rho_0^2(\psi)}{\sqrt{\rho_0^2(\psi) + \rho_0'^2(\psi)}}, \quad \varphi = \psi - \arcsin\left(\frac{\rho_0'(\psi)}{\sqrt{\rho_0^2(\psi) + \rho_0'(\psi)}}\right).$$

In other words, with time, the shape of the growing contour ceases to vary. This effect of the "freezing" of the contour's shape is due to geometric divergence of directions of its growth. The frozen shape of a growing contour, for the initial contour given by Eq. (2.103), and at different values of the parameter ε, is shown in Fig. 2.19.

2.6.3 Contour envelopes

Let us discuss the following problem: a two-dimensional ice floe bounded by the contour $\mathscr{L}_0$, is floating on the surface of a swimming pool. Water in the pool may be cold or warm. In cold water, the floe grows at a speed c, and in warm water, it melts at the same speed. The floe is first frozen in cold water during the time interval T.

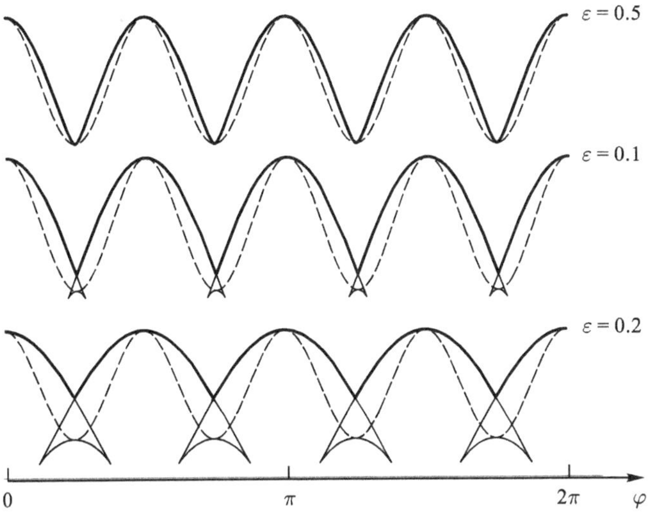

Fig. 2.19 Limiting shape of the contour as a function of the angle φ and at different ε. The vertical scales in the graphs are adjusted to match changes in the height of the initial line (dashed lines). In the lower panels, there are intervals of multivaluedness. Within these intervals, the real shape of the contour coincides with the upper branch of the function $\rho_\infty(\varphi)$. The real contour is accentuated by the bold line.

As a result, the floe takes the shape bounded by the contour $\mathscr{L}_T$. Then water is instantaneously heated and the floe is being defrosted during the same time T. What must be the profile of the contour $\mathscr{L}_0$, so that after defrosting, the flow returned to the original shape?

Let us find the shape of the ice floe at the moment of time $t = T$ by rolling a circle of the radius $R = cT$ around the contour $\mathscr{L}_0$. The locus of the centers of the circles tangent to the the contour $\mathscr{L}_0$ gives the profile $\mathscr{L}_T$ of the floe (see Fig. 2.20).

It may so happen that the circle rolling around the contour $\mathscr{L}_0$ does not reach all its points, similarly to the case depicted in Fig. 2.17. Then the shape of the contour $\mathscr{L}_T$ does not change, if the contour $\mathscr{L}_0$ is replaced with its *envelope* $\mathscr{H}_{cT}$. We call a closed contour, composed of all contact points of a contour $\mathscr{L}_0$ with outer circles of a radius R, and supplemented, if a circle is tangent to the contour simultaneously at two points, by the arc connecting these points, the envelope $\mathscr{H}_R$ of the contour $\mathscr{L}_0$.

Let us now investigate the defrosting of the floe assuming, for the time being, that the initial contour $\mathscr{L}_0$ coincides with its envelope $\mathscr{H}_{cT}$. In order to find the shape of the floe after defrosting, we need to roll the same circle of the radius cT, but now around the inner side of the contour$\mathscr{L}_T$. The locus of the centers of all circles tangent to the contour $\mathscr{L}_T$ from inside forms the shape of the floe after defrosting.

Let us prove that the new shape of the floe coincides with $\mathscr{L}_0$. To this end, it is necessary and sufficient for the outer normal to the contour $\mathscr{L}_0$ at any point $\mathscr{M}_0$ and the inner normal to the contour $\mathscr{L}_T$ at the point $\mathscr{M}$, where the point $\mathscr{M}_0$ is mapped, to lie on the same line. Let us prove that this condition is satisfied. For that, let us

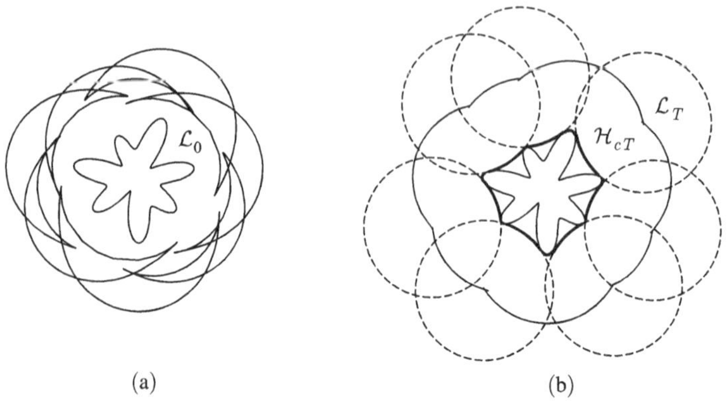

Fig. 2.20 Determination of the shape of a growing ice floe. **(a)** Initial contour of the floe $\mathscr{L}_0$ and its mapping given by Eqs. (2.100), (2.102). **(b)** Only those branches of the mapping are retained, which form the real shape of the contour $\mathscr{L}_T$. The bold line highlights the envelope $\mathscr{H}_{cT}$ of the initial contour $\mathscr{L}_0$. All circles of the radius $R = cT$, tangent to the contour at two points at the same time, are also shown here. Arcs of these circles, between the points of contact, take part in forming the envelope $\mathscr{H}_{cT}$.

differentiate Eq. (2.100) of an arbitrary growing line with respect to s and take the scalar (dot) product of the result with the normal $\mathbf{n}$ to the initial line at an arbitrary point:

$$(\mathbf{n} \cdot \dot{\mathbf{r}}) = (\mathbf{n} \cdot \dot{\mathbf{r}}_0) + ct(\mathbf{n} \cdot \dot{\mathbf{n}}). \tag{2.105}$$

The above-formulated condition is satisfied, when this dot product is equal to zero. Let us show that the right-hand side of Eq. (2.105) indeed vanishes. Indeed, the first term is equal to zero, since the vector $\dot{\mathbf{r}}_0(s)$ tangent to the line $\mathbf{r}_0(s)$ is orthogonal to the normal vector $\mathbf{n}$. The second term is also equal to zero, since the derivative of a unit vector is always orthogonal to it: $\mathbf{n} \perp \dot{\mathbf{n}}$.

Hence, if the contour $\mathscr{L}_0$ coincides with its envelope $\mathscr{H}_{cT}$; then after defrosting, the floe will regain its original shape. Otherwise, it easy to realize, the ice floe takes on the shape of the envelope $\mathscr{H}_{cT}$.

Note. If the time of freezing $T \to \infty$; after defrosting, the floe assumes the shape of its *convex hull*. Recall that in order to find it, one needs to wrap the contour taut by an elastic band. Precisely the shape of the elastic band is the convex hull of the contour.

Physicists, in their minds, like to turn time back, being curious whether the events, having occurred until a certain moment of time T, would recur in the reverse order. To please the physicists, it is possible to interpret the melting of an ice floe as its evolution under the change of time flow to the opposite. The analysis carried out above shows that contour growth would be time-reversible, only if the initial contour coincided with its envelope. But in a general case, the process of contour growth is irreversible. This happens, because, during growth, the information about the shape of the parts of the initial contour lying inside its envelope gets lost.

Note. Mathematically, the mappings (2.100), (2.102) $\mathscr{L}_0 \to \mathscr{L}_T$ may be interpreted as the solutions of the line-growth equation at an initial contour $\mathscr{L}_0$. As long as the initial contour $\mathscr{L}_0$ coincides with its envelope $\mathscr{H}_{cT}$, these mappings give the classical solution. Otherwise, rolling a circle around the contour $\mathscr{L}_0$ gives the weak solution. Note an important physical property of weak solutions: unlike classical solutions of first order partial differential equations, weak solutions describe *irreversible physical processes*.

2.7 Problems to Chapter 2

Problem 1. Let a cone of a solid angle Ω be filled with a neutral substance of a volume density ρ, and at the base of the cone, at $r \leqslant \varepsilon \to 0$, where r is the distance from the apex of the cone $\mathscr{O}$, explosives of the same density are laid. At the initial moment of time $t = 0$, the explosives acquire a momentum p_0 (its density is uniformly distributed within the explosives and is equal to p_0/ε). Assume the solid angle to be so small ($\Omega \ll 1$), that the substance practically moves along the inner r-axis of the cone. Also assume that, during compression, the substance forms an infinitesimally thin pancake of inelastically coalesced particles spanning the whole of the cross-section of the cone. Let us call the pancake's motion a *detonation wave*. By applying the global principle, find the law of motion of the detonation wave and growth of the mass accumulated by it.

Solution. Let us introduce a one-dimensional density of the substance along the r-axis:

$$\rho_0(r) = \rho\,\Omega\, r^2.$$

According to the global principle, solving this problem is reduced to finding the coordinate $q(r,t)$ of the absolute minimum of the function

$$P(q)t + N(q) - r M(q) \quad (q > 0), \tag{2.106}$$

where

$$M(q) = \int_0^q \rho_0(r)\, dr = \frac{1}{3}\rho\,\Omega\, q^3, \tag{2.107}$$

and $P(q)$ and $N(q)$ are given by the expressions similar to (2.87):

$$P(q) = \begin{cases} \dfrac{p_0}{\varepsilon} q, & 0 < q < \varepsilon, \\ p_0, & \varepsilon < q, \end{cases} \qquad N(q) = \frac{1}{4}\rho\,\Omega\, q^4.$$

According to the global principle, in order to find the of motion of the detonation wave, it is necessary to determine the line $M(q)r + h$ tangent to the curve at two points (2.106) q^- and q^+ simultaneously. The position of the left point is obvious: $y_- = 0$. Hence $h = 0$. We find the position of the right point by equating the functions $\phi(q,t)$ and $M(q)r$ and their derivatives with respect to q. As a result, we obtain two equations for q and r:

$$\gamma t + 3q^4 = 4q^3 r, \quad q = r.$$

Here we used an auxiliary parameter $\gamma = 12p_0/\sigma\Omega$. Thus

$$r = q^+ = \sqrt[4]{\gamma t}.$$

This is the sought-for law of motion of the detonation wave. By substituting it for q in the expression for the mass on the left (2.107), we find the law of growth of mass accumulated by the detonaton wave:

$$M(t) = (4p_0 t)^{3/4} \left(\frac{\sigma\Omega}{3}\right)^{1/4}.$$

Problem 2. By means of the absolute minimum principle, find the weak solution of the Riemann equation (2.10) in the case, if the initial condition is proportional to a delta function $v_0(x) = s\,\delta(x)$. Give a physical interpretation of the solution in terms of a flow of inelastically coalescing particles.

Solution. Recall the weak solution of the Riemann equation has the following form:

$$v_w(x,t) = \frac{x - y_w(x,t)}{t}, \tag{2.108}$$

where $y_w(x,t)$ is the coordinate of the point of tangency of the initial potential

$$s_0(y) = s\,\Theta(y)$$

and the parabola (2.47). The sought-for mapping $y = y_w(x,t)$ and relevant geometric constructions are given in Fig. 2.21. From this figure and relation (2.108), it is seen that the weak solution of the Riemann equation

$$v(x,t) = \begin{cases} 0, \ x < 0, \\ \dfrac{x}{t}, \ 0 < x < x^*(t), \\ 0, \ x > x^*(t) \end{cases} \tag{2.109}$$

has the shape of a right-angled triangle. Here

$$x^*(t) = \sqrt{2st} \tag{2.110}$$

is the coordinate of the point of discontinuity of the weak solution.

Let us give a physical explanation of the weak solution (2.109). It follows from comparing the global principle with the absolute minimum principle that the latter describes motion of inelastically coalescing particles with a homogeneous initial density. Let it equal ρ_0. Then the delta-like initial condition given in the problem means that at $t = 0$ all substance is immobile apart from the particle situated at the point $x = 0$, to which a momentum of $\rho_0 s$. is transferred. Its current coordinate is given by the expression (2.110), and the velocity is equal to

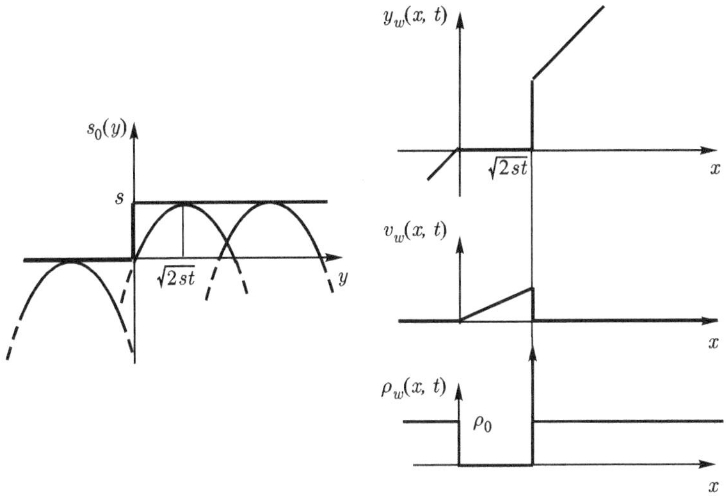

Fig. 2.21 Left hand side: initial potential of the velocity and parabolas tangent to it. Three characteristic positions of the parabolas are shown, corresponding to different parts of the mapping $y = y_w(x,t)$. Right hand side: Eulerian-to-Lagrangian coordinate transformation, velocity and density fields of the flow of coalescing particles. Bold arrow in the lower panel represents the singular component of the generalized density field.

$$v^*(t) = \frac{d}{dt}\sqrt{2st} = \sqrt{\frac{s}{2t}}.$$

While moving this particle turns into a macroparticle by picking up substance initially situated to the right of it, within the interval $x \in [0, x^*]$. The mass of thus-formed macroparticle is obviously equal to

$$m^*(t) = \rho_0 x^*(t) = \rho_0 \sqrt{2st}.$$

By multiplying it by the velocity of the macroparticle, let us verify the law of conservation of momentum

$$p^* = m^*(t)\, v^*(t) = \rho_0 \sqrt{2st}\sqrt{\frac{s}{2t}} = s = const$$

holds.

Let us find the density of the substance $\rho_w(x,t)$ at some point x. Recall that the mass to the left of a flow of coalescing particle is given by the expression (2.97):

$$m(x,t) = M(y_w(x,t)).$$

In our case, $M(x) = \rho_0 x + C$, where C is an inessential, albeit infinite, constant. After discarding it, we have

$$m(x,t) = \rho_0 y_w(x,t).$$

In order to find the current density of the flow, it remains to differentiate both sides of the last equality with respect to x. It is the easiest to reconstruct the sought-for derivative from the graph of the mapping $y = y_w(x,t)$ depicted in Fig. 2.21. As a result, we obtain

$$\rho_w(x,t) = m^*(t)\delta(x^*(t) - x) + \rho_c(x,t),$$

where

$$\rho_c(x,t) = \begin{cases} \rho_0, & x < 0, \\ 0, & 0 < x < x^*(t), \\ \rho_0, & x^*(t) < x. \end{cases}$$

Note. Let us note that within the interval $x \in [0, x^*]$ the density of the flow is equal to zero (see Fig. 2.21). It is clear why: the macroparticle sweeps out the substance in its path, collecting it into a cluster with a singular density. Thereby the triangular field $v_w(x,t)$ (2.109), if interpreted as the velocity field of a flow of coalescing particles, happens to be a *ghost field*, i.e. it describes the velocity of a substance of zero density and mass.

In view of the ghost character of the velocity field (2.109), it may seem that the obtained weak solution of the Riemann equation does not have any physical value. Far from it. In nonlinear acoustics, where $v_w(x,t)$ gives a pressure field, this solution is quite tangible, and the corresponding pressure field can be experimentally measured.

Problem 3. Let the initial velocity field of a flow of inelastically coalescing particles equal

$$v_0(x) = V\Theta(-x),$$

and the initial density $\rho_0(x)$ is such that the total mass is bounded:

$$\int_{-\infty}^{\infty} \rho_0(x)\,dx = M < \infty.$$

Derive the equation, which is obeyed by the coordinate $x^*(t)$ of the emerging macroparticle. Study its asymptotic at $t \to \infty$.

Solution. According to the global principle, the coordinate of the macroparticle $x^*(t)$ is determined from the condition that the function (2.85) has two identical absolute minima at different point with the coordinates y^- and y^+. In this problem, it is easy to find the connection between these coordinates. Indeed, since the particles to the right of the discontinuity are stationary, their Lagrangian coordinates coincide with the Eulerian ones. This also applies to the particle immediately adjacent to the discontinuity on the right. And this means that

$$y^+(t) = x^*(t) > 0.$$

Similar considerations concerning the particles on the left, moving with the same velocity V, give another useful formula:

$$y^-(t) = x^*(t) - Vt < 0.$$

In order to compose the equation for $x^*(t)$, it remains to equate the values of the function (2.85) at the points specified above by putting $x = x^*$ on both sides of the equality. Thus the sought-for equation has the following form:

$$x^*[M(x^*) - M(x^* - Vt)] = [N(x^*) - N(x^* - Vt)] - VtM(x^* - Vt). \qquad (2.111)$$

Here we used the definitions (2.87) and took into account that at the velocity field given in the formulation of the problem, we have

$$P(y) = V\,M(y)\,\Theta(-x).$$

Let us study the limiting cases of Eq. (2.111). If, for instance, the initial density is everywhere the same, then

$$M(y) = y, \quad N(y) = \frac{y^2}{2}.$$

Here we took into account that the homogeneous initial density can be set equal to unity. By substituting the last expressions into Eq. (2.111), we, after trivial algebraic manipulations, arrive at the formula

$$x^*(t) = \frac{V}{2}t.$$

From here, and from the initial condition, it follows that the weak solution of the Riemann equation found by means of the absolute minimum principle is equal to

$$v_w(x,t) = V\,\Theta\left(\frac{V}{2}t - x\right).$$

In other words, the step of the field $v(x,t)$ moves at a speed of $V/2$ — half the magnitude of the step.

Let us find the asymptotic solution of Eq. (2.111) at $t \to \infty$, assuming that the mass of the flow is bounded. Physically, it is evident that at $t \to \infty$ practically all substance of the flow accumulates into a single macroparticle moving at a constant velocity. In this case, physical intuition agrees with mathematical conclusions. Namely, it is possible rigorously to show that the following asymptotics hold:

$$\begin{aligned} M(x^*) - M(x^* - Vt) &\to M \\ N(x^*) - N(x^* - Vt) &\to x_c M \quad (t \to \infty). \\ M(x^* - Vt) &\to -M_- \end{aligned}$$

Here M is the total mass of the flow mentioned in the formulation of the problem, x_c is its center of mass at the initial moment of time, and

$$M_- = \int_{-\infty}^{0} \rho_0(y)\,dy$$

is the mass of particles moving at the moment of time $t = 0$. By substituting the above-listed asymptotes into (2.111), we obtain the following physically evident expression for the limiting law of motion of the macroparticle, which accumulated all mass of the flow:

$$x^*(t) = x_c + \frac{M_-}{M} Vt.$$

References

1. M.J. Lighthill, *Waves in Fluids*, 2nd edn. (Cambridge University Press, 2002)
2. B.L. Rozhdestvenskii, N.N. Yanenko, *Systems of Quasilinear Equations* (Nauka, Moscow, 1978). In Russian
3. G.B. Whitham, *Linear and Nonlinear Waves* (Wiley, New York, 1974)
4. O.V. Rudenko, S.I. Soluyan, *Theoretical Foundations of Nonlinear Acoustics* (Plenum, New York, 1977)
5. M.B. Vinogradova, O.V. Rudenko, A.P. Sukhorukov, *Theory of Waves* (Nauka, Moscow, 1979). In Russian
6. R. Richtmyer, *Principles of Advanced Mathematical Physic*, vol. 1 (Springer, Berlin, 1978)
7. W. E, Y. Rykov, Y. Sinai, Generalized variational principles, global weak solutions and behavior with random initial data for systems of conservation laws arising in adhesion particle dynamics, Commun. Math. Phys. **177**, 349–380 (1996)

Chapter 3
Nonlinear Equations of the Second Order

In this chapter, we discuss the main ideas and solution methods for nonlinear partial differential equations of the second order, which allow us to investigate the important for applications features and evolution stages of nonlinear waves due to competition of nonlinearity and dissipation. Additional useful information on this topic can be found in Refs. [1–5].

3.1 Regularization of nonlinear equations

We already know that description of nonlinear processes leads, within the framework of first order nonlinear partial differential equations, to the gradient catastrophe. Certainly, this is just a mathematical catastrophe meaning a failure of the classical solutions of the above mentioned equations. Meanwhile, the real life and, along with it, the investigated physical, economic and other processes are taking their course.

This contradiction between mathematics and real life was circumvented in the preceding chapter by constructing weak solutions. But physicists are not always satisfied with these. Based on too global principles, they are not capable of uncovering fine details and mechanisms of formation of singularities (discontinuities of the solution itself or its derivatives) inherent in weak solutions. There is another fruitful approach to the problem of the gradient catastrophe. It consists of *regularization of equations*, i.e. introduction of additional terms containing higher order derivatives. The latter impede development of the gradient catastrophe, thereby prolonging the life of classical solutions. Regularized solutions are also valuable in that they explicitly introduce into consideration parameters (coefficients at higher-order derivatives) having an evident meaning for applications. All this makes regularized equations an important tool for analysis of real life phenomena. Let us illustrate the above said by examples of surface growth and nonlinear acoustic waves.

3.1.1 The Kardar-Parisi-Zhang equation

Let us consider simple physical reasons leading to the well-known nonlinear equation of surface growth, suggested in Ref. [6]. Let us take a certain line $z = h(x,t)$, growing due to adhesion to it of micro-particles sedimenting from above. From the previous chapters, it is clear that if the intensity of the particle flow from different directions is the same, and the angles between the normal to the line and the z-axis are small, then, in the small angle approximation, the equation of the line is reduced to

$$\frac{\partial h}{\partial t} = \frac{c}{2}\left(\frac{\partial h}{\partial x}\right)^2 . \tag{3.1}$$

Here c is the speed of line growth in the direction perpendicular to the line. In the following, in order to simplify derivations, we will assume that $c = 1$, restoring the speed c in its rights only where it is necessary for the understanding of line-growth properties.

While deriving Eq. (3.1), we assumed that micro-particles cling to the line. But in reality, once on the line, micro-particles may move along it, for example, by sliding down a steep slope under the action of gravity. Let us take possible motion of particles into account by introducing into Eq. (3.1) the following additional term:

$$\frac{\partial h}{\partial t} + \frac{\partial g}{\partial x} = \frac{1}{2}\left(\frac{\partial h}{\partial x}\right)^2 . \tag{3.2}$$

The new function g entering this expression has a transparent physical meaning. This is *a flow* along the line $z = h(x,t)$ of micro-particles sedimented on it. It is natural to assume that the steeper the slope of the line to the x-axis, the stronger the tendency of particles to slide down and the greater the flow of particles toward the falling off of the line. The simplest mathematical model expressing such properties of a flow is :

$$g = \mu \frac{\partial h}{\partial x} . \tag{3.3}$$

The coefficient μ serves as a measure of particles' mobility. Fig. 3.1 illustrates the falling of micro-particles down onto a line and their sliding down along this line.

Apart from mobility of particles ended up on the line $z = h(x,t)$, inhomogeneity of the flow is also taken into account. The latter is accounted for by adding the term $F(x,t)$ to Eq. (3.2). As a result, the equation of line assumes the following form:

$$\frac{\partial h}{\partial t} = \frac{1}{2}\left(\frac{\partial h}{\partial x}\right)^2 + \mu \frac{\partial^2 h}{\partial x^2} + F(x,t). \tag{3.4}$$

We have arrived at the one-dimensional version of the well-known *Kardar–Parisi–Zhang (KPZ) equation*, which adequately describes, e.g., the process of deposition of semiconductor films.

The corresponding to Eq. (3.4) homogeneous (at $F \equiv 0$) KPZ equation

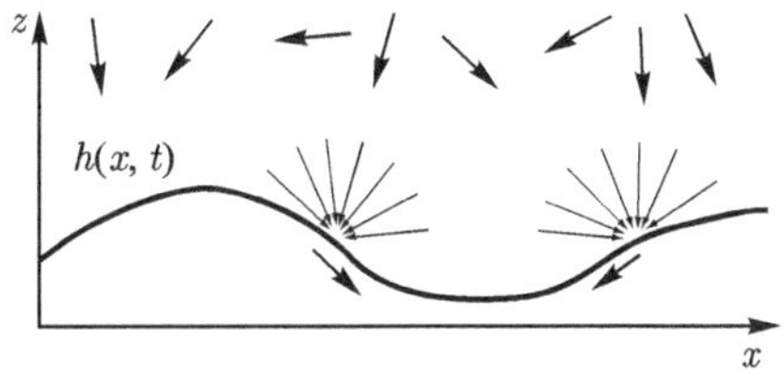

Fig. 3.1 Illustration of growth of the line $z = h(x,t)$, deposited by an isotropic flow of micro-particles. The arrows at the top symbolize the falling particles. The arrows below show the direction of particles' sliding along the line.

$$\frac{\partial h}{\partial t} = \frac{1}{2}\left(\frac{\partial h}{\partial x}\right)^2 + \mu \frac{\partial^2 h}{\partial x^2} \tag{3.5}$$

represents a regularized version of the original line-growth equation (3.1). In the following, we will ensure that at $\mu > 0$ this equation, along with an arbitrary initial condition

$$h(x,t=0) = h_0(x), \tag{3.6}$$

has a solution valid at all $t > 0$.

3.1.2 The Burgers equation

Let us take the equation of nonlinear acoustics as the next illustration of regularization of a first order partial differential nonlinear equation. From the previous chapter, it is known that one-dimensional nonlinear acoustic waves obey the Riemann equation

$$\frac{\partial v}{\partial t} + v\frac{\partial v}{\partial x} = 0. \tag{3.7}$$

Here $v(x,t)$ is the pressure deviation of a medium (e.g. air) from an equilibrium value, caused by the propagation of an acoustic wave. Eq. (3.7) does not take into account an important physical effect, *viz.* the viscosity of a medium, which absorbs the energy of the acoustic wave. The derivation of the nonlinear acoustics equation accounting for viscosity gives the following regularized equation:

$$\frac{\partial v}{\partial t} + v\frac{\partial v}{\partial x} = \mu \frac{\partial^2 v}{\partial x^2}, \quad v(x,t=0) = v_0(x). \tag{3.8}$$

The coefficient μ here expresses the degree of viscosity of the medium.

Equation (3.8) bears the name of Burgers, who proposed it as a model equation of strong hydrodynamic turbulence. Later it has found diverse application. In particular, as we already know, it is used to describe intense acoustic waves.

Note. By differentiating Eq. (3.5) term-by-term with respect to x, we arrive at an equation for the field:

$$v(x,t) = -\frac{\partial h(x,t)}{\partial x},$$

coinciding with the Burgers equation (3.8). Thus $v(x,t)$ has, apart from the acoustic meaning, also a clear geometric interpretation as the slopes of a growing line.

3.2 Properties of the Burgers equation

Let us turn to an analysis of solutions to the Burgers equation and to a discussion of their properties. This equation has an analytic solution nearly for any initial condition $v_0(x)$. We will not rush to present it to the reader: to have an exact solution of a nonlinear equation at our disposal is a rare stroke of luck. Without it, an investigator attempts to get an idea about the solution by studying characteristic special cases using various methods of qualitative and asymptotic analysis. We take this opportunity to illustrate some tools of the above mentioned arsenal by using the KPZ and Burgers equations as examples. The exact analytic solution will later provide an opportunity to appreciate the effectiveness of standard methods of investigating nonlinear phenomena.

3.2.1 Galilean invariance

First of all, let us discuss the properties of symmetries of the KPZ and Burgers equations. Note that if $v(x,t)$ obeys the Burgers equation, the fields $v(x+a,t)$ and $v(x,t+\tau)$, where a and τ are arbitrary space and time translations, respectively, also obey this equation. Let us denote the presence of a symmetry by the sign $\Longleftrightarrow$. For instance, we express the above mentioned translational symmetries by the following relations:

$$\begin{aligned} v(x,t) &\Longleftrightarrow v(x+a,t+\tau), \\ h(x,t) &\Longleftrightarrow h(x+a,t+\tau). \end{aligned} \tag{3.9}$$

The latter relation states the obvious fact that the properties of the translational symmetry are also inherent in the homogeneous KPZ equation.

The *odd reflection symmetry* also belongs to the symmetry properties characteristic of the Burgers equation: if $v(x,t)$ obeys the Burgers equation, $-v(-x,t)$ also obeys the same equation:

$$v(x,t) \Longleftrightarrow -v(-x,t). \tag{3.10}$$

The KPZ equation also possesses a reflection symmetry, but it is the even one:

$$h(x,t) \Longleftrightarrow h(-x,t).$$

It expresses the equivalence of line-growth direction (left-right).

Apart from the translation and reflection symmetries listed above, the Burgers equation has another one, which plays a key role in physics, *viz.* the *Galilean in-*

variance. Let us illustrate it by using the velocity field $u(x,t)$ of a one-dimensional flow of particles as an example. Let $\tilde{u}(x',t)$ is the velocity field of the flow in the coordinate system x' moving at a velocity V. Then the same field in the stationary coordinate system x, such that $x' = x - Vt$, is written as:

$$u(x,t) = V + \tilde{u}(x - Vt, t).$$

The Galilean invariance of the Burgers equation means that this equation is invariant under the above mentioned transformation

$$v(x,t) \iff V + v(x - Vt, t). \tag{3.11}$$

Let us mention consequences of the Galilean invariance of the Burgers equation as applied to finding solution of this equation. The Galilean invariance means that by finding one solution of the Burgers equation, we simultaneously acquire an infinite family of solutions to this equation generated by the Galilean transformation (3.11), i.e. if the solution of the Burgers equation with the initial condition $\tilde{v}_0(x)$ is known, then also known are the solutions with the initial conditions

$$v_0(x) = \tilde{v}_0(x) + V,$$

where V is an arbitrary constant.

3.2.2 Reynolds number

Apart from the symmetry properties, it useful to find out how the pace and character of evolution of a solution to the Burgers equation are varying under a change of the length scales and characteristic magnitudes of the initial field. To this end, we assume that the initial field $v_0(x)$ has the characteristic length scale ℓ and the magnitude U, i.e. it is representable in the following form:

$$v_0(x) = U u_0\left(\frac{x}{\ell}\right), \tag{3.12}$$

where $u_0(s)$ is a dimensionless function of a dimensionless argument.

Let us transform in the Burgers equation (3.8) to the dimensionless coordinate s and field $u(s,t)$ connected with the original variables by the following equalities:

$$s = \frac{x}{\ell}, \quad u(s,t) = \frac{v(s\ell,t)}{U}. \tag{3.13}$$

As a result, the Burgers equation assumes the form:

$$\frac{\partial u}{\partial t} + \frac{U}{\ell} u \frac{\partial u}{\partial s} = \frac{\mu}{\ell^2} \frac{\partial^2 u}{\partial s^2}, \quad u(s,t=0) = u_0(s). \tag{3.14}$$

Note that at $\mu = 0$ it turns into

$$\frac{\partial u}{\partial t} + \frac{U}{\ell} u \frac{\partial u}{\partial s} = 0, \quad u(s,t=0) = u_0(s).$$

Solution of the latter equation does not depend on the length scales of the original field, if we take the time scale to be $T = \ell/U$, i.e. we introduce the dimensionless time

$$\tau = \frac{t}{T} = \frac{U}{\ell} t. \tag{3.15}$$

Thereby the previous equation turns into the Riemann equation:

$$\frac{\partial u}{\partial \tau} + u \frac{\partial u}{\partial s} = 0, \quad u(s,t=0) = u_0(s).$$

Hence, in the absence of viscosity ($\mu = 0$), identical in shape and differing only in length scale and magnitude initial fields $v_0(x)$ generate similarly varying solutions $v(x,t)$. Only the pace of their evolution is different. It is natural that this property of *scale invariance* of solutions to the Riemann equation is also applicable to its weak discontinuous solutions.

At $\mu \neq 0$, Eq. (3.14) is transformed into the following equation:

$$\frac{\partial u}{\partial \tau} + u \frac{\partial u}{\partial s} = \frac{\mu}{\ell U} \frac{\partial^2 u}{\partial s^2}, \quad u(s,t=0) = u_0(s), \tag{3.16}$$

and the behavior of solutions to the Burgers equation becomes considerably more complex. It depends on the magnitude of the dimensionless parameter

$$\mathrm{R} = \frac{U\ell}{\mu}, \tag{3.17}$$

which appeared on the right-hand side of Eq. (3.16). It is called the *acoustic Reynolds number* or simply the *Reynolds number*. If it is small ($\mathrm{R} \ll 1$) (the viscosity is large), the last term of the Burgers equation (3.8) dominates over the nonlinear term, and the equation itself can be replaced with the linear diffusion equation

$$\frac{\partial v}{\partial t} = \mu \frac{\partial^2 v}{\partial x^2}. \tag{3.18}$$

But is the Reynolds number is large, to the forefront come effects of nonlinear distortion of the field $v(x,t)$. In other words, *the Reynolds number serves as a measure of the influence of nonlinearity on the behavior of the field $v(x,t)$.*

Let us have a look at the Reynolds number from another viewpoint. It can be represented as the ratio of two spatial scales

$$\mathrm{R} = \ell/\delta,$$

where ℓ is an external, with respect to the Burgers equation, spatial scale introduced by the initial condition, and

$$\delta = \mu/U \tag{3.19}$$

is the internal spatial scale, more inherent in the Burgers equation itself (more precisely, in the laws, which this equation describes). Let us call ℓ the *external*, and δ the *internal* length scales.

The notions of the internal and external length scales are difficult to express in the language of formal logic. Nevertheless, they possess a heuristic value while studying nonlinear fields. By specifying the external $\ell(t)$ and internal $\delta(t)$ length scales of the current nonlinear field $v(x,t)$, we obtain the current, time-dependent Reynolds number

$$\mathrm{R}(t) = \frac{\ell(t)}{\delta(t)}. \tag{3.20}$$

3.2.3 Hubble expansion

Until now, we have studied the general properties of the Burger equation. In order for the knowledge of the general properties to come in handy at the right moment, one needs to have a set of partial solutions of the equation. Let us start with a search for such solutions, without neglecting the simplest of them. Let us find out, for instance, if the linear function of x

$$v(x,t) = \beta(t)x \quad (\beta(t=0) = \alpha)$$

is a solution of the Burgers equation. By substituting it into (3.8), we discover that it indeed obeys the Burgers equation (and, at the same time, the Riemann equation), if the coefficient $\beta(t)$ satisfying the equation:

$$\frac{d\beta}{dt} + \beta^2 = 0, \quad \beta(t=0) = \alpha.$$

By solving it, we arrive at the following solution of the Burgers equation:

$$\beta(t) = \frac{\alpha}{1+\alpha t} \Rightarrow v(x,t) = \frac{\alpha x}{1+\alpha t}. \tag{3.21}$$

This, at first glance, trivial expression deserves a detailed discussion. It will later help better to understand the properties of solutions of the Burgers equation with an arbitrary initial solution.

While looking at the solution (3.21), let us imaging a (one-dimensional) expanding (at $\alpha > 0$) Universe. Indeed, the formula (3.21) follows from analysis of motion of uniformly scattering particles, whose velocities at the initial moment of time have been equal to $v_0(y) = \alpha y$, where y is the initial (Lagrangian) coordinate of a particle. Such particles' motion is given by the expressions:

$$v = \alpha y, \quad x = y + \alpha y t.$$

By eliminating y from here, we arrive at the relation (3.21).

Let us call the solution (3.21) the *Hubble expansion*. Its distinctive feature is in that with time the field $v(x,t)$ (3.21) loses information of the initial profile (in our case of the coefficient α). Indeed, at $t \to \infty$ the field v (3.21) tends to the field

$$v(x,t) \sim \frac{x}{t}, \tag{3.22}$$

which does not depend on the initial slope α. We also emphasize that at a negative $\alpha < 0$ the solution (3.21) expresses not expansion, but compression. The latter leads to a gradient catastrophe, when, during a finite time, the field everywhere becomes infinite. As it will be clear later, similar, but only local, gradient catastrophes are typical for solutions of the Burgers equation at small μ.

While continuing to interpret $v(x,t)$ of the velocity field of the one-dimensional Universe, we note that in reality there is motion of matter deviating from the Hubble expansion. Let us find out, within the framework of the Burgers equation, how the Hubble expansion affects the behavior of such excitations. In other words, we attempt to solve the Burgers equation with the initial condition

$$v(x,t=0) = \alpha x + \hat{v}_0(x),$$

where the first term take the Hubble expansion into account, and the second accounts for perturbations of the velocity fields. We will look for a solution of the Burgers equation in the form of a similar sum

$$v(x,t) = \frac{\alpha x}{1+\alpha t} + \hat{v}(x,t) \tag{3.23}$$

of a homogeneous Hubble expansion and field $\hat{v}(x,t)$, which is called the *peculiar velocity* in astrophysics. It reflects the development of excitations with respect to an expanding background. Let us investigate the behavior of the peculiar velocity by transforming to such a coordinate system, expanding with the background, that the new coordinate z is connected with the old one x by the following obvious equality:

$$z = \frac{x}{1+\alpha t}.$$

In the new coordinate system, the unknown field assumes the following form:

$$v(x,t) = \alpha z + u(z,t), \tag{3.24}$$

where

$$u(z,t) = \hat{v}\left(z(1+\alpha t),t\right).$$

By substituting (3.24) into (3.8), we arrive at the equation for the peculiar velocity:

$$\frac{\partial u}{\partial t}+\frac{1}{1+\alpha t}u\frac{\partial u}{\partial z}=-\frac{\alpha u}{1+\alpha t}+\frac{\mu}{(1+\alpha t)^2}\frac{\partial^2 u}{\partial z^2}.$$

From here, it is seen that the expanding background reduces the effect of nonlinearity and weakens dissipation of the field, and also weakens (at $\alpha > 0$) the field itself. The latter is due to the fact that the "particles" having a large velocity overtake the Hubble expansion, which reduces the velocity difference between the peculiar perturbation and the Hubble background.

Let us explicitly take into account the weakening of the peculiar velocity by using the following substitution:

$$u(z,t)=\frac{w(z,t)}{1+\alpha t}.$$

As a result, we arrive at the equation:

$$\frac{\partial w}{\partial t}+\frac{1}{(1+\alpha t)^2}w\frac{\partial w}{\partial z}=\mu\frac{1}{(1+\alpha t)^2}\frac{\partial^2 w}{\partial z^2}.$$

Let us pay attention to the mutual consistency of the coefficients of nonlinearity and viscosity in this equation. It consists in that after the transformation to the new time

$$\tau=\frac{t}{1+\alpha t}, \tag{3.25}$$

which takes into account the above mentioned suppression of nonlinearity and viscosity in the expanding background, we, surprisingly, return to original Burgers equation:

$$\frac{\partial w}{\partial \tau}+w\frac{\partial w}{\partial z}=\mu\frac{\partial^2 w}{\partial z^2},\quad w(z,\tau=0)=\hat{v}_0(z). \tag{3.26}$$

By combining all the previous transformations, we finally obtain:

$$\hat{v}(x,t)=\frac{1}{1+\alpha t}w\left(\frac{x}{1+\alpha t},\frac{t}{1+\alpha t}\right). \tag{3.27}$$

From here, it is seen that interaction of the perturbation $\hat{v}(x,t)$ with the expanding (at $\alpha > 0$) background reduces the amplitude of the field and increases its spatial scale. Due to this, the Hubble expansion slows down development of the peculiar field, which, in the absence of expansion, is equal to $w(x,t)$. As a consequence, during an infinite time $t \in (0,\infty)$, only a part of evolution of the field $w(x,t)$ is realized, which corresponds to the interval $(0,t^*)$ ($t^* = 1/\alpha$).

Otherwise, when $\alpha < 0$, a global gradient catastrophe takes place, i.e an avalanche-like growth of the amplitude of the peculiar field and compression of the length scales of the initial excitation occur. Because of this, the course of events is dramatically accelerated. Namely, all the stages of the development of the perturbation $w(x,t)$ from an infinite time interval happen during a finite time $t \in (0,t^*)$ ($t^* = 1/|\alpha|$).

3.2.4 Stationary wave

There is a "gentlemanly set" of partial solutions of partial differential nonlinear equations, which are looked for in the first instance. *Stationary waves* undoubtedly belong to this set. As far as one-dimensional waves are concerned, these are the solutions of the following form:

$$v(x,t) = \upsilon(x - Vt),$$

which depends only on the coordinate $z = x - Vt$. In other words, stationary waves propagate at a constant velocity V without changing its shape.

Let us find the stationary solution of the Burgers equation. Due to the Galilean invariance, it is sufficient to find a fixed $\upsilon(x)$ solution, and then "make it move" by means of the relation (3.11). Time-independent solution $\upsilon(x)$ satisfies the equation

$$\frac{d}{dx}\left[\frac{1}{2}\upsilon^2(x) - \mu\frac{d\upsilon(x)}{dx}\right] = 0. \tag{3.28}$$

It is written in the form, from which the first integral of this ordinary second order differential equation is immediately seen:

$$\mu\frac{d\upsilon(x)}{dx} + \frac{1}{2}\left[U^2 - \upsilon^2(x)\right] \equiv 0. \tag{3.29}$$

Here U is a constant of integration, which is obviously equal to the extremum value of $\upsilon(x)$. Because of the translational symmetry, an arbitrary translation a of the solution along the x-axis serves as the second integration constant: $\upsilon = \upsilon(x-a)$. While omitting this constant, by means of elementary methods of integration, we find the final expression for the fixed field:

$$\upsilon(x) = -U\tanh\left(\frac{Ux}{2\mu}\right). \tag{3.30}$$

We recreate the stationary wave from (3.30), by using the Galilean transformation (3.11) and adding an arbitrary translation:

$$v(x,t) = V - U\tanh\left(\frac{U}{2\mu}(x - Vt - a)\right). \tag{3.31}$$

From here, it is seen that the stationary wave describes the drop from the maximum v_- (on the left) to the minimum v_+ (on the right) value of the field. Here

$$v^- = v(x = -\infty, t) = V + U, \quad v^+ = v(x = \infty, t) = V - U.$$

From (3.31) follows that the effective width of the transition layer is equal to the internal length scale δ (3.19), and the velocity of the stationary wave$V$ and its amplitude U are connected with the maximum and minimum values of the stationary

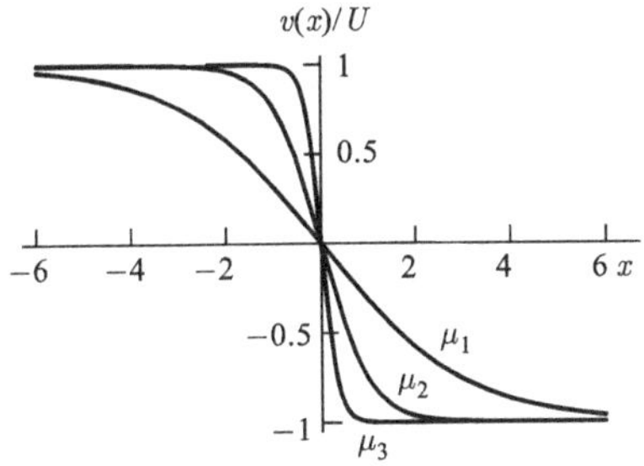

Fig. 3.2 Fixed solution of the Burgers equation for the following three values of the viscosity coefficient: $\mu_1, \mu_2 = \mu_1/3, \mu_3 = \mu_2/3$.

wave by already familiar relationships:

$$V = \frac{v^+ + v^-}{2}, \qquad U = \frac{v^+ - v^-}{2}. \tag{3.32}$$

We encountered them while discussing weak solutions following from the absolute minimum principle. There, such equalities expressed the velocity and amplitude of a discontinuity of a weak solution $v_w(x,t)$ through the values of the field immediately before and after the discontinuity.

The connection between a stationary wave and the local conditions at a discontinuity of a weak solution becomes evident, if we note that at $\mu \to 0_+$ the stationary solution (3.31) weakly converges to the discontinuous one

$$v_w(x,t) = V - U \operatorname{sgn}(x - Vt - a). \tag{3.33}$$

If the internal length scale of some discontinuity of the weak solution $v_w(x,t)$ is much less than the external length scale ($\delta(t) \ll \ell(t)$), then the fine structure of the discontinuity is reconstructed by means of the stationary solution (3.31) and of the relationships (3.32) by substituting into them the current values of $v^{\pm}(t)$ on the right and on the left of the investigated discontinuity of the weak solution $v_w(x,t)$. Fixed solution of the Burgers equation for different values of the viscosity coefficient μ is plotted in Fig. 3.2.

3.2.5 *Khokhlov's solution*

The stationary solution considered above has a fixed shape. We obtain a more "lively" partial solution[1] of the Burgers equation, by substituting the fixed field $\upsilon(x)$ (3.30) for w into Eqs. (3.27) and (3.23):

[1] This, important for understanding the competitive interaction of nonlinearity and viscosity, solution of the Burgers equation is named after the academician Rem Viktorovich Khokhlov, who is one of the founders of the nonlinear theory of acoustic waves.

$$v(x,t) = \frac{1}{1+\alpha t}\left[\alpha x - U \tanh\left(\frac{Ux}{2\mu(1+\alpha t)}\right)\right]. \tag{3.34}$$

In order better to understand the essence of the Khokhlov solution, let us have a look at the skeleton of this solution

$$v_w(x,t) = U(t)\left[\frac{x}{\ell} - \operatorname{sgn}(x)\right], \tag{3.35}$$

which is the weak limit of the exact solution (3.34) at $\mu \to 0_+$. In the last formula, we used the following notation:

$$U(t) = \frac{U}{1+Ut/\ell}, \quad \ell = \frac{U}{\alpha}. \tag{3.36}$$

Here $U(t)$ is the time-dependent shock amplitude, and ℓ is the distance from the origin of the coordinate system to the zeros of the weak solution (3.35). It is natural to consider ℓ as the external length scale of the fields (3.34) and (3.35). By substituting into (3.19) the current amplitude $U(t)$ (3.36) of the shock, we find the internal length scale:

$$\delta(t) = \frac{\mu}{U(t)} = \frac{\mu}{U}\left(1+\frac{Ut}{\ell}\right). \tag{3.37}$$

By dividing the external length scale by the internal one, we obtain the *current Reynolds number*

$$\mathrm{R}(t) = \frac{\ell}{\delta(t)} = \mathrm{R}\left(1+\frac{U}{\ell}t\right)^{-1}, \quad \mathrm{R} = \mathrm{R}(t=0) = \frac{U\ell}{\mu}. \tag{3.38}$$

With time, it monotonously decreases. In this case, acousticians say that due to dissipation of the wave in a viscous medium, the role of nonlinearity in the formation of the profile of the acoustic field weakens.

Let us consider an important special case of the Khokhlov solution. Formally, it follows from (3.34), when U and α tend to infinity, but in such a way that the ratio of these quantities remains equal $\ell < \infty$. The corresponding limit of the function (3.34), obviously, will also be an exact solution of the Burgers equation. This limit solution can easily be found:

$$v(x,t) = \frac{1}{t}\left[x - \ell \tanh\left(\frac{\ell x}{2\mu t}\right)\right]. \tag{3.39}$$

Its current internal length scale and Reynolds number are equal to

$$\delta = \frac{\mu t}{\ell}, \quad \mathrm{R} = \frac{\ell^2}{\mu t}. \tag{3.40}$$

The solution (3.39) describes the universal profile, to which, with time, tends the Khokhlov solution at all α and U. The field (3.39)

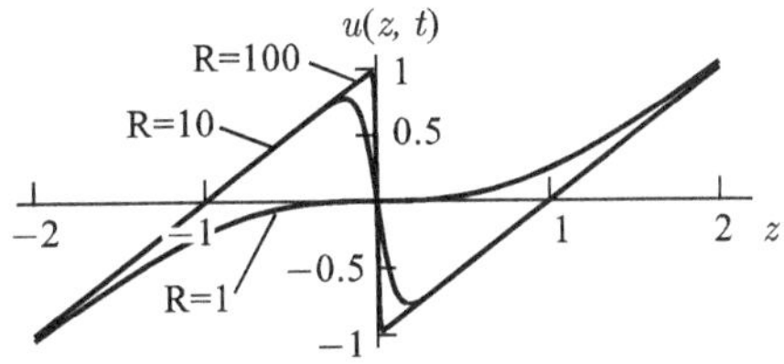

Fig. 3.3 Partial solution (3.41) of the Burgers equation as a function of $z = x/\ell$ at the following different values (inversely proportional to time) of the Reynolds number: R = 100; 10; 1. It is seen that the more R, the closer the graph to the limiting discontinuous function $u(z) = z - \mathrm{sgn}(z)$.

$$u(z,t) = \frac{t}{\ell} v(z\ell,t) = z - \tanh(\mathrm{R}z) \tag{3.41}$$

at different values of t and as a function of $z = x/\ell$ is plotted in Fig. 3.3.

3.2.6 *Rudenko's solution*

Another class of particular solutions of nonlinear partial differential equations attracting theoreticians' attention are *self-similar solutions*[2]. Let us find them for the Burgers and KPZ equations.

We start with a search for a self-similar solution of the homogeneous KPZ equation (3.5). Let us look for a solution depending on a single argument $\rho = t^n x$

$$h(x,t) = f(\rho) = f(t^n x), \tag{3.42}$$

assuming that $f(\rho)$ is a smooth bounded function. By substituting (3.42) into (3.5), after obvious manipulations, we have

$$nt^{n-1}xf' = \frac{1}{2}t^{2n}(f')^2 + \mu t^{2n} f''.$$

Here the primes denote derivatives with respect to ρ. By dividing the last equation by t^{2n}, we arrive at the following equation:

$$n\frac{x}{t^{n+1}}f' = \frac{1}{2}(f')^2 + \mu f''.$$

It is consistent with the requirement of self-similarity of the solution only if

---

[2] A self-similar solution of the Burgers equation had been found and analyzed by O.V. Rudenko in application to problems of nonlinear acoustics for plane and cylindrical waves. An analysis of the self-similar solution for intense acoustic waves is given in the book [7]. Self-similar solutions of the generalized Burgers equation are described by B. Enflo and O. Rudenko in [8].

$$n+1=-n \Rightarrow n=-\frac{1}{2}, \quad \rho=\frac{x}{\sqrt{t}}.$$

In view of these relations, the equations for $f(\rho)$ assumes the following form:

$$2\mu g' = g^2 - \rho g, \quad g = -f'. \tag{3.43}$$

Let us solve the equation for $g(\rho)$ by reducing it to a linear equation for the function $p = 1/g$. By dividing Eq. (3.43) by $1/p^2$, we obtain $2\mu p' = \rho p - 1$. From here, by the method of arbitrary constant variation, we obtain

$$p(\rho) = \sqrt{\frac{\pi}{\mu}} \exp\left(\frac{\rho^2}{4\mu}\right) \left[C - \Phi\left(\frac{\rho}{2\sqrt{\mu}}\right)\right].$$

Here we used the following auxiliary function:

$$\Phi(z) = \frac{1}{\sqrt{\pi}} \int_{-\infty}^{z} e^{-w^2} dw = \frac{1}{2}\left[1 + \operatorname{erf}(z)\right]. \tag{3.44}$$

Thus

$$g(\rho) = \frac{1}{p(\rho)} = \sqrt{\frac{\mu}{\pi}} \frac{\exp\left(-\frac{\rho^2}{4\mu}\right)}{C - \Phi\left(\frac{\rho}{2\sqrt{\mu}}\right)}. \tag{3.45}$$

In order to find $f(\rho)$, it remains to integrate this expression with respect to ρ. Let us assign, for definitiveness, $f(-\infty) = 0$ and express the arbitrary constant C via a geometrically illustrative quantity, *viz.* the limiting value of the sought-for solution at $\rho \to \infty$: $S = -f(\infty)$. Simple computations show that there exists the only bounded function $f(\rho)$ satisfying the above listed conditions:

$$f(\rho) = 2\mu \ln\left[1 - \left(1 - e^{-\mathrm{R}}\right) \Phi\left(\frac{\rho}{2\sqrt{\mu}}\right)\right]. \tag{3.46}$$

Here we used the following notation:

$$\mathrm{R} = \frac{S}{2\mu}. \tag{3.47}$$

Hence the self-similar solution of the homogeneous KPZ equation has the following form:

$$h_{\mathrm{R}}(x,t) = f\left(\frac{x}{2\sqrt{\mu t}}\right). \tag{3.48}$$

By differentiating (3.48) with respect to x, we find the self-similar solution of the Burgers equation:

$$v = -\frac{\partial h}{\partial x} \Rightarrow v(x,t) = \sqrt{\frac{\mu}{\pi t}}\, \mathscr{V}_{\mathrm{R}}\left(\frac{x}{2\sqrt{\mu t}}\right). \tag{3.49}$$

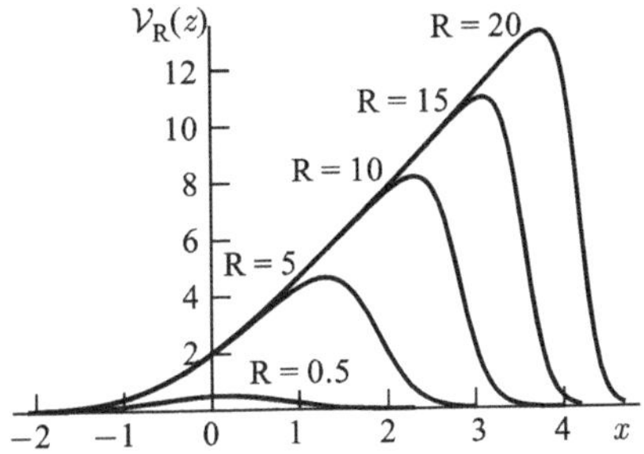

Fig. 3.4 $\mathscr{V}_R(z)$ as a function of z and at the values of R = 0.5, 5, 10, 15, 20. It is seen that the greater R, the more asymmetric (triangular) the shape of the self-similar solution of the Burgers equation.

Here we introduces another self-similar function

$$\mathscr{V}_R(z) = \frac{(1-e^{-R})e^{-z^2}}{1-(1-e^{-R})\,\Phi(z)}, \quad z = \frac{x}{2\sqrt{\mu t}}. \tag{3.50}$$

It is plotted in Fig. 3.4 at different values of R.

In order to comprehend the essence of the obtained solution, it is useful to uncover the mechanisms of its formation. Let us first find out, to which initial conditions correspond the obtained self-similar solutions. It is easy to figure out that the weak limit of the right-hand side of the relation (3.48) is proportional to the Heaviside function

$$h(x,t=0) = -S\Theta(x),$$

and the self-similar solution (3.49) of the Burgers equation weakly converges to a delta function

$$v(x,t=0) = S\delta(x). \tag{3.51}$$

As the next step on the way to understanding the essence of the self-similar solutions, let us discuss the meaning of the parameter R entering these solutions. Let us apply the scaling (3.13), (3.15) to the Burgers equation. Then it transforms into Eq. (3.16). While the initial condition, accounting for the properties of a delta function, assumes the following form:

$$u_0(s) = \frac{S}{U\ell}\,\delta(s).$$

It will not depend on the length scales of the initial field, only it $U\ell \sim S$. By comparing this equality with (3.47) and (3.17), we arrive at the conclusion that R (3.47) is the *Reynolds number of the singular initial condition* (3.51). In support of this conclusion, we note that the main asymptotic of $v(x,t)$ (3.49), (3.50)

$$v(x,t) \sim \frac{S}{2\sqrt{\pi\mu t}}\exp\left(-\frac{x^2}{4\mu t}\right), \quad R \to 0 \tag{3.52}$$

coincides with the self-similar solution of the linear diffusion equation (3.18). This should have been expected, since, at small Reynolds numbers, nonlinear effects are insignificant. Note also that the analogous "linearized" asymptotic

$$v(x,t) \sim \sqrt{\frac{\mu}{\pi t}}(1 - e^{-\mathrm{R}}) \exp\left(-\frac{x^2}{4\mu t}\right), \quad z < 0 \tag{3.53}$$

takes place at all R, only if the values of the function $\Phi(z)$ are sufficiently small. This is practically so at all $z < 0$.

Let us further discuss the behavior of the self-similar solution (3.49), (3.50) at large values of the Reynolds number ($\mathrm{R} \gg 1$) and at $z \gg 1$. For that, we need to know the asymptotic of the function $\Phi(z)$ at $z \to \infty$. It is equal to

$$\Phi(z) \sim 1 - \frac{1}{2z\sqrt{\pi}} e^{-z^2}, \quad z \to \infty. \tag{3.54}$$

By substituting it into (3.49), (3.50), we have

$$v(x,t) \approx \frac{x}{t} \frac{1}{2z\sqrt{\pi}\exp(z^2 - \mathrm{R}) + 1}, \quad z = \frac{x}{2\sqrt{\mu t}}. \tag{3.55}$$

As long as the first term in the denominator is small, i.e. while

$$2z\sqrt{\pi}\exp(z^2 - \mathrm{R}) \ll 1, \tag{3.56}$$

from (3.55) follows the already familiar to us characteristic linear (with respect to x) asymptotic of solutions to the Burgers equation

$$v(x,t) \approx \frac{x}{t}. \tag{3.57}$$

The boundary value z_*, at which the linear growth (3.57) is replaced with an exponential decay, is determined by the transcendental equation

$$2z_*\sqrt{\pi}e^{z_*^2} = e^{\mathrm{R}}.$$

A coarse estimate of its solution gives

$$z_* \approx \sqrt{\mathrm{R}} = \sqrt{\frac{S}{2\mu}}. \tag{3.58}$$

It allows us to estimate time variation of the characteristic length scale along the x-axis of the self-similar solution

$$z_* \approx \frac{\ell}{2\sqrt{\mu t}} \Rightarrow \ell(t) \approx \sqrt{2St}. \tag{3.59}$$

In its turn, by substituting the characteristic length scale of the self-similar solution $\ell(t)$ (3.59) for x in (3.57), we find it characteristic amplitude

$$U(t) \approx \frac{\ell(t)}{t}. \tag{3.60}$$

The obtained $\ell(t)$ and $U(t)$ allow us to estimate time behavior of the current Reynolds number. According to (3.17), (3.59), (3.60), we have [3]

$$\mathrm{R} = \frac{\ell^2(t)}{2\mu t} \approx \frac{2S}{\mu} = const. \tag{3.61}$$

We have arrived at an important conclusion: the *Reynolds number of the self-similar solution of the Burgers equation does not change with time.*

Let us discuss the profile of the self-similar solution to the Burgers equation in the boundary region, at a large Reynolds number ($\mathrm{R} \gg 1$), in detail. In this case, in this region, we can rewrite the expression (3.55) as

$$v(x,t) \approx \frac{\ell(t)}{t} \frac{1}{e^{z^2 - z_*^2} + 1}. \tag{3.62}$$

By using the fact that, in the case of interest, $z_* \gg 1$; let us further simplify the expression (3.62). Let us represent z as $z = z_* + s$ and replace in (3.62) the difference $z^2 - z_*^2$ with $2z_*s$. As a result, we obtain

$$v(x,t) \approx U(t) \frac{1}{e^{2z_*s} + 1}.$$

By using then the formula

$$\frac{1}{e^{2a} + 1} = \frac{1}{2} - \frac{1}{2}\tanh(a),$$

we have

$$v(x,t) \approx U(t) - U(t)\tanh\left(\frac{U(t)}{2\mu}[x - \ell(t)]\right), \quad x \gtrsim \ell(t). \tag{3.63}$$

Note that, up to the substitutions of V for the first term and of the law of uniform motion of the shock $X(t) = Vt + a$ for the actual law of motion in the case under discussion $X(t) = \ell(t)$, the obtained expression coincides with the expression for the stationary wave (3.31).

We note, in conclusion, that if we had been a little more observant, we could have assembled the self-similar solution of the Burgers equation, as if from lego construction-set pieces, from the already familiar particular solutions (3.53), (3.57), (3.63) of this equation:

---

[3] The Reynolds number (3.61) is 4 times greater than the previously introduced R (3.47). There is no contradiction in that, since the Reynolds number is of a semi-qualitative character and, without any adverse effect, may be changed by a reasonable amount. The definition of R (3.47) has been chosen on the basis of notational convenience for the consequent formulas. In the future, we will adhere precisely to the definition (3.47).

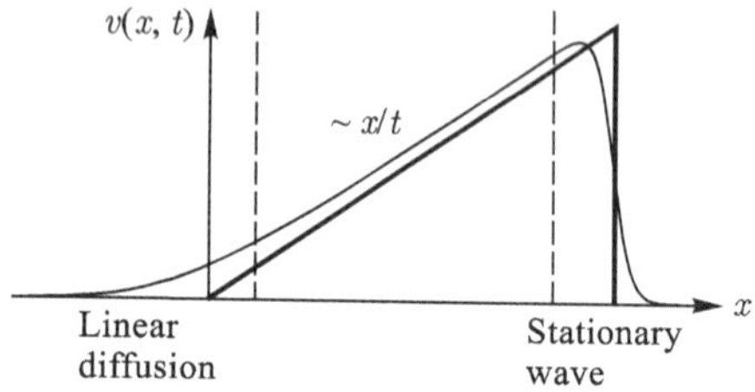

Fig. 3.5 Self-similar solution at R = 50. The regions, where the solution practically coincides with the solution of the linear diffusion equation and with the stationary wave are marked. The triangular skeleton of the self-similar solution is also shown.

$$v(x,t) \approx \begin{cases} \sqrt{\dfrac{\mu}{\pi t}} \exp\left(-\dfrac{x^2}{4\mu t}\right), & x \lesssim 0, \\ \dfrac{x}{t}, & 0 < x < \ell, \\ U - U \tanh\left(\dfrac{U}{2\mu}(x-\ell)\right), & x \gtrsim \ell. \end{cases} \tag{3.64}$$

The first line here is the solution of the linear diffusion equation (3.18) with the initial condition

$$v_0(x) = 2\mu\delta(x) = \frac{2}{\mathrm{R}} S\delta(x).$$

The second line in (3.64) coincides with the characteristic slope (3.57) due to effect of nonlinearity. Finally, the third line gives the sharp precipice of the self-similar solution having the shape of the stationary wave.

It remains to note that by virtue of the obvious invariant

$$\int_{-\infty}^{\infty} v(x,t)\,dx = const, \tag{3.65}$$

the area under the profile of the self-similar solution of the Burgers equation does not vary with time and is equal to S, and the self-similar solution itself (3.49), (3.64) at $\mathrm{R} \to \infty$ converges to the triangular weak solution of the Riemann equation obtain on the basis of the absolute minimum principle:

$$v_w(x,t) = \frac{x}{t}\left[\Theta(x) - \Theta(x-\ell)\right]. \tag{3.66}$$

In analogy with this solution, we also call the self-similar solution of the Burgers equation (3.49) at $\mathrm{R} \gg 1$ a *triangular* solution. The triangular solution $v(x,t)$ (3.49), (3.64) of the Burgers equation is depicted in Fig. 3.5.

3.3 General solution of the Burgers equation

After familiarizing ourselves with the material of the previous sections, we are sufficiently prepared to proceed with the general solution of the Burgers equation obtained in Refs. [2,9]. In order to kill two birds with one stone, i.e. to solve the Burgers equation (3.8) and the related to it line-growth equation (3.5), let us again discuss the KPZ equation (3.4).

3.3.1 The Hopf-Cole substitution

Let us return to the KPZ equation:

$$\frac{\partial h}{\partial t} = \frac{1}{2}\left(\frac{\partial h}{\partial x}\right)^2 + \mu \frac{\partial^2 h}{\partial x^2} + F(x,t), \quad h(x,t=0) = h_0(x). \tag{3.67}$$

Let us uncover its close relation with the Burgers equation. Purely psychologically, this is more conveniently done from the standpoint of a mathematician. To a mathematician, it is irrelevant that these equations describe phenomena of different physical nature, but it is important that there is an intrinsic mathematical relationship between these equations. Indeed, by introducing the new function

$$v(x,t) = -\frac{\partial h(x,t)}{\partial x} \tag{3.68}$$

and differentiating the KPZ equation (3.67) with respect to x term by term, we arrive at the (inhomogeneous) Burgers equation

$$\frac{\partial v}{\partial t} + v\frac{\partial v}{\partial x} = \mu \frac{\partial^2 v}{\partial x^2} + f(x,t), \quad v(x,t=0) = v_0(x). \tag{3.69}$$

Here

$$f(x,t) = -\frac{\partial F(x,t)}{\partial x}, \quad v_0(x) = -\frac{\partial h_0(x)}{\partial x}. \tag{3.70}$$

For the further discussion, it is also important that the KPZ and Burgers equations, in their turn, are the "closest relatives" of the linear diffusion equation

$$\frac{\partial \varphi}{\partial t} = \mu \frac{\partial^2 \varphi}{\partial x^2} + \frac{1}{2\mu} F(x,t)\,\varphi. \tag{3.71}$$

This can be easily verified by writing $\varphi(x,t)$ in the following form:

$$\varphi(x,t) = \exp\left(\frac{h(x,t)}{2\mu}\right). \tag{3.72}$$

According to the chain rules of differentiation,

$$\frac{\partial \varphi}{\partial t} = \frac{1}{2\mu}\frac{\partial h}{\partial t} e^{h/2\mu}, \quad \frac{\partial^2 \varphi}{\partial x^2} = \frac{1}{2\mu}\left[\frac{1}{2\mu}\left(\frac{\partial h}{\partial x}\right)^2 + \frac{\partial^2 h}{\partial x^2}\right] e^{h/2\mu}.$$

By substituting (3.72) and the last equalities into (3.71), after reduction of common multipliers, we discover that if $\varphi(x,t)$ is a solution of the linear equation (3.71), then the function $h(x,t)$ in the exponential (3.72) *satisfies the KPZ equation* (3.67)!

Hence the solution of the KPZ equation (3.67) is expressed through the solution of the linear diffusion equation (3.71) by means of the formula

$$h(x,t) = 2\mu \ln \varphi(x,t). \tag{3.73}$$

In order for this solution also to satisfy the initial condition specified in (3.67), Eq. (3.71) should be solved with the consistent initial condition

$$\varphi_0(x) = \exp\left(\frac{h_0(x)}{2\mu}\right). \tag{3.74}$$

Eq. (3.73), reducing the nonlinear KPZ equation (3.67) to the linear diffusion equation (3.71), is known as the *Hopf-Cole* substitution.

3.3.2 General solution of the Burgers equation

By differentiating (3.73) with respect to x and keeping in mind Eq. (3.68), we arrive at a conclusion that the solution of the inhomogeneous Burgers equation (3.69) is expressed via the solution of the Cauchy problem (3.71), (3.74) in the following way:

$$v(x,t) = -2\mu \frac{\partial}{\partial x} \ln \varphi(x,t) \tag{3.75}$$

or

$$v(x,t) = -\frac{2\mu}{\varphi}\frac{\partial \varphi}{\partial x}. \tag{3.76}$$

From here, it follows, in particular, that the homogeneous Burgers equation

$$\frac{\partial v}{\partial t} + v\frac{\partial v}{\partial x} = \mu \frac{\partial^2 v}{\partial x^2}, \quad v(x,t=0) = v_0(x), \tag{3.77}$$

be means of the substitution (3.75), is reduced to the linear diffusion equation

$$\frac{\partial \varphi}{\partial t} = \mu \frac{\partial^2 \varphi}{\partial x^2}, \quad \varphi_0(x) = \exp\left(-\frac{s_0(x)}{2\mu}\right). \tag{3.78}$$

Here

$$s_0(x) = \int^x v_0(x')\, dx' \tag{3.79}$$

is the familiar from the previous chapters initial potential of the solution to the Burgers equation. The solution of the Cauchy problem (3.78) is well known:

$$\varphi(x,t) = \frac{1}{2\sqrt{\pi\mu t}} \int_{-\infty}^{\infty} \varphi_0(y) \exp\left(-\frac{(y-x)^2}{4\mu t}\right) dy. \quad (3.80)$$

In the case we are considering now, it assumes the following form:

$$\varphi(x,t) = \frac{1}{2\sqrt{\pi\mu t}} \int_{-\infty}^{\infty} \exp\left(-\frac{1}{2\mu t}\left[s_0(y)t + \frac{(y-x)^2}{2}\right]\right) dy. \quad (3.81)$$

Note that the already familiar from the absolute minimum principle function (2.44)

$$\mathcal{G}(y;x,t) = s_0(y)t + \frac{1}{2}(y-x)^2 \quad (3.82)$$

enters the argument of the exponential function in the integrand. By using this function, it is convenient to write $\varphi(x,t)$ in a more compact form:

$$\varphi(x,t) = \frac{1}{2\sqrt{\pi\mu t}} \int_{-\infty}^{\infty} \exp\left(-\frac{\mathcal{G}(y;x,t)}{2\mu t}\right) dy. \quad (3.83)$$

3.3.3 Averaged Lagrangian coordinate

If the integral (3.80) can be taken analytically, the solution of the Burgers equation is found by the direct substitution of the known function $\varphi(x,t)$ into the right-hand side of Eq. (3.76). But for an analysis of general properties of the Burgers equation, writing its solution in another form happens to be more convenient. Let us find it, by differentiating the integral in (3.80) with respect to x and substituting the result into Eq. (3.76):

$$v(x,t) = \frac{x - \{y\}(x,t)}{t}. \quad (3.84)$$

Here the braces $\{\dots\}$ symbolize the procedure of spatial averaging by means of the non-negative normalized function

$$f(y;x,t) = \frac{\exp\left[-\frac{1}{2\mu}\mathcal{G}(y;x,t)\right]}{\int_{-\infty}^{\infty} \exp\left[-\frac{1}{2\mu}\mathcal{G}(y;x,t)\right] dy}. \quad (3.85)$$

The above mentioned procedure of spatial averaging of an arbitrary function $g(y)$ is defined by the following equality:

$$\{g(y)\} \equiv \int_{-\infty}^{\infty} g(y) f(y;x,t)\, dy. \quad (3.86)$$

Equation (3.84) demonstrates the close connection of the solution the Burgers equation with the classical solution of the Riemann equation (1.12) and its weak solution (2.40), since the function $\{y\}(x,t)$ serves as a natural generalization of the

Lagrangian coordinate to the case $\mu > 0$. Therefore we call $\{y\}(x,t)$ an . *averaged Lagrangian coordinate*. Let us list the properties of $\{y\}(x,t)$ analogous to the properties of Lagrangian coordinates:

1. As any Lagrangian coordinate of a single-stream gas, $\{y\}(x,t)$ also does not decrease with growing x.

Let us show this by noting that, by direct differentiation of Eqs. (3.85), (3.86); it is not difficult to prove validity of the following relation:

$$\frac{\partial}{\partial x}\{g(y)\} = \frac{1}{2\mu t}\left[\{g(y)y\} - \{g(y)\}\{y\}\right].$$

By substituting here $g(y) = y$, we arrive at the required inequality

$$\frac{\partial\{y\}}{\partial x} = \frac{1}{2\mu t}\left[\{y^2\} - \{y\}^2\right] = \frac{1}{2\mu t}\{(y - \{y\})^2\} \geqslant 0. \tag{3.87}$$

From here, and from (3.84), it follows that the solution of the Burgers equation obeys the inequality

$$\frac{\partial v(x,t)}{\partial x} \leqslant \frac{1}{t}. \tag{3.88}$$

Another, natural for Lagrangian coordinates, property of $\{y\}(x,t)$ is:

2. Let $\{y\}(x,t)$ correspond to the initial field $v_0(x)$, and $\{y\}(x,t|V)$ correspond to the field $v_0(x) + V$. Then these functions are linked by the following equality:

$$\{y\}(x,t|V) = \{y\}(x - Vt, t). \tag{3.89}$$

This property follows from the Galilean invariance of the solution to the Burgers equation (3.84) and from the fact that the function x/t does not change under the Galilean transformation:

$$V + \frac{x - Vt}{t} \equiv \frac{x}{t}.$$

3.3.4 Solution of the Burgers equation with vanishing viscosity

Recall that sometimes the Burgers equation (3.8) is interpreted as the regularized Riemann equation (3.7), which is formally obtained from the Burgers equation (3.8) at $\mu = 0$. In order better to comprehend the "mutual relationships" between the Riemann and Burgers equations, it is useful to know how the solution of the latter equation is transformed at $\mu \to 0$. It so happens that, at $\mu \to 0$, an effect of the *"Cheshire cat"* occurs, i.e. viscosity vanishes, while its action remains. Namely, at $\mu \to 0$, the solution of the Burgers equation converges to the weak solution (2.46) of the Riemann equation found from the absolute minimum principle. This effect demonstrates a phenomenon characteristic of nonlinear equations, whereby addition of a term with a higher derivative, even with an infinitesimal coefficient, qualitatively influences the solution.

In order to demonstrate this, we evaluate the weak limit $\lim_{\mu\to 0} v(x,t)$ of the solution to the Burgers equation on the basis of its representation (3.84) by means of the averaged Lagrangian coordinate

$$\{y\}(x,t) = \int_{-\infty}^{\infty} y f(y;x,t)dy, \tag{3.90}$$

where the function $f(y;x,t)$ is given by the equality (3.85). From the generalized function theory, it is known that the weak limit of the function $f(y;x,t)$ (3.85) at $\mu \to 0$ is equal to the delta function

$$\lim_{\mu\to 0} f(y;x,t) = \delta(y - y_w(x,t)), \tag{3.91}$$

where $y_w(x,t)$ is the absolute minimum of the function (3.82). By substituting the right-hand side of the last equality for the function $f(y;x,t)$ into the integral (3.90) and using the well-known sifting property of the delta function, we obtain

$$\lim_{\mu\to 0} \{y\}(x,t) = y_w(x,t).$$

Hence, at $\mu \to 0$, the solution of the Burgers equation converges to the weak solution (2.46) of the Riemann equation found from the absolute minimum principle.

3.4 Model equations of gas dynamics

Let us discuss some modifications and generalizations of the Burgers equation permitting general solutions and, at the same time, more fully than the Burgers equation itself modeling actual gasodynamic processes.

3.4.1 One-dimensional model of a polytropic gas

As it has been mentioned above, the equation

$$\frac{\partial v}{\partial t} + v\frac{\partial v}{\partial x} = \mu\frac{\partial^2 v}{\partial x^2} \tag{3.92}$$

was suggested by Burgers as a model equation for strong hydrodynamic turbulence, taking into account the effect of competition of inertial nonlinearity and viscosity on formation of the properties of strong hydrodynamic turbulence. But, from the point of view of experts in gasodynamics, the Burgers equation is not a very successful model of gasodynamic motion. First of all, it does not take into account the forces of pressure, which prevent excessive thickening of gases. Let us take the pressure forces into account by introducing an additional term

$$\frac{\partial v}{\partial t}+v\frac{\partial v}{\partial x}+\frac{1}{\rho}\frac{\partial P}{\partial x}=\mu\frac{\partial^2 v}{\partial x^2} \tag{3.93}$$

into Eq. (3.92). Here $P(x,t)$ is the pressure of a model gas, and $\rho(x,t)$ is its density. Physicists often investigate behavior of a *polytropic gas*, in which the pressure and density are linked by the relation

$$P(x,t)=\frac{\kappa^2}{\gamma}\rho^{\gamma}(x,t), \quad \kappa>0, \quad \gamma>0. \tag{3.94}$$

Note also that the Burgers equation, interpreted as the equation for the velocity field $v(x,t)$, is “immaterial”, since does not reflect the distribution of matter in a gas. The latter is described by the continuity equation for the density $\rho(x,t)$ of a gas

$$\frac{\partial \rho}{\partial t}+\frac{\partial}{\partial x}(\rho v)=\nu\frac{\partial^2 \rho}{\partial x^2}. \tag{3.95}$$

Here ν is the coefficient of molecular diffusion, which takes in account the effect of Brownian motion of molecules of a gas on evolution of its density.

The system of Eqs. (3.93)~(3.95) gives a much more adequate, than the Burgers equation itself (3.92), mathematical model of nonlinear motion of a one-dimensional compressible gas. The value of this model for studying the behavioral features of nonlinear fields of the gasodynamical type is greatly increased by the fact that when

$$\gamma=3 \quad \text{and} \quad \nu=\mu, \tag{3.96}$$

Equations (3.93)~(3.95) have an analytic solution for a wide class of initial conditions

$$v(x,t=0)=v_0(x), \quad \rho(x,t=0)=\rho_0(x). \tag{3.97}$$

Let us show this by writing down the system of equations

$$\begin{aligned}
&\frac{\partial v}{\partial t}+v\frac{\partial v}{\partial x}+c\frac{\partial c}{\partial x}=\mu\frac{\partial^2 v}{\partial x^2},\\
&\frac{\partial c}{\partial t}+v\frac{\partial c}{\partial x}+c\frac{\partial v}{\partial x}=\mu\frac{\partial^2 c}{\partial x^2},
\end{aligned} \tag{3.98}$$

which follows from (3.93), (3.95) under the condition that Eqs. (3.96) hold. Here we introduced the *local sound-speed* field

$$c(x,t)=\kappa\rho(x,t). \tag{3.99}$$

Let us introduce two more auxiliary fields

$$u_{\pm}(x,t)=v(x,t)\pm c(x,t), \tag{3.100}$$

such that the original velocity and density fields are expressed via them by the following equalities:

$$v(x,t) = \frac{u_+(x,t)+u_-(x,t)}{2}, \quad \rho(x,t) = \frac{u_+(x,t)-u_-(x,t)}{2\kappa}. \tag{3.101}$$

By adding and subtracting Eqs. (3.98), we observe that each of the auxiliary fields (3.100) satisfies its own Burgers equation

$$\frac{\partial u_\pm}{\partial t} + u_\pm \frac{\partial u_\pm}{\partial x} = \mu \frac{\partial^2 u_\pm}{\partial x^2} \tag{3.102}$$

with the initial condition

$$u_\pm(x,t=0) = v_0(x) \pm \kappa\rho_0(x). \tag{3.103}$$

The solutions (3.101) of the equations of a model gas (3.98) are of the greatest interest for physicists in the particular case of a constant initial density

$$\rho(x,t=0) = \rho_0 = const. \tag{3.104}$$

This is because in this case, as it will soon be clear, these solutions satisfy the fundamental : *law of conservation of momentum*:

$$\int \rho(x,t)v(x,t)\,dx = const. \tag{3.105}$$

For this reason, we consider the case (3.104) in more detail. If the initial density is everywhere constant, the initial conditions (3.103) for the Burgers equation (3.102) assume the following form:

$$u_\pm(x,t=0) = v_0(x) \pm c_0 \quad (c_0 = \kappa\rho_0 = const),$$

and, due to the Galilean invariance (3.11), the sought-for solutions of Eq. (3.102) are such that

$$u_+(x,t) = u(x-c_0t,t)+c_0, \quad u_-(x,t) = u(x+c_0t,t)-c_0. \tag{3.106}$$

The only auxiliary field $u(x,t)$ remaining here satisfies the Burgers equation with the standard initial condition

$$\frac{\partial u}{\partial t} + u\frac{\partial u}{\partial x} = \mu\frac{\partial^2 u}{\partial x^2}, \quad u(x,t=0) = v_0(x). \tag{3.107}$$

By substituting (3.106) into (3.101), we express the solutions of the model equations of gasodynamics (3.98) via the solution of the Burgers equation (3.107):

$$v(x,t) = \frac{1}{2}\left[u(x-c_0t,t)+u(x+c_0t,t)\right] \tag{3.108}$$

and

$$\rho(x,t) = \rho_0 \left[1 - \frac{u(x+c_0 t,t) - u(x-c_0 t,t)}{2c_0} \right]. \tag{3.109}$$

Let us verify that these solutions obey the law of conservation of momentum (3.105). By taking the product of the right-hand sides of (3.108) and (3.109), we have

$$\begin{aligned} \rho(x,t)\, v(x,t) &= \frac{\rho_0}{2} \left[u(x-c_0 t,t) + u(x+c_0 t,t) \right] \\ &+ \frac{1}{2\kappa} \left[u^2(x-c_0 t,t) - u^2(x+c_0 t,t) \right]. \end{aligned} \tag{3.110}$$

Let us integrate both side of the obtained equality over infinite limits with respect to x. The integral of the last term on the right-hand side, by virtue of its symmetry, is equal to zero. But the integral of the first term does not depend on time, since the solution of the Burgers equation (3.107) has the invariant

$$\int u(x,t)\, dx = \int v_0(x)\, dx = const.$$

Thus the total momentum of a model gas does not depend on time and equals

$$\int \rho(x,t) v(x,t)\, dx = \rho_0 \int v_0(x)\, dx.$$

3.4.2 *Discussion of physical properties of a model gas*

While discussing various physical phenomena, physicists usually start with an analysis of the time and length scales inherent in them. Following their lead, let us introduce the characteristic magnitude U and length scale ℓ of the initial field $v_0(x)$. Evolution of the solution to the Burgers equation qualitatively depends on the ratio of the characteristic times of development of nonlinear and dissipative effects:

$$t_n = \frac{\ell}{U}, \quad t_d = \frac{\ell^2}{\mu}, \tag{3.111}$$

which forms the initial Reynolds number

$$\mathrm{R} = \frac{t_d}{t_n} = \frac{U\ell}{\mu}.$$

Motion of the gas is characterized by yet another characteristic time scale

$$t_a = \frac{\ell}{c_0}. \tag{3.112}$$

Let us call it an *acoustic time* of relaxation (spreading) of initial excitations present in the gas. Its ration to the characteristic time of development of nonlinearity t_n form the famous *Mach number*:

$$\mathrm{M} = \frac{t_a}{t_n} = \frac{U}{c_0}. \tag{3.113}$$

If it is small, then deviations of the density

$$\delta\rho(x,t) = \rho(x,t) - \rho_0 = \rho_0 \frac{u(x - c_0 t, t) - u(x + c_0 t, t)}{2c_0} \tag{3.114}$$

from the initial density of the gas ρ_0 are also small. In other words, pressure forces, in this case, prevent appearance of large variations of the gas density. Moreover, as long as the current time is much less the characteristics times of nonlinearity and dissipation ($t \ll \min\{t_n, t_d\}$), the field $u(x,t)$ in (3.108) can be replaced with the initial field $v_0(x)$. Accordingly, the solution (3.108) describes the characteristic for linear acoustics spreading of waves at a sound speed c_0 without changing their shape:

$$v(x,t) = \frac{1}{2}\left[v_0(x - c_0 t) + v_0(x + c_0 t)\right].$$

In the limit $\mu \to 0_+$, the field $u(x,t)$ of the right-hand sides of (3.108), (3.109) should be replaced with the weak solutions $u_w(x,t)$ of the Riemann equation, described in detail in the previous chapter, which have been found by means of the global minimum principle. The corresponding expressions

$$\begin{aligned} v_w(x,t) &= \frac{1}{2}\left[u_w(x - c_0 t, t) + u_w(x + c_0 t, t)\right], \\ \rho(x,t) &= \rho_0 \left[1 - \frac{u_w(x + c_0 t, t) - u_w(x - c_0 t, t)}{2c_0}\right] \end{aligned} \tag{3.115}$$

are appropriately interpreted as the generalized, satisfying the law of conservation of momentum, solutions of the equations

$$\begin{cases} \dfrac{\partial v}{\partial t} + v\dfrac{\partial v}{\partial x} + \kappa^2 \rho \dfrac{\partial \rho}{\partial x} = 0, \\ \dfrac{\partial \rho}{\partial t} + \dfrac{\partial}{\partial x}(\rho v) = 0 \end{cases} \tag{3.116}$$

of a one-dimensional polytropic gas with a polytrope exponent of $\gamma = 3$. In this case, at long time ($t \gtrsim t_n$), the fields $v(x,t)$ and $\rho(x,t)$ become discontinuous, but they always remain bounded due to the action of pressure forces preventing formation of domains with a very high density.

Example 1. We will better understand peculiarities of behavior of the generalized velocity and density fields (3.115) the vicinities of shocks (discontinuities) at large Mach numbers, if we trace the behavior of these fields in the case, when the auxiliary field $u(x,t)$ is described by the Khokhlov solution. In the limit studied here ($\mu = 0_+$), the field $u(x,t)$ coincides with the skeleton of the Khokhlov solution (3.35). During

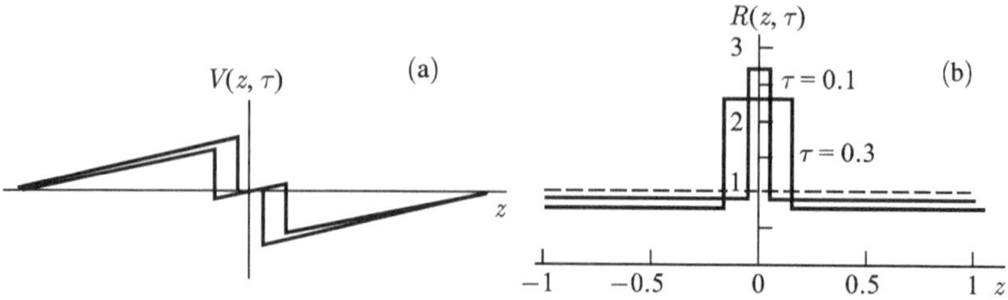

Fig. 3.6 Generalized velocity and density fields (3.117) of a polytropic gas at $\mathrm{M} = 2$ and at the moments of time $\tau = 0.1$ and $\tau = 0.3$.

an analysis of the skeleton and its ramifications, it is convenient to transform to the dimensionless coordinate and time

$$z = \frac{x}{\ell}, \quad \tau = \frac{Ut}{\ell},$$

and also to the dimensionless velocity and density fields

$$V(z,\tau) = \frac{v}{U}, \quad R(z,\tau) = \frac{\rho}{\rho_0}.$$

From (3.115) and (3.35) follows that these fields are equal to

$$\begin{aligned} V(z,\tau) &= \frac{1}{2(1+\tau)}\left[g\left(z+\frac{\tau}{\mathrm{M}}\right)+g\left(z-\frac{\tau}{\mathrm{M}}\right)\right], \\ R(z,\tau) &= 1-\frac{\mathrm{M}}{2(1+\tau)}\left[g\left(z+\frac{\tau}{\mathrm{M}}\right)-g\left(z-\frac{\tau}{\mathrm{M}}\right)\right], \\ g(z) &= z-\operatorname{sgn}(z). \end{aligned} \tag{3.117}$$

Their profiles are shown in Fig. 3.6. It is seen that in a vicinity of the point $z = 0$, where the discontinuity of the initial velocity field has been located, there appears a high-density domain Thereby pressure forces cause this domain to expand with time, thus reducing the density within it.

Let us discuss the behavior of the model gas in another limiting case $\mathrm{M} \to \infty$. Physically, it corresponds to a gas without pressure, whose behavior is determined by competition of only inertial nonlinearity and viscosity. In this case, the model-gas equations assume the following form:

$$\begin{cases} \dfrac{\partial v}{\partial t} + v\dfrac{\partial v}{\partial x} = \mu\dfrac{\partial^2 v}{\partial x^2}, \\ \dfrac{\partial \rho}{\partial t} + \dfrac{\partial}{\partial x}(\rho v) = \mu\dfrac{\partial^2 \rho}{\partial x^2}, \end{cases} \tag{3.118}$$

and the density field is described by the relation

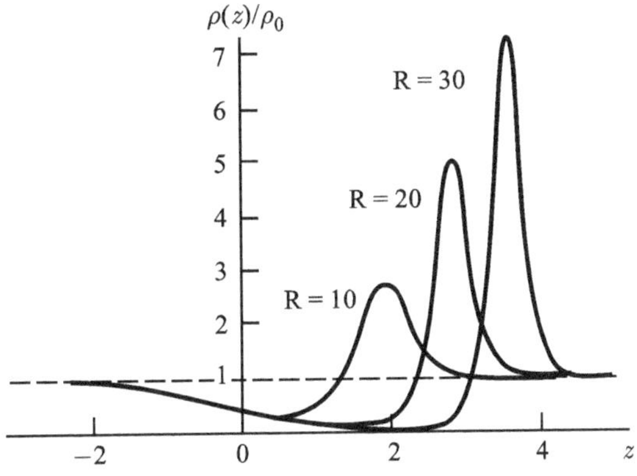

Fig. 3.7 Density of a pressureless gas in the case, when at the initial moment of time the gas acquired a momentum at the origin of the coordinate system. Thereby appearing motion leads to development of a cluster accompanied by a long tail, i.e. a region of reduced density to the left of the cluster. The greater the Reynolds number (smaller μ), the greater the maximum value of the density inside the cluster.

$$\rho(x,t) = \rho_0 \left[1 - t\frac{\partial v(x,t)}{\partial x}\right], \tag{3.119}$$

which follows from Eqs. (3.108), (3.109) at $c_0 \to 0$. At $\mu > 0$, the density field (3.119) is everywhere bounded. Only contrary to the previous case, where excessive growth of the gas density has been prevented by pressure forces, here limitation of the density magnitude occurs due to viscosity of the gas and molecular diffusion. ∎

Example 2. Let, at the initial moment of time and at the point $x = 0$, a gas acquire a momentum $\rho_0 S$. Then the velocity field of the pressureless gas is described by the expressions (3.49), (3.50). The density field of such a gas (3.119) is self-similar and equals

$$\rho(x,t) = \rho_0 \left[1 - \frac{1}{2\sqrt{\pi}} \frac{d\mathscr{V}_{\mathrm{R}}(z)}{dz}\right], \quad z = \frac{x}{2\sqrt{\mu t}}.$$

It is plotted at different values of the Reynolds number $\mathrm{R} = S/\mu$ in Fig. 3.7. ∎

3.5 Problems to Chapter 3

Problem 1. Although the stationary wave (3.30) is immobile, it describes a dynamic equilibrium of inertial and dissipative processes. Therefore it is useful to evaluate the rate of decay

$$\Gamma = \mu \int_{-\infty}^{\infty} \left(\frac{\partial v}{\partial x}\right)^2 dx \tag{3.120}$$

of the (infinite) energy of the stationary wave. Analyze the dependence of Γ on the amplitude U of the wave and on the viscosity coefficient μ.

Solution. Let us evaluate the derivative of the stationary solution entering the integrand in (3.120). It is equal to

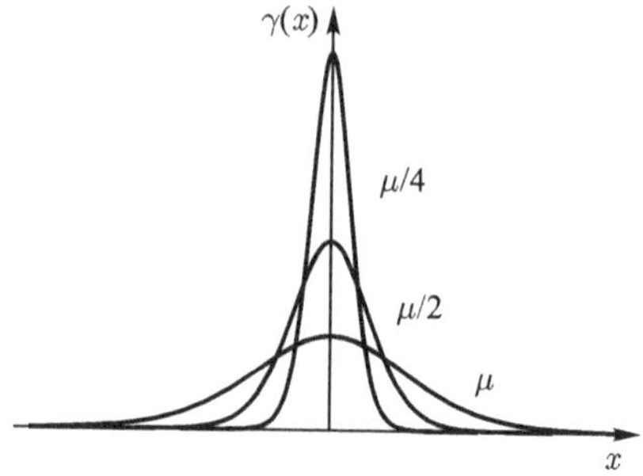

Fig. 3.8 Dissipation density $\gamma(x)$ of the stationary wave at the same U and different μ: $\mu_1 = \mu$, $\mu_2 = \mu/2$, $\mu_3 = \mu/4$. With decreasing μ, the density compresses and elongates upwards, but the area under the curves does not change.

$$\frac{dv(x)}{dx} = -\frac{U^2}{2\mu\cosh^2\left(\frac{Ux}{2\mu}\right)}.$$

By substituting this expression in the integral (3.120), we obtain

$$\Gamma = \frac{U^4}{4\mu}\int_{-\infty}^{\infty}\frac{dx}{\cosh^4\left(\frac{Ux}{2\mu}\right)} = \frac{U^3}{2}\int_{-\infty}^{\infty}\frac{dz}{\cosh^4(z)}.$$

By taking the remaining integral, we have

$$\Gamma = \frac{2}{3}U^3. \tag{3.121}$$

Note. The rate of energy decay depends only on the amplitude of the wave U, but it does not depend on the viscosity coefficient μ. This is the secret of the "Cheshire cat" effect mentioned in Sect. 3.3, according to which viscosity vanishes ($\mu \to 0_+$), but dissipation of the field remains. For a detailed understanding of the mechanism of realization of the Cheshire-cat effect, it is useful to investigate the *dissipation-density* field

$$\gamma(x,t) = \mu\left(\frac{\partial v(x,t)}{\partial x}\right)^2, \tag{3.122}$$

the integral of which with respect to x determines the rate of dissipation of the field (3.120). Dissipation density

$$\gamma(x) = \frac{U^4}{4\mu\cosh^4\left(\frac{Ux}{2\mu}\right)} \tag{3.123}$$

of the stationary wave at the same U and different values of μ is shown in Fig. 3.8.

It is easy to show that at $\mu \to 0_+$ the dissipation density (3.123) weakly converges to the delta function

$$\lim_{\mu\to\mu_+}\gamma(x) = \frac{2}{3}U^3\,\delta(x).$$

This limit mathematically expresses the fact that, in the limit $\mu \to 0$, all dissipative processes occur in infinitesimal neighborhoods of discontinuities of weak solutions to nonlinear equations.

Problem 2. The initial condition of the stationary solution to the Burgers equation coincides with the stationary solution (3.30) itself. Find and analyze the solution of the Burgers equation, when its initial condition is equal to the superposition of stationary waves:

$$v_0(x) = -U_1 \tanh\left(\frac{U_1}{2\mu}(x-\ell_1)\right) - U_2 \tanh\left(\frac{U_2}{2\mu}(x-\ell_2)\right). \tag{3.124}$$

Solution. Let us recreate the initial condition of the diffusion equation (3.78) according to the given initial condition of the Burgers equation. First of all, let us find the initial potential

$$s_0(x) = \int_0^x v_0(y)\,dy = -2\mu \ln\left[\cosh\left(\frac{U_1}{2\mu}(x-\ell_1)\right)\cosh\left(\frac{U_2}{2\mu}(x-\ell_2)\right)\right].$$

From here and from (3.78), we have

$$\varphi_0(x) = \cosh\left(\frac{U_1}{2\mu}(x-\ell_1)\right)\cosh\left(\frac{U_2}{2\mu}(x-\ell_2)\right)$$

or

$$\varphi_0(x) = \cosh\left(\frac{U_+}{2\mu}(x-\ell_+)\right) + \cosh\left(\frac{U_-}{2\mu}(x-\ell_-)\right).$$

Here we have taken into account that just as the initial potential $s_0(x)$ is defined up to a constant term, so the initial field $\varphi_0(x)$ is defined up to a constant factor. In the last formula, we introduce the following notation:

$$U_\pm = U_2 \pm U_1, \quad \ell_\pm = \frac{U_2\ell_2 \pm U_1\ell_1}{U_2 \pm U_1}.$$

We obtain the current solution $\varphi(x,t)$ of the linear diffusion equation by realizing that the diffusion equation with the initial condition $\cosh(ax)$ has a solution with separable variables:

$$e^{\mu a^2 t}\cosh(ax).$$

Thus

$$\varphi(x,t) = \exp\left(\frac{U_+^2}{4\mu}t\right)\cosh\left(\frac{U_+}{2\mu}(x-\ell_+)\right) + \exp\left(\frac{U_-^2}{4\mu}t\right)\cosh\left(\frac{U_-}{2\mu}(x-\ell_-)\right).$$

By substituting this expression into (3.76), we finally obtain

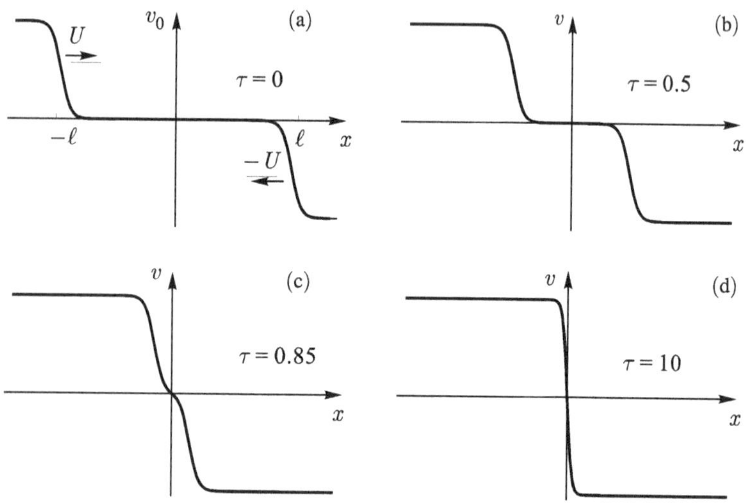

Fig. 3.9 Illustration of coalescence of stationary waves as functions of x at different moments of time $\tau = Ut/\ell$ and at a value of the dimensionless parameter of $U\ell/\mu = 25$. Note that the effective width of the transition region of the resultant stationary wave is twice as narrow as that of the original stationary waves.

$$v(x,t) = -\frac{U_+ \sinh\left(\frac{U_+}{2\mu}(x-\ell_+)\right) + \exp\left(-\frac{U_1U_2}{\mu}t\right) U_- \sinh\left(\frac{U_-}{2\mu}(x-\ell_-)\right)}{\cosh\left(\frac{U_+}{2\mu}(x-\ell_+)\right) + \exp\left(-\frac{U_1U_2}{\mu}t\right)\cosh\left(\frac{U_-}{2\mu}(x-\ell_-)\right)}. \tag{3.125}$$

Let, for definiteness, $U_1U_2 > 0$. Then, with growing t, the first terms in the numerator and denominator of (3.125) become increasingly greater in comparison with the second terms, and the solutions of the Burgers equation asymptotically tends to the stationary solution

$$\lim_{t\to\infty} v(x,t) = -U_+ \tanh\left(\frac{U_+}{2\mu}(x-\ell_\infty)\right).$$

In other words, out of the two "stationary waves", with time, a single stationary wave with the total amplitude $U_+ = U_1 + U_2$ and center at the point

$$\ell_+ = \frac{U_2\ell_2 + U_1\ell_1}{U_2 + U_1} \tag{3.126}$$

is formed. Solution of the Burgers equation (3.125) at $U_1 = U_2 = U$, $\ell_2 = -\ell_1 = \ell$, illustrating the process of coalescence of shocks, is shown in Fig. 3.9.

Problem 3. By means of the skeleton of the solution (3.125) of the Burgers equation, explain the origin of Eq. (3.126). For definitiveness, assume that

$$U_1 > 0, \quad U_2 > 0, \quad \ell_2 > \ell_1.$$

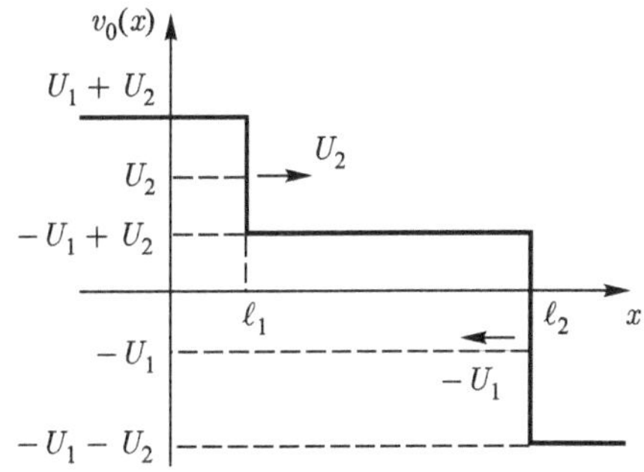

Fig. 3.10 Skeleton of the initial field $v_0(x)$ (3.124). The arrows show the directions of motion of the shocks.

Solution. The skeleton (limit at $\mu \to 0_+$) of the initial field $v_0(x)$ (3.124) is plotted in Fig. 3.10. From the theory of weak solutions of the Riemann equation, it is known that the velocity of motion of a shocks is equal to the half-sum of the velocities before and after the shock. Here, this means that the left shock moves to the right at a speed of U_2, and the right shock moves to the left at a speed of U_1. Hence the equations of motion of the shocks before the collision are equal to

$$\ell_1(t) = \ell_1 + U_2 t, \quad \ell_2(t) = \ell_2 - U_1 t.$$

At the moment of collision

$$\ell_1(t_*) = \ell_2(t_*) \Rightarrow t_* = \frac{\ell_2 - \ell_1}{U_2 + U_1}$$

the shocks merge, forming am immobile stationary wave, whose coordinate of the shock is equal to $\ell_1(t_*) = \ell_2(t_*) = \ell_+$.

References

1. J.M. Burgers, Mathematical examples illustrating relations occurring in the theory of turbulent fluid motion, Kon. Ned. Akad. Wet. Verh. **17**, 1–53 (1939).
2. J.D. Cole, On a quasi-linear parabolic equation occurring in aerodynamics, Quart. Appl. Math. **9**, 225–236 (1951)
3. S.N. Gurbatov, A.N. Malakhov, A.I. Saichev, *Nonlinear Random Waves and Turbulence in Nondispersive Media: Waves, Rays and Particles.* (Manchester University Press, 1991)
4. V.I. Karpman, *Non-linear Waves in Dispersive Media* (Pergamon Press, Oxford, 1974)
5. Y. Kuramoto, *Chemical Oscillations, Waves and Turbulence* (Springer, Berlin, 1985)
6. M. Kardar, G. Parisi, Y.C. Zhang, Dynamical scaling of growing interfaces, Phys. Rev. Lett. **56**, 889–892 (1986)
7. O.V. Rudenko, S.I. Soluyan, *Theoretical Foundations of Nonlinear Acoustics* (Plenum, New York, 1977)
8. B.O. Enflo, O.V. Rudenko, To the theory of generalized Burgers' equations, Acta Acustica **88**, 155–162 (2002)
9. E. Hopf, The partial differential equation $u_t + uu_x = u_{xx}$, Comm. Pure Appl. Mech. **3**, 201–230 (1950)

Chapter 4
Field Evolution Within the Framework of the Burgers Equation

In this chapter, we describe some solutions of the Burgers equation for single-scale fields, discuss properties of solutions to the Burgers equation for multi-scale fields, which, in one way or another, help to understand laws of evolution of noise fields.

4.1 Evolution of one-dimensional signals

Let us discuss typical scenarios of evolution of solutions to the Burgers equation realized under various initial conditions. We pay special attention to strongly nonlinear regimes, and also to specific features of the way a solution of the Burgers equation approaches the linear stage.

Solutions of the Burgers equation, typical for nonlinear acoustics, are also discussed in Refs. [1,2] and in the second part of the present book.

4.1.1 Self-similar solution, once more

Let us return to the solution (3.84) of the Burgers equation. It is easy rigorously to prove that it exists at any $t \in (0,\infty)$ and gives the unique solution of the Cauchy problem (3.77), if $v_0(x)$ grows at $x \to \pm\infty$ slower than the first power of x:

$$|v_0(x)| < A + B|x|^\gamma \quad (x \in \mathbb{R},\ A, B < \infty,\ 0 \leqslant \gamma < 1). \tag{4.1}$$

Note, however, that while this condition of existence and uniqueness guarantees availability of a solution to the Burgers equation, it does not prohibit to seek other solutions of this equation with initial conditions, which are beyond the framework of the inequalities (4.1). Sometimes such "exotic" solutions are very instructive for theory and valuable for applications. The Khokhlov solution (3.34), its particular case (3.39) or even the simplest solution of this class (3.18) satisfying a linear initial condition $v_0(x) = \alpha x$ serve as examples. Its exoticism consists in that at $\alpha < 0$ the field (3.18) "lives" only for a finite time, everywhere turning to infinity at $t^* = 1/|\alpha|$. But even this trivial "end of the world" may serve as a convenient model of the gradient catastrophe known from the previous chapter.

Example. Let us find a solution of the Burgers equation with the initial condition

$$v_0(x) = S\delta(x). \tag{4.2}$$

We already know the corresponding field $v(x,t)$, because we earlier established that the self-similar solution (3.49) weakly converges at $t \to 0$ to the delta function. Nevertheless, it is always useful to investigate different paths towards one and the same solution, since, as a rule, this helps shed new light upon the problem at hand.

The initial potential $s_0(x) = S\Theta(x)$ corresponds to the initial condition (4.2). Consequently, the initial condition for the auxiliary linear diffusion equation (3.78) is representable in the following form:

$$\varphi_0(x) = 1 - (1 - e^{-\mathrm{R}})\Theta(x).$$

By substituting it into the solution (3.80) of the diffusion equation, we have

$$\varphi(x,t) = 1 - (1 - e^{-\mathrm{R}})\Phi\left(\frac{x}{2\sqrt{\mu t}}\right). \tag{4.3}$$

Here R is the initial Reynolds number familiar from the self-similar solution, and $\Phi(z)$ is the auxiliary function (3.44).

By substituting (4.3) into (3.76), we find the sought-for solution of the Burgers equation with a singular initial condition. Naturally, it coincides with the self-similar solution (3.49). But this does not mean that we have wasted our time by looking for an already known solution. Based on the experience of solving the linear diffusion equation, we will formulate a statement radically changing our understanding of the role of the self-similar solution. Until now we have thought it to be one of particular solutions of the Burgers equation. Now we are capable, based on the obtained general solution and the theory of the linear diffusion equation, of rigorously proving that:

if the integral of the initial condition $v_0(x)$ is finite and equal to

$$\int_{-\infty}^{\infty} v_0(x)\,dx = S,$$

then at $t \to \infty$ the solution $v(x,t)$ of the Burgers equation asymptotically tends to the self-similar solution (3.49) with the Reynolds number $\mathrm{R} = S/2\mu$.

Thus, self-similar solutions serve as a powerful instrument for analysis of asymptotic properties of solutions to nonlinear equations. ∎

Note. We note that the above statement contradicts "common sense", according to which the current Reynolds number, due to dissipation of an acoustic wave in a viscous ($\mu \neq 0$) medium, must tend to zero ($\mathrm{R} \to 0$, $t \to \infty$), and the field, sooner or later, enters the linear stage of its evolution. We see that in the case under discussion, this is not so: The characteristic amplitude of the field $U(t)$ (3.60) indeed tends to zero at $t \to \infty$, but, at the same time, at the same rate grows the external length-scale $\ell(t)$ (3.59). As a result, the Reynolds number remains constant, and nonlinearity, as before, substantially determines the form of the field's profile.

4.1.2 Approach to the linear stage

Note that the above mentioned "common sense" does not let us down, is the initial field has a wave-like character:

$$\int_{-\infty}^{\infty} v_0(x)\,dx = 0. \tag{4.4}$$

In this case, at any, however large initial Reynolds number R, the solution of the Burgers equation eventually is asymptotically described by the linear diffusion equation. In other words, the nonlinear stage of evolution of the field $v(x,t)$ is succeeded by the linear stage.

Let us find the asymptotic of the solution of the Burgers equations at the linear stage. Note that the equality (4.4), as applied to the potential $s_0(x)$ of the initial field $v_0(x)$, means that the limiting values of $s_0(x)$ at $x \to \pm\infty$ are the same:

$$\lim_{x\to-\infty} s_0(x) = \lim_{x\to\infty} s_0(x).$$

Since the potential is defined with an accuracy up to an arbitrary constant, we assign these limits to be equal to zero. In other words, the initial potential is *localized* in a certain region of the x-axis. In order for the further constructions to be more rigorous, we require, for definitiveness, the initial potential $s_0(x)$ to be a finite functions, not equal to zero only within the interval $|x| < \ell$. Then the initial condition for the corresponding linear diffusion equation (3.78) assume the following form:

$$\varphi_0(x) = 1 + q_0(x), \tag{4.5}$$

where

$$q_0(x) = \exp\left(-\frac{s_0(x)}{2\mu}\right) - 1 \tag{4.6}$$

is also a finite function identically equal to zero at $|x| \geqslant \ell$.

From the properties of linear diffusion equations, it is known that if

$$t \gg t_d, \quad t_d = \frac{\ell^2}{4\mu}, \tag{4.7}$$

then the solution of Eq. (3.78) with the initial condition (4.5) is described by the asymptotic formula

$$\varphi(x,t) \sim 1 + Q(t)\exp\left(-\frac{x^2}{4\mu t}\right). \tag{4.8}$$

Here

$$Q(t) = \frac{Q_0}{2\sqrt{\pi\mu t}}, \quad Q_0 = \int_{-\infty}^{\infty} q_0(y)\,dy. \tag{4.9}$$

By substituting the asymptotic formula (4.8) into the right-hand side of the relationship (3.76), we obtain the asymptotic of the solution to the Burgers equation

$$v(x,t) \sim \frac{x}{t}\,\frac{Q(t)}{\exp\left(\frac{x^2}{4\mu t}\right) + Q(t)}. \tag{4.10}$$

The function $Q(t)$, which enters this expression, with time monotonically tends to zero. Hence, at $t \gg t_l$, where t_l is the characteristic time of approach to the linear regime:

$$Q(t_l) \simeq 1 \Rightarrow t_l = \frac{Q_0^2}{4\pi\mu}, \tag{4.11}$$

the asymptotic of the solution to the Burgers equation (3.77) will practically coincide with the solution of the linear diffusion equation

$$v(x,t) \sim \frac{x}{t}\,\frac{Q_0}{2\sqrt{\pi\mu t}}\exp\left(-\frac{x^2}{4\mu t}\right). \tag{4.12}$$

4.1.3 N-wave and U-wave

Earlier, we have found the characteristic time t_l (4.11) of approach of the solution to the Burgers equation to the linear regime. But this time itself, and also the mechanism of the transition to the linear stage, strongly depend on the shape of the initial field $v_0(x)$. In the nonlinear wave theory, there are even special terms: *N-wave* and *U-wave* [1], in order to distinguish regimes of evolution of nonlinear waves and their transition to the linear stage. Below we consider examples illustrating the notion of N- and U-waves.

Example 1. Let the initial field equal the difference of the two delta functions

$$v_0(x) = S\left[\delta(x+\ell) - \delta(x-\ell)\right]. \tag{4.13}$$

To this field correspond the rectangular potential $s_0(x)$ and function $q_0(x)$ (4.6):

[1] Note that in nonlinear acoustics, where the graphs of an acoustic field can be found by a mirror reflection of the studied in this section solutions of the Burgers equation, different terminology is used. So N-waves, discussed here, correspond to acoustic S-waves, and U-waves correspond to acoustic N-waves.

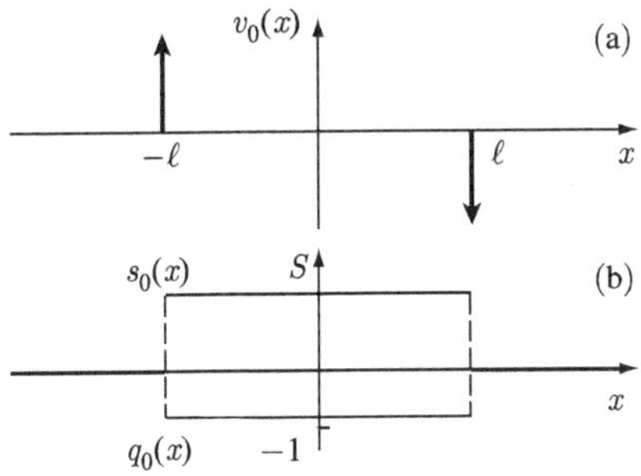

Fig. 4.1 Initial field $v_0(x)$ (4.13) **(a)** and fields $s_0(x)$, $q_0(x)$ **(b)**.

$$s_0(x) = [\Theta(x+\ell) - \Theta(x-\ell)],$$
$$q_0(x) = \left(e^{-R} - 1\right)[\Theta(x+\ell) - \Theta(x-\ell)]. \tag{4.14}$$

The initial condition (4.13) and functions (4.14) are plotted in Fig. 4.1.

In (4.14), the initial Reynolds number (3.47) $R = S/2\mu$ is introduced. In the most interesting case $R \gg 1$ from (4.14), (4.9), (4.11) we have

$$q_0(x) \simeq -[\Theta(x+\ell) - \Theta(x-\ell)] \Rightarrow Q_0 \simeq -2\ell \Rightarrow t_l \simeq \frac{4}{\pi} t_d.$$

Thus, in this case, the time of approach to the linear stage is close to the characteristic time of linear diffusion t_d (4.7).

Let us trace stages of evolution of the field $v(x,t)$ corresponding to the initial condition (4.13), by using the exact solution of the Burgers equation:

$$v(x,t) = -\frac{2\mu}{\ell}\sqrt{\frac{R}{\pi\tau}} \frac{\left(1-e^{-R}\right)\exp\left(-R\frac{z^2+1}{\tau}\right)\sinh\left(\frac{2Rz}{\tau}\right)}{1-\left(1-e^{-R}\right)\left[\Phi\left(\sqrt{\frac{R}{\tau}}(1-z)\right) - \Phi\left(-\sqrt{\frac{R}{\tau}}(1+z)\right)\right]}. \tag{4.15}$$

Here we introduced the dimensionless coordinate and time $z = x/\ell$, $\tau = 2St/\ell^2$, and the function Φ is defined by the equality (3.44). The field $v(x,t)$ is plotted in Fig. 4.2 for different values of τ and at $R = 25$ At the moment of time $\tau = 0.5$, the field consists of two triangular waves. At $\tau = 1$, the triangular waves collided and started to "devour" each other. At $\tau = 2$, mutual absorption of the triangular waves strongly decreases their amplitude. But the absolute magnitude of the parameter (4.9)

$$Q(\tau) \simeq -\sqrt{\frac{4R}{\pi\tau}}$$

is still appreciable ($|Q(\tau = 1)| \simeq 4$), and the nonlinear stage of evolution still continues. Characteristic features of the field $v(x,t)$ at $\tau = 1$ and $\tau = 2$, having the shape of a stylized letter N, are reflected in the way such type nonlinear fields are referred to: N-waves. Finally, at $\tau = R = 30$, when $|Q(\tau = 30)| \simeq 1$, mutual annihilation of the triangular waves ends in entering the linear stage. ∎

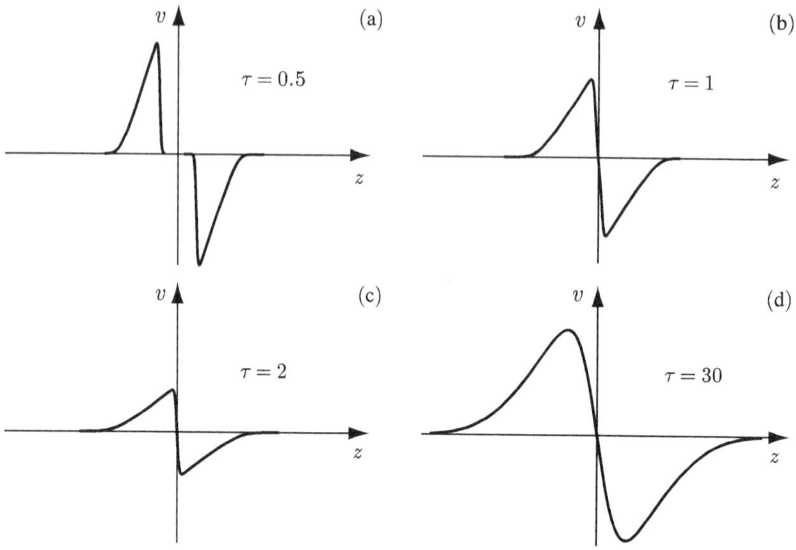

Fig. 4.2 Solution of the Burgers equation of the N-wave type, with the initial condition (4.13) and initial Reynolds number R=25, at different moments of time. The scales of the horizontal axes match, and the vertical scale of the latter graph is much greater than the scale of the former ones, in order for the weakened by dissipation solution of the Burgers equation at the linear stage to be seen.

Example 2. We obtain an example of U-waves by studying the solution of the Burgers equation with the initial condition

$$v_0(x) = S[\delta(x-\ell) - \delta(x+\ell)]. \tag{4.16}$$

The corresponding exact solution

$$v(x,t) = -\frac{2\mu}{\ell}\sqrt{\frac{\mathrm{R}}{\pi\tau}} \frac{(1-e^{\mathrm{R}})\exp\left(-\mathrm{R}\frac{z^2+1}{\tau}\right)\sinh\left(\frac{2\mathrm{R}z}{\tau}\right)}{1-(1-e^{\mathrm{R}})\left[\Phi\left(\sqrt{\frac{\mathrm{R}}{\tau}}(1-z)\right)-\Phi\left(-\sqrt{\frac{\mathrm{R}}{\tau}}(1+z)\right)\right]}, \tag{4.17}$$

is, at the first sight, very similar to the solution (4.15). But its behavior drastically differs from the behavior of the N-wave considered above in that the triangular waves, generated by the delta-like components of the initial condition (4.16), travel away from each other (see. Fig. 4.3). Therefore, in contrast to the N-wave, the triangular components of the U-wave interact only with their "tails". At a large R, this interaction is much weaker than the mutual extinguishing of the fronts for N-waves. As a result, the nonlinear stage of U-waves lasts much longer than for N-waves.

Let us confirm the above-said by quantitate derivations, by computing the time (4.11) of approach to the linear stage. In this case, it is equal to

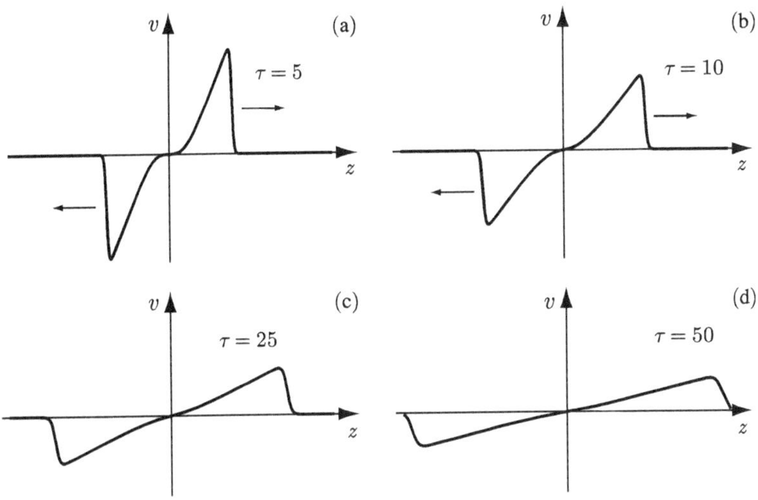

Fig. 4.3 Solution of the Burgers equation of the U-wave type with the initial condition (4.16) and R=25, at different moments of time.

$$t_l = \frac{4}{\pi}\left(e^{\mathrm{R}} - 1\right) t_d .$$

Hence, at the same (large) initial Reynolds number, the nonlinear stage of a U-wave lasts unimaginably longer than that of an N-wave. So, for the initial Reynolds number used in the examples $\mathrm{R} = 25$, the time of approach to the linear stage for the U-wave is approximately 10^{10} times greater than that for the N-wave. ∎

Note. Let us emphasize the importance of the notion of N- and U-waves. They describe typical elements of universal nonlinear structures appearing in the process of evolution of nonlinear fields with various initial conditions. Universality of N- and U-waves is expressed by the fact that the asymptotic formula (4.10) does not depend on fine details of the initial conditions $v_0(x)$, but does depend only on their integral characteristic Q_0 (4.9). If the latter quantity is positive, the field with acquires an N-like shape, whereas if $Q_0 < 0$, the field "rolls down" to a U-wave.

4.1.4 Sawtooth waves

Until now we used to specify an initial field $v_0(x)$ and monitor the corresponding solution of the Burgers equation. Sometimes, another approach is no less fruitful, whereby an initial condition $\varphi_0(x)$ of the linear diffusion equation (4.11) is given and the generated by it solution of the Burgers equation is studied. In what follows, the above mentioned approach will allow us illustratively to clarify the notion of *sawtooth waves* playing a key role in the analysis of behavior of nonlinear fields satisfying the Burgers equation.

Example. Let us take an initial condition of the linear diffusion equation (3.78) as the sum of delta functions:

$$\varphi_0(x) = \delta(x+\ell) + Q^2\delta(x-\ell). \tag{4.18}$$

Up to a common factor, which does not depend on x. the solution of the linear diffusion equation (3.78) has the following form:

$$\varphi(x,t) = \exp\left(-\frac{(x+\ell)^2}{4\mu t}\right) + Q^2 \exp\left(-\frac{(x-\ell)^2}{4\mu t}\right).$$

By substituting it into (3.76) and reducing the common factor factors in the numerator and denominator, we have

$$v(x,t) = \frac{x}{t} - \frac{\ell}{t}\,\frac{Q^2\exp\left(\frac{x\ell}{2\mu t}\right) - \exp\left(-\frac{x\ell}{2\mu t}\right)}{Q^2\exp\left(\frac{x\ell}{2\mu t}\right) + \exp\left(-\frac{x\ell}{2\mu t}\right)}.$$

We will better understand the physical meaning of the parameter Q by representing it in the following form:

$$Q = \exp\left(-\frac{s}{2\mu}\right). \tag{4.19}$$

As a result, we finally obtain

$$v(x,t) = \frac{1}{t}\left[x - \ell\tanh\left(\frac{\ell}{2\mu t}(x-Vt)\right)\right], \quad V = \frac{s}{\ell}.$$

This is the already familiar (but moving at a velocity V) solution (3.39) of the Burgers equation. By giving the artificial initial condition (4.18), we arrived at a natural, having a visual physical meaning solution of the Burgers solution. ∎

Let us build on the success by taking $\varphi_0(x)$ in the form of an arbitrary superposition of delta functions:

$$\varphi_0(x) = \sum_k Q_k\,\delta(x-y_k), \tag{4.20}$$

and in analogy with (4.19), assigning the coefficients to be equal to

$$Q_k = \exp\left(-\frac{s_k}{2\mu}\right). \tag{4.21}$$

Let us call the field corresponding to the initial condition (4.20) a *sawtooth wave*. Let us write the sawtooth wave in the form (3.84)

$$v(x,t) = \frac{x - \{y\}(x,t)}{t}, \tag{4.22}$$

where $\{y\}(x,t)$ is the mean Lagrangian coordinate, which here is equal to

$$\{y\}(x,t) = \frac{\sum_k y_k \exp\left(-\frac{1}{2\mu t}\left[s_k t + \frac{(x-y_k)^2}{2}\right]\right)}{\sum_k \exp\left(-\frac{1}{2\mu t}\left[s_k t + \frac{(x-y_k)^2}{2}\right]\right)}. \tag{4.23}$$

In order more clearly to comprehend the geometric meaning of the obtained solution, let us pick out the skeleton of the mean Lagrangian coordinate $\{y\}(x,t)$ and the corresponding skeleton of the sawtooth wave $v(x,t)$. Obviously, at $\mu \to 0_+$, in each point x, is sufficient to retain one (the largest) term in both numerator and denominator of Eq. (4.23). The dominant term is determined by plotting graphs of the *critical parabolas*

$$\Pi_k(x) = s_k t + \frac{(x-y_k)^2}{2}, \tag{4.24}$$

and choosing that one, which, in the point x, is less than the rest of them. Accordingly, $\{y\}(x,t)$ turns out to be a stepwise function, which is equal to

$$\{y\}(x,t) = y_k,$$

where k is the number of a given parabola. At the points of intersection of the lowest critical parabolas, the skeleton of the function $\{y\}(x,t)$ has discontinuities. Let us find the points $x_{k,m}(t)$ if intersection of the kth and mth parabolas:

$$\begin{gathered} \Pi_k(x) = \Pi_m(x) \Rightarrow x_{k,m}(t) = x^0_{k,m} + V_{k,m} t, \\ x^0_{k,m} = \frac{y_k + y_m}{2}, \quad V_{k,m} = \frac{s_m - s_k}{M_{km}}, \quad M_{k,m} = y_m - y_k \quad (k < m). \end{gathered} \tag{4.25}$$

If, immediately to the left and right of the point $x_{k,m}(t)$, the parabolas Π_k and Π_m are less than the other parabolas, then at the point $x_{k,m}(t)$ the function $\{y\}(x,t)$ undergoes a discontinuity. Thereby

$$\{y\}(x_{k,m}(t) - 0, t) = y_k, \quad \{y\}(x_{k,m}(t) + 0, t) = y_m \quad (k < m).$$

Critical parabolas (4.24) illustrating the construction of a stepwise function $\{y\}(x,t)$ are shown in Fig. 4.4.

If the discontinuities (shocks) move at different velocities $V_{k,m}$, some of them coalesce forming a new shock moving at its own velocity. Let us study the laws of coalescence of shocks in detail.

Let in a small neighborhood of $t \in (t_{k,m,n} - \varepsilon, t_{k,m,n})$ of the moment $t_{k,m,n}$ of intersection of the straight lines $x_{k,m}(t)$ and $x_{m,n}(t)$, and in a small neighborhood of the intersection point $x_{k,m,n}$, the smallest parabolas consecutively are Π_k, Π_m and Π_n $(k < m < n)$. This means that at the points $x_{k,m}(t)$ and $x_{m,n}(t)$ the function $\{y\}(x,t)$ has discontinuities. At the moment of time $t_{k,m,n}$, the middle parabola Π_m happens to be everywhere higher than the other ones, and at the position of two coalesced shocks, a new one emerges, with the coordinate $x_{k,n}(t)$ and velocity $V_{k,n}$. From (4.25) follows that the velocity of the shock created at the point of coalescence of the old shocks is connected with the velocities of the latter ones by the following equality:

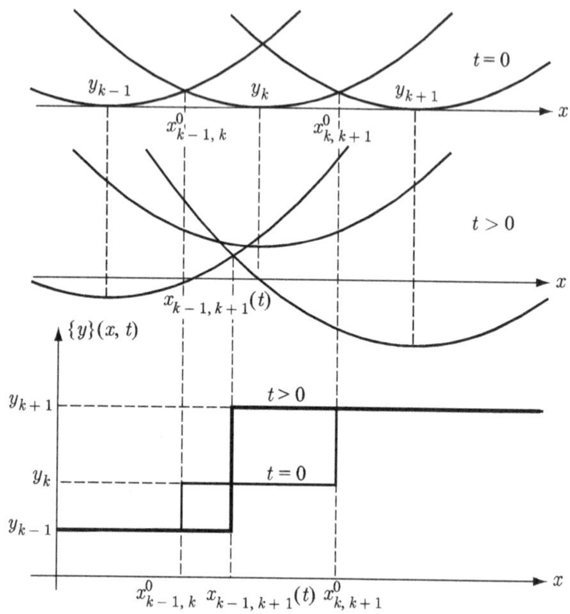

Fig. 4.4 Illustration to the construction of the skeleton of the function $\{y\}(x,t)$ by means of the comparison of parabolas. At the top, the parabolas at $t = 0$, and below, the parabolas at $t > 0$ are shown. It is seen that the middle parabola is everywhere higher than at least one of the rest parabolas. Therefore, instead of two discontinuities of the function $\{y\}(x,t)$ at the points $x^0_{k-1,k}$ and $x^0_{k,k+1}$, only one discontinuity is left at the point $x_{k-1,k+1}(t)$.

$$V_{k,n} = \frac{s_n - s_k}{y_n - y_k} = \frac{M_{k,m}V_{k,m} + M_{m,n}V_{m,n}}{M_{k,m} + M_{m,n}}. \tag{4.26}$$

This formula coincides with the law of velocity change of particles with masses $M_{k,m}$ and $M_{m,n}$ at an absolutely inelastic collision.

The fact that, until coalescence, the shock velocities are constant, and at the moment of coalescence they change according to the law of absolutely inelastic collisions, allows us to describe the behavior of a sawtooth wave in the parlance of a one-dimensional flow of inelastically colliding particles. The constructed according to the formula (3.84) skeleton of the sawtooth field $v(x,t)$ is shown in Fig. 4.5. The typical pattern of the trajectories of coalescing shocks is depicted in Fig. 4.6.

Until now we studied the skeleton of a sawtooth wave corresponding to the limit $\mu \to 0_+$. The expression (4.23) for the mean coordinate $\{y\}(x,t)$, however, also describes the smearing of the shocks because of viscosity ($\mu > 0$) and the approach to the linear stage. The latter is reached, when for any x the neighboring terms in the sums (4.23) have comparable magnitudes.

Let us briefly discuss an application scheme of the sawtooth-wave approximation. In order to do this, we recall the initial condition of the linear diffusion equation (4.6). Let s_k be the minimum value of the initial potential $s_0(x)$ attained at the point $x = y_k$. Then, at small μ and in a vicinity of the position of the minimum, this function may be replaced by the Gaussian:

$$\varphi_0^k(x) \sim \exp\left[-\frac{s_k}{2\mu} - \frac{\sigma_k}{4\mu}(x - y_k)^2\right]. \tag{4.27}$$

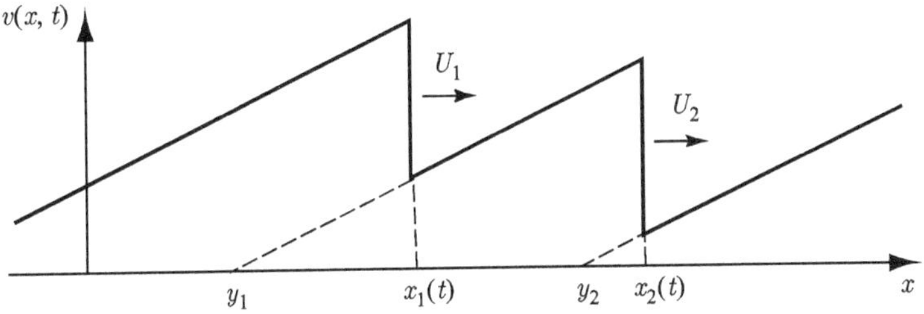

Fig. 4.5 Skeleton of a sawtooth wave. "Zeros" of the linear intervals and the coordinates of discontinuities are shown.

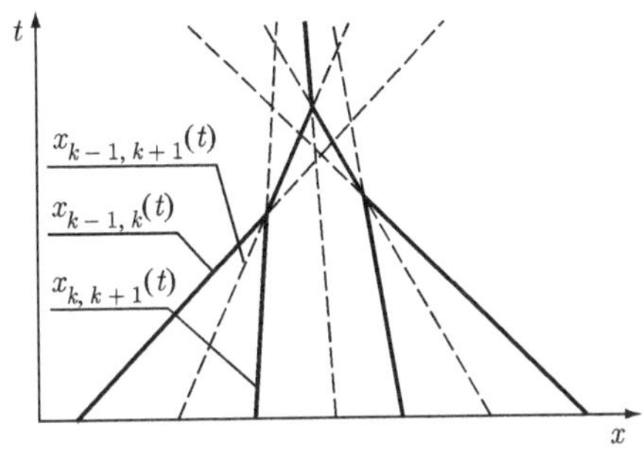

Fig. 4.6 Pattern of trajectories of coalescing shocks. Solid lines denote the trajectories of actually existing shocks.

Here

$$s_k = \sigma(y_k), \quad \sigma(x) = \frac{\partial^2 s_0(x)}{\partial x^2} = \frac{\partial v_0(x)}{\partial x}. \tag{4.28}$$

In the following, we assume that there is such ε that for for all k the following inequality holds:

$$\sigma_k > \varepsilon > 0.$$

By substituting (4.27) in (3.80), we find the solution of the linear diffusion equation

$$\varphi^k(x,t) = \frac{1}{\sqrt{1+\sigma_k t}} \exp\left[-\frac{\sigma_k t}{1+\sigma_k t}\frac{(x-y_k)^2}{4\mu t}\right]. \tag{4.29}$$

In the region

$$\varepsilon t \gg 1, \quad |x-y_k| \ll 2\sqrt{\varepsilon\mu t}, \tag{4.30}$$

the function $\varphi^k(x,t)$ (4.29) practically does not change, if we replace the right-hand side of the relationship (4.27) by the delta function:

$$\varphi_0^k(x) \sim \sqrt{\frac{4\pi\mu}{\sigma_k}} \exp\left(-\frac{s_k}{2\mu}\right) \delta(x-y_k).$$

By combining the contributions of all minimum points of the initial potential and taking into account the fact that the initial potential is defined up to an arbitrary constant factor, we arrive at the following assertion: *if the conditions* (4.30) *are satisfied, the solution of the Burgers equation is described by the expression (3.76), where $\varphi(x,t)$ is the solution of the linear Burgers equation with initial condition (4.20), and*

$$Q_k = \frac{1}{\sqrt{\sigma_k}} \exp\left(-\frac{s_k}{2\mu}\right).$$

The factor in front of the exponential can be interpreted as a small correction to s_k:

$$\frac{1}{\sqrt{\sigma_k}} \exp\left(-\frac{s_k}{2\mu}\right) = \exp\left(-\frac{s'_k}{2\mu}\right), \quad s'_k = S_k + \frac{\mu}{2} \ln \sigma_k,$$

which, at small μ, can be neglected. As a result, we arrive at the initial condition (4.20), (4.21).

4.1.5 Periodic waves

In applied problems, for instance in nonlinear acoustics, evolution of periodic waves is of greatest interest. Therefore we devote some attention to the features of the solution of the Burgers equation with periodic initial conditions by examining them in the approximation of sawtooth waves.

First of all, let us discuss behavior of an initially harmonic field with the initial condition

$$v_0(x) = a\sin(\kappa x) \Rightarrow s_0(x) = -\frac{a}{\kappa}\cos(\kappa x). \tag{4.31}$$

Let us determine the condition of applicability of the sawtooth-wave approximation in relation to the originally harmonic wave. The characteristic curvature of the minimum points of the initial potential is here the same and equal to

$$\sigma_k = \varepsilon = a\kappa = \frac{1}{t_n}, \quad t_n = \frac{1}{a\kappa},$$

where t_n is the moment of shock formation. Apart from this, since the relative, and not absolute, values of the terms in the expression (4.23) are important, it is possible to rewrite the conditions (4.30) in the following form:

$$t \gg t_n, \quad \ell \ll \sqrt{\frac{\mu}{t_n} t} \quad \left(\ell = \frac{\pi}{\kappa}\right). \tag{4.32}$$

Let us find the sawtooth wave corresponding to the harmonic initial field (4.31). Since the minima of $s_0(x)$ within each period are the same, the values s_k in (4.23) can be assigned to be equal to zero. In addition to that, $y_k = 2\pi k/\kappa$. As a result, the expression for the sawtooth wave approximating the initially harmonic field assumes the following form:

$$v(x,y) = \frac{a}{\tau}\left(z - 2\pi \frac{\sum_k k \exp\left[-\frac{\mathrm{R}}{8\tau}(z-2\pi k)^2\right]}{\sum_k \exp\left[-\frac{\mathrm{R}}{8\tau}(z-2\pi k)^2\right]}\right). \tag{4.33}$$

Here we used the following notation:

$$z = \kappa x, \quad \tau = a\kappa t, \quad \mathrm{R} = \frac{2a}{\mu\kappa}. \tag{4.34}$$

The field $v(x,t)$ (4.33) for different values of τ are plotted in Fig. 4.7.

We also note that, at a large Reynolds number $\mathrm{R} \gg 1$, the conditions of applicability of the sawtooth-wave approximation (4.32) are reduced to the following inequality:

$$t \gg t_n\sqrt{\mathrm{R}}.$$

Let us discuss how the Reynolds number of the initial harmonic wave changes with time. If $\mathrm{R} \gg 1$, then there are three clearly distinct evolution stages of the field $v(x,t)$. At times

$$t < t_n$$

shocks are as yet absent, and the Reynolds number is close to its inititial value:

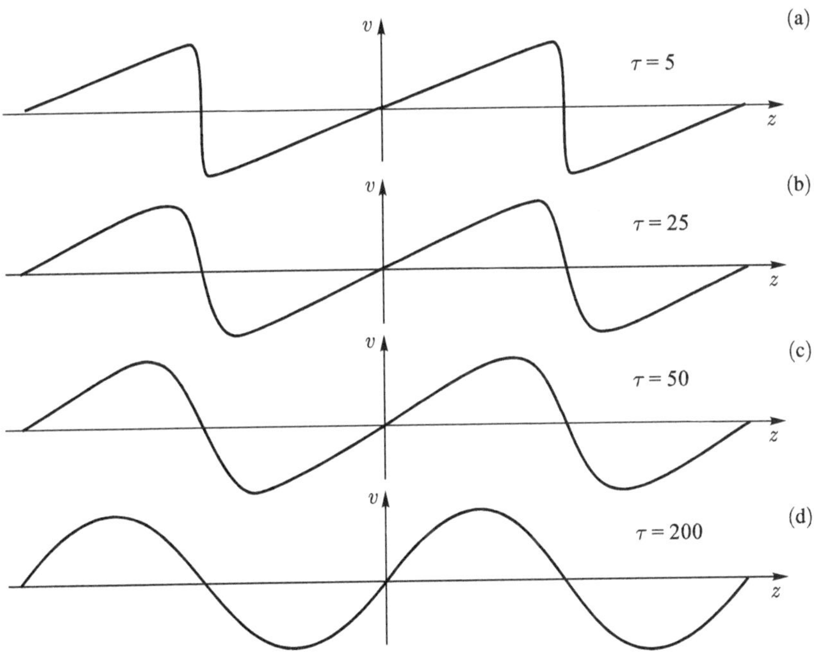

Fig. 4.7 Sawtooth wave (4.33) at $\mathrm{R} = 100$. The vertical scales of the plots are chosen so that the shape of the field $v(x,t)$ is clearly seen. It is seen that, with growing τ, the shocks get smeared out, and the field acquires a more and more sinusoidal profile, characteristic of the linear stage of evolution.

$$R(t) \simeq \frac{a\ell}{\mu} = \frac{\pi a}{\mu\kappa} \simeq R \quad (\ell = \frac{\pi}{\kappa}).$$

At $t \gg t_n$, the shock magnitude $U(t)$ and width $\delta(t)$ vary according to the laws

$$U(t) \simeq \frac{\ell}{t}, \quad \delta(t) \simeq \frac{2\mu}{U(t)},$$

and the Reynolds number decreases as $1/t$:

$$R(t) \simeq \frac{U(t)\ell}{\mu} \simeq \frac{\ell^2}{\mu t}.$$

Finally, at $t \gtrsim t_l$, where t_l is the time at which the shock width becomes equal to the half-period of the field $v(x,t)$:

$$\delta(t_l) \simeq \ell \Rightarrow t_l \simeq \frac{\pi^2}{2\mu\kappa^2} \simeq R t_n,$$

the linear stage sets in, and the Reynolds number tends to zero. A semi-qualitative graph of the current Reynolds number $R(t)$ of the initially harmonic field $v(x,t)$ is depicted in Fig. 4.8.

Note. Let us note that the sawtooth wave, into which the initially harmonic field turns at $R \gg 1$, possesses features of both N- and U-waves. Since the dissipation mechanism of N-waves is much more effective, the evolution of an initially harmonic wave and its approach to the linear stage develop according to the scenario of N-waves.

Let us also pay attention to the fact that the expression (4.33) does not contain information on the harmonicity of the initial field. The latter means that if a periodic field originally consists of several harmonic fields, then its asymptotic is determined by the wave with the largest period. Apart from that, the "final victory" of the large-scale component may be accelerated by the coalescence of shocks corresponding to a wave with a smaller period. The above-said illustrates the graphs of the solution of the Burgers equation, shown in Fig. 4.9, with the initial condition

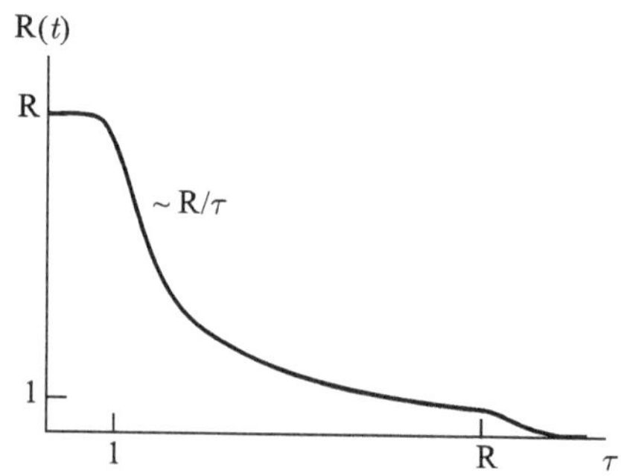

Fig. 4.8 Semi-qualitative graph of the current Reynolds number of a periodic field at a large initial Reynolds number $R \gg 1$ as a function of the dimensionless time $\tau = a\kappa t$.

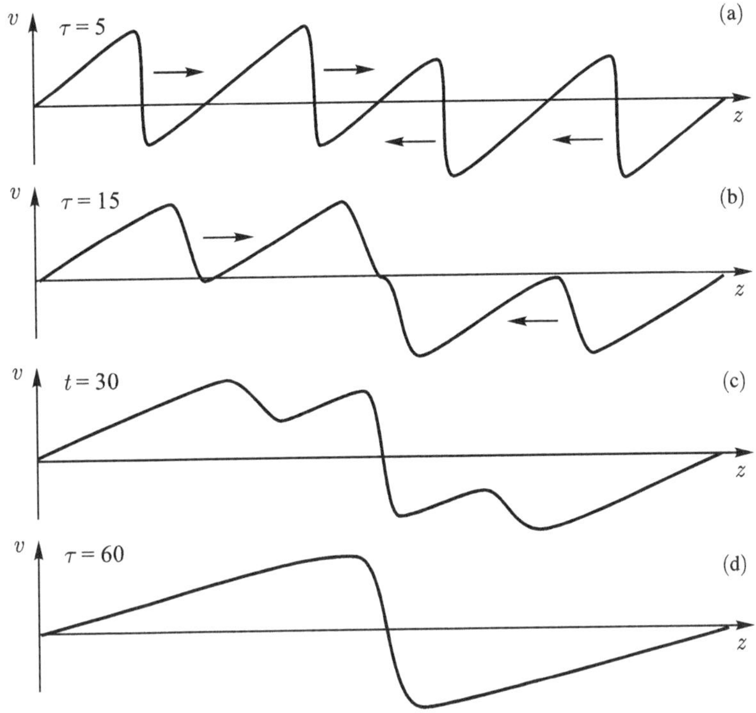

Fig. 4.9 Evolution of the solution to the Burgers equation with the initial condition (4.35) and R = 50. It is seen that the coalescence of shocks leads to the formation of a sawtooth wave with the period of the large-scale component of the initial condition.

$$v_0(x) = a\left[\sin(\kappa x) + \tfrac{1}{4}\sin\left(\tfrac{1}{4}\kappa x\right)\right] \tag{4.35}$$

at R = 50. The definition of the initial Reynolds number and other dimensionless parameters is borrowed from (4.34).

From this figure, it is seen that first shock corresponding to the small-scale component of the initial condition (4.35) are formed. Then, due to modulation of shock velocities of the large-scale component, the shocks coalesce, forming, in the end, one shock per period of the large-scale component of the initial condition.

4.2 Evolution of complex signals

In this section, we discuss several examples of evolution of complex signals having not one, but a set of characteristic length scales. Their behavior may qualitatively differ from evolution of single-scale signals. So it is conventional to believe that dissipation leads to a relative decrease of the role of nonlinear effects, and the nonlinear stage of evolution is succeeded by the linear stage. But the reverse sequence of events is possible, when the linear stage of evolution precedes the the nonlinear one. Let, for instance, the initial field have the form of a sequence of N spaced pulses with the initial Reynolds number $\mathrm{R}_0 \ll 1$. Because of linear diffusion, the pulses spread out, assume a Gaussian shape, and then merge into a single pulse with the Reynolds number $\mathrm{R}(t) = N\mathrm{R}_0$. If thereby $\mathrm{R}(t) \gg 1$, then the subsequent evolution has a pronounced nonlinear character. Below we discuss other characteristic examples of complex signal evolution.

4.2.1 Quasiperiodic complex signals

Let us illustrate, in detail, a possible "anomalous" behavior of complex signals consisting in that their effective current Reynolds number may not only decrease or stay constant, but also grow with time. We do so by discussing the behavior of periodic and quasiperiodic fields as an example.

Let the initial field equal the sum of the harmonic components:

$$v_0(x) = a\left[\sin(\kappa x) + \beta^{\gamma-1}\sin(\beta\kappa x)\right] \quad (\beta \ll 1). \tag{4.36}$$

Let us introduce, in analogy with the way it has been done above, the characteristic times of nonlinearity and approach to the linear regime for the second harmonic term. They are equal to

$$t_n(\beta) \simeq \beta^{-\gamma} t_n, \quad t_l(\beta) \simeq \beta^{-2} t_l \simeq \beta^{-2}\mathrm{R}\, t_n.$$

If the following inequality holds:

$$t_l \lesssim t_n(\beta) \Rightarrow \mathrm{R}\beta^{\gamma} \lesssim 1 \Rightarrow \gamma > 0,$$

then, at $t < t_l$, the second term has practically no influence on the evolution of the shape of the first periodic wave, and by the moment of time $t \gtrsim t_l$, which it practically completely dissipates, the resultant field is approximately equal to

$$v(x, t \gtrsim t_l) \simeq a\beta^{\gamma-1}\sin(\beta\kappa x).$$

Its Reynolds number is:

$$\mathrm{R}(t_n(\beta)) \simeq \frac{t_l(\beta)}{t_n(\beta)} \simeq \mathrm{R}\beta^{\gamma-2}.$$

Thus, when the condition

$$0 < \gamma < 2 \tag{4.37}$$

holds, the Reynolds number by the beginning of the nonlinear stage of development of the large-scale component in (4.36) becomes greater than the initial Reynolds number.

Let us consider a more complex quasiperiodic initial field

$$v_0(x) = a\sum_{k=1}^{\infty}\beta^{(\gamma-1)k}\sin(\beta^k\kappa x+\theta_k), \tag{4.38}$$

where θ_k are arbitrary phase shifts. If the above-listed limitations of β hold, and γ satisfies the inequalities (4.37), then by the moment of time

$$t^k \simeq \beta^{-k\gamma}t_n$$

the nonlinear stage for the kth term of the sum (4.38) sets in, the previous terms have been eliminated due to dissipation, and the next ones produce a quasi-constant background. Accordingly, the current Reynolds number is equal to

$$\mathrm{R}(t^k) \simeq \mathrm{R}\,\beta^{k(\gamma-2)}.$$

By eliminating β from the two latter inequalities, we find that, when the condition (4.37) holds, the Reynolds number, on average, grows with time without limit according to the power law

$$\mathrm{R}(t) \simeq \mathrm{R}\left(\frac{t}{t_n}\right)^{(2-\gamma)/\gamma}.$$

4.2.2 Evolution of fractal signals

Behavior of fields qualitatively changes even more for complex signals having a fractal structure [3].

Let, e.g., there exist N unidirectional pulses with the period L_1 and this structure is reproduced N times with the period $L_2 = \beta L_1$. Then the number of pulses within the specified length scale is equal to N^2. Let this procedure be repeated M times, whereas $L_i = \beta L_{i-1}$, $\beta = (N-1)\gamma$ and $\gamma > 1$. Within the length scale L_M, the pulse duration is equal to $T_M = L_M(N-1)$, and the number of pulses in the sequence is equal to N^M. At $M \gg 1$, it is possible to introduce the fractal dimension of such a signal as $D = \lim(\ln R/\ln L)$, where $R = N^i$ is the number of pulses within the interval $L = L_1 N\beta^{i-1}$ and

$$D = \ln N/\ln[(N-1)\gamma].$$

If $(N-1)\gamma = N$, then $D = 1$ and we have a periodic signal with the period L_1. But if the external period $T_M = 1$, and $M \to \infty$, then it is easy to see that the sequence of the pulse coordinates forms a Cantor set. So, if $N = 2$, $\beta = 3$, then $D = \ln 2/\ln 3$. Illustration of Cantor set signal evolution is depicted, schematically, in Fig. 4.10.

Let us discuss evolution of a signal at the smallest scale L_1. The Reynolds number of a single pulse is equal to $\mathrm{R}_0 = m/2\mu$, and if $\mathrm{R}_0 \ll 1$, then we have the linear stage

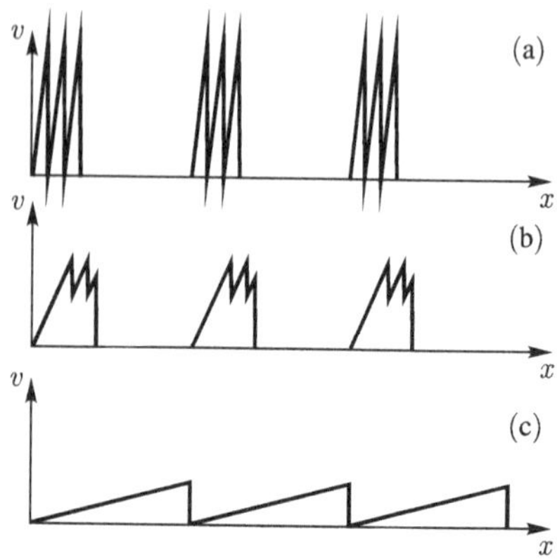

Fig. 4.10 Evolution of a Cantor set.

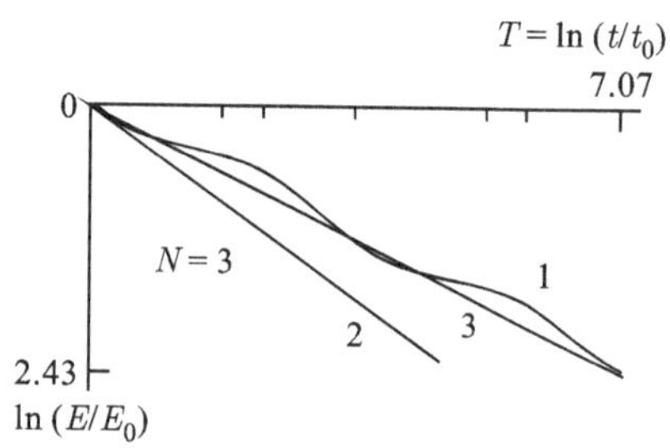

Fig. 4.11 Energy decay of the Cantor set (curve 1), decay of a single pulse (curve 2), average law of decay (curve 3).

of decay, where the width of each pulse grows as $l(t) = (2\mu t)^{1/2}$. At times, when $l(t) \gg L_1 N$, the sequence of N pulses, due to *linear diffusion*, will turn into a single pulse with the Reynolds number $\mathrm{R}_1 = mN/2\mu = N\mathrm{R}_0 > \mathrm{R}_0$. Thus, because of linear diffusion, the Reynolds number grows, the linear stage is eventually succeeded by the nonlinear one, and we can limit ourselves to an analysis in the limit of $\mu \to 0$. At the smallest scale, each separate pulse turns into a triangular one of length $x_s(t) = (2mt)^{1/2}$, and its energy decays as $E(t) = x_s^3/3t^2 = (2m)^{3/2}t^{1/2}$. Interaction between pulses starts at $t > t_0$, where $t_0 = L_1^2/2m$ is determined from the condition $x_s(t) = L_1$. After coalescence of all shocks at the smallest scale, the N pulses turn into a single triangular pulse of length $x_s(t) = (2Nmt)^{1/2}$, and its energy is $N^{1/2}$ times greater than the energy of N noninteracting pulses. At the moment of time $t_1 = L_2N^2/2m = t_0\beta^2/N$, coalescence of pulses at the second scale begins. As a result, the field's evolution is logarithmically self-similar, i.e. within the time interval $t \in [t_0(\beta^2/N)^i, t_0(\beta^2/N)^{i+1}]$, the field reproduces the evolution within the interval $t \in [t_0, t_0\beta^2/N]$. The average law of energy decay is thereby determined by the signal's fractal dimension D:

$$E(t) = C_E(t/t_0)^{-p}, \quad p = (1-D)/(2-D), \quad 0 < p < 1/2.$$

In Ref. [4], spectral, diffusive and convective properties of one-dimensional homogeneous fractal non-alternating pulse fields displaying a well-defined Kolmogorov capacity D was investigated. The energy spectrum of fractal or spiral alternating pulse fields scales as k^D. The energy spectrum of scales as k^D. Both these scaling laws hold in a range of wavenumbers between η^{-1} and L^{-1}, where η is the smallest distance between pulses and $L(\gg \eta)$ is a characteristic large scale of the structure. The space-filling geometry, which is quantified by the Kolmogorov capacity D, makes the field less autocorrelated (more singular) in the alternating case, whereas it makes it more autocorrelated (less singular) in the non-alternating case. For homogeneous fractal non-alternating pulse fields energy decays also as

$$E(t) = C_E(t/t_0)^{-p}, \quad p = (1-D)/(2-D).$$

4.2.3 *Evolution of multi-scale signals — a dynamic turbulence model*

Analysis of the so-called Burgers turbulence is an important example of evolution of complex signals. It is a common convention to call evolution of random fields satisfying the Burgers equation "the Burgers turbulence" (see, e.g., [5–8]). In the case of vanishingly small viscosity, a continuous field is transformed into a random sawtooth wave, i.e. a sequence of triangular pulses with the same slope $\partial_x v = 1/t$ and with random positions of shocks. Due to multiple coalescence of shocks, statistical properties of such a random field become self-similar and are characterized by the only integral length scale $L(t)$. Because of the coalescence of shocks, the integral length scale grows, which causes the energy of the turbulence

$$\sigma^2(t) \sim L^2(t)/t^2 \tag{4.39}$$

to decay at a slower rate than the energy of a periodic signal. The evolution type of the turbulence is determined by the behavior of large-scale components of the initial energy spectrum

$$E_0(k) = \alpha^2 k^n b_0(k); \tag{4.40}$$

$$E_0(k) = \frac{1}{2\pi}\int \langle v_0(x), v_0(x+z)\rangle e^{ikz} dz. \tag{4.41}$$

Here $b_0(k)$ is a function, which decays sufficiently rapidly at $k > k_0 \sim l_0^{-1}$, and $b_0(0) = 1$. We also note that the angular brackets $\langle \cdots \rangle$ here and in the following denote statistical averaging.

At $n < 1$, the integral scale of the turbulence $L(t)$ grows as

$$L(t) = (\alpha t)^{2/(3+n)}. \tag{4.42}$$

(see, e.g., [9]). From (4.39), for the energy of the turbulence, we thereby have:

$$\sigma^2(t) \sim t^{-p}, \; p = \frac{2(n+1)}{n+3}. \tag{4.43}$$

Let us also discuss the example of the damping of a *multiscale* deterministic signal with an initial discrete spectrum, whose average properties (the integral length scale and energy) are similar to the decay laws of the Burgers turbulence with a continuous initial spectrum [10].

Let the initial field have the following form:

$$v_0(x) = \sum_{p=0}^{\infty} a_p A_{inv}(k_p x + \phi_p). \tag{4.44}$$

Here a_p, k_p are the amplitude and wavenumber of a mode, and ϕ_p is its phase. We assume that the spatial frequencies of modes k_p form a Weierstrass spectrum (accumulate towards the zero frequency), and their amplitudes are chosen from the condition $a_p^2 = E_0(k_p)\Delta_p$, $E_0(k) \sim k^n$, where $E_0(k)$ is the energy spectrum of the continuous signal

$$k_p = k_0 \varepsilon^p, \quad a_p = a_0 \varepsilon^{-hp}, \quad h = -\frac{n+1}{2}, \quad a_0 = \alpha k_0^{(n+1)/2}. \tag{4.45}$$

Here h is a similarity parameter.

We choose the modes to be of the form of the following 2π-periodic inverse sawtooth function $A_{inv}(x)$,

$$A(x) = \pi - x, \quad x \in [0, 2\pi) \tag{4.46}$$

whose feature is the formation of a finite-amplitude shock.

4.2.3.1 Evolution and interaction of inverse sawtooth modes

As it was shown above, the solution of the Burgers equation with the initial linear profile $v_0 = -\gamma(x - x_+)$ has the following form:

$$v(x,t) = \frac{-\gamma(x - x_+)}{1 - \gamma t}.$$

The quantity γ^{-1} has the dimension of time, and, for $\gamma > 0$ during a finite time period $t = \gamma^{-1}$, the gradient $\partial_x v$ becomes infinite. For $\gamma < 0$, the gradient becomes equal to $\partial_x v = t^{-1}$, regardless of the initial gradient γ, at times $t \gg |\gamma|^{-1}$. Thus, from the previous relationships, we have that the evolution of the pth mode is characterized by the nonlinear time

$$t_p = \gamma_p^{-1} = a_p k_p{}^{-1} = t_0/(\varepsilon^{(n+3)/2})^p, \quad t_0 = 1/\alpha k_0^{n+3/2}. \tag{4.47}$$

From the solution (3.21), it is easy to see that, at the moment of time $t = t_p$, the pth mode is transformed into an "ordinary" sawtooth wave with the slope $\partial_x v = 1/t$ independent of the amplitude and wavenumber of this mode. Thereby, the energy density of this mode $\sigma^2(t) = \langle v^2(x,t)\rangle_L$, where $\langle \cdots \rangle_L$ denotes averaging over the period, is conserved at $t < t_p$ and decays as $(k_p t)^{-2}$ at $t > t_p$.

As it was shown in Sect. 4.1.4, evolution of the velocity field in the Burgers equation at $\mu \to 0$ is equivalent to evolution of a gas of coalescing particles with a constant initial velocity. For the pth mode at the initial stage, for the density, we have

$$\rho(x,t) = \rho_0 \frac{1}{1 - t/t_p}, \qquad \left| \frac{\pi}{k_p} - x \right| < \frac{t}{t_p} \frac{\pi}{k_p}, \tag{4.48}$$

and ρ is equal to zero outside this interval. At the moment of time $t = t_p$, all light particles merge into a heavy particle of a mass

$$m_p = \rho_0 L_p = \rho_0 \frac{2\pi}{k_p}, \tag{4.49}$$

with the coordinate

$$x_{p,l} = \frac{\pi}{k_p} - \frac{\phi_p}{k_p} + \frac{2\pi}{k_p} l; \quad l = 0, \pm 1, \pm 2, \ldots \tag{4.50}$$

equivalent to the zero of the pth mode. The process of the velocity evolution and of the coalescence of particles is depicted in Fig. 4.12.

Let us now consider interaction of two adjacent modes, the pth and $(p+1)$th. From Eq. (4.47), it is seen that the ratio of nonlinear times of these consecutive modes is equal to

$$\frac{t_{p+1}}{t_p} = \varepsilon^{-(n+3)/2} \equiv \varepsilon^{1-h} \tag{4.51}$$

and does not depend on p. The gradient of the initial field $v_{(p)}(x) + v_{(p+1)}(x)$ is equal to $-(\gamma_p + \gamma_{p+1})$, and the effective nonlinear time of this field is

$$t_{p,\text{eff}} = t_{p,p+1} = \frac{1}{\gamma_p + \gamma_{p+1}} = \frac{t_p}{1 + t_p/t_{p+1}}. \tag{4.52}$$

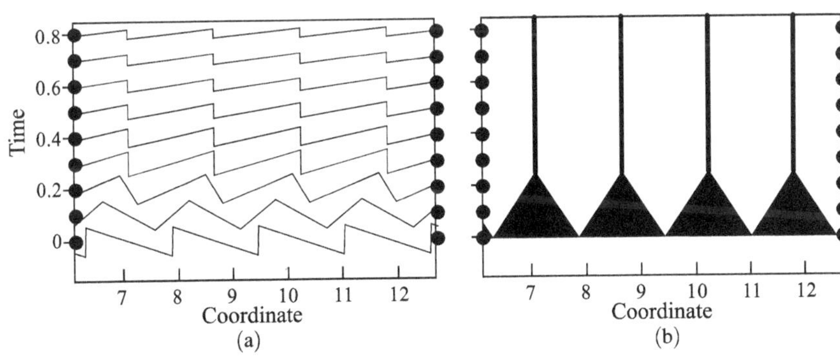

Fig. 4.12 Evolution of an inverse mode and coalescence of light particles into clusters.

Thus the large-scale mode leads to a faster appearance of shocks in the small-scale mode. Since the initial gradient is the same for all points of the initial profile, all light particles coalesce at the same time $t = t_{p,p+1}$. Suppose the following relationship between the phases of the consecutive modes holds:

$$k_{p+1}\phi_{p+1} = k_p\phi_p + 2\pi r/N. \tag{4.53}$$

In this case, the shocks of the low-frequency $(p+1)$th mode lead to appearance of additional shocks in the total field $v_{(p)}(x) + v_{(p+1)}(x)$ compared with the pth mode. Thus, at times $t > t_{r,\text{eff}}$, the masses of all heavy particles will be the same as in the absence of the large-scale mode.

The coordinates of these particles at the moment of time $t = t_{p,\text{eff}}$ are equal to

$$X_{(p,l)}(t_{p,\text{eff}}) = x_{p,l} + v_{(p+1)}(x_{p,l})t_{p,\text{eff}}, \tag{4.54}$$

where $x_{p,l}$ are the positions of the zeros of the pth mode (4.50). The velocity of these particles is equal to $v_{(p+1)}(x_{p,l})$. Eq. (4.54) becomes obvious if we use the trivial equality $v_{(p)}(x_{p,l}) + v_{(p+1)}(x_{p,l}) = v_{(p+1)}(x_{p,l})$. From Eq. (4.54) we immediately have that at times greater than $t_{p,\text{eff}}$, the coordinates of heavy particles behave as

$$X_{(p,l)}(t) = x_{(p,l)} + v_{(p+1)}(x_{p,l})t. \tag{4.55}$$

The distance between consecutive heavy particles $X_{p,l}(t)$ and $X_{p,l+1}(t)$ decreases with time proportionally to the initial gradient of the large-scale mode $v_{(p+1)}(x)$:

$$\begin{aligned} X_{p,l+1}(t) - X_{p,l}(t) &= (x_{p,l+1} - x_{p,l}) - t\frac{\partial v_{(p+1)}(x)}{\partial x}(x_{p,l+1} - x_{p,l}) \\ &\equiv (x_{p,l+1} - x_{p,l})(1 - t/t_{p+1}). \end{aligned} \tag{4.56}$$

From here it is seen that at the moment of time $t = t_{p+1}$ these particles coalesce, and the newly merged particles have have the masses

$$m_{(p+1)} = \rho_0 L_{p+1} \tag{4.57}$$

and coordinates

$$x_{p+1,l} = \frac{\pi}{k_{p+1}} - \frac{\phi_{p+1}}{k_p} + \frac{2\pi l}{k_{p+1}}; \quad l = 0, \pm 1, \pm 2, \ldots \tag{4.58}$$

Their velocities are equal to zero.

Thus, if t is greater than t_{p+1}, the evolution of the initial excitation $v_0(x) = v_{(p)}(x) + v_{(p+1)}(x)$ is the same as the evolution of only one large-scale mode $v_{(p+1)}(x)$. Evolution of the velocity field of two consecutive modes and the corresponding process of particle coalescence are depicted in Fig. 4.13.

It is evident that under a suitable choice of the wavenumbers $k_p = k_0/N^p$ and phases of modes and for a finite total $v(x) = v_{(p)}(x) + v_{(p+1)}(x) + \ldots + v_{(M)}(x)$, the evolution of the field at long times greater than t_M will be the same as the evolution

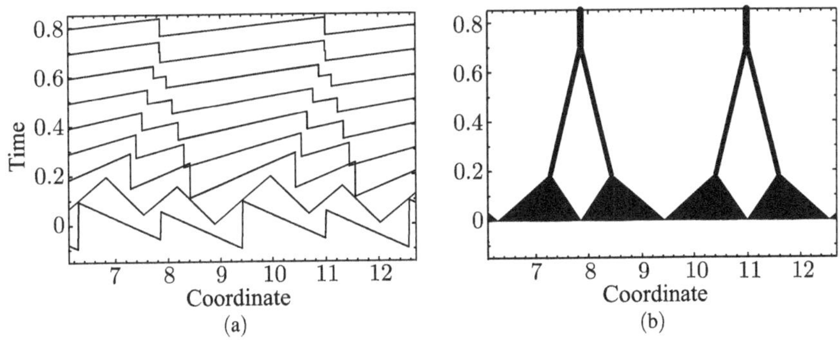

Fig. 4.13 Interaction of two consecutive inverse modes and coalescence of light particles into clusters.

of the only large-scale mode $v_{(M)}(x)$. For integral N, the minimum combination frequency of all interacting harmonics is equal to the wavenumber of the largest mode $k_M = k_0/N^M$. Hence nonlinear interaction does not lead to generation of new components with wavenumbers less than k_M.

4.2.3.2 Interaction of a small-scale inverse sawtooth mode with a large-scale structure

Let us consider interaction of the pth small-scale mode with the field in the form of an infinite series of large-scale modes

$$W_p(x) = \sum_{r=p+1}^{\infty} v_r(x) \equiv \sum_{r=p+1}^{\infty} a_r A(k_r x + \phi_r), \tag{4.59}$$

assuming that the phases of these modes satisfy the condition (4.53), and for the wavenumbers, as before, the relationship $k_r = k_0 \varepsilon^r$, $a_r = a_0 \varepsilon^{-hr}$, $h = -(n+1)/2$ holds. The interaction process can, thereby, be conveniently interpreted in terms of particles. From (4.59) and (4.47) for the gradient of the initial excitation $v_0(x) = v_p(x) + W_p(x)$ we have

$$\begin{aligned} \frac{\partial v_0(x)}{\partial x} &= \frac{\partial v_p(x)}{\partial x} + \frac{\partial W_p(x)}{\partial x} = \sum_{r=p}^{\infty} \gamma_p \\ &= \gamma_0 \sum_{r=p}^{\infty} (\varepsilon^{\frac{(n+3)}{2}})^r = \gamma_0 \varepsilon^{\frac{(n+3)}{2} p} \frac{1}{1 - \varepsilon^{\frac{(n+3)}{2}}}. \end{aligned} \tag{4.60}$$

For convergence of the series, it is here assumed that $n > -3$ ($h < 1$). From this equation follows that the effective nonlinearity time of the pth mode is equal to

$$\tilde{t}_p = \left(\frac{\partial v_0(x)}{\partial x}\right)^{-1} = t_p\left(1 - \varepsilon^{\frac{(n+3)}{2}}\right), \qquad (4.61)$$

where t_p is determined by Eq. (4.47).

Thus, at the moment of time $\tilde{t}_p$, light particles coalesce into heavy ones of a mass $m_p = \rho_0 L_p$ (4.57). Coordinates of these particles are determined by the equation analogous to Eq. (4.55):

$$x_{p,l}(t) = x_{p,l}(t) + W_p(x_{p,l})t, \qquad (4.62)$$

where the particle velocities are determined by the function $W_p(x)$ (4.59), which represents an infinite sum of large-scale modes, and $x_{p,l}$ are the coordinates of the zeros of the pth mode.

The distance between the coordinates of two adjacent heavy particles $x_{p,l}$ and $x_{p,l}$ decreases with time as $(1 - t/\tilde{t}_{p+1})$, where $\tilde{t}_{p+1} = t_{p+1}(1 - \varepsilon^{(n+3)/2})$ is the reciprocal of the gradient of the function $W_p(x)$, (see relationships (4.59) and (4.60)). Hence the time of coalescence of particles of this generation is determined by Eq. (4.61) with $p = p+1$, and the masses of new particles will be determined by the period of the $(p+1)$th — see Eq. (4.57).

Extrapolation of the process of heavy particle coalescence in the following generations is obvious. Particle collision in the qth generation takes place at the moment of time $\tilde{t}_{p+q} = t_{p+q}(1 - \varepsilon^{\frac{n+3}{2}})$, and the masses of these particles at this moment of time are determined by the period of the $(p+q)$th mode $m_{p+q} = \rho_0 L_{p+q} = 2\pi\rho_0/k_{p+q}$. During the interval between collisions $t \in [\tilde{t}_{p+q}, \tilde{t}_{p+q+1}]$

$$\frac{\tilde{t}_{p+q+1}}{\tilde{t}_{p+q}} = \varepsilon^{-\frac{(n+3)}{2}} = N^{\frac{n+3}{2}}, \qquad (4.63)$$

the particle coordinates will be determined by Eq. (4.62) with $p = p+q$. Here $W_{p+q}(x)$ is the sum of velocities of all large-scale modes with $r > p+q$, and $x_{p+q,l}$ are the zeros of the $(p+q)$th mode. It is important to emphasize that, at $t > \tilde{t}_{p+q}$, the evolution of particles is completely determined only by large-scale modes with $r \geqslant p+q$. This means that, at times $t > \tilde{t}_{p+q}$, the particle positions do not depend on the presence of small-scale excitations with $r < p+q$ in the initial excitation.

Thus, for two different initial velocities: a field with small-scale modes $\tilde{v}_0(x)$ and a field without smal-scale modes $v_0(x)$:

$$v_0(x) = W_{p+q-1}(x); \quad \tilde{v}_0(x) = W_{p-1}(x) \qquad (4.64)$$

the fields will be the same at $t > \tilde{t}_{p+q-1}$. Even if $p \to -\infty$ (when in the initial excitation there are modes with very small scales $L_p \sim \varepsilon^{-p} = N^p$ and very large amplitudes $a_p \sim a_0(\varepsilon^{(n+1)/2})^p = a_0(N^{(n+1)/2})^{-p}$) multiple coalescence of particles leads to independent evolution of large-scale excitations with respect to small-scale modes.

This effect is similar to the effect of self-preservation of large-scale structures in the Burgers turbulence [11–13]. If the initial excitation $v_0(x)$ represents a noise field, then multiple coalescence of shocks leads to continuous growth of the integral length scale of the turbulence $L(t)$. In the presence of small-scale perturbations $v_h(x)$, the shock coordinates of the large-scale structure will deviate from unperturbed positions, and these deviations $\Delta x_k(t)$ grow with time. Thus evolution of large-scale structures is determined by competition of two factors: the growth of the integral length scale $L(t)$ due to coalescence of large-scale shocks and the growth of deviations of shock positions $\Delta x_k(t)$ from the unperturbed value because of the presence of small-scale perturbations $v_h(x)$. For the Burgers turbulence having the energy spectrum (4.40) with $n < 1$, multiple coalescence of shocks leads to stability of large-scale structures with respect to small-scale perturbations. For the model signal considered above, this effect occurs for arbitrary n due to a special choice of the wavenumbers and phases of the interacting modes.

As it has been mentioned several times, the evolution of the velocity field in the Burgers equation has a one-to-one correspondence with the evolution of a gas of coalescing particles. At the stage, when all light particles merged into heavy ones, the gradient of the velocity field at all points of space is the same $\partial_x v = 1/t$. At this stage, the profile of the field $v(x,t)$ is completely determined by the coordinates and velocities of heavy particles. Their coordinates coincide with the shock coordinates $X_s(t)$, and the shock velocities satisfy the well-known relationship

$$v_s(t) = \frac{dX_s(t)}{dt} = \frac{v_s(x_s - 0,t) + v_s(x_s + 0,t)}{2} \tag{4.65}$$

and are equal to the velocity of heavy particles. The shock amplitudes

$$\Delta v_s(x) = v(x_s - 0,t) - v(x_s + 0,t) = \frac{m}{t} \tag{4.66}$$

are determined by the mass of heavy particles ($\rho_0 \equiv 1$).

Thus the investigation of heavy particle motion allows us completely to reconstruct the velocity field $v(x,t)$ of the Burgers equation.

4.2.3.3 Weierstrass-Mandelbrot sawtooth function

As is has been shown above, evolution of heavy particles (shocks) is determined by the function $W_p(x)$ (4.59). The base functions $W_p(x)$ are the periodic inverse sawtooth functions with the wavenumbers $k_r = k_0\varepsilon^r$ and amplitudes $a_r = a_0\varepsilon^{-hr}$, $h = -(n+1)/2$. The wavenumbers form a geometric progression as in the Weierstrass function (see, e.g., [14]), and accumulate toward the point $k = 0$.

In the standard Weierstrass function, the situation is the opposite, i.e. its frequencies continuously grow. Nevertheless, the function $W_p(x)$ possesses many properties of the Weierstrass function and of its generalization, viz. the Weierstrass-Mandelbrot function (see [14, 15]).

Here we consider a deterministic function $W_p(x)$ with special phase relations between mode phases $\phi_p = (2\pi k/N)p$ $(k = 1,2,\ldots,N; N = 1/\varepsilon)$, so that shocks of the large-scale modes $r > p+1$ coincide with some of the shocks of the small-scale mode $r = p+1$. The function $W_p(x)$ is continuous within the intervals $2\pi/k_{p+1} = 2\pi/(k_0\varepsilon^{p+1})$ and has there the same slope (gradient). The reciprocal of this gradient has the dimension of time $\tilde{t}_{p+1}$

$$\tilde{t}_{p+1} = t_{p+1}(1-\varepsilon^{\frac{n+3}{2}}); \quad t_{p+1} = t_0(\varepsilon^{\frac{n+3}{2}})^{p+1} \tag{4.67}$$

and is proportional to the nonlinearity time t_{p+1} of the smallest-scale mode. Evidently, we assume that $n > -3$, which guarantees convergence of (4.60) and validity of the inequality $t_{p+1} > t_p$. The amplitudes of modes are proportional to $\varepsilon^{(n+1)/2}$ and at $n > -1$ the function $W_p(x)$ is bounded

$$W_p(x) \leqslant \sum_{r=p+1}^{\infty} a_r = a_0(\varepsilon^{\frac{n+1}{2}})^{p+1} \frac{1}{1-\varepsilon^{\frac{n+1}{2}}}. \tag{4.68}$$

Thus, at finite p, the energy of $W_p(x)$ is also finite. Thereby the function possesses scaling properties

$$W_p(x) = \varepsilon^{-hp} W_0(\varepsilon^p x); \quad W_p(\varepsilon^m x) = \varepsilon^{hm} W_{m+p}(x). \tag{4.69}$$

The case $-1 < n < 1$ is here equivalent to initial conditions for the Burgers turbulence in the form of white noise. The energy of the initial noise is thereby determined by the ultraviolet cutoff frequency, which in this model corresponds to the smallest length scale p. If $p \to -\infty$, the energy of the model signal (as well as the energy of white noise) tends to infinity. But, as it follows from the analysis given above, during a finite time due to nonlinear dissipation t, all modes with $t_p < t$ have a finite energy $\sim L_p^2/t^2$ and, thus, the total energy of the wave is also finite. Hence, even if there is divergence of initial conditions ($p \to -\infty$), there exist a solution with a finite energy for any time $t > 0$.

The case $n < -1$ is similar to the fractal Brownian motion for the velocity in the Burgers turbulence. The series (4.68) in this case diverges and the initial excitation $W_p(x)$ is unbounded. For the Burgers turbulence, however, here only relative motion of particles (shocks) is important. Thus it is possible to perform regularization of the function $W_p(x)$, similar to regularization of the Weierstrass function [15].

So, assuming that $\phi_p \equiv 0$, it is possible, according to [15], to introduce the function $W_p^\infty(x) = W_p(x) - W_p(0)$, bounded within any finite interval.

4.2.3.4 Self-similar properties of a multi-scale signal

By using the scaling characteristics of the Weierstrass-Mandelbrot function $W_p(x)$, let us show that its evolution in the framework of the Burgers equation is of a logarithmically periodic, self-similar character.

Let us discuss evolution of the multi-scale signal

$$v_0(x) = v_p(x) + W_p(x). \tag{4.70}$$

As it has been shown, at times $t > \tilde{t}_p$, all light particles coalesce and form heavy particles of a mass $M_p = \rho_0 L_p$, and their motion is determined by Eq. (4.63). These particles coalesce at the moment of time $\tilde{t}_{p+1}$, ($\tilde{t}_{p+1}/\tilde{t}_p = N^{\frac{(n+3)}{2}}, N = \varepsilon^{-1}$), and new heavy particles have the mass $m_{p+1} = \rho_0 L_{p+1} = m_p N$. Their motion is determined by the same laws (4.63), but with a change of the subscript of the Weierstrass-Mandelbrot function $p \to p+1$. By using the scaling properties of $W_p(x)$ (4.69) we have that the motion of particles in this time interval is similar to the motion of particles in the interval $[\tilde{t}_p, \tilde{t}_{p+1}]$, if renormalize time $t/\tilde{t}_p \Rightarrow t/\tilde{t}_{p+1}$. Since the ratio of the coalescence times t_{p+1}/t_p does not depend on p, we can speak about logarithmically periodic self-similarity of particle motion. This means that within an arbitrary time interval $[\tilde{t}_q, \tilde{t}_{q+1}]$, particle motion will be similar to motion of particles within the interval $\tilde{t}_p, \tilde{t}_{p+1}$, with similarity parameters $x_p/x_q = \varepsilon^{p-q}$ in the coordinate space and $t_p/t_q = (\varepsilon^{-\frac{n+3}{2}})^{p-q}$ in time. But since the coordinates and masses of particles completely determine the velocity field, then the solution of the Burgers equation with such initial conditions will also be logarithmically periodic self-similar.

After each collision, the mass of particles $M(t)$ increases $N = 1/\varepsilon$ times. The time intervals between consecutive collisions grow as $t_{p+1}/t_p = N^{\frac{n+3}{2}}$. Thus, by approximating the piecewise-constant function $m(t)$ by the power law

$$m(t) \simeq m_0 (t/t_0)^{(n+3)/2}, \tag{4.71}$$

we obtain the same law as the law of growth of the integral length scale $L(t) \sim m(t)$ for the Burgers turbulence.

For the case $n > -1$, it is also not difficult to estimate the law of decay of the energy of the model signal. At $n > -1$ and $\varepsilon \ll 1$, the main energy of the signal at the moment of time t is in the mode with the smallest period and it is proportional to $L^2(t)/t^2$. Thus, also for the averaged law of energy decay of the model signal we obtain the same law of energy decay as for the Burgers turbulence.

In order to illustrate evolution of model self-similar signals, we show the velocity profiles at different moments of time and trajectories of coalescing particles for initial conditions of the "white noise" ($n = 0$, $h = -1/2$) and "Brownian" motion ($n = -2$, $h = 1/2$) types. In experiments, ten modes have been taken with the ratio of the consecutive wavenumbers of $\varepsilon = 1/N = 1/2$. In Figs. 4.14, 4.15, the initial stage of evolution is depicted in a certain sufficiently small spatial interval, when the finiteness of the number of modes has not yet manifested itself.

From Fig. 4.14, it is seen that for $n = 0$ the initial sawtooth multi-scale function oscillates about $v = 0$ similarly to a "white noise" with a finite variance. After coalescence of light particles, when the "inverse" sawtooth function is transformed into a sawtooth wave with the same positive gradient $\partial_x v = 1/t$, the structure of the signal is relatively simple and, even at $N = 2$, the main energy is concentrated in the mode with the smallest wavenumber.

In the case $n = -2$, the initial profile has large deviations, which is typical of Brownian motion. After coalescence of light particles, the wave profile represents a

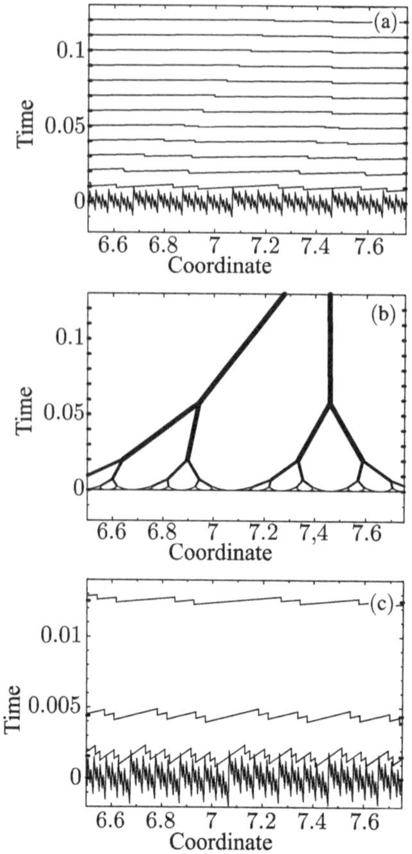

Fig. 4.14 Profile of the field (**a**) and trajectories of clusters (shocks) (**b**) for the initial conditions of the "white noise" type ($n = 0$, $h = -1/2$). In the last panel (**c**), the profiles of the field at the moments of similarity are shown.

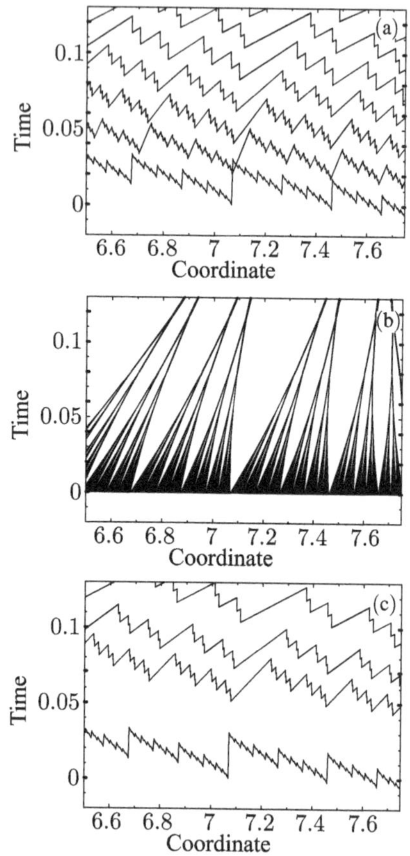

Fig. 4.15 Profile of the field (**a**) and trajectories of clusters (shocks) (**b**) for the initial conditions of the "Brownian motion" type ($n = -2$, $h = 1/2$). In the last panel (**c**), the profiles of the field at the moments of similarity are shown.

sequence of shocks of different amplitude, which also imitates properties of Brownian motion in the Burgers turbulence [16].

In the latter graphs, the velocity profiles at three consecutive moments of coalescence of heavy particles $t_*/t_{**} = N^{(n+3)/2}$ are shown. These figures illustrate the logarithmically periodic self-similarity of evolution of multi-scale signals.

4.2.3.5 Evolution of multi-scale fields in the vector Burgers equation

The Burgers equation admits a generalization to the multidimensional case

$$\partial_t \mathbf{v} + (\mathbf{v}\cdot\nabla)\mathbf{v} = \mu\nabla^2\mathbf{v}.$$

Its detailed discussion is deferred until Chapter 6, where, in particular, it will be shown that for potential fields, it is also reduced to the linear diffusion equation. Its asymptotic solution at vanishing viscosity is completely analogous to the corresponding solution of the one-dimensional Burgers equation.

Here we only note that multi-scale solutions, similar to the ones considered above, can be constructed and for the vectorial Burgers equation. Suppose that the initial excitation $\mathbf{V}_p(\mathbf{x})$ represents an infinite sum of "inverse" modes $\mathbf{v}_r(\mathbf{x})$:

$$\mathbf{V}_p(\mathbf{x}) = \sum_{r=p}^{\infty} \mathbf{v}_r(\mathbf{x}). \tag{4.72}$$

In the two-dimensional case, the rth "inverse" mode may be constructed as a system of linear functions in equilateral triangles of a side L_r, densely covering the plane. Inside each triangle, in the rth mode, the velocity has the linear profile $\mathbf{v}_r(\mathbf{x}) = -\gamma_r(\mathbf{x}-\mathbf{x}_+)$, where $\mathbf{x}_+$ is the coordinate of the center of the triangle. It is easy to verify that the solution of the multi-dimensional Burgers equation for such an initial condition has the form

$$\mathbf{v}(\mathbf{x},t) = \frac{-\gamma(\mathbf{x}-\mathbf{x}_+)}{1-\gamma t} \tag{4.73}$$

and is valid inside a triangle of a size $L_r(t) = L_r(1-t\gamma_r)$. The quantity γ_r^{-1} has the dimension of time and, during the finite time $t_r = \gamma_r^{-1}$, the gradient of the field become infinite. In other words, at the moment of time $t = t_r$, the mode is transformed into a "straight" sawtooth wave with the universal behavior inside a new set of triangles and with the gradient $1/t$, which does not depend on the wavenumber and amplitude of the mode:

$$\mathbf{v}(\mathbf{x},t) = \frac{\mathbf{x}-\mathbf{x}_c}{t}, \tag{4.74}$$

where $\mathbf{x}_c$ now are the centers of triangles, which coincide with the vertices of the initial set of triangles. By considering the corresponding density of a gas of coalescing particles, we see that inside a "collapsing" triangle of a side length $L_r(t) = L_r(1-t\gamma_r)$, the density grows as

$$\rho(\mathbf{x},t) = \rho_0 \frac{1}{(1-t/t_p)^2}, \tag{4.75}$$

and the density ρ is equal to zero outside the "compensating" triangles. At the moment of time $t = t_r$, all light particles coalesce into heavy particles of a mass

$$m_r = \rho_0 L_r^2 \frac{\sqrt{3}}{4}, \tag{4.76}$$

and the coordinates of heavy particles coincide with the coordinates of the initial triangles $\mathbf{x}_+$.

Fig. 4.16 Tessellation of the plane with hierarchical triangles, in which the modes of the multi-scale signal are defined.

For a multi-scale field, let us consider here a special case, when the ratio of the length scales of two consecutive modes is equal to $L_{r+1}/L_r = \varepsilon^{-1} = N = 2$. We also assume the presence of a special symmetry and special phase relations for all modes. In this case, a large triangle of the large-scale mode is divided into four small triangles of the consecutive small-scale mode so that no new shocks appear from the large-scale mode (see Fig. 4.16).

Let us now consider evolution of the vector field $\mathbf{V}_p(\mathbf{x})$ (4.72), which represents a superposition of an infinite number of "inverse" modes Suppose that evolution of the rth mode is characterized by the same nonlinear time t_r as in the one-dimensional case(4.47):

$$t_r = \gamma_r^{-1} = t_0/(2^{-(n+3)/2})^r. \tag{4.77}$$

Evolution of such a vector field is very similar to that considered by us in the one-dimensional case (4.59). So, for the gradient of the initial excitation $\mathbf{V}_p(\mathbf{x})$, we have the same expression (4.60) as in the one-dimensional case. The effective nonlinearity time of the small small-scale pth mode of the vector field (4.72) in the presence of all large-scale modes is, as before, determined by Eq. (4.61). Thus, after time $\tilde{t}_p$ has elapsed, there appear heavy particles of a mass m_p (4.76). The velocity of this particles is determined by the two-dimensional Weierstrass-Mandelbrot function $\mathbf{V}_{p+1}(\mathbf{x})$ (4.72), which is equal to the sum of all large-scale modes. At the moment of time $\tilde{t}_{p+1}$, we have a collision of four heavy particles for the next mode. Further process of the length-scale enlargement can be easily constructed by recursion. In Fig. 4.17, the hierarchical process of coalescence of particle is seen. While, in the one-dimensional case, the particle trajectories formed a structure similar to the flat model of an umbrella tree (see. [15]); in the two-dimensional case, this analogy is even more suitable. Whereas, as it has been shown, these structures possess the property of self-similarity.

In conclusion of this chapter, we note that despite the simplicity of the Burgers equation and availability of an exact solution, the evolution of fields in the frame-

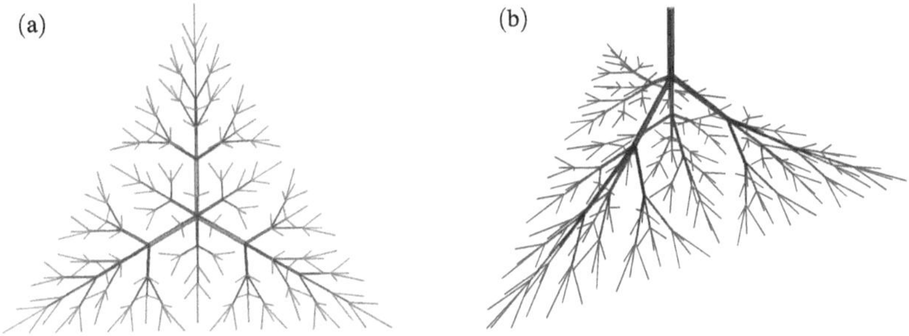

Fig. 4.17 Trajectories of particles for a multi-scale signal in the two-dimensional case, represented in the three-dimensional case (two coordinates vs time). The thickness of the trajectories reflects the mass of particles: **(a)** — top view; **(b)** — side view.

work of this equation is very diverse. Thereby the mechanical interpretation of solutions to the Burgers equation as evolution of a gas of coalescing particles is very intuitive and useful.

4.3 Problems to Chapter 4

Problem 1. Find the solution of the Burgers equation with the initial condition

$$v_0(x) = S[\delta(x) + \delta(x-\ell)] \quad (\ell > 0, \quad S > 0). \tag{4.78}$$

Plot $v(x,t)$ at $\mathrm{R} = S/2\mu \gg 1$ for different values of dimensionless time $\tau = 2St/\ell^2$.

Solution. In this case, the initial potential and the initial condition of the linear diffusion equation (3.78) are equal to:

$$s_0(x) = S[\Theta(x) + \Theta(x-\ell)],$$
$$\varphi_0(x) = 1 + (e^{-\mathrm{R}} - 1)\,\Theta(x) + (e^{-2\mathrm{R}} - e^{-\mathrm{R}})\,\Theta(x-\ell).$$

By substituting the latter expression in (3.80), we have

$$\varphi(x,t) = 1 + (e^{-\mathrm{R}} - 1)\,\Phi\left(\frac{x}{2\sqrt{\mu t}}\right) + (e^{-2\mathrm{R}} - e^{-\mathrm{R}})\,\Phi\left(\frac{x-\ell}{2\sqrt{\mu t}}\right).$$

Hence the solution of the Burgers equation is such:

$$v(x,t) = -\sqrt{\frac{\mu}{\pi t}}\,\frac{(e^{-\mathrm{R}} - 1)\exp\left(-\frac{x^2}{4\mu t}\right) + (e^{-2\mathrm{R}} - e^{-\mathrm{R}})\exp\left(-\frac{(x-\ell)^2}{4\mu t}\right)}{1 + (e^{-\mathrm{R}} - 1)\,\Phi\left(\frac{x}{2\sqrt{\mu t}}\right) + (e^{-2\mathrm{R}} - e^{-\mathrm{R}})\,\Phi\left(\frac{x-\ell}{2\sqrt{\mu t}}\right)}. \tag{4.79}$$

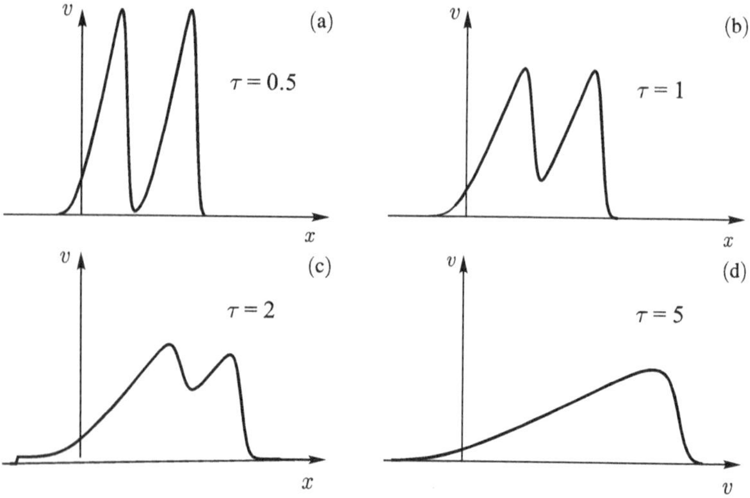

Fig. 4.18 Solution (4.79) of the Burgers equation at R = 16 illustrating the process of coalescence of triangular waves.

Its plots, constructed for different values of τ, are shown in Fig. 4.18. They illustrate the process of coalescence of two triangular waves corresponding to two delta functions in the initial condition (4.78).

Problem 2. Indicate the skeleton of the solution to the previous problem. By using the fact that the shock velocity is equal to the half-sum of the values of the field $v(x,t)$ before and after the shock, write down the equations of motion of the shocks and estimate the time of coalescence of the two triangular waves into one triangular wave.

Solution. In the beginning, the field's skeleton consists of separate triangles of the same area S bounded on the right by the shocks. Let us denote the shock coordinates $x_1(t)$ and $x_2(t)$. As long as the triangles do not overlap (see the top panel in Fig. 4.19), the shock coordinates can be easily found by using the fact that the areas of the triangles are conserved:

$$x_1(t) = \ell\sqrt{\tau}, \quad x_2(t) = \ell(1+\sqrt{\tau}), \quad \tau = \frac{t}{t^*} = \frac{2St}{\ell^2}. \tag{4.80}$$

At the moment of time

$$t^* = \frac{\ell^2}{2S} \quad (\tau = 1),$$

the left shock runs into the right one (the lower panel in Fig. 4.19), due to which the law of motion of the left shock changes. Let us find it by solving the equation of motion of the shock

$$\frac{dx_1(t)}{dt} = \frac{1}{t}\left(x_1(t) - \frac{\ell}{2}\right), \quad x_1(t^*) = \ell.$$

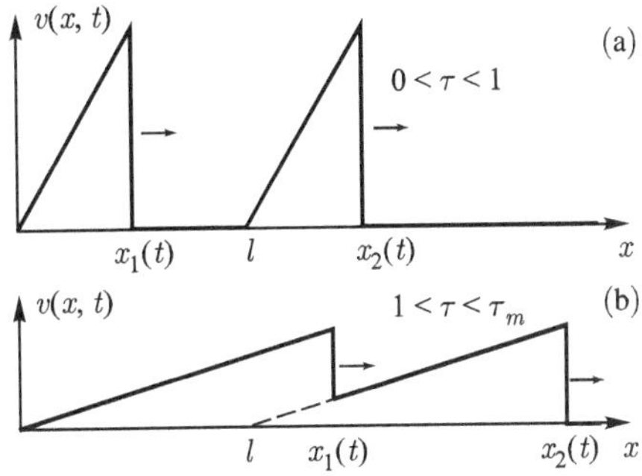

Fig. 4.19 Skeleton of the solution (4.79) of the Burgers equation.

As a result, we obtain

$$x_1(t) = \frac{\ell}{2}(\tau + 1). \tag{4.81}$$

By equating the coordinates of the right (4.80) and left (4.81) shocks, we find the sought-for time of their coalescence:

$$\tau_m = (1 + \sqrt{2})^2 \approx 5.83.$$

Note. Initially (at $\tau < 1$), the field $v(x,t)$ consists of non-overlapping triangular waves, with the Reynolds number of each of them being equal to $\mathrm{R} = S/2\mu$. Further on, the merge into a single triangular wave with twice the area and Reynolds number. Thus the coalescence of the shocks leads *to the growth of the current Reynolds number.*

Problem 3. Find the shape of the smeared discontinuities of the averaged Lagrangian coordinate $\{y\}(x,t)$ (4.23) by taking into account two dominant terms in the vicinity of a shock.

Solution. Let, in the considered point of discontinuity of the function $\{y\}(x,t)$, two parabolas $\Pi_1(x)$ and $\Pi_2(x)$ intersect. By retaining the two corresponding terms in the sums (4.23), let us rewrite $\{y\}(x,t)$ in the following form:

$$\{y\}(x,t) \approx \frac{y_1 \exp\left(-\frac{1}{2\mu t}\left[s_1 t + \frac{(x-y_1)^2}{2}\right]\right) + y_2 \exp\left(-\frac{1}{2\mu t}\left[s_2 t + \frac{(x-y_2)^2}{2}\right]\right)}{\exp\left(-\frac{1}{2\mu t}\left[s_1 t + \frac{(x-y_1)^2}{2}\right]\right) + \exp\left(-\frac{1}{2\mu t}\left[s_2 t + \frac{(x-y_2)^2}{2}\right]\right)}. \tag{4.82}$$

Let us introduce new notation

$$x_1 = \frac{y_1 + y_2}{2}, \quad \ell = \frac{y_2 - y_1}{2}, \quad z = x - x_1.$$

By using this notation, after cancellation of common factors, we rewrite the expression (4.82) in the form

$$\{y\} \approx x_1 + \ell \frac{\exp\left(-\frac{s_2 t - z\ell}{2\mu t}\right) - \exp\left(-\frac{s_1 t + z\ell}{2\mu t}\right)}{\exp\left(-\frac{s_2 t - z\ell}{2\mu t}\right) + \exp\left(-\frac{s_1 t + z\ell}{2\mu t}\right)}.$$

From here, after simple manipulations, we finally have

$$\{y\} \approx \frac{y_1 + y_2}{2} + \frac{y_2 - y_1}{2} \tanh\left(\frac{\ell}{2\mu t}(x - x_1 - Ut)\right), \quad U = \frac{s_2 - s_1}{y_2 - y_1}.$$

Problem 4. By using the well-known formula

$$e^{\mathrm{R}\cos(\kappa x)} = I_0(R) + 2\sum_{n=1}^{\infty} I_n(\mathrm{R})\cos(n\kappa x),$$

where $I_n(z)$ is the modified Bessel function of the nth order, find the asymptotic behavior, at the linear stage, of the solution to the Burgers equation with the harmonic initial condition

$$v_0(x) = a\sin(\kappa x). \tag{4.83}$$

Investigate the dependence of the field amplitude at the linear stage on the initial amplitude a.

Solution. Let us first write down the corresponding solution of the linear diffusion equation (3.78):

$$\varphi(x,t) = I_0(R) + 2\sum_{n=1}^{\infty} I_n(\mathrm{R})\exp\left(-\frac{n^2\tau}{2\mathrm{R}}\right)\cos(nz). \tag{4.84}$$

Here we introduce the following notation:

$$z = \kappa x, \quad \tau = a\kappa t, \quad \mathrm{R} = \frac{a}{2\mu\kappa}.$$

By substituting (4.84) into (3.76) and retaining only the first terms in the numerator and denominator, we have:

$$v \approx \frac{2a}{\mathrm{R}}\frac{I_1(\mathrm{R})}{I_0(\mathrm{R})}e^{-\tau/2\mathrm{R}}\sin(z) \quad (\tau \gg \mathrm{R}). \tag{4.85}$$

In this case, it is appropriate to give the Reynolds number R a more suitable, from the viewpoint of acoustic applications, interpretation: it is equal to the ratio of the initial amplitude a of the field to the characteristic amplitude of development of nonlinear effects

$$a_n = \frac{1}{2\mu\kappa} \Rightarrow \mathrm{R} = \frac{a}{a_n}.$$

Apart from that, it is natural to investigate the dimensionless field

$$u = \frac{v}{a_n} = f(\mathrm{R})\,\exp\left(-\frac{\tau}{2\mathrm{R}}\right)\sin(z).$$

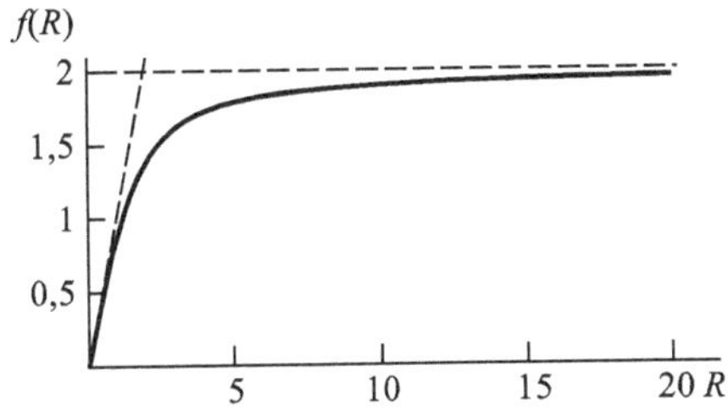

Fig. 4.20 Dimensionless amplitude of the initially harmonic field at the linear stage. As long as it practically coincides with the straight line R, nonlinear effects of evolution of the field $v(x,t)$ can be neglected.

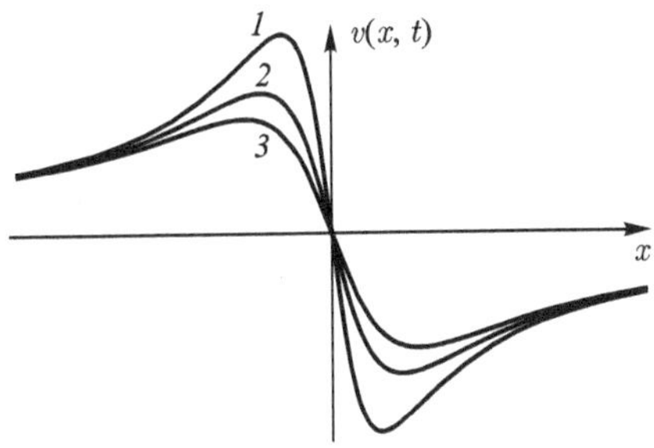

Fig. 4.21 Solution (4.85) of the Burgers equation at the moments of time $t_1, t_2 = 2t_1, t_3 = 3t_1$. "Anomalous" behavior of the solution is explained by the dominance of the diffusive smearing over the nonlinear inertial effects.

Here

$$f(\mathrm{R}) = 2\frac{I_1(\mathrm{R})}{I_0(\mathrm{R})},$$

where $f(\mathrm{R}) \simeq \mathrm{R}$, the field (4.85) replicates the solution of the linear equation with the initial condition (4.83), and it is possible to neglect the nonlinear effects. $f(\mathrm{R})$ is plotted in Fig. 4.20. It is seen that at large values of R, the function $f(\mathrm{R})$ saturates at the level of 2. This expresses a well-known fact that a nonlinear field with time "forgets" the initial condition and, in particular, its amplitude.

Problem 5. Find the solution of the Burgers equation, if

$$\varphi_0(x) = x^2.$$

Solution. The solution of the linear diffusion equation is here equal to

$$\varphi(x,t) = 2\mu t + x^2.$$

Accordingly, the solution of the Burgers equation has the following form:

$$v(x,t) = -\frac{x}{t}\,\frac{2}{1+z^2}, \quad z = \frac{x}{\sqrt{2\mu t}}. \tag{4.86}$$

It is plotted for three consecutive moments of time in Fig. 4.21. At first glance, the obtained solutions contradict intuition acquired by us: according to our understanding, at $x < 0$, where $v(x,t) > 0$, the field must move to the right, and the negative field, at $x > 0$, must move to the left. An analysis of the solution, and of the graphs, reveals that exactly the opposite happens. This is due to the fact that the effective

Reynolds number of the field (4.86) is close to unity, and the diffusive smearing dominates over the expected inertial effects.

References

1. O.V. Rudenko, S.N. Gurbatov, C.M. Hedberg, *Nonlinear Acoustics through Problems and Examples* (Trafford, 2010)
2. O.V. Rudenko, S.I. Soluyan, *Theoretical Foundations of Nonlinear Acoustics* (Plenum, New York, 1977)
3. S.N. Gurbatov, D.B. Crighton, The nonlinear decay of complex signals in dissipative media, Chaos **5**, 524–530 (1995)
4. J.R. Angilella, J.C. Vassilicos, Spectral, diffusive and convective properties of fractal and spiral fields, Physica D **124**, 23–57 (1998)
5. J.M. Burgers, *The Nonlinear Diffusion Equation* (D. Reidel, Dordrecht, 1974)
6. U. Frisch, *Turbulence: the Legacy of A.N. Kolmogorov* (Cambridge University Press, 1995)
7. S. Kida, Asymptotic properties of Burgers turbulence, J. Fluid Mech. **93**, 337–377 (1979)
8. S.A. Molchanov, D. Surgailis, W.A. Woyczynski, Hyperbolic asymptotics in Burgers' turbulence and extremal processes, Comm. Math. Phys. **168**, 209–226 (1995)
9. S.N. Gurbatov, A.N. Malakhov, A.I. Saichev, *Nonlinear Random Waves and Turbulence in Nondispersive Media: Waves, Rays and Particles.* (Manchester University Press, 1991)
10. S.N. Gurbatov, A.V. Troussov, The decay of multiscale signals — deterministic model of the Burgers turbulence, Phys. D **145**, 47–64 (2000)
11. E. Aurell, S.N. Gurbatov, I.I. Wertgeim, Self-preservation of large-scale structures in Burgers turbulence, Phys. Lett. A **182**, 109–113 (1993)
12. S.N. Gurbatov, G.V. Pasmanik, Self-preservation of large-scale structures in a nonlinear viscous medium described by the Burgers equation, J. Exp. Theoret. Phys. **88**, 309–319 (1999)
13. S.N. Gurbatov, A.I. Saichev, Degeneracy of one-dimensional acoustic turbulence at large Reynolds numbers, Sov. Phys. JETP **80**, 589–595 (1981)
14. M.V. Berry, Z.V. Lewis, On the Weierstrass–Mandelbrot fractal function, Proc. Roy. Soc. A **340**, 459–484 (1980)
15. B.B. Mandelbrot, *The Fractal Geometry of Nature* (Freeman, New York, 1982)
16. M. Vergassola, B. Dubrulle, U. Frisch, A. Noullez, Burgers' equation, devil's staircases and the mass distribution for large-scale structures, Astron. Astrophys. **289**, 325–356 (1994)

Chapter 5
Evolution of a Noise Field Within the Framework of the Burgers Equation

This chapter gives a brief review of evolution of random fields satisfying the Burgers equation. Often such random fields are called the Burgers turbulence, or even Burgulence, and also, bearing in mind applications to evolution of intense acoustic noise, acoustic turbulence. More details on probabilistic and spectral-correlational properties of the Burgers turbulence are contained in [1–16] and references therein.

5.1 Burgers turbulence — acoustic turbulence

Let us discuss in this chapter statistical properties of solutions to the Burgers equation

$$\frac{\partial v}{\partial t} + v\frac{\partial v}{\partial x} = \mu\frac{\partial^2 v}{\partial x^2} \tag{5.1}$$

in the limit of a vanishing diffusion coefficient μ. This equation was introduced by Burgers [17] as a model for hydrodynamic turbulence.

A large body of work has been devoted to investigations of dynamic and static properties of solutions to the one-dimensional and, in recent years, three-dimensional Burgers equation (see, e.g., references in monographs [18–21]). Despite of the fact that the Burgers equation has an exact solution, *viz.* the Hopf-Cole solution, an analysis of deterministic and, especially, random fields is a very complex mathematical problem. So first serious results for a Brownian initial potential were obtained only 30 years [22] after the equation itself had appeared [17], and an exact statistical description of this particular case had been produced relatively recently [3].

As it has already been mentioned, the Burgers equation (5.1) describes two main effects inherent in any turbulence [23]: the nonlinear redistribution of energy over the spectrum and influence of viscosity at small spatial scale. This is why, apart from direct physical applications, the Burgers equation is of great interest for verification of the theory and various models of developed turbulence.

First of all, let us note that in the case of the Riemann equation ($\mu = 0$ in Eq. (5.1)), it is possible to find exact expressions for both the spectra and probability distributions of a random field [18, 19, 24, 25]. Some of these results will be given in the next section.

Since there are no external forces in Eq. (5.1), evolution of a random initial field may be interpreted as a model of a decay of turbulence. Here, for instance, it is important to know the laws of energy decay at long time. Before proceeding to the Burgers equation itself, let us briefly discuss the situation with the decay laws of the three-dimensional Navier-Stokes turbulence.

Karman and Howarth [26] (see also [27]) studied the decay of three-dimensional homogeneous and isotropic hydrodynamic Burgers turbulence at large Reynolds numbers. Under the assumption that evolution of the spatial correlation function is self-similar, i.e. its shape does not change, it was obtained that the integral scale of turbulence $L(t)$ and the mean square velocity $u(t)$ have a power-law behavior. Then from the Karman-Howarth equation, which connects the correlation function and the third-moment function, it follows that the two exponents are linked. In the process, additional conditions are required in order to find the exponent in the turbulence-decay law.

Kolmogorov realized that and suggested [28] to use the so-called Loitsyanski "invariant" [29] as an additional condition and, accordingly, derived the decay law for three-dimensional turbulence $u^2(t) \sim t^{-10/7}$. But later, Proudman and Reid [30], and Batchelor and Proudman [31] showed that the integral considered by Loitsyanski is not a true invariant. Under the assumption that the turbulence-energy spectrum at small wavenumbers obeys the powers law $E(k,t) \sim k^4$, the Loitsyanski integral, up to a numerical coefficient, is nothing else but a coefficient in front of k^4. For the three-dimensional hydrodynamic turbulence, nonlinear interaction of spatial harmonics leads to generation of large-scale components and their contribution is proportional to k^4 at small wavenumbers k [23, 32]. Accordingly, precisely this fact leads to the dependence of the Loitsyanski "invariant" on time. Nevertheless, if the initial spectrum $E(k) \sim |k|^n$, and the exponent $n < 4$, then the coefficient in front of $|k|^n$ will be invariant. In the theory of turbulence it is called the principle of "permanence of large eddies" (PLE). Kolmogorov's arguments are easily adaptable to this case, which leads to the following three-dimensional-turbulence-decay law $u^2(t) \sim t^{-2(n+1)/(n+3)}$ (see, e.g., [23]).

A similar analysis may also be carried out for the one-dimensional Burgers turbulence. In the one-dimensional case, the contribution due to parametric generation of large-scale components is proportional to k^2. Accordingly, if the initial energy spectrum is $E_0(k) \sim |k|^n \quad -1 < n < 2$, than Kolmogorov's arguments again predict that $u^2(t) \sim t^{-2(n+1)/(n+3)}$. But a rigorous analysis shows [11] that this is valid only if $-1 < n < 1$. A similar result had later also been obtained for the three-dimensional Navier-Stokes turbulence [33].

In this chapter, we will provide a classification of different regimes of evolution of the Burgerce turbulence. Physically, differences between various regimes are determined by competition between the initial spectrum and new spatial frequencies arising due to the nonlinear evolution of the spectrum. For large wavenumbers, the universal k^{-2} behavior aways takes place, which is due to the creation of discontinuities. If $n < 1$, the large-scale part of the spectrum is conserved with time and spectrum evolution turns out to be self-similar. If $n > 2$, the long-time spectrum evolution is also self-similar, whereas the shape of the spectrum does not depend on the form of the initial spectrum and has the universal asymptotic k^2 at small wavenumbers. But if $1 < n < 2$, it is possible to identify three regions in the spectrum, all with a power-law behavior: the region of low wavenumbers, where the spectrum is proportional to $|k|^n$ with a prefactor which does not depend on time; the intermediate region where the spectrum is proportional to k^2, and the prefactor grows with time; and, finally, the region of high k where the spectrum is proportional to k^{-2}. But if $n < -3$, it is necessary to introduce an infrared cutoff for the spectrum and its evolution does not depend on the exponent n.

5.2 The Burgers turbulence at the initial stage of evolution

In the most interesting, from the viewpoint of analysis of the Burgers turbulence, case of vanishing viscosity (at $\mu \to 0$) and at the initial stage until the appearance of discontinuities, the Burgers equation (5.1) may be replaced by the Riemann equation

$$\frac{\partial v}{\partial t} + v\frac{\partial v}{\partial x} = 0. \tag{5.2}$$

Let us supplement it by the initial condition

$$v(x,t=0) = v_0(x), \tag{5.3}$$

where $v_0(x)$ is a random function whose statistical properties are considered to be given. In particular, we assume that the probability density

$$w_0(v,x) = \langle \delta(v - v_0(x)) \rangle \tag{5.4}$$

is known. Here the angular brackets, as before, designate a statistical average. In this case, the averaging is with respect to the statistical ensemble of the initial random field $v_0(x)$.

In this section, we will find some statistical characteristics of the random field $v(x,t)$ satisfying the Riemann equation (5.2) and a random initial condition (5.3), while paying particular attention to the case of the statistically homogeneous Burgers turbulence, for which $v_0(x)$ is a statistically homogeneous function of its argument x. Therewith the initial probability density introduced above does not depend on x: $w_0(v,x) = w_0(v)$. In this case, evolution of spectra of the Burgers turbulence at the initial stage is completely determined by both the form of the probability density $w_0(v)$ and the initial spatial spectrum

$$E_0(k) = \frac{1}{2\pi}\int_{-\infty}^{\infty} B_0(s)ds, \tag{5.5}$$

where

$$B_0(s) = \langle v_0(x) v_0(x+s) \rangle \tag{5.6}$$

is the correlation function of the initial random field $v_0(x)$, which we also assume to be known. Size limitations of the monograph do not allow us to give here a comprehensive review of the properties of the Burgers turbulence at the initial stage. Further information on this topic can be found in [18, 18, 25, 34–38].

Recall that a solution $v(x,t)$ of the Riemann equation describes the initial stage of the Burgers turbulence in the Eulerian representation. Accordingly, the field $v(x,t)$ is sometimes called Eulerian. Nonlinearity of the Riemann equation makes a statistical analysis of the Eulerian field $v(x,t)$ very difficult. It is much easier to study statistical properties of solutions to the Riemann equation in the Lagrangian representation. Therefore we will first study statistical properties of the corresponding Lagrangian fields $X(y,t)$ and $V(y,t)$ satisfying the following equations:

$$\frac{dX}{dt} = V, \quad \frac{dV}{dt} = 0, \tag{5.7}$$

and initial conditions

$$X(y,0) = y, \quad V(y,0) = v_0(y), \tag{5.8}$$

and then, by using the well-known formulas connecting statistical characteristics of Lagrangian and Eulerian fields, we will find statistical properties of the Eulerian field $v(x,t)$.

In order to take the influence of effects of nonlinear compression and expansion of the wave profile $v(x,t)$ on the statistics of the field $v(x,t)$ into account, it is necessary to supplement the Lagrangian equations (5.7) by equations for the auxiliary Lagrangian fields

$$J(y,t) = \frac{\partial X(y,t)}{\partial y}, \quad U(y,t) = \frac{\partial V(y,t)}{\partial y}. \tag{5.9}$$

Evidently, the above fields satisfy the following equations:

$$\frac{dJ}{dt} = U, \quad \frac{dU}{dt} = 0 \tag{5.10}$$

and initial conditions

$$J(y,0) = 1, \quad U(y,0) = v_0'(y). \tag{5.11}$$

Solutions of the lagrangian equations (5.7), (5.10) with the initial conditions (5.8), (5.11) are obvious:

$$\begin{aligned} X(y,t) &= y + v_0(y)t, \quad V(y,t) = v_0(y), \\ J(y,t) &= 1 + v_0'(y)t, \quad U(y,t) = v_0'(y). \end{aligned} \tag{5.12}$$

Let us first find the Lagrangian probability density of the fields $X(y,t)$, $V(y,t)$ and $J(y,t)$. By definition, it is equal to

$$w_1(x,v,j;y,t) = \langle \delta(X(y,t)-x)\delta(V(y,t)-v)\delta(J(y,t)-j)\rangle . \tag{5.13}$$

By substituting here Eqs. (5.12) and by using the properties of the delta function, we obtain

$$w_1(x,v,j;y,t) = \frac{1}{t}\, w_0\left(v, \frac{j-1}{t}; y\right)\delta(x-y-vt), \tag{5.14}$$

where

$$w_0(v,u;x) = \left\langle \delta(v_0(x)-v)\delta(v_0'(x)-u)\right\rangle \tag{5.15}$$

is the joint probability density of the random fields $v_0(x)$ and $v_0'(x)$.

5.2.1 *One-point probability density of a random Eulerian velocity field*

Let us first find the one-point Eulerian probability distribution of a random field $v(x,t)$

$$w_e(v;x,t) = \langle \delta(v(x,t)-v)\rangle . \tag{5.16}$$

In order to do this, let us integrate both parts of Eq. (5.13) with respect to y. By using the fact that the operations of integrations and statistical averaging may be performed in any order, we arrive at the following equality:

$$\int_{-\infty}^{\infty} w_e(x,v,j;y,t)dy = \left\langle \int_{-\infty}^{\infty} \delta(X(y,t)-x)\delta(V(y,t)-v)\delta(J(y,t)-j)dy \right\rangle . \tag{5.17}$$

Let us use the following relationship from the generalized function theory (see Appendix):

$$\begin{aligned}\delta(X(y,t)-x)&\delta(V(y,t)-v)\delta(J(y,t)-j)\\ &= \frac{1}{j(x,t)}\delta(y(x,t)-y)\delta(v(x,t)-v)\delta(j(x,t)-j),\end{aligned} \tag{5.18}$$

which holds at the initial stage of development of the Burgers turbulence, when the function $X(y,t)$ may be considered a strictly monotonous, smooth function of the Lagrangian coordinate y. Here $y(x,t)$ is the Lagrangian coordinate in the Eulerian representation and $j(x,t)$ is the Eulerian divergence field.

By substituting Eq. (5.18) into the right-hand side of Eq. (5.17) and by using the sifting property fo the delta function $\delta(y(x,t)-y)$, we obtain

$$\int_{-\infty}^{\infty} w_e(x,v,j;y,t)dy = \frac{1}{j} w_e(v,j;x,t), \tag{5.19}$$

where

$$w_e(v,j;x,t) = \langle \delta(v(x,t)-v)\delta(j(x,t)-j)\rangle \tag{5.20}$$

is the joint Eulerian probability density of the fields $v(x,t)$, $j(x,t)$ at the moment of time t and at the point with the Eulerian coordinate x. Let us rewrite the resultant relationship (5.19) between the Lagrangian and Eulerian probability densities in a form more convenient for analysis

$$w_e(v,j;x,t) = j\int_{-\infty}^{\infty} w_e(x,v,j;y,t)dy. \tag{5.21}$$

By inserting here the expression (5.14) for the Lagrangian probability density and by eliminating the integral by means of the sifting property of the delta function $\delta(x-y-vt)$, we finally obtain

$$w_e(v,j;x,t) = \frac{j}{t}\,w_0\left(v,\frac{j-1}{t};x-vt\right). \tag{5.22}$$

Recall that we are interested in the probability density $w_e(v;x,t)$ (5.16) of a random field $v(x,t)$. It is expressed via the Eulerian probability density, which has been determined above, $w_e(v,j;x,t)$ by the following obvious equality:

$$w_e(v;x,t) = \int_{-\infty}^{\infty} w_e(v,j;x,t)dj. \tag{5.23}$$

By inserting the right-hand side of Eq. (5.22) into the integrand, we obtain

$$w_e(v;x,t) = \frac{1}{t}\int_{-\infty}^{\infty} w_0\left(v,\frac{j-1}{t};x-vt\right)jdj. \tag{5.24}$$

By transforming to the new integration variable $u=(j-1)/t$, we obtain

$$w_e(v;x,t) = \int_{-\infty}^{\infty}(1+ut)w_0(v,u;x-vt)du. \tag{5.25}$$

By using the property of consistency of the probability density $w_0(v,u;x)$:

$$\int_{-\infty}^{\infty} w_0(v,u;x)du = w_0(v),$$

let us rewrite Eq. (5.25) as

$$w_e(v;x,t) = w_0(v;x-vt) + t\int_{-\infty}^{\infty} uw_0(v,u;x-vt)du. \tag{5.26}$$

Let us write down the remaining integral by using the language of statistical averages:

$$\int_{-\infty}^{\infty} uw_0(v,u;x-vt)du = \left\langle v_0'(x-vt)\delta(v_0(x-vt)-v)\right\rangle.$$

By using the relationship from the generalized function theory (see Appendix)

$$v_0'(x-vt)\delta(v_0(x-vt)-v) = -\frac{\partial}{\partial x}\int_{-\infty}^{v}\delta(v_0(x-vt)-z)dz,$$

we transform the above equality to the following form:

$$\int_{-\infty}^{\infty} uw_0(v,u;x-vt)du = -\frac{\partial}{\partial x}\int_{-\infty}^{v}\langle\delta(v_0(x-vt)-z)\rangle dz,$$

which is equivalent to the following equality for the probability densities:

$$\int_{-\infty}^{\infty} uw_0(v,u;x-vt)du = -\frac{\partial}{\partial x}\int_{-\infty}^{v} w_0(z;x-vt)dz.$$

Here, as before, $w_0(v;x)$ is the probability density of the initial random field $v_0(x)$.

By substituting the last equality into Eq. (5.26), we find that

$$w_e(v;x,t) = w_0(v;x-vt) - t\int_{-\infty}^{v}\frac{\partial}{\partial x}w_0(z;x-vt)dz.$$

By using the standard differentiation rules, we finally obtain

$$w_e(v;x,t) = \frac{\partial}{\partial v}\int_{-\infty}^{v} w_0(z;x-vt)dz. \tag{5.27}$$

5.2.2 *Properties of the probability density of a random velocity field*

Let us discuss in detail evolution of the probability density (5.27) of a random field satisfying the Riemann equation (5.2). Let us first consider a statistically homogeneous random initial field $v_0(x)$, whose probability density $w_0(v)$ is independent of x. Then from Eq. (26) we obtain

$$w_e(v;x,t) = w_0(v) \tag{5.28}$$

that the one-point probability density of a statistically homogeneous field $v(x,t)$ is time independent. In other words, nonlinear self-action of the field $v(x,t)$ has no effect on the shape of its one-point probability density. This, at first sight unexpected result is easily understood by means of the well-known relationship between the probability density of a statistically homogeneous random function and behavior of its realizations: the probability density of a statistically homogeneous and ergodic with respect to x field $v(x,t)$ can be expresses via the limit of the relative length of time the realization $v(x,t)$ spends within the interval $[v, v+dv]$:

$$w_e(v;t) = \lim_{\ell\to\infty}\frac{1}{\ell dv}\sum_k dx_k, \tag{5.29}$$

where dx_k are lengths of intervals on the x-axis, within which the values of $v(x,t)$ belong to the interval $[v, v+dv]$. Due to the linear dependence of the Lagrangian field $X(y,t)$ (5.12) on time, the length of each interval dx_k varies with time according to the following law:

$$dx_k(t) = dx_k(0) \pm t\,dv, \tag{5.30}$$

where the negative sign corresponds to the intervals at steepening parts of the profile of the field $v(x,t)$, and the positive sign corresponds to the stretching parts. Evidently, as long as the solution of the Riemann equation (5.2) is a single-stream one the sum of any two neighboring intervals is conserved

$$dx_k + dx_{k+1} = const,$$

the relative length of time the field $v(x,t)$ spends within any given interval $[v, v+dv]$ does not change, and so the one-point probability density of a statistically homogeneous field $v(x,t)$ remains invariant as well.

Let us now use Eq. (5.27) for an analysis of signal-noise interaction. Let the initial field $v_0(x)$ equal the sum of a deterministic signal $v_s(x)$ and a statistically homogeneous noise $v_n(x)$, whose probability density $w_n(v)$ is known:

$$v_0(x) = v_s(x) + v_n(x). \tag{5.31}$$

Then the initial probability density is equal to

$$w_0(v;x) = w_n(v - v_s(x)),$$

and Eq. (5.27) is transformed into

$$w_e(v;x,t) = w_n(v - v_s(x - vt)) \frac{\partial}{\partial v} [v - v_s(x - vt)]. \tag{5.32}$$

From here, it is seen that nonlinear interaction of the signal with noise, with growing t, changes the probability density of noise, and also makes the shape of the signal, which may naturally be taken as the mean field $\langle v(x,t) \rangle$, depend on the statistics of noise.

One of the peculiarities of the probability density (5.32) of the signal-noise mixture (5.31), whose geometric explanation is akin to the given above explanation of the invariance of the probability density of the statistically homogeneous Riemann field, consists in that the resultant probability density $w_e(v;x,t)$ (31) does not depend on the form of realizations of the initial noise $v_n(x)$: at the same one-point probability density $w_n(v)$, the probability density of the signal-noise ration (5.32) is the same for both quasi-harmonic and broadband noise, and for the case when all realizations $v_n(x)$ are constant along x. Only the applicability limits of the expression (5.32), valid until formation of discontinuities in the random field $v(x,t)$, change. This insensitivity of the probability density (5.32) with respect to behavior of realizations of noise allows us to write down the probability density of the signal-noise mixture in a different, equivalent to (5.32), form. The idea is that instead of the initial condition (5.31) the following simpler condition may be used:

$$v_0(x) = v_s(x) + v_n, \tag{5.33}$$

where v_n is simply a random value with the probability density $w_n(v)$. The solution of the Riemann equation (5.2) with the initial condition (5.33) is connected with the field in the absence of noise $v_s(x,t)$ — the solution of Eq. (5.2) with the initial condition

$$v(x,0) = v_s(x),$$

by the Galilean relationship

$$v(x,t) = v_s(x - v_n t, t) + v_n. \tag{5.34}$$

Accordingly, the probability density of the field $v(x,t)$ (5.34) is by definition equal to

$$w_e(v;x,t) = \langle \delta(v - v_n - v_s(x - v_n t, t)) \rangle,$$

where averaging is performed with respect to an ensemble of values of the random variable v_n. By explicitly expanding the averaging operation, we obtain

$$w_e(v;x,t) = \int_{-\infty}^{\infty} w_n(z)\delta(v - z + v_s(x - zt, t))dz. \tag{5.35}$$

From here, in particular, it follows that at $\langle v_n \rangle = 0$ the mean field is equal to

$$\langle v(x,t) \rangle = \int_{-\infty}^{\infty} w_n(v) v_s(x - vt, t) dv. \tag{5.36}$$

Equation (5.35) for the probability density of the signal-noise mixture, which is equivalent to Eq. (5.32), is convenient when the solution, i.e. the shape of the signal in the absence of noise, is known $v_s(x,t)$. Note also that contrary to Eq. (5.32), Eqs. (5.35), (5.36) are also valid at times when discontinuities form in the wave profile, under the condition that the noise sufficiently slowly, in comparison with the signal, changes along the x-axis.

Let us consider the example of an initially sinusoidal signal

$$v_s(x) = v_0 \sin(k_0 x) \tag{5.37}$$

and a Gaussian noise with the variance σ_n^2 in more detail. Therewith the probability density (5.32) takes on the following form:

$$w_e(v;x,t) = [1 - v_0 \cos k_0(x - vt)] \frac{1}{\sqrt{2\pi}\sigma_n} \exp\left\{ -\frac{[v - v_0 \sin k_0(x - vt)]^2}{2\sigma_n^2} \right\}. \tag{5.38}$$

The right-hand side of this equality is positive and has the meaning of a probability density as long as the solution of the Riemann equation $v_s(x,t)$ is single-stream, i.e. while

$$\tau \leqslant 1, \quad \text{where} \quad \tau = v_0 k_0 t. \tag{5.39}$$

Recall that the dimensionless parameter τ characterizes the degree of nonlinear distortions of the signal.

From Eq. (5.38) it is seen that as a result of interaction between the signal and noise, with growing t, the probability density of the field $v(x,t)$ becomes non-Gaussian. It is of interest to investigate evolution of the probability density at the points $s = 0$ and $s = \pi$, where $s = k_0 x$ is a dimensionless coordinate; i.e. at the point of the maximum stretching and steepening of the signal, respectively. At these points, for the probability distribution of the normalized field $\alpha = v/\sigma_\mathrm{n}$ we have

$$w_\pm(\alpha;t) = \frac{1}{\sqrt{2\pi}} \left[1 \pm \tau \cos\left(\frac{\alpha\tau}{\nu}\right)\right] \exp\left\{-\frac{1}{2}\left[\alpha \pm \nu \sin\left(\frac{\alpha\tau}{\nu}\right)\right]^2\right\}, \tag{5.40}$$

where the negative sign corresponds to the point $s = \pi$, and the positive sign corresponds to the point $s = 0$. The parameter $\nu = v_0/\sigma_\mathrm{n}$ entering Eq. (5.40) is the signal-to-noise ratio. Let us discuss evolution of the probability density of the signal-noise mixture at $\nu \gg 1$. Therewith, not too close to the moment of overturn of the field and formation of multistreamness ($\tau < 1$), it is possible to Taylor-expand the sinusoid and to retain only the first term of the series. In this approximation, the probability density for α turns out to be Gaussian with the variance

$$\sigma_\pm^2(\tau) = (1 \pm \tau)^{-2}. \tag{5.41}$$

From here, and also from an analysis of the more general expression (5.40) it is seen that at the steepening parts of the signal, at $s = \pi$, the variance of the noise grows with growing τ. This is due to the fact that, at a steepening front, even a small drift of the signal because of the noise velocity leads to a strong change of the field $v(x,t)$. On the contrary, at stretching parts of the signal profile, at $s = 0$, there occurs suppression of the noise by the signal, because, within such intervals, the signal drifting with the velocity v_n tends to compensate the noise component of the field.

While nearing the moment of overturn of the signal, $\tau = 1$, the variance of the noise at the steepening part strongly grows, and the probability density itself becomes substantially non-Gaussian. In Figs. 5.1 and 5.2, the probability densities (5.40) at different values of τ and at $\nu = 4$ are plotted in order to illustrate evolution of the shape of the probability density with time.

5.2.3 *Spectra of a velocity field*

The spatial spectra of random fields contain much more information on evolution of space-time properties of these fields than the one-point probability densities considered above. It is possible to show (see, e.g., [18, 19, 36, 37]) that in the case of a statistically homogeneous Riemann field $v(x,t)$ its spatial spectrum

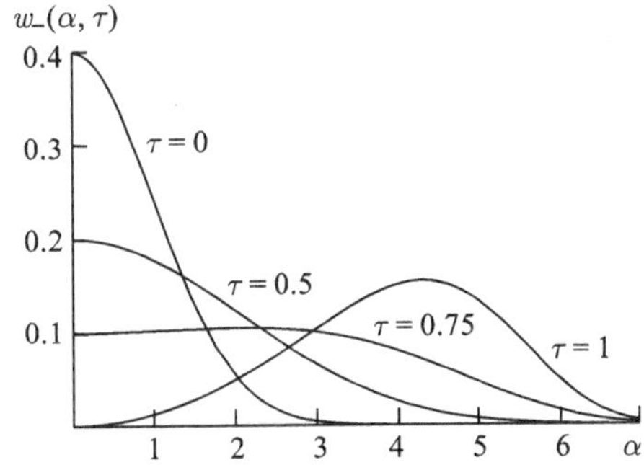

Fig. 5.1 Probability density $w_-(\alpha;\tau)$ (5.40) of the signal-noise mixture at the point of the maximum steepening of the signal, at the signal-to-noise ration $\nu=4$ and different values of $\tau=0$; 0.5; 0.75; 1.

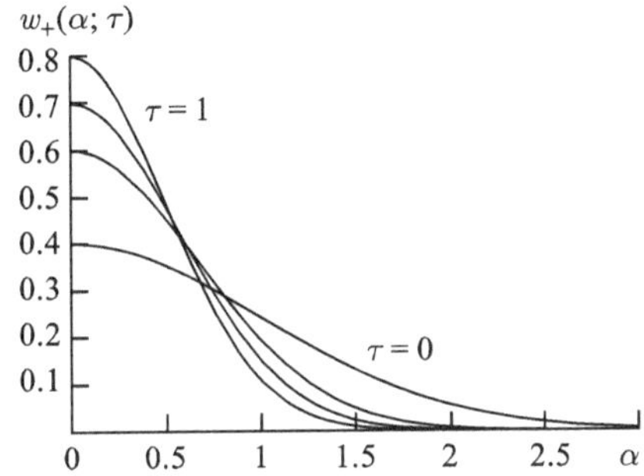

Fig. 5.2 Probability density $w_+(\alpha;\tau)$ (5.40) of the singnal-noise mixture at the point of the maximum stretching of the signal, at the signal-to-noise ratio $\nu=4$ and different values of $\tau=0$; 0.5; 0.75; 1.

$$E(k,t)=\frac{1}{2\pi}\int_{-\infty}^{\infty}B(s,t)e^{-iks}ds, \tag{5.42}$$

where

$$B(s,t)=\langle v(x,t)v(x+s,t)\rangle \tag{5.43}$$

is the correlation function of the Eulerian field $v(x,t)$, is equal to

$$E(k,t)=\frac{1}{2\pi(kt)^2}\int_{-\infty}^{\infty}e^{-iks}\left[\theta_2(kt,-kt,s)-\theta_1(kt)\theta_1(-kt)\right]. \tag{5.44}$$

Here

$$\theta_2(k_1,k_2,s)=\left\langle e^{i[k_1v_0(x)+k_2v_0(x+s)]}\right\rangle,\quad \theta_1(k)=\left\langle e^{ikv_0(x)}\right\rangle \tag{5.45}$$

are the two-point and one-point characteristic functions of the initially statistically homegeneous field $v_0(x)$.

Let us discuss some characteristic features of evolution of the spectral density of the statistically homogeneous Riemann field $v(x,t)$ by using the initially Gaussian field $v_0(x)$ with a zero mean and a given correlation function $B_0(s)$, $B_0(0)=\sigma_0^2$ as an example. In this case, the spectral density (5.44) takes on the form

$$E(k,t)=\frac{1}{2\pi(kt)^2}e^{-(\sigma_0kt)^2}\int_{-\infty}^{\infty}\left(e^{B_0(s)k^2t^2}-1\right)e^{-iks}ds. \tag{5.46}$$

Note above all that from Eq. (5.46), as well as from the more general expression (5.44), follows the invariant

$$E(0,t) = \frac{1}{2\pi}\int_{-\infty}^{\infty} B_0(s)ds = const. \tag{5.47}$$

This invariant plays a special role in the theory of the Burgers turbulence, because, as it will be shown in the following sections, during the stage with discontinuities, evolution of the spectral-correlational and probabilistic properties of the Burgers turbulence is qualitatively different at $E(0,t) \neq 0$ and at $E(0,t) = 0$.

Let us also note that the rate of nonlinear self-action and generation of new harmonics of the field $v(x,t)$ depends on the spatial frequency k in the following way: the smaller k the slower these processes. From this point of view, the invariant (5.47) is a consequence of an infinite characteristic time of self-action and generation of the harmonic at zero frequency. Therefore at $\sigma_0 kt \ll 1$, it is possible to expand the exponents in (5.46) into a Taylor series and retain several first terms, e.g.:

$$E(k,t) = E_0(k) + \frac{1}{2}(kt)^2\left[E_0(k)\otimes E_0(k) - 2S_0(0)E_0(k)\right] + \ldots \tag{5.48}$$

where $E_0(k)$ is the spectrum of the initial field $v_0(x)$, the sign $\otimes$ denotes the convolution operation. Taking only the first term on the right-hand side into account corresponds to neglecting nonlinear effects; two first terms take nonlinear interaction of pairs of initial field harmonics into account, which leads to appearance of spectral components with difference and sum wavenumbers (single interaction); etc.

Let us now consider behavior of the spectral density of the field $v(x,t)$ at large wavenumbers k. In this case, to evaluate the integral (5.46), it is possible to use the method of steepest descent. By retaining in Eq. (5.46) the first few terms of the Taylor expansion of the correlation function $B_0(s)$ with respect to powers of s, we obtain:

$$B_0(s) = \sigma_0^2\left(1 - \frac{k_1^2 s^2}{2!} + \frac{k_1^2 s^4}{4!} - \ldots\right), \tag{5.49}$$

$$E(k,t) = \frac{\sigma_0^2}{k_1\sqrt{2\pi}(\kappa\tau)^3}\exp\left(-\frac{1}{2\tau}\right), \quad \tau = \sigma_0 k_1 t, \quad \kappa = k/k_1. \tag{5.50}$$

From here, it follows that the spectral density of the Riemann field decays at $k \to \infty$ according to the universal power law

$$E(k,t) \sim k^{-3}. \tag{5.51}$$

From an analysis of behavior of Riemann fields carried out in Chapter 2 follows that such an asymptotic of the spectrum may be due to the presence of singularities of the type $v(x,t) \sim \sqrt{x}$ in realizations of the field $v(x,t)$. Multistream solutions of the Riemann equation do indeed have such singularities. Therefore the asymptotic (5.51) signifies the appearance of multistreamness. For the Burgers turbulence, the approximation of multistream Riemann solutions is unacceptable, since in this case discontinuities form at the positions of multistream regions. The discontinuities lead to another, slower asymptotic of the spectral density at large values of k:

$$E(k,t) \sim k^{-2}. \tag{5.52}$$

Nevertheless, the asymptotic (5.51) still correctly reflects the behavior of the spectral density of the Burgers turbulence in a certain intermediate region of wavenumbers during the stage preceding the formation of discontinuities and during the initial stage of their appearance.

Let us illustrate the temporal evolution of a random Riemann field for three characteristic initial spectra:

$$E_0(k) = \gamma \alpha_n \left(\frac{k}{k_*}\right)^{2n} e^{-k^2/2k_*^2}, \tag{5.53}$$

$$\gamma = \frac{\sigma_0^2}{k_* \sqrt{2\pi}}, \quad \alpha_0 = \alpha_1 = 1, \quad \alpha_2 = \frac{1}{3}. \tag{5.54}$$

Here $n = 0, 1, 2$, and the constants α_n are chosen so that all three spectra have the same variance σ_0^2. Let us introduce in Eq. (5.46) dimensionless reduced spatial frequency $\kappa = k/k_*$, time $\tau = \sigma_0 k_* t$ and new integration variable $z = k_* s$. Then, for the normalized spectrum $g_n(\kappa;\tau) = S/\gamma$ from (5.46), we have

$$g_n(\kappa;\tau) = \sqrt{\frac{2}{\pi}} \frac{1}{(\kappa\tau)^3} e^{-(\kappa\tau)^2} \int_0^\infty \left[e^{(\kappa\tau)^2 R_n(z)} - 1\right] \cos(\kappa z) dz, \tag{5.55}$$

where $R_n(z)$ are the correlation coefficients for the three types of the initial spectrum (5.53):

$$R_0(z) = e^{-z^2/2}, \quad R_1(z) = (1 - z^2) e^{-z^2/2},$$
$$R_2(z) = \left(1 - 2z^2 + \frac{z^4}{3}\right) e^{-z^2/2}. \tag{5.56}$$

Log-log plots of the spectra (5.55) are shown in Figs. 5.3–5.5. From these figures, it is seen that nonlinear interaction of the spectral components of the field $v(x,t)$, without changing the value of the spectrum at zero frequency, influences its behavior near $k = 0$ in different ways depending on the form of the initial spectrum. If $S_0(0) \neq 0$ and the spectrum $E_0(k)$ monotonously decays with growing k, the process of pumping the energy from the low-frequency region into the high spatial frequencies prevails. But if $S_0(0) = 0$, together with this process, a parametric generation of low frequency components occurs and, if in the initial spectrum

$$E_0(k) \sim k^{2n}, \quad n > 1,$$

then, as follows from Eq. (5.48), in the region of low spatial frequencies, nonlinear interaction leads to a universal asymptotic

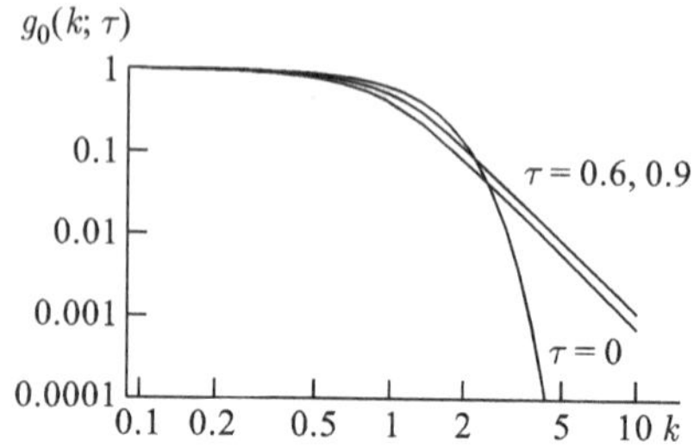

Fig. 5.3 Riemann-wave spectrum $g_0(k;\tau)$ (5.55) at $\tau = 0$, 0.6, 0.9.

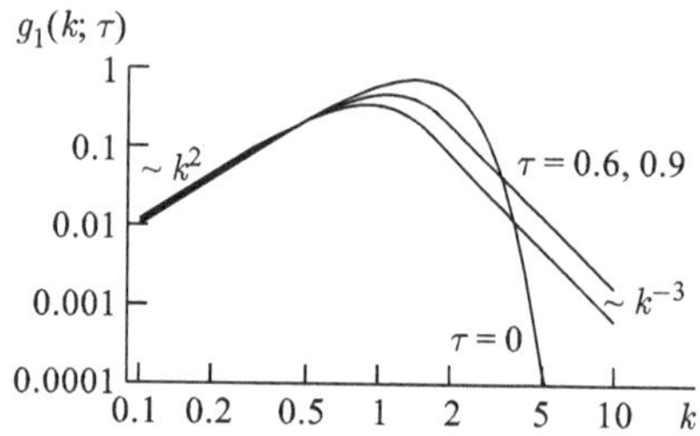

Fig. 5.4 Riemann-wave spectrum $g_1(k;\tau)$ (5.55) at $\tau = 0$, 0.6, 0.9.

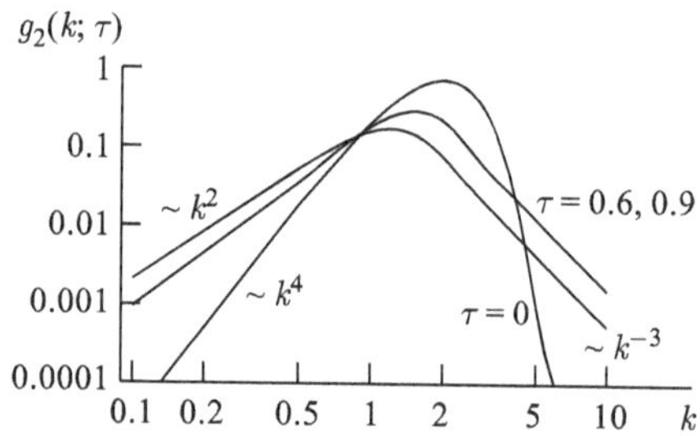

Fig. 5.5 Riemann-wave spectrum $g_2(k;\tau)$ (5.55) at $\tau = 0, 0.6, 0.9$.

$$E(k,t) = \frac{(kt)^2}{2} \int_{-\infty}^{\infty} S_0^2(k)dk. \tag{5.57}$$

In the region of high frequencies, for all three spectral types (5.55), (5.56), formation of slowly decaying in agreement with the asymptotic (5.51) power-law tails $g_n(\kappa;\tau) \sim \kappa^{-3}$ is observed.

5.3 Turbulence evolution at the stage of developed discontinuities

In the previous section we discussed, in detail, the influence of nonlinear interaction and self-action of fields on the statistical properties of the Burgers turbulence at the stage until formation of discontinuities. This section is devoted to a discussion of the properties of the Burgers turbulence by taking formation and chaotic coalescence of discontinuities of a field $v(x,t)$ into account. Further information on statistics of the developed Burgers turbulence and related problems of statistical description of nonlinear acoustic noise waves may be found in Refs. [2, 3, 13, 16, 39–51].

5.3.1 *Phenomenology of the Burgers turbulence*

Let us discuss the properties of the Burgers turbulence assuming that the spectral density at large scales (small wavenumbers k) is in the form of a power law: $E_0(k) \sim |k|^n$. We also assume that this law is valid in a bounded interval $k_i \leqslant |k| \leqslant k_u$, where k_i and k_u are the spatial frequencies cutting off the spectrum at large and small scales, i.e. in the infrared and ultraviolet regions of the spectrum, respectively. We assume that, at both ends of this interval, the spectrum decays to zero faster than any power law:

$$E_0(k) = \alpha^2 |k|^n b_0(k), \quad (k_i \leqslant |k| \leqslant k_u) \tag{5.58}$$

where n is the exponent, $b_0(k) \approx 1$ in the region of wavenumbers $[k_i, k_u]$ and rapidly decays to zero outside this region.

In the theory of the Burgers turbulence, it is customary to introduce a potential $\psi(x,t)$ differing from the above-introduced action $s(x,t)$ only in its sign. In the limit $\mu \to 0$, the potential is representable in the following form:

$$\psi(x,t) = \max_y \left[\psi_0(y) - \frac{(x-y)^2}{2t} \right], \tag{5.59}$$

where $\psi_0(x)$ is the initial potential of the velocity field. Accordingly, for the velocity field we have

$$v(x,t) = -\psi_x(x,t) = \frac{x - y(x,t)}{t}, \tag{5.60}$$

where $y(x,t)$ is the coordinate of the maximum of (5.59) for given x and t.

At long time, the parabola $(x-y)^2/2t$ in Eq. (5.59) becomes a smooth function at the scale of the initial potential $\psi_0(y)$, and the coordinates of the global maxima in (5.59) practically coincide with the coordinates of some local minima of $\psi_0(y)$, which are zeros of the velocity field with positive Hence, at long time, a continuous random field is transformed into a random sawtooth wave — a sequence of cells with the universal behavior within each cell $v(x,t) = (x - y_k)/t$, but with random positions of discontinuities separating the cells. Coalescence of the cells leads to the growth of the overall scale of the turbulence $L(t)$ (the mean mass of a macro-particle), therefore the energy of the random field $E(t) \sim L^2(t)/t^2$ decreases slower that the energy of a periodic signal.

The rate of coalescence of discontinuities is determined by the statistical characteristics of the discontinuity velocities, which, in their turn, depend on the initial potential $\psi_0(x)$. At long time, after multiple coalescence of discontinuities, the properties of the turbulence are determined by the statistical properties of the increments $\psi_0(x+L) - \psi_0(x)$ at large separations L, and at Gaussian statistics of the initial field — by the asymptotic behavior of the structure function of the initial potential. Thus, the turbulence-development scenario is determined by the behavior of the large-scale part of the initial energy spectrum $E_0(k)$ of the velocity field.

For a continuous initial field, the start time of the discontinuity formation is determined by the velocity gradient

$$t_{s,\text{first}} = -1\Big/\min\left(\frac{\partial v_0(x)}{\partial x}\right).$$

Accordingly, the variance of the gradient of the initial field (if it exists) is equal to

$$\sigma_q^2 \equiv \left\langle\left(\frac{\partial v_0(x)}{\partial x}\right)^2\right\rangle = \int_{-\infty}^{\infty} k^2 E_0(k)\,dk \tag{5.61}$$

and determines the characteristic time of formation of the first discontinuity $t_s = 1/\sigma_q$.

Let us also define the velocity variance — the initial energy of the turbulence:

$$\sigma_v^2 \equiv \langle v_0^2(x)\rangle = \int_{-\infty}^{\infty} E_0(k)\,dk \tag{5.62}$$

and the variance of the initial potential

$$\sigma_\psi^2 \equiv \langle \psi_0^2(x)\rangle = \int_{-\infty}^{\infty} \frac{E_0(k)}{k^2}\,dk. \tag{5.63}$$

If the initial spectrum is non-zero within a bounded interval non including the point $k = 0$, then all three variances σ_q, σ_v and σ_ψ exist and are finite. In particular, such situation is realized in numerical experiments, where k_i is determined by the size of the simulated region L_{box}, and k_u is inversely proportional to the discretization step (mesh size).

Since we are interested in the evolution of the Burgers turbulence at long time, where it is determined by the low-frequency part of the spectrum, we assign $k_i = 0$. Accordingly, for the potential $\psi_0(x)$ entering the solution (5.59) we have: if $n > 1$, then the initial potential is statistically homogeneous with a finite variance σ_ψ^2, but if $n < 1$, then the variance σ_ψ^2 is unlimited and the potential only has statistically homogeneous increments. In the first case, it is possible to introduce for the potential the correlation function $B_{0\psi}(x)$, whose Fourier transform is equal to $E_0(k)/k^2$. In the case $n < 1$, the potential is characterized by the structure function

$$D_{0\psi}(x) = \langle(\psi_0(x+y) - \psi_0(y))^2\rangle, \tag{5.64}$$

which is independent of the displacement y and exists only if $n > -1$. It is connected with the energy spectrum by the following relationship

$$D_{0\psi}(x) = 4\alpha^2 \int_0^{\infty} (1-\cos(kx))\,k^{n-2}\,b_0(k)\,dk. \tag{5.65}$$

If $n > 1$, the structure function tends to a finite limit at large increments of the coordinates, but if $n < 1$, its growth is unbounded:

$$D_{0\psi}(x) \sim \begin{cases} \sigma_\psi^2 & n > 1, \\ \alpha^2 |x|^{1-n} & n < 1, \end{cases} \qquad |x| \to \infty. \tag{5.66}$$

From the asymptotic solution of the Burgers solution (5.59) it is possible to identify a spatial scale $L(t)$ proportional to a typical value of $|x - \tilde{y}(x,t)|$. From Eq. (5.60) it is seen that between the discontinuities ($x_{\text{shock},m} < x < x_{\text{shock},m+1}$), the velocity field has a universal structure $v(x,t) = (x - a_m)/t$ and therefore the turbulence energy behaves as $E(t) \sim L^2(t)/t^2$.

The increment of the potential in the solution (5.59) may be estimated as the square root of the structure function (5.66) and, consequently, $(\psi_0(x) - \psi_0(0)) \sim \alpha x^{(1-n)/2}$ for $n < 1$ ($k_i = 0$) and $\sim \sigma_\psi$ for $n > 1$ [18,50]. At long time, by equating the two terms in the solution (5.59), it is possible to estimate the spatial scale $L(t)$ and energy $E(t)$ of the turbulence. At a fixed coordinate x, the maximum in Eq. (5.59) corresponds to the point $y(x,t)$, where the potential's increments are comparable with the change of the parabolic term. This gives the following equation for the turbulence scale $L(t)$:

$$\sqrt{S_{0\psi}(L)} \sim \frac{L^2}{t}. \tag{5.67}$$

Thus, depending on the exponent n of the initial spectrum (5.58), for long times, we find the estimates of the spatial scale $L(t)$ and energy $E(t)$ of the turbulence listed in Table 5.1. Recall that we assumed in the case $n > -3$ that $k_i = 0$ and that there exists a certain ultraviolet spatial cutoff frequency $k_u < \infty$. In the region $n < -3$ it is always necessary to introduce $k_i > 0$, since only in this case a solution of the Burgers equation exists.

Table 5.1 Separation of regions of the exponent n of the initial spectrum according to the typical laws of scale growth and energy decay of the turbulence with time t.

n		-3		-1		1	
$L(t)$	$(\sigma_\psi t)^{1/2}$		$(\alpha t)^{2/(3+n)}$		$(\alpha t)^{2/(3+n)}$		$(\sigma_\psi t)^{1/2}$
$E(t)$	σ_ψ/t		$\alpha^2 k_i^{n+1}$		$(\alpha t)^{2(n+1)/(3+n)}$		σ_ψ/t

If the Burgers turbulence is indeed characterized by a single-scale, then, assuming self-similarity, its spectrum may be represented in the self-similar form:

$$E(k,t) = \frac{L^3(t)}{t^2} \tilde{E}(kL(t)). \tag{5.68}$$

As it has been mentioned above, for the initial spectrum with $n > 2$, parametric interaction of spatial harmonics leads to the universal behavior of the spectrum $E(k,t) \sim k^2$ in the region of small spatial frequencies k; and for $n < 2$, conservation of the initial spectrum $E(k,t) = E_0(k) = \alpha^2 |k|^n$ is observed in the region of small wavenumbers k, which is the spectral formulation of the principle of "permanence of large eddies" (PLE) [11,23]. In the Fourier space, the assumption of self-similarity (5.68) along with the PLE give the same laws of scale growth and turbulence decay, which are given in the table, but now they occur only at $-3 < n < 2$. Evidently, such arguments cannot be used for initial excitations with the exponent $n \geqslant 2$, because, due to the parametric pumping of energy into the low-frequency region, the spectrum has the universal form k^2 in the low-k region with a time-dependent coefficient. By comparing the above-said with the data in Table 5.1, where the domain of applicability of the law $L(t) \sim (\alpha t)^{2/(3+n)}$ is in the interval $n < 1$, we find that the region $1 < n < 2$ requires a separate treatment. Indeed, in the interval $1 < n < 2$, the assumption of self-similarity is no longer valid [11]. This is because of the competitions between the initial spectrum $|k|^n$ (with a time-independent coefficient) and the newly generated part of the spectrum, which is proportional to k^2 and grows with time. If $n > 2$, the initial spectrum at low k is rapidly exceeded by the newly appearing components, whose spectrum is proportional to k^2. In this case the spectrum at long time is universal, is characterized by the only scale $L(t)$, and its behavior does not depend on the exponent n.

For sufficiently large wavenumbers, the behavior of the spectrum is always determined by discontinuities. Therefore

$$E(k,t) \sim \frac{B(t)}{k^2} \quad (\text{large } k), \tag{5.69}$$

and, from Eq. (5.68), it follows that $B(t) \sim L(t)/t^2$. The amplitude of the short-wave part of the spectrum is decreasing with time at $n > -2$ and grows with time at $-3 < n < -2$. The latter fact should not be surprising, since, in this case, the total energy of the turbulence is infinite.

Let us note, in conclusion, that the above mentioned semi-qualitative analysis gives an incomplete description of the behavior of the Burgers turbulence. So, for instance, the spectrum k^{-2}, according to the self-similar solution (5.68), does not change with time, while the characteristics of discontinuities (amplitude distribution, distances between discontinuities, etc.) do change with time (see, e.g., [48–50]).

Thus a general property of the decaying Burgers turbulence is establishment of self-similarity at long times and, in particular, the self-similar behavior of the spectrum (5.68). Therewith it is possible to identify the critical exponents $n_* = -3, -1, 1, 2$, such that the properties of self-similarity for n lying in different intervals between the critical exponents $n_* = -3, -1, 1, 2$ are qualitatively different.

In what follows, we briefly discuss the main regimes of Burgers-turbulence evolution and illustrate the spectrum evolution by numerical experiments borrowed from Ref. [13]. In this work, numerical simulations of the Burgers turbulence demonstrated that, even in the presence of cutoff factors in the regions of small and large scales, spectrum evolution in a limited frequency-time domain is still self-similar. The use of the fast Legendre transform allowed to perform averaging with respect to 3000 realizations with 10^6 sample points in each realization.

5.3.2 Evolution of the Burgers turbulence: statistically homogeneous potential and velocity ($n > 1$ and $n < -3$)

In this section, we discuss evolution of the Burgers turbulence at $n > 1$, when the initial field has Gaussian statistics, and the velocity and potential are statistically homogeneous. The latter means that there is an ultraviolet spectrum cutoff at the spatial frequency $k_u < \infty$. Accordingly, the function $b_0(k)$ is characterized by the wavenumber k_u, near which most of the initial energy is concentrated, and which, by the order of magnitude, is inversely proportional to the initial integral scale L_0. Similar situation is also characteristic of spectra with $n < -3$ and an infrared cutoff at small wavenumbers k_i.

We will not provide a detailed statistical analysis here, but we will just show the key ideas, which form the basis for such an analysis, and will discuss the basic properties of turbulence at the self-similar stage. One of the first works, where serious results in this direction had been obtained, was the work by Kida [52], albeit for a discrete model of initial conditions. Kida considered a model of discrete initial conditions with a statistically independent potential in each cell. Therewith, any connection of the model with statistical characteristics of a continuous initial field (in particular, initial spectrum) remained open. For the case when the probability distribution of the potential has Gaussian tails, Kida obtained an expression for the correlation function, spectrum, and also a logarithmic correction to the law $1/t$ for the energy decay $E(t) \sim t^{-1}\sigma_\psi \ln^{-1/2}(t/t_{\mathrm{nl}})$, where, however, the nonlinearity time t_{nl} was a free parameter and was determined by the cell size of the discrete model.

While analyzing evolution of continuous fields, the asymptotic solution (5.59), (5.60) of the Burgers equation was used As it follows from this solution, the field $v(x,t)$ at a point x and a moment of time t is determined by the coordinate $y(x,t)$ of the absolute maximum. Hence, the statistics of the velocity field is determined by the statistical characteristics of the absolute maximum coordinates. At long times, the parabola in (5.59) becomes a smooth function at the scale of the initial action $\psi_0(x)$, and for the right to be the absolute maximum in (5.59) competes a large number of local maxima of $\psi_0(x)$. This made it possible to use for an analysis of the Burgers turbulence at long time [8], [41] (see also [18]) the statistical theory of large overshoots [53]. It was, in particular, shown that the points of the absolute maxima represent a Poisson process. These results obtained at a physical level of rigor were later confirmed by a rigorous mathematical analysis [54]. In particular, it was rigorously proved that the probability density of the absolute maximum points in the plane (x, ψ) is asymptotically homogeneous along the x-axis and exponentially decays along the ψ-axis.

For the one-dimensional Burgers turbulence (as well as for its three-dimensional generalization [18]) it is, therewith, possible to give a practically exhaustive statistical description. In particular, one-point and two-point probability distributions of the velocity field [8], N-point probability distributions [54] and, respectively, multi-point moment functions have been found. Therewith, at Gaussian initial statistics, all properties of the turbulence at long times are determined by only two integral characteristics of the initial spectrum, *viz.* the variances of the initial velocity σ_v^2 and the initial potential σ_ψ^2. But in a general case, the asymptotic behavior of the turbulence at long time, in both one-dimensional and multidimensional cases, is determined by the "tails" of the distribution function of the initial potential [4]. Therewith, depending on the form of the initial distribution of the potential, three universal self-similar regimes of turbulence decay may be realized.

In the limit of vanishing viscosity, when the time t tends to infinity, the statistical characteristics of the Burgers turbulence become self-similar and, in particular, the energy spectrum assumes the form (5.68). The integral scale of the turbulence $L(t)$ and its energy $E(t)$ are given by the following expressions

$$L(t) \approx (t\sigma_\psi)^{1/2} \ln^{-1/4}\left(\frac{t}{2\pi t_{\mathrm{nl}}}\right), \; E(t) \simeq t^{-1}\sigma_\psi \ln^{-1/2}\left(\frac{t}{2\pi t_{\mathrm{nl}}}\right), \tag{5.70}$$

where

$$t_{\mathrm{nl}} \equiv L_0^2/\sigma_\psi = L_0/\sigma_v, \quad L_0 \equiv \sigma_\psi/\sigma_v \tag{5.71}$$

is the nonlinearity time and the initial integral scale of the turbulence, respectively. Based on these laws, it is possible, in the first approximation, to write the laws of change of the turbulence scale and energy as

$$L(t) \simeq L_0 (t/t_{\mathrm{nl}})^{1/2}, \quad E(t) \simeq E_0 (t/t_{\mathrm{nl}})^{-1}. \tag{5.72}$$

One-point distribution of the velocity field is, therewith, Gaussian with the variance $\sigma_v^2(t) = E(t)$ (5.72). The dimensionless correlation function $\tilde{B}_v(\tilde{x})$ depending on the dimensionless coordinate $\tilde{x} = x/L(t)$ is defined by the following expression:

$$\tilde{B}_v(\tilde{x}) = \frac{d}{d\tilde{x}}\left(\tilde{x}P(\tilde{x})\right), \tag{5.73}$$

where for $x \geqslant 0$

$$P(\tilde{x}) = \frac{1}{2}\int_{-\infty}^{\infty} \frac{dz}{g\left(\frac{\tilde{x}+z}{2}\right)\exp\left[\frac{(\tilde{x}+z)^2}{8}\right] + g\left(\frac{\tilde{x}-z}{2}\right)\exp\left[\frac{(\tilde{x}-z)^2}{8}\right]}, \tag{5.74}$$

$$g(z) \equiv \int_{-\infty}^{z} e^{-\frac{s^2}{2}}\, ds.$$

Here the normalization by $E(t) = L^2(t)/t^2$ is chosen so that for the dimensionless spectrum the following equality would hold:

$$\int_{-\infty}^{\infty} \tilde{E}(\tilde{k})\, d\tilde{k} = 1.$$

Note also that the function $P(\tilde{x})$ also serves as the probability of the absence of discontinuities in the interval of length $\tilde{x}L(t)$ [18].

Recall once more that in this case the properties of the self-similar turbulence are universal and are determined by the two integral characteristics of the initial spectrum: σ_ψ and σ_v.

The dimensionless spectrum

$$\tilde{E}(\tilde{k}) = \frac{1}{2\pi}\int_{-\infty}^{\infty} \tilde{B}_v(\tilde{x})\exp(ik\tilde{x})\,d\tilde{x} = -\frac{ik}{2\pi}\int_{-\infty}^{\infty} \tilde{x}P(\tilde{x})\exp(ik\tilde{x})\,d\tilde{x} \tag{5.75}$$

has the following asymptotics:

$$\tilde{E}(\tilde{k}) \simeq \begin{cases} 0.36\,\tilde{k}^{-2}, & \tilde{k} \gg 1, \\ 1.08\,\tilde{k}^{2}, & \tilde{k} \ll 1, \end{cases} \qquad \tilde{k} \equiv kL(t). \tag{5.76}$$

The asymptotic of the spectrum k^{-2} reflects appearance of discontinuities, while the asymptotic k^2 is formed due to the parametric pumping of energy into the region of low spatial frequencies k. In normal (not dimensionless) variables, evolution of the low-frequency part of the spectrum has the following form:

$$E(k,t) \simeq \frac{L^5(t)}{t^2}k^2 \simeq A(t)\,k^2, \quad kL(t) \ll 1, \tag{5.77}$$

where

$$A(t) = \sigma_v^2 L_0^3 \left(\frac{t}{t_{\mathrm{nl}}}\right)^{1/2} \ln^{-5/4}\left(\frac{t}{2\pi t_{\mathrm{nl}}}\right). \tag{5.78}$$

Thus, at low wavenumbers, the universal power law k^2 takes place, whereas the coefficient in front of it $A(t)$ grows with time.

5.3.3 *Exact self-similarity* ($n > 2$)

The situation becomes more complex at long times [11]. If $n > 2$, the component k^2 (5.77) formed due to nonlinear self-action dominates over the initial spectrum $|k|^n$ and self-similar behavior of the spectrum appears within the entire interval of wavenumbers (see Fig. 5.6), but the time of establishment of self-similarity t_{ss} depends on n. In a general case, the condition $t/t_{\mathrm{nl}} \gg 1$ is not sufficient in order to for the points of absolute maxima in (5.59) to form a Poisson sequence and, consequently, for the self-similar regime of the turbulence to appear. Let us introduce a correlation scale of the initial potential Δ_{corr}, which may be greater than the initial integral scale L_0 (5.71). The self-similar regime of evolution appears when the integral scale of the turbulence $L(t)$ (5.72) becomes much greater than the initial correlation scale Δ_{corr}. This leads to the following expression for the time of establishment of the self-similar regime t_{ss} [11]:

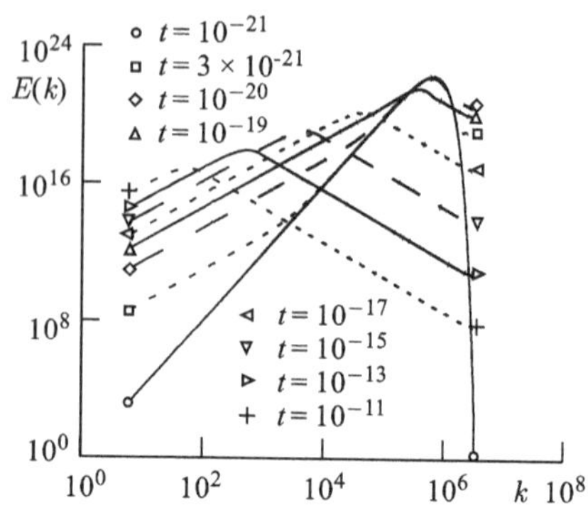

Fig. 5.6 Evolution of the Burgers-turbulence spectrum with the initial spectrum being proportional to k^4 at low wavenumbers k. Marks correspond to the following times: $t_1/t_{nl} = 0.033$, $t_2/t_{nl} = 0.098$, $t_3/t_{nl} = 0.33$ and then $t_i/t_{nl} = 3.310^{2(i-4)}$.

$$t_{ss} \sim t_{nl} \left(\frac{\Delta_{corr}}{L_0} \right)^2 . \tag{5.79}$$

Quasi-monochromatic signals serve as typical examples of the case when the inequality $(\Delta_{corr}/L_0)^2 \gg 1$ holds. Let us consider the initial spectrum $E_0(k)$ (5.2) with $n \gg 1$ and the function $b_0(k)$ rapidly decreasing at $k > k_u$. In this case, the velocity field represents a quasi-monochromatic signal with the central wavenumber $k_u \sim L_0^{-1}$ and the spectral width $\Delta k \sim [\Delta_{corr}]^{-1} \ll k_u$. At the initial stage of evolution

$$t_{nl} \ll t \ll t_{nl}(\Delta_{corr}/L_0),$$

suppression of the amplitude modulation occurs, and displacements of discontinuities of the appearing sawtooth wave are much less than the period of the quasi-monochromatic signal. The energy of such a signal is approximately the same as the energy of the periodic wave: $E(t) \simeq L_0^2/12t^2$ [42]. Nevertheless, because of the finite width of the initial spectrum, generation of low-frequency components $v_l(x,t)$ with the energy $E_l(t) \sim E_0(L_0/\Delta_{corr})^2 \ll E_0$ takes place, whose spectrum lies much lower than the carrier frequency k_u. At

$$t_{nl}(\Delta_{corr}/L_0) \ll t \ll t_{nl}(\Delta_{corr}/L_0)^2$$

the energy of low-frequency components becomes greater than the energy of the high-frequency quasi-periodic wave, but, due to the large spatial scale, relatively weak distortion of the low-frequency signal is observed. And, finally, only at

$$t \gg t_{ss} \sim t_{nl}(\Delta_{corr}/L_0)^2$$

the self-similar regime of turbulence evolution occurs. Physically, this is connected with the fact that, at the initial stage, discontinuities of the quasi-periodic sawtooth wave are strongly correlated, which resists their coalescence. Note that a similar situation also appears for the spectrum with $n \ll -3$ and a nonzero cutoff frequency k_i at small wavenumbers.

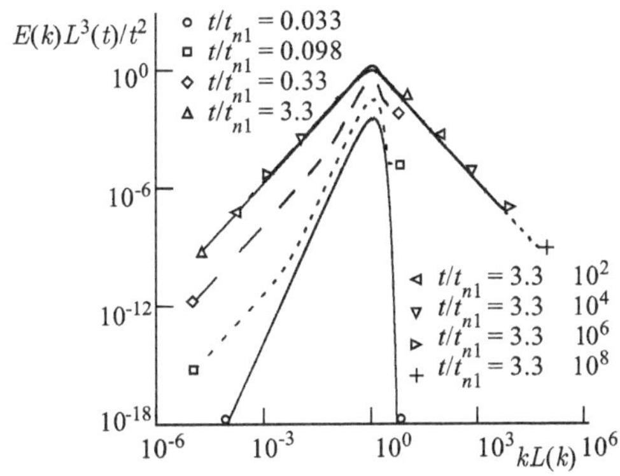

Fig. 5.7 Evolution of the normalized spectrum $E(k,t)L_{\mathrm{exp}}^3(t)/t^2$ $(n=4)$ at the same times as a function of the dimensionless wavenumber $kL_{\mathrm{exp}}(t)$.

Let us cite the results of numerical experiments from Ref. [13], which illustrate establishment of self-similar regimes of spectrum evolution. The use of the fast Legendre transform [45] made it possible to simulate the process of evolution with a large number of points $N=2^{20}$ and perform spectrum averaging with respect to 3000 realizations. In that work, a smooth spectrum cutoff at high frequencies was used:

$$E_0(k)=\alpha_n^2|k|^n e^{-\frac{k^2}{2k_0^2}} \tag{5.80}$$

with $k_u=k_0=N/16$. In all experiments, the periodic initial conditions were used and, thus, the infrared cutoff frequency was determined by the size of the simulated domain and $k_i=2\pi$. In order to test the hypothesis of self-similarity, evolution of the spectrum $E(k,t)$, energy $E(t)=\langle v^2(x,t)\rangle$ and the integral scale $L_{\mathrm{exp}}(t)$, which has been measured from experimental data as

$$L_{\mathrm{exp}}^2(t)=\langle\psi^2(x,t)\rangle/\langle v^2(x,t)\rangle, \tag{5.81}$$

have been considered.

Fig. 5.6 shows evolution of the spectrum at several moments of time from $t/t_{\mathrm{nl}}=0.033$ to $t/t_{\mathrm{nl}}=3.3\cdot 10^8$. At low wavenumbers k, the initial spectrum grew according to the power law k^4. Fig. 5.7 shows evolution of the normalized spectrum $E(k,t)L^3(t)/t^2$ for the same moments of time as a function of the dimensionless wavenumber $kL(t)$. Generation of new components $A(t)k^2$ with a growing amplitude $A(t)$ at low k and k^{-2} at large wavenumbers is clear seen. The point $k_s(t)$ of transition from the $A(t)k^2$ to $\alpha^2|k|^n$ regions of the spectrum moves towards the maximum of the spectrum, and, at long time, the spectral region with α^2k^4 vanishes.

From these plots, establishment of the self-similar regime of evolution and universal power laws k^2 and k^{-2} at $t/t_{\mathrm{nl}}\gtrsim 10$ is clearly seen. In Fig. 5.7, the dimensionless wavenumber $kL_{\mathrm{exp}}(t)$ is used. In order to compare the experimental data with the theoretical expression for the spectrum $\tilde{E}(\tilde{k})$ (5.75), let us take the following relationships between $L_{\mathrm{exp}}(t)$ and $L(t)$ (5.68) into account:

$$L_{\mathrm{exp}}^2(t)=L^2(t)\frac{\int_{-\infty}^{\infty}\tilde{E}(\tilde{k})/\tilde{k}^2\,d\tilde{k}}{\int_{-\infty}^{\infty}\tilde{E}(\tilde{k})\,d\tilde{k}}=L^2(t)\int_0^{\infty}\tilde{x}P(\tilde{x})\,d\tilde{x}\approx 1.65\,L^2(t). \tag{5.82}$$

For the dimensionless spectrum $\tilde{E}(\kappa)$, from experimental data we obtain that al low wavenumbers $\tilde{E}(\kappa) \simeq 1.10\kappa^2$ and $\kappa E(\kappa) \simeq 0.37/\kappa^2$, which is by two percent greater than it follows from the theory (5.76). This small discrepancy is connected with the finite size of the simulation domain.

5.3.4 *Violation of self-similarity* $(1 < n < 2)$

Violation of the self-similar regime of the turbulence evolution is characteristic of this case [11]. For very small wavenumbers $|k| \ll k_s(t)$, the initial spectrum of the turbulence is conserved

$$E(k,t) \simeq \alpha^2 |k|^n \quad \text{for } k \to 0. \tag{5.83}$$

This holds only in the region of wavenumbers, where (5.83) prevails over (5.77). The wavenumber $k_s(t)$ of the boundary between the two regimes, is found from the condition of equality of (5.77) and (5.83), and is defined by the expression

$$k_s(t) \simeq \left(\frac{\alpha^2 t^2}{L^5(t)}\right)^{1/(2-n)} \simeq L_0^{-1} \left(\frac{t}{t_{\mathrm{nl}}}\right)^{-1/[2(2-n)]} \ln^{5/[4(2-n)]} \left(\frac{t}{2\pi t_{\mathrm{nl}}}\right). \tag{5.84}$$

The greater part of the turbulence energy is concentrated within a neighborhood of the integral wavenumber $k_L(t) = L^{-1}(t)$. With accuracy up to the logarithmic factor from (5.81), we have $k_L(t) \sim (t\sigma_\psi)^{-1/2}$. Accordingly:

$$\frac{k_s(t)}{k_L(t)} \sim \left(\frac{t}{t_{\mathrm{nl}}}\right)^{-(n-1)/[2(2-n)]}. \tag{5.85}$$

Thus, the wavenumber demarcating the change of the two power laws tends with time to zero much faster than the integral wavenumber. The ratio of energy in the region $0 < k < k_s(t)$ to the total energy of the turbulence decreases as $(t/t_{\mathrm{nl}})^{-3(n-1))/(n-2)}$ (up to a logarithmic factor) and becomes vanishingly small if $t \gg t_{\mathrm{nl}}$, apart from the case when n is very close to unity. Thus, at finite times with $1 < n < 2$, there is no global self-similar evolution of the spectrum.

In Fig. 5.8, again, generation of the universal low-frequency asymptotic of the spectrum $A(t)k^2$ with a growing amplitude $A(t)$ and appearance of the universal spectrum k^{-2} at large wavenumbers are seen. The position $k_s(t)$ of the boundary of the regions with $A(t)k^2$ and $\alpha^2|k|^n$ rapidly tends to zero and, at long time, the region $\alpha^2|k|^n$ practically vanishes (see Fig. 5.7). The fact that the power-law part of the spectrum $\alpha^2|k|^n$ practically has no effect on the behavior of the integral scale of the turbulence $L(t)$ (5.81) and its energy $E(t)$ even at $1 < n < 2$, when self-similarity is violated, is illustrated by the results of the numerical experiment, as it is seen in Fig. 5.9, and also in Fig. 5.10, where evolution of $L_{\exp}(t)$ and $E(t)$ for different $n = 1.5; 2; 3; 4$ and theoretical curves are shown.

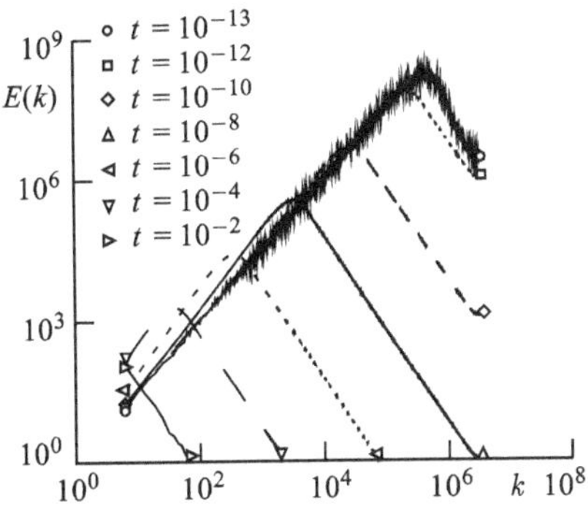

Fig. 5.8 Evolution of the energy spectrum with the initial spectrum being proportional to $|k|^n$ ($n = 1.5$) at small wavenumbers k. The curves correspond to times $t_1/t_{\rm nl} = 0.18$, and then $t_i/t_{\rm nl} = 1.8 10^{2(i-2)}$ ($i = 2,3,\ldots,8$).

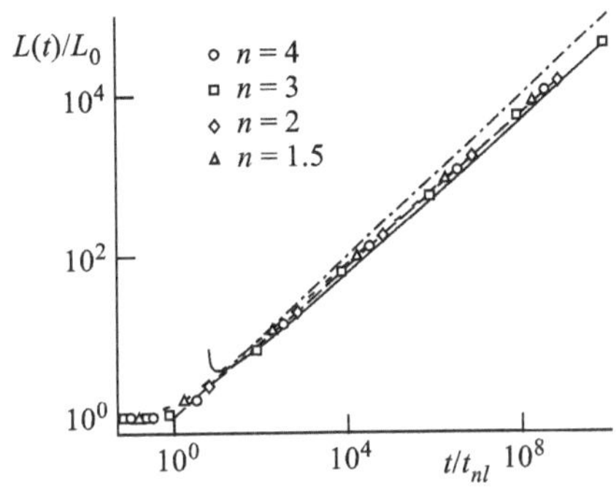

Fig. 5.9 Evolution of the integral length scale $L_{\rm exp}(t)$ obtained in the numerical experiment for $n = 1.5, 2, 3, 4$ (dotted curves), the theoretical curve $\tilde{L}_{\rm exp} = 1.28L(t)$ (5.81), (5.82) (solid curve) and the theoretical curve without the logarithmic correction (dashed curve).

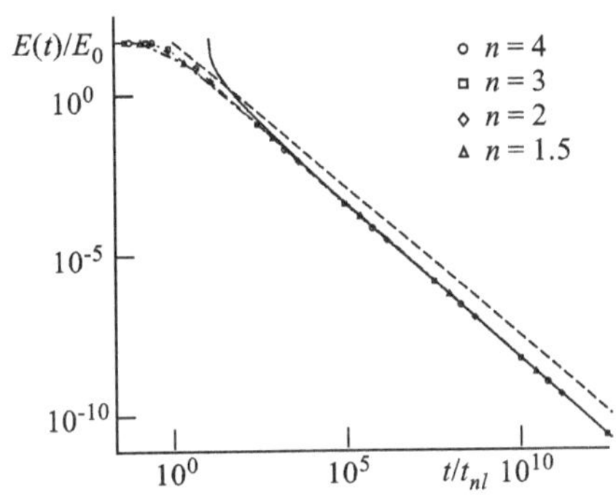

Fig. 5.10 Evolution of the energy $E(t)$ obtained in the numerical experiment for $n = 1.5, 2, 3, 4$ (dotted curves), the theoretical curve $E(t) = L^2(t)/t^2$ (5.81) (solid curve) and the theoretical curve without the logarithmic correction (dashed curve).

Note that, in all experimental results shown here, the condition $k_L(t) \gg k_i$ for the integral wavenumber is satisfied. The latter means that in the considered interval, there many discontinuities. If this condition is violated, there is only one discontinuity per period, and the spectrum has the universal asymptotic $E(k,t) \sim (kt)^{-2}$ at all wavenumbers.

At finite Reynolds numbers $\mathrm{R}_0 = \sigma_\psi/2\mu$, the Reynolds number decreases very slowly due to multiple coalescences of discontinuities:

$$\mathrm{R}(t) = V(t)L(t)/\mu \sim \mathrm{R}_0 \ln^{-1/2}\left(\frac{t}{2\pi t_{\rm nl}}\right),$$

the linear regime is reached at a late stage, when

$$t \gg t_{\mathrm{nl}} \exp(\mathrm{R}_0^2)/\mathrm{R}_0,$$

where $t_{\mathrm{nl}} = \sigma_\psi / l_0^2$ is the time of appearance of nonlinear effects. During the linear stage, the energy decays as $Ct^{-3/2}$, where the constant $C \simeq l_0 \exp(\mathrm{R}_0^2)/\mathrm{R}_0$.

5.3.5 Evolution of turbulence: statistically inhomogeneous potential $(-3 < n < 1)$

For $n < 1$, the variance of the potential is unbounded, and for $n < -1$, the variance of the initial field is also infinite. The first serious statistical results for the solution of Eq. (5.1) had been obtained in the case $n = 0$, when the initial potential represents Brownian motion, only 30 years [22] after the equation itself appeared in press [17]. The exact statistical description of this special case has been produced relatively recently [3].

At a purely power-law initial spectrum, the initial potential represents a Brownian or fractal Braunian realization which makes it possible to rescale the global solution of the Burgers equation [50]

$$\psi_0(\lambda x) = \lambda^{h+1}\psi_0(x); \quad h = -\frac{1}{2}(n+1),$$

$$\psi_0(x) \sim |x|^{h+1} = |x|^{(1-n)/2},$$

$$v(x,t) = t^{h/(1-h)} v\left(xt^{-h/(1-h)}, 1\right).$$

Accordingly, the turbulence turns out to be self-similar from the very beginning of evolution, the spectrum evolution is described by the expression (5.68), and the integral scale $L(t)$ grows as

$$L(t) = (\alpha t)^{2/(3+n)}. \tag{5.86}$$

The spectrum of the turbulence is conserved at low k, and the dimensionless spectrum (5.68) can be represented in the following form:

$$\tilde{E}(\tilde{k}) = \begin{cases} \gamma_n \tilde{k}^{-2}, & \tilde{k} \gg 1, \\ \tilde{k}^n, & \tilde{k} \ll 1, \end{cases} \qquad \tilde{k} \equiv kL(t). \tag{5.87}$$

For the turbulence energy (when it exists, $-1 < n < 1$), we have, respectively

$$E(t) = a_n L^2(t)/t^2 = a_n \alpha^{\frac{4}{3+n}} t^{-\frac{2(n+1)}{3+n}}. \tag{5.88}$$

Here and above, γ_n and a_n are dimensionless constants, which can, in principle, be derived theoretically or computed in a numerical experiment [13].

5.3.6 *Statistically homogeneous velocity and inhomogeneous potential* $(-1 < n < 1)$

For an initial spectrum with $-1 < n < 1$, the potential is divergent in the infrared part of the spectrum, and because of this it is already impossible to define an initial spatial length scale on the basis of Eq. (5.71). Here we define the nonlinear time and the initial spatial scale as

$$t'_{\rm nl} = L'_0/\sigma_v = 1/\sigma_q, \quad L'_0 \equiv \sigma_v/\sigma_q. \tag{5.89}$$

It is easy to see that $t'_{\rm nl}$ coincides with a characteristic time of formation of the first discontinuity (shock) t_s. By using the latter expressions, let us rewrite the laws of growth of the external scale $L(t)$ and decay of the energy $E(t)$ in the following form:

$$L(t) \simeq L'_0(t/t'_{\rm nl})^{2/(3+n)}, \quad E(t) \simeq E_0(t/t'_{\rm nl})^{-2(n+1)/(3+n)}. \tag{5.90}$$

Self-similar behavior of the spectrum may be realized in a certain region of the (k,t)-plane, even if the initial spectrum is cut off in the infrared k_i or ultraviolet k_u parts of the spectrum. From the asymptotic solution of the Burgers equation (5.59), it follows that the statistical properties of the turbulence are determined by the behavior of the structure function of the initial potential, In a general case, for the structure function of the initial potential (5.64) we have

$$D_{0\psi}(x) = g(x)\beta^2\alpha^2|x|^{1-n}, \quad \beta^2 = \alpha^2\frac{2\pi}{\Gamma(2-n)\sin\frac{\pi(n-1)}{2}}. \tag{5.91}$$

If the initial spectrum has the spatial cutoff frequencies k_i and k_u, the function $g(x) \simeq 1$ in a certain spatial interval $L_{\rm u} < x < L_{\rm i}$, where $L_{\rm u} \sim L_{\rm u} = 1/k_u$ and $L_{\rm i} = 1/k_i$, and at $x > L_{\rm i}$ tends to a constant. Note that precisely such conditions are always realized in numerical modeling.

But if the integral scale of the turbulence $L(t)$ is situated within the interval $L_{\rm i} \gg L(t) \gg L_{\rm u}$, then the self-similar law of decay of the integral scale $L(t)$ and energy $E(t)$ of the turbulence, where $t_{\rm u} \ll t \ll t_{\rm i}$ with $t_{\rm u}$, $t_{\rm i}$ being determined from the conditions $L(t_{\rm i}) = L_{\rm i}$, $L(t_{\rm u}) = L_{\rm u}$, is still valid. The energy spectrum proves to be self-similar at $k > k_i$. For the asymptotic behavior of the spectrum at long time, two scenarios are possible. If the initial signal is periodic, and the period is determined precisely by the infrared cutoff frequency $L_{\rm box} = L_{\rm i} = 2\pi/k_i$, then, at very large times, there appears one triangular wave per period, and the energy decays as $E(t) = L_{\rm i}^2/12t^2$. But if the initial spectrum is continuous, then generation of low-frequency components $E(k,t) \sim A(t)k^2$ takes place in the region $k < k_i$, and the final behavior of the turbulence will be the same as in the case $n > 1$ (see Sect. 5.3.2).

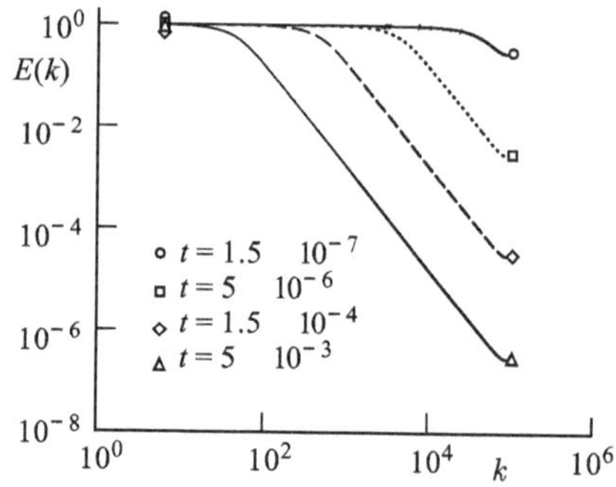

Fig. 5.11 Evolution of the spectrum $E(k,t)$ with $E_0(k) \sim k^n$, $n = 0$ at small wavenumbers k.

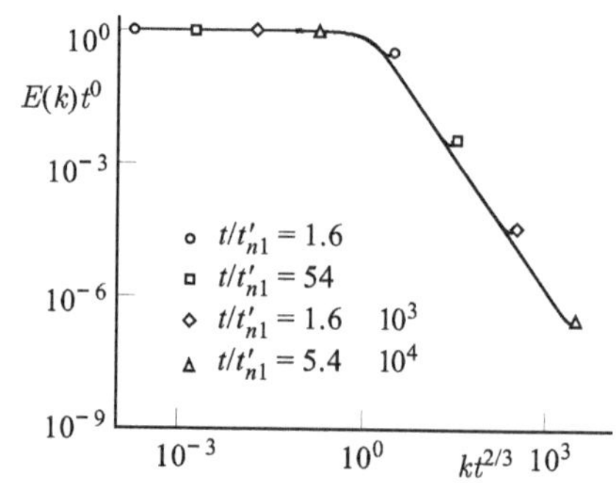

Fig. 5.12 Evolution of the normalized energy spectrum $E(k,t)t^0$ as a function of the normalized wavenumber $kt^{2/3}$ for $E_0(k) \sim k^n$, $n = 0$ at small wavenumbers k.

Fig. 5.11 shows evolution of the energy spectrum $E(k,t)$ for the moments of time $t/t'_{\rm nl} = 1.6\, t/t'_{\rm nl} = 5.4 \cdot 10^5$, when the initial spectrum represents the classical white noise ($n = 0$). Fig. 5.12 shows evolution of the normalized spectrum $E(k,t)t^{\,0}$ as a function of the normalized wavenumber $kt^{\,2/3}$. For the dimensionless constant of the dimensionless spectrum (5.87), we have $\gamma_n = 1.43$.

Thus the asymptotic behavior of the turbulence with a power-law initial spectrum cut off at high frequencies is also self-similar, while it does not depend on the spatial scale of the initial spectrum l_0. Moreover, at long time, even the behavior of separate realizations of a random field weakly depends on small-scale fluctuations and is determined by large-scale components of the initial excitation [43].

At finite viscosity ($\mu > 0$), the Reynolds number

$$\mathrm{R}(t) = \frac{V_c(t)L_c(t)}{\mu} \sim t^{\frac{1-n}{n+3}}$$

grows with time. Here $V_c(t)$, $L_c(t)$ are the amplitude and scale of the turbulence. The latter is connected with the fact that the characteristic scale of the turbulence grows faster than the shock-front broadening due to viscosity.

5.3.7 *Statistically inhomogeneous velocity and inhomogeneous potential* $(-3 < n < -1)$

The initial self-similar spectrum with $-3 < n < -1$ is characterized in the infrared part by divergence of both potential and velocity, and also by divergence of the velocity gradient in the ultraviolet part of the spectrum. If an ultraviolet cutoff frequency is introduced, it is possible to define the nonlinear time via the velocity gradient $t'_{\rm nl} = 1/\sigma_q$ (5.89). Evidently, it is equal to the characteristic time t_s of formation of the first discontinuity (shock). Because of the divergence of energy in the infrared region, energy dissipation at shocks never leads a finite value of energy. Nevertheless, it is possible to introduce an integral length scale of the turbulence $L(t)$, which signifies a region where the power law of the initial spectrum $E(k,t) \sim |k|^n$ is transformed into the universal power law $E(k,t) \sim k^{-2}$. The same length scale determines characteristic changes of other statistical properties of the turbulence, such are the shock-amplitude distribution, distances between them, etc. From the spectral form of the "permanence of large eddies" principle, we, as before, have that the integral scale grows according to the law (5.86). From the expression (5.69), it is seen that the amplitude of the high-frequency part of the spectrum decreases at $n > -2$ and grows with time at $-3 < n < -2$.

Let us first consider a special case when $n = -2$ and the integral scale grows as $L(t) \sim (\alpha t)^2$. From Eq. (5.68), it is seen that, in this case, the spectrum does change with time. Fig. 5.13 shows evolution of the spectrum $E(k,t)$ for different moments of time, and Fig. 5.14 shows realizations of a random field at two different moments of time. It is clearly seen that even at $t/t'_{\rm nl} \gg 1$, the spectrum does not change with time. Nevertheless, statistical properties of the turbulence, such as the shock-amplitude distribution, change with time and are determined precisely by this integral scale.

Fig. 5.15 shows evolution of the spectrum $E(k,t)$ for the case when the initial spectrum $E(k,t) \sim |k|^n$ with $n = -2.5$. Generation of the universal power-law tail k^{-2} with growing amplitude is clearly seen. It is also seen that the boundary between the power laws $k^{-2.5}$ and k^{-2} moves into the region of small wavenumbers inversely proportionally to the integral scale.

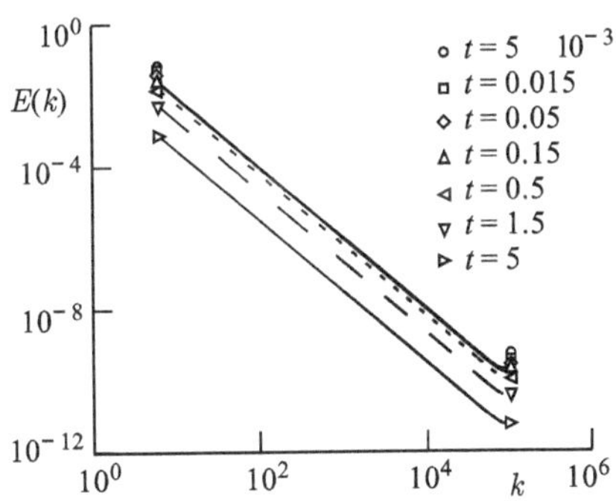

Fig. 5.13 Evolution of the energy spectrum for the initial spectrum proportional to $|k|^n$ $(n = -2)$.

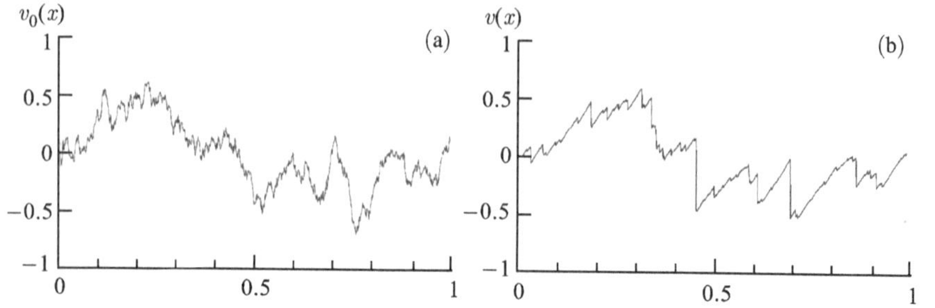

Fig. 5.14 Realizations of the velocity field at two different moments of time for the initial energy spectrum proportional to $|k|^n$ ($n = -2$).

Fig. 5.15 Evolution of the energy spectrum with the initial spectrum proportional to $|k|^n$ ($n = -2.5$) at small wavenumbers k.

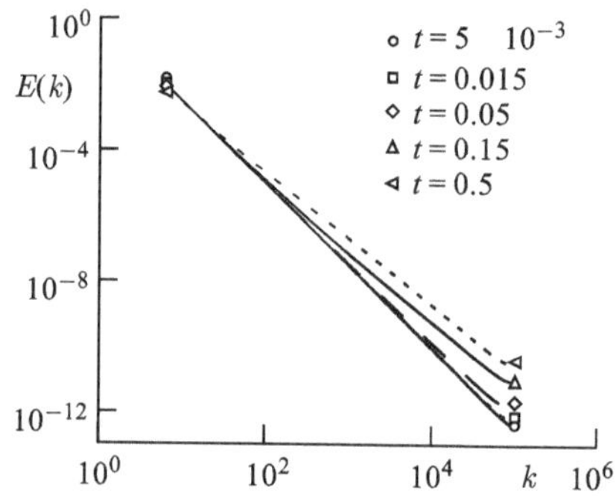

5.3.8 Evolution of intense acoustic noise

Let us discuss the main effects inherent in evolution of intense acoustic noise waves. Recall once more that, in a quadratic medium, interaction of three waves is effective if the conditions of synchronism $\omega_1 + \omega_2 = \omega_3$, $k_1 + k_2 = k_3$ are satisfied. Evidently, in acoustics, the process of finding such waves is extremely simple — from the dispersion equation for sound waves $\omega = ck$, it follows that the conditions of synchronism are satisfied for any three unidirectional interacting waves. As a result, for a harmonic input excitation, there is an avalanche-like growth of the number of higher harmonics $\omega_n = n\omega_1$. Whereas at the initial stage, the amplitude of the n-th harmonic $A_n \sim A_1^{n-1} z^{n-1}$, where A_1 is the amplitude of the initial harmonic signal, and z is the distance from the source of radiation.

Peculiarities of behavior of a randomly modulated quasi-harmonic signal at this stage can be easily explained by means of the well-known statistical inequality $\langle A^2 \rangle > \langle A \rangle^2$. From it follows that nonlinearity emphasizes large overshoots, due to which nonlinear processes for a noise signal happen more effectively than for a harmonic wave. So at Gaussian statistics of quasi-harmonic noise, the intensity of the n-th harmonic is $n!$ times greater than the intensity of a monochromatic signal of the same initial intensity. This fact has been observed in experiments [46] on propagation of narrow-band acoustic noise with intensity of 200 Pa in an air-filled 75-meter tube.

Avalanche-like growth of the number of higher harmonics leads to formation of shocks, at which the energy dissipates. In the case of a monochromatic excitation, the wave is transformed into a sequence of sawtooth pulses with the amplitude $A(z) \sim A_1/(1+\beta z A_1 \omega_1)$. At a given distance from the input z, the limiting amplitude $A_*(z) \sim 1/\beta z \omega_1$ is determined by the frequency ω_1 and the nonlinearity parameter β. Thus, for an amplitude-modulated wave $A_1 = A_1(t)$, suppression of large overshoots takes place, and, therefore, the probability distribution of the noise is narrowing with time, vanishes outside the interval $[-A_*, A_*]$ and tends to a uniform distribution of width $2A_*(z)$ independent of the initial amplitude and proportional to the wave period. Such a universal form of the distribution is also characteristic of an arbitrary quasi-periodic wave.

In an analysis of statistical wave problems, as a rule, first of all, evolution of the spectrum of the wave $E_0(\omega) \to E_0(\omega, z)$ is of interest. At a finite width of the initial spectrum $\Delta\omega_1$, the width of the spectrum of the n-th harmonic grows with the harmonic's number. Whereas, depending on the form of the initial phase modulation, $\Delta\omega_n \simeq n\Delta\omega_1$ or $\Delta\omega_n \simeq n^{1/2}\Delta\omega_1$. At the stage with shocks, the phase modulation of the initial wave gives rise to fluctuations in shock positions and, as a consequence, to a random modulation of the amplitude of the sawtooth wave. At $\Delta\omega_n \simeq \omega_1$, the spectra of neighboring harmonics overlap and form a continuous spectrum $\sim \omega^{-2}$. Fig. 5.16 shows evolution of the spectrum of intense quasi-monochromatic noise in an air-filled tube [40] with the central frequency of 1.5 kHz, width of the spectrum of 316 Hz and intensity of 150 dB. Here curve 1 is the spectrum near the source of radiation $z = 0.35$ m, curve 2 is the same at the distance of 10.35 m (shown with the amplification of 20 dB), and dots show the amplitudes of a single-tone signal of the same intensity in the cross-section at 10.35 m.

A principal distinction of the behavior of a quasi-harmonic signal from evolution of a single-tone signal consists in generation of difference combinational frequencies. Although effectiveness of low-frequency component generation is small, they decay slower than the high-frequency components, and, in the end, they determine the asymptotic behavior of the field at long time. The amplitude of a low-frequency component is of the order of magnitude of $v_n \simeq (\Delta\omega_1/\omega_1)A_1$. At the sawtooth stage, its behavior is determined by the motion of sawtooth fronts leading to an additional broadening of the spectral lines of high-frequency harmonics. Because of a more intensive attenuation of the high-frequency harmonics, the entire energy of the wave is, in the end, concentrated in the low-frequency part of the spectrum, and its attenuation starts, when shocks of the sawtooth wave will coalesce. By the order of magnitude, this happens at distances $z \sim z_n(\omega_1/\Delta\omega_1)^2 A_1$, because the shock velocities are strongly correlated.

Both generation of high-frequency components caused by shock formation and appearance of a low-frequency part of the spectrum are inherent in evolution of a broadband noise. Shocks, therewith, are weakly correlated, and gradual coalescence of small shocks leads to a growth of the characteristic scale of the noise and to a shift of the spectrum towards low frequencies. Due to appearance of shocks, information of the fine structure of the initial signal is lost, and, because of multiple coalescence of shocks, the spectrum acquires a universal form practically indepen-

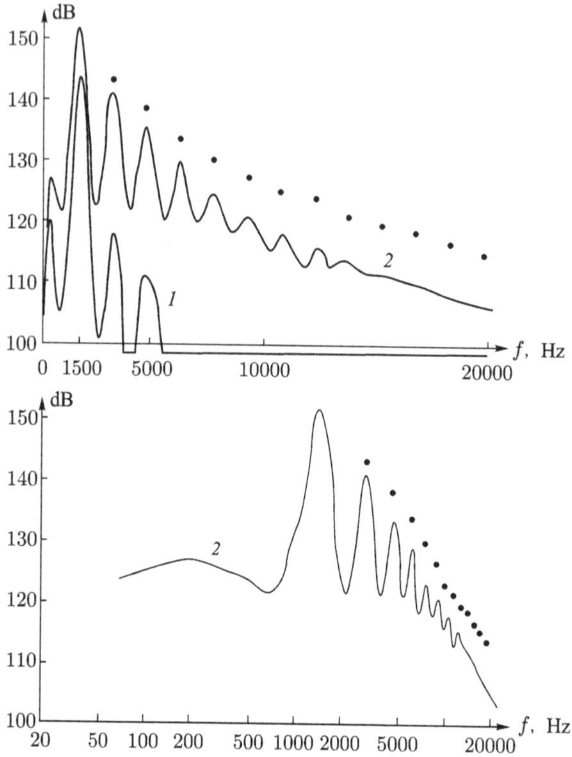

Fig. 5.16 Evolution of the spectrum of a quasi-monochrmatic noise.

dent of the shape of the initial spectrum. These nonlinear phenomena explain the effect of an anomalously strong high-frequency "wing", formed in the atmosphere during propagation of noise from powerful aircraft and rocket engines.

In the case of interaction between noise and regular signals, formation of shocks also radically changes the spectral composition of a wave. In particular, noise components appear in a very broad frequency interval [51]. So, during interaction of a high-frequency harmonic wave and a low-frequency noise, it is possible to assume that the noise gives only quasi-statical phase shift of the high-frequency signal proportional to the low-frequency signal, the harmonic's frequency and the distance to the source. In other words, the noise-component spectrum of the n-th harmonic reproduces the spectrum of the low-frequency noise.

At the stage with shocks, when the amplitudes of harmonics are inversely proportional to $zn\omega_1$, the amplitude of the spectrum of the noise component of the n-th harmonic does not depend on the distance z and is equal to the amplitude of the low-frequency noise for a large number of harmonics. It is natural to call this phenomenon the effect of anomalous noise amplification.

Let us once again emphasize that, for acoustic waves, it is possible to neglect dispersion in a wide range of frequencies. In media without dispersion, a large number

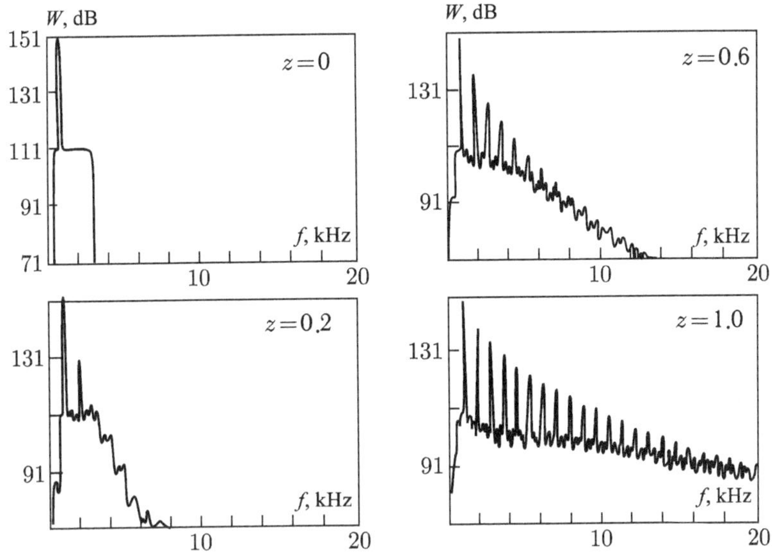

Fig. 5.17 Interaction of a noise and a single-tone signal.

of harmonics effectively interact, as it is seen in Fig. 5.17, whereas this interaction leads to a strong coherence of their phases. Therefore here it is not possible to use the method of slowly varying amplitudes, which is effective in nonlinear optics, where, because of a strong dispersion, it is enough to limit oneself by taking a small number of linear modes into account. The strong coherence of spectral components makes it also impossible to apply the approximation of chaotic phases, which is used in the theory of weak turbulence, where it is possible to reduce a description of interaction of a large number of linear modes to kinetic equations for the mode intensity.

References

1. M. Avellaneda, W. E, Statistical properties of shocks in Burgers turbulence, Comm. Math. Phys. **172**, 13–38 (1995)
2. J. Bec, K. Khanin, Burgers turbulence, Physics Reports. **447**, 1–66 (2007)
3. L. Frachebourg, P.A. Martin, Exact statistical properties of the Burgers equation, J. Fluid Mech. **417**, 323–349 (2000)
4. S.N. Gurbatov, Universality classes for self-similarity of noiseless multidimensional Burgers turbulence and interface growth, Phys. Rev. E. **61**, 2595–2604 (2000)
5. S.N. Gurbatov, I.Y. Demin, A.I. Saichev, Establishment of self-similar regimes of nonlinear random waves in dissipative media, Sov. Phys. JETP **60**, 284–292 (1984)
6. S.N. Gurbatov, I.Y. Demin, A.I. Saichev, On properties of the Burgers turbulence at the stage of shock-front interaction, Izv. Vyssh. Uchebn. Zaved. Radiofiz. [Radiophys. Quantum Electron.] **27**, 1079–1081 (1984). In Russian

7. S.N. Gurbatov, A.I. Saichev, Asymptotic properties of one-dimensional acoustic turbulence, Sov. Phys. Dokl. **26**, 651–653 (1981)
8. S.N. Gurbatov, A.I. Saichev, Degeneracy of one-dimensional acoustic turbulence at large Reynolds numbers, Sov. Phys. JETP **80**, 589–595 (1981)
9. S.N. Gurbatov, A.I. Saichev, Probability distribution and spectra of potential hydrodynamic turbulence, Radiophys. Quantum Electron. **27**, 303–313 (1984)
10. S.N. Gurbatov, A.I. Saichev, One-dimensional turbulence in a viscous polytropic gas, Radiophys. Quantum Electron. **31**, 1043–1054 (1988)
11. S.N. Gurbatov, S. Simdyankin, E. Aurell, U. Frisch, G. Toth, On the decay of Burgers turbulence, J. Fluid Mech. **344**, 349–374 (1997)
12. G.M. Molchan, Burgers equation with self-similar Gaussian initial data: tail probabilities, J. Stat. Phys. **88**, 1139–1150 (1997)
13. A. Noullez, S.N. Gurbatov, E. Aurell, S.I. Simdyankin, The global picture of self-similar and not self-similar decay in Burgers turbulence, Phys. Rev E. **71**, 056305:1-14 (2005)
14. A.I. Saichev, W.A. Woyczynski, Density fields in Burgers and KdV-Burgers turbulence, SIAM J. Appl. Math. **56**, 1008–1038 (1996)
15. A.I. Saichev, W.A. Woyczynski, in *The IMA Volumes in Mathematics and its Applications*, vol. 77 (Springer, New York, 1996), pp. 167–192
16. A.I. Saichev, W.A. Woyczynski, Evolution of Burgers' turbulence in the presence of external forces, J. Fluid Mech. **331**, 313–343 (1997)
17. J.M. Burgers, Mathematical examples illustrating relations occurring in the theory of turbulent fluid motion, Kon. Ned. Akad. Wet. Verh. **17**, 1–53 (1939)
18. S.N. Gurbatov, A.N. Malakhov, A.I. Saichev, *Nonlinear Random Waves and Turbulence in Nondispersive Media: Waves, Rays and Particles.* (Manchester University Press, 1991)
19. O.V. Rudenko, S.I. Soluyan, *Theoretical Foundations of Nonlinear Acoustics* (Plenum, New York, 1977)
20. M.B. Vinogradova, O.V. Rudenko, A.P. Sukhorukov, *Theory of Waves* (Nauka, Moscow, 1979). In Russian
21. W.A. Woyczynski, *Burgers-KPZ Turbulence. Gottingen Lectures* (Springer, Berlin, 1998)
22. J.M. Burgers, *The Nonlinear Diffusion Equation* (D. Reidel, Dordrecht, 1974)
23. U. Frisch, *Turbulence: the Legacy of A.N. Kolmogorov* (Cambridge University Press, 1995)
24. A.N. Malakhov, A.I. Saichev, Kinetic equations in the theory of random waves, Radiophys. Quantum Electron. **17**, 526–534 (1974)
25. A.I. Saichev, Probabilistic analysis of plane random waves of gas dynamics, Izv. AN SSSR: Mekh. Zhidk. Gaza (5), 99–104 (1982). In Russian
26. T. Kármán, L. von Howarth, On the statistical theory of isotropic turbulence, Proc. R. Soc. Lond. **164**, 192–215 (1938)
27. C.C. Lin, W.H. Reid, in *Handbuch der Physik, Fluid Dynamics*, vol. 2, ed. by S. Flügge, C. Truesdell (Springer, Berlin, 1963), pp. 438–523
28. A.N. Kolmogorov, To degenerence of isotropic turbulence in incompressible viscous liquid, Dokl. Akad. Nauk SSSR [Sov. Phys. Dokl.] **31**, 538–541 (1941). In Russian
29. L.G. Loitsanskii, in *Trudy Tsentral'nogo Aerogidrodinamicheskogo Instituta* (1939), pp. 3–23. In Russian
30. I. Proudman, W.H. Reid, On the decay of a normally distributed and homogeneous turbulent velocity field, Phil. Trans. R. Soc. Lond. A **247**, 163–189 (1954)
31. G.K. Batchelor, I. Proudman, The large-scale structure of homogeneous turbulence, Philos. Trans. Roy. Soc. **248**, 69–405 (1956)
32. A.S. Monin, A.M. Yaglom, *Statistical Fluid Mechanics*, vol. 2 (MIT Press, Cambridge, Mass, 1975)
33. G.L. Eyink, D.J. Thomson, Free decay of turbulence and breakdown of self-similarity, Phys. Fluids **12**, 477–479 (2000)
34. S.N. Gurbatov, A.I. Saichev, I.G. Yakushkin, Nonlinear waves and one-dimensional turbulence in nondispersive media, Sov. Phys. Usp. **26**, 857–864 (1983)
35. A.N. Malakhov, A.I. Saichev, Probabilistic description of random fields satisfying simplest equations of the hydrodynamic type, Sov. Phys. JETP **40**, 467–477 (1974)

36. O.V. Rudenko, A.P. Chirkin, Theory of nonlinear interaction between monochromatic and noise waves in weakly dispersive media, Sov. Phys. JETP **67**, 945 (1974)
37. A.I. Saichev, Spectra of certain random waves propagating in nonlinear media, Radiophys. Quantum Electron. **17**, 781–787 (1974)
38. S.N. Gurbatov, A.I. Saichev, Inertial nonlinearity and chaotic motion of particle fluxes, Chaos **3**, 333–358 (1993)
39. E. Aurell, S.N. Gurbatov, I.I. Wertgeim, Self-preservation of large-scale structures in Burgers turbulence, Phys. Lett. A **182**, 109–113 (1993)
40. L. Björnö, S.N. Gurbatov, Evolution of universal high-frequency asymptotic forms of the spectrum in the propagation of high-intensity acoustic noise, Sov. Phys. Acoust. **31**, 179–182 (1985)
41. J.D. Fournier, U. Frisch, L'équation de Burgers déterministe et statistique, J. Méc. Théor. Appl. (Paris) **2**, 699–750 (1983)
42. S.N. Gurbatov, A.N. Malakhov, Statistical characteristics of random quasi monochromatic waves in nonlinear media, Sov. Phys. Acoust. **23**, 325–329 (1977)
43. S.N. Gurbatov, G.V. Pasmanik, Self-preservation of large-scale structures in a nonlinear viscous medium described by the Burgers equation, J. Exp. Theoret. Phys. **88**, 309–319 (1999)
44. S.N. Gurbatov, O.V. Rudenko (eds.), *Acoustics in Problems* (Fizmatlit, Moscow, 2009). In Russian
45. A. Noullez, M. Vergassola, A fast algorithm for discrete Legendre transforms, J. Sci. Comp. **9**, 259–281 (1994)
46. D.F. Pernet, R.C. Payne, Nonlinear propagation of signals in air, J. Sound and Vib. **17**, 383–387 (1971)
47. O.V. Rudenko, Interactions of intense noise waves, Sov. Phys. Usp. **29**, 620–641 (1986)
48. Z.S. She, E. Aurell, U. Frisch, The inviscid Burgers equation with initial data of Brownian type, Commun. Math. Phys. **148**, 623–641 (1992)
49. Y. Sinai, Statistics of shocks in solutions of inviscid Burgers equation, Commun. Math. Phys. **148**, 601–622 (1992)
50. M. Vergassola, B. Dubrulle, U. Frisch, A. Noullez, Burgers' equation, Devil's staircases and the mass distribution for large-scale structures, Astron. Astrophys. **289**, 325–356 (1994)
51. D.F. Webster, D.T. Blackstock, Collinear interaction of noise with a finite-amplitude tone, J. Acoust. Soc. America. **63**, 687–691 (1978)
52. S. Kida, Asymptotic properties of Burgers turbulence, J. Fluid Mech. **93**, 337–377 (1979)
53. M.R. Leadbetter, G. Lindgren, H. Rootzen, *Extremes and Related Properties of Random Sequences and Processes* (Springer, Berlin, 1983)
54. S.A. Molchanov, D. Surgailis, W.A. Woyczynski, Hyperbolic asymptotics in Burgers' turbulence and extremal processes, Comm. Math. Phys. **168**, 209–226 (1995)

Chapter 6
Multidimensional Nonlinear Equations

6.1 Nonlinear equations of the first order

Until now, we have analyzed the properties of one-dimensional fields as a function of time t and only one spatial coordinate. Such fields usually appear in an idealized, simplified description of real processes happening in the three-dimensional space. On the other hand, many ideas and methods of solving partial differential nonlinear equations for one-dimensional fields are in a natural way carried over to the richer with geometric and mechanical developments multidimensional case. Therefore, for completeness, let us discuss multidimensional equations related to those one-dimensional partial differential nonlinear equations of the first order which have been studied in the previous chapter. Complementary information on dynamics and statistics of three-dimensional fields of the hydrodynamic type can be found in [1–13].

6.1.1 *Main equations of three-dimensional flows*

First of all, this is the equation of the vector velocity field $\mathbf{v}(\mathbf{x},t)$ of a three-dimensional flow of uniformly moving particles:

$$\frac{\partial \mathbf{v}}{\partial t} + (\mathbf{v}\nabla)\mathbf{v} = 0, \quad \mathbf{v}(\mathbf{x},t=0) = \mathbf{v}_0(\mathbf{x}). \tag{6.1}$$

Here the *del operator* is represented by the nabla symbol:

$$\nabla = \mathbf{j}_1 \frac{\partial}{\partial x_1} + \mathbf{j}_2 \frac{\partial}{\partial x_2} + \mathbf{j}_3 \frac{\partial}{\partial x_3},$$

and is equal to the sum of partial derivatives with respect to the Cartesian coordinates $\{x_1, x_2, x_3\}$ multiplied by their basis vectors $\{\mathbf{j}_1, \mathbf{j}_2, \mathbf{j}_3\}$.

If the velocity field is a potential one, i.e. there is such a scalar function $s(\mathbf{x},t)$ that

$$\mathbf{v}(\mathbf{x},t) = \nabla s(\mathbf{x},t), \tag{6.2}$$

then it satisfies the following equation

$$\frac{\partial s}{\partial t} + \frac{1}{2}(\nabla s)^2 = 0, \quad s(\mathbf{x},t=0) = s_0(\mathbf{x}). \tag{6.3}$$

In what follows, we will always assume that the velocity is a potential field, and Eq. (6.2) holds. In this case

$$(\nabla s)^2 = v^2 = (\mathbf{v} \cdot \nabla) s,$$

and the last equation may be rewritten in a form more convenient for analysis:

$$\frac{\partial s}{\partial t} + (\mathbf{v}\nabla) s = \frac{v^2}{2}. \tag{6.4}$$

A geometric illustration of the behavior of three-dimensional fields requires to plot them in a four-dimensional space. 3D plots are, however, much more visual. Therefore we will, as a rule, illustrate many results from the nonlinear wave theory of the hydrodynamic type by using two dimensional fields as examples. Sometimes such fields are of interest by themselves. So the function $s(\mathbf{x},t)$ in the two-dimensional space $\mathbf{x} = \{x_1, x_2\}$ has another familiar interpretation — it describes, in the small angle approximation, flame-surface growth or the wave front of an optic wave propagating along the third spatial coordinate $z = x_3$.

Regrouping of moving particles leads to a change of the density $\rho(\mathbf{x},t)$ of the particles in space and time. The density obeys the universal continuity equation:

$$\frac{\partial \rho}{\partial t} + (\nabla \cdot \rho \mathbf{v}) = 0, \quad \rho(\mathbf{x},t=0) = \rho_0(\mathbf{x}). \tag{6.5}$$

Let us introduce two more equations useful for the subsequent analysis. Recall, that apart from the Eulerian coordinates $\mathbf{x} = \{x_1, x_2, x_3\}$, it is possible to introduce in space the Lagrangian coordinate system $\mathbf{y} = \{y_1, y_2, y_3\}$ "frozen" into the particle flow under study. If some quantity Q keeps it value in a vicinity of an arbitrary particle of the flow, its Lagrangian field $Q = Q(\mathbf{y})$ does not depend on time. The corresponding Eulerian field $q(\mathbf{x},t)$ in its turn satisfies the following partial differential equation:

$$\frac{\partial q}{\partial t} + (\mathbf{v}\nabla) q = 0, \quad q(\mathbf{x},t=0) = q_0(\mathbf{x}). \tag{6.6}$$

This holds not only for scalar fields, but also for vector ones. Thus the vector transformation $\mathbf{y} = \mathbf{y}(\mathbf{x},t)$ of Eulerian coordinates into Lagrangian ones satisfies the same equation:

$$\frac{\partial \mathbf{y}}{\partial t} + (\mathbf{v}\nabla) \mathbf{y} = 0, \quad \mathbf{y}(\mathbf{x},t=0) = \mathbf{x}. \tag{6.7}$$

6.1.2 Lagrangian and Eulerian description of a three-dimentional flow

In Lagrangian coordinates, the nonlinear partial differential equations listed above are reduced to ordinary differential equations for the Eulerian coordinates

$$\frac{d\mathbf{X}}{dt} = \mathbf{V}, \quad \mathbf{X}(\mathbf{y}, t=0) = \mathbf{y}, \tag{6.8}$$

Lagrangian velocity field $\mathbf{V}(\mathbf{y}, t)$

$$\frac{d\mathbf{V}}{dt} = 0, \quad \mathbf{V}(\mathbf{y}, t=0) = \mathbf{v}_0(\mathbf{y}), \tag{6.9}$$

and its potential $S(\mathbf{y}, t)$

$$\frac{dS}{dt} = \frac{1}{2}V^2, \quad S(\mathbf{y}, t=0) = s_0(\mathbf{y}). \tag{6.10}$$

Solution of the first two equations gives at our disposal the Lagrangian-to-Eulerian coordinate transformation

$$\mathbf{x} = \mathbf{X}(\mathbf{y}, t) = \mathbf{y} + \mathbf{v}_0(\mathbf{y})t, \tag{6.11}$$

and solution of the second and third equations gives the Lagrangian fields of velocity and its potential

$$\mathbf{V}(\mathbf{y}, t) = \mathbf{v}_0(\mathbf{y}), \quad S(\mathbf{y}, t) = s_0(\mathbf{y}) + \frac{1}{2}v_0^2(\mathbf{y})t. \tag{6.12}$$

In order to determine the corresponding Eulerian fields, it is necessary to find the inverse of (6.11) Eulerian-to-Lagrangian coordinate transformation:

$$\mathbf{y} = \mathbf{y}(\mathbf{x}, t). \tag{6.13}$$

If it is known, the fields of the velocity and its potential are determined by the following equations:

$$\mathbf{v}(\mathbf{x}, t) = v_0(\mathbf{y}(\mathbf{x}, t)), \quad s(\mathbf{x}, t) = s_0(\mathbf{y}(\mathbf{x}, t)) + \frac{1}{2}v_0^2(\mathbf{y}(\mathbf{x}, t))t. \tag{6.14}$$

Another, more convenient form to express these fields explicitly via the transformation (6.13) of Eulerian coordinates into Lagrangian ones is

$$\mathbf{v}(\mathbf{x}, t) = \frac{\mathbf{x} - \mathbf{y}(\mathbf{x}, t)}{t}, \tag{6.15}$$

$$s(\mathbf{x}, t) = s_0(\mathbf{y}(\mathbf{x}, t)) + \frac{(\mathbf{y}(\mathbf{x}, t) - \mathbf{x})^2}{2t}. \tag{6.16}$$

6.1.3 Jacobian matrix for the transformation from Lagrangian to Eulerian coordinates

The Jacobian

$$J(\mathbf{y},t)=\left|\frac{\partial \mathbf{X}(\mathbf{y},t)}{\partial \mathbf{y}}\right| \tag{6.17}$$

of the Lagrangian-to-Eulerian coordinate transformation plays an important role for analysis of three-dimensional flow behavior. By substituting here the expression (6.11) while taking the potentiality of the velocity field into account, let us rewrite it in the form

$$J(\mathbf{y},t)=\left|\delta_{ij}+s_{ij}t\right|, \tag{6.18}$$

where δ_{ij} is the Kroneker symbol, and s_{ij} are the components of a symmetric tensor $\hat{s}$ composed of partial derivatives of the initial potential of the velocity field

$$\hat{s}=\left\|s_{ij}\right\|, \quad s_{ij}(\mathbf{y})=\frac{\partial^2 s_0(\mathbf{y})}{\partial y_i \partial y_j}. \tag{6.19}$$

It is well known that by a coordinate-system rotation, its own for each point $\mathbf{y}=\{y_1,y_2,y_3\}$, a symmetric tensor can be reduced to a diagonal form:

$$\hat{s}=\left\|\lambda_i\delta_{ij}\right\|,$$

where $\{\lambda_1,\lambda_2,\lambda_3\}$ are the eigenvalues of the tensor $\hat{s}$. In this local coordinate system, the Jacobian (6.18) happens to be equal to

$$J=\prod_{i=1}^{3}(1+\lambda_i t). \tag{6.20}$$

Everywhere in what follows, we assume that the eigenvalues are numbered in the ascending order:

$$\lambda_1(\mathbf{y})\leqslant\lambda_2(\mathbf{y})\leqslant\lambda_3(\mathbf{y}).$$

Recall, that the Jacobian of the Lagrangian-to-Eulerian coordinate transformation $J(\mathbf{y},t)$ has an illustrative geometric meaning. It is equal to the following ratio of infinitesimal (elementary) volumes:

$$J(\mathbf{y},t)=\frac{\delta \mathrm{v}}{\delta \mathrm{v}_0},$$

where $\delta \mathrm{v}_0$ is the volume of the region $\delta\mathbb{V}_0$ occupied by a certain portion of particles at the initial moment of time $t=0$, and $\delta \mathrm{v}$ is the volume of the region $\delta\mathbb{V}$ occupied by the same particles at the current moment of time. The sign of $\delta \mathrm{v}$ is positive, if the corresponding Lagrangian local basis may be superposed with the Eulerian one by means of rotations and deformations, and negative, if these attempts fail (i.e. if for success, apart from rotations, inversion of basis vectors is needed).

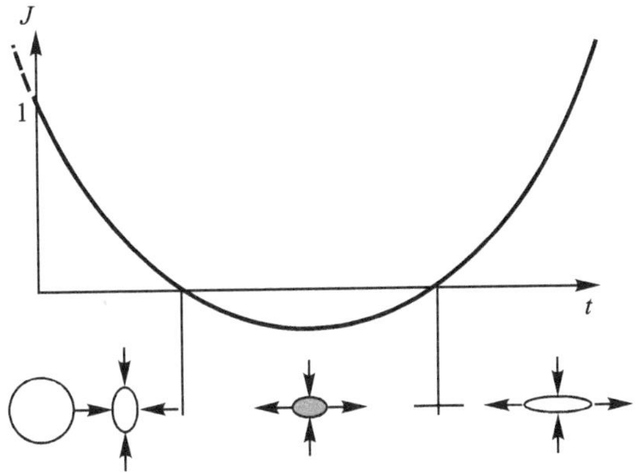

Fig. 6.1 Transformation of an elementary ellipse in two dimensions and in the "most rich" for two dimensions case $\lambda_1 < \lambda_2 < 0$. It is seen that in the beginning (in the interval $0 < t < -1/\lambda_1$) the ellipse is compressed in both directions, and then (in the interval $-1/\lambda_1 < t < -1/\lambda_2$) expands along the y_1-axis, but keeps being compressed along the y_2-axis. Finally, when $t > -1/\lambda_2$, it expands in all directions. Shaded ellipse is the one, whose volume should be considered negative.

A local Lagrangian basis corresponding to a diagonal tensor (6.19) also has a clear geometric meaning. Its axes point in the directions of compressions and expansions of an elementary region. In other words, if the initial region $\delta\mathbb{V}_0$ was a sphere, then the region $\delta\mathbb{V}$ would have the shape of an ellipsoid, whose principal axes coincided with the axes of the above mentioned local basis. A plot illustrating various stages of a two-dimensional sphere's $\delta\mathbb{V}$ transformation with time is shown in Fig. 6.1.

6.1.4 Density of a multidimensional flow

Compressions and expansions of a flow lead to changes of its density. It is known that the solution of the three-dimensional continuity equation, in the most general case, has the following form:

$$\rho(\mathbf{x},t) = \int_{-\infty}^{\infty} \rho_0(\mathbf{y})\delta\left(\mathbf{X}(\mathbf{y},t) - \mathbf{x}\right) d^3y, \tag{6.21}$$

where $\mathbf{x} = \mathbf{X}(\mathbf{y},t)$ is the Lagrangian-to-Eulerian coordinate transformation generated by the velocity field $\mathbf{v}(\mathbf{x},t)$.

In the case of transformation (6.11), which holds for a flow of uniformly moving particles, as in the one-dimensional case, single-flow and multi-flow regimes should be distinguished. Within the time interval $t < t_n$, where

$$t_n = -\min_{\mathbf{y}} \frac{1}{\lambda_1(\mathbf{y})}, \tag{6.22}$$

the single-flow regime takes place. In this regime the Jacobian (6.17), (6.20) is strictly positive, the transformation $\mathbf{x} = \mathbf{X}(\mathbf{y},t)$ realizes a one-to-one mapping of

$\mathbb{R}^3$ onto $\mathbb{R}^3$, and, while determining the right-hand side of Eq. (6.21), it is possible to use the standard formulas for evaluation of functionals of delta functions of a composite argument. This gives

$$\rho(\mathbf{x},t) = \frac{\rho_0(\mathbf{y}(\mathbf{x},t))}{J(\mathbf{y}(\mathbf{x},t),t)}. \tag{6.23}$$

At times $t > t_n$, in three dimensions, islands of multi-flow motion appear in space. Here the total density of a substance, which is equal to the total of the densities of all flows, continues to have a clear physical meaning:

$$\rho(\mathbf{x},t) = \sum_i^n \frac{\rho_0(\mathbf{y}_i(\mathbf{x},t))}{|J(\mathbf{y}_i(\mathbf{x},t),t)|}, \tag{6.24}$$

where summation is with respect to all n branches of the multivalued in a general case transformation $\mathbf{y} = \mathbf{y}(\mathbf{x},t)$.

A discussion of a generalized density field in two dimensions and in the case of a discontinuous transformation $\mathbf{y} = \mathbf{y}(\mathbf{x},t)$ will be given in the last section of this chapter.

6.1.5 Weak solution of the surface-growth equation

In many physical and other applications, multi-flow solutions are prohibited. Therefore at $t > t_n$, when motion of uniformly moving particles becomes a multi-flow one, and classical solutions of above mentioned multidimensional partial differential equations of the first order no longer exist, non-differentiable or discontinuous weak solutions are defined in their place. It is most instructive to do this with an example of an optic wave front or a bulk fire surface. For this reason, let us return to the problem of fire propagation.

Let us consider the forefront of a bulk flame propagating with unit velocity in the direction perpendicular to the front. By reasoning in a similar way as while deriving Eq. (1.48), it is not difficult to show that the front surface

$$z = h(\mathbf{x},t) \tag{6.25}$$

satisfies the following nonlinear partial differential equation:

$$\frac{\partial h}{\partial t} = \sqrt{1 + (\nabla h)^2}. \tag{6.26}$$

Here $\mathbf{x} = \{x_1, x_2\}$ is a two-dimensional vector in the horizontal plane, and $z = x_3$ is the vertical coordinate.

If the fire propagates predominantly upwards, along the z-axis, then the following inequality holds

$$(\nabla h)^2 \ll 1$$

and Eq. (6.26) may be transformed into a simpler approximate equation. In order to achieve this, the right-hand side of (6.26) is expanded into the Taylor series with respect to $(\nabla h)^2$ and only the first two terms of the expansion are retained:

$$\sqrt{1+(\nabla h)^2} \approx 1+\frac{1}{2}(\nabla h)^2.$$

The first, constant term is then discarded, since it describes the trivial surface growth with a constant velocity, and the latter term is retained. As a result, the approximates equation has a form

$$\frac{\partial h}{\partial t} = \frac{1}{2}(\nabla h)^2, \quad h(\mathbf{x}, t=0) = h_0(\mathbf{x}), \tag{6.27}$$

similar to Eq. (1.50).

Let us introduce another, closely linked to the geometry of a fire front, field:

$$\mathbf{u}(\mathbf{x},t) = -\nabla h(\mathbf{x},t). \tag{6.28}$$

This two-dimensional field has a transparent geometric meaning: its absolute value is equal to the tangent of the angle between the normal to the fire front and the z-axis. By applying the del operator term-by-term to (6.27), we arrive at the following equation for the vector field $\mathbf{u}(\mathbf{z},t)$:

$$\frac{\partial \mathbf{u}}{\partial t} + (\mathbf{u}\cdot\nabla)\mathbf{u} = 0 \tag{6.29}$$

— a two-dimensional analogue of Eq. (6.1) for the velocity field of uniformly moving particles.

As in the case of a flow of uniformly moving particles, the surface-growth equations (6.27), (6.29) are solved by the method of characteristics. Namely, a transformation is made from them to the following system of characteristic equations

$$\frac{d\mathbf{X}}{dt} = \mathbf{U}, \quad \frac{d\mathbf{U}}{dt} = 0, \quad \frac{dH}{dt} + \frac{1}{2}U^2 = 0. \tag{6.30}$$

Solutions of the latter have the following form:

$$\mathbf{X}(\mathbf{y},t) = \mathbf{y} - \nabla h_0(\mathbf{y})t, \quad \mathbf{U}(\mathbf{y},t) = -\nabla h_0(\mathbf{y}), \tag{6.31}$$

and also

$$H(\mathbf{y},t) = h_0(\mathbf{y}) - \frac{1}{2}(\nabla h_0(\mathbf{y}))^2 t. \tag{6.32}$$

As long as the vector function

$$\mathbf{x} = \mathbf{X}(\mathbf{y},t) = \mathbf{y} - \nabla h_0(\mathbf{y})t \tag{6.33}$$

and its inverse (6.13) realize an one-to-one mapping of $\mathbb{R}^2$ onto $\mathbb{R}^2$, the expressions (6.31), (6.32) allow one to reconstruct the sought-for fields

$$h(\mathbf{x},t) = h_0((\mathbf{y}(\mathbf{x},t)) - \frac{(\mathbf{y}(\mathbf{x},t) - \mathbf{x})^2}{2t} \tag{6.34}$$

and

$$\mathbf{u}(\mathbf{x},t) = \frac{\mathbf{x} - \mathbf{y}(\mathbf{x},t)}{2t} \tag{6.35}$$

at any point of the plane $\mathbf{x}$. But if the transformation $\mathbf{y} = \mathbf{y}(\mathbf{x},t)$ becomes multivalued, the real fire surface $h_w(\mathbf{x},t)$, which also is a weak solution of Eq. (6.27), is found by selecting from all branches of the multivalued field $h(\mathbf{x},t)$ the one which, in a given point x, has the maximum value.

It is most convenient to find the above mentioned weak solution of Eq. (6.27) on the basis of the *absolute maximum principle*, which is a natural modification of the absolute maximum method described earlier for the case considered here.

Let us introduce an auxiliary function

$$\mathscr{G}(\mathbf{y};\mathbf{x},t) = h_0(\mathbf{y}) - \frac{(\mathbf{y} - \mathbf{x})^2}{2t} \tag{6.36}$$

of the argument $\mathbf{y}$ and parameters $\mathbf{x}$, t.

It is known that the necessary condition of extremum of a smooth function $\mathscr{G}(\mathbf{y};\mathbf{x},t)$ of a vector argument $\mathbf{y}$ is the equality to zero of the gradient of this function:

$$\nabla\mathscr{G}(\mathbf{y};\mathbf{x},t) = 0.$$

A direct evaluation of the gradient gives

$$\nabla h_0(\mathbf{y}) = \frac{1}{2}(\mathbf{y} - \mathbf{x}).$$

By comparing this equation with (6.32)–(6.34), we are convinced that all extremum points $\mathbf{y}(\mathbf{x},t)$ turn the transformation (6.33) into identity, while the function $\mathscr{G}(\mathbf{y};\mathbf{x},t)$ at this points is equal to the values of the Eulerian field $h(\mathbf{x},t)$ (6.34) of the heights of the growing surface. Hence, by substituting the coordinates $\mathbf{y}_w(\mathbf{x},t)$ of the absolute maximum of the function (6.36) into (6.34) and (6.35), we will find the required weak solutions $h_w(\mathbf{x},t)$ and $\mathbf{u}_w(\mathbf{x},t)$.

Figure 6.2, a, b shows some initial surface $h_0(\mathbf{x})$ consisting of three peaks and the surface $h(\mathbf{x},t)$ after a sufficiently large interval of time, when the shape of the surface is given by the weak solution of the surface-growth equation (6.27). The weak solution is drawn as a 3D parametric plot by means of the expressions (6.32) and (6.33). The Mathematica software, which was used to plot this surface, conceals the lower branches of the multivalued function $h(\mathbf{x},t)$, and due to this fact we can see the plot of the weak solution. It clearly shows the characteristic lines of non-differentiability, where the partial derivatives of the weak solution undergo a discontinuity.

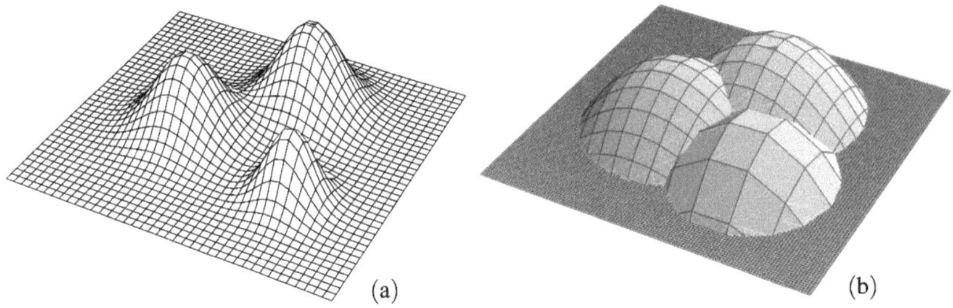

Fig. 6.2 Initial shape of the surface containing three well expressed peaks **(a)**. The same surface after some time **(b)**. Clearly seen are fracture lines of the surface, which are due to a nonlinear overlap of the peaks.

6.1.6 Flows of locally interacting particles and a singular density field

In what follows, we will interpret Eq. (6.29) as the equation for the velocity field of a two-dimensional particle flow. As long as the solution of this equation is single-valued, the field $\mathbf{u}(\mathbf{x},t)$ has an apparent physical meaning — it is the velocity of a two-dimensional hydrodynamical flow of uniformly moving particles. As we already well know, starting from a certain moment of time t_n, some particles begin to overtake others and, if the particles do not interact, a multistream regime is entered. But if, during the overtaking, the particles interact, hindering the multistreamness, then instead of multistream fields there can appear discontinuous single-flow fields $\mathbf{u}_w(\mathbf{x},t)$, which we call weak solutions of Eq. (6.29).

Unlike the case of a one-dimensional flow, where the mechanical meaning of weak solution formation because of nonelastic coalescence of particles, in a multidimensional case, it is difficult to suggest a physical interaction mechanism leading to a comparatively simple mathematical algorithm for a choice of a weak solution. Therefore our approach to the particle-interaction problem will be a purely formal one. We postulate that a local interaction at the moment of a collision gives rise to a discontinuous Eulerian-to-Lagrangian coordinate transformation $\mathbf{y} = \mathbf{y}_w(\mathbf{x},t)$ and, consequently, a weak solution for the particle-velocity field follows from the absolute maximum principle. To justify such a choice, we note that, based on the above mentioned approach, a theory of nonlinear gravitational interaction has been successfully developed, which allowed for a qualitative, and even quantitative, explanation of evolution of the large-scale matter distribution in the Universe.

Let us apply the method outlined above to an analysis of the generalized density field $\rho_w(\mathbf{x},t)$ of a two-dimensional flow of particles locally interacting at the moment of overtaking. As we know, independently of the character of interaction of the flow's substance, its density may be written as

$$\rho_w(\mathbf{x},t) = \rho_0 \int_{-\infty}^{\infty} \delta(\mathbf{X}_w(\mathbf{y},t) - \mathbf{x})\, d^2y, \tag{6.37}$$

where $\mathbf{x} = \mathbf{X}_w(\mathbf{y},t)$ is the transformation inverse of the transformation $\mathbf{y} = \mathbf{y}_w(\mathbf{x},t)$ in this case following from the absolute maximum principle. Apart from this, we assumed, for simplicity, that the initial density of an imaginary gas, interacting according to the absolute maximum law, is the same everywhere in the plane $\mathbf{x}$: $\rho_0(\mathbf{x}) = \rho_0 = const.$

In a general case $\rho_w(\mathbf{x},t)$ is a singular generalized function. Therefore we find out the algorithm of its action on a test function $\phi(\mathbf{x})$. Following simple mathematical calculations, we obtain

$$\int_{-\infty}^{\infty} \phi(\mathbf{x})\rho_w(\mathbf{x},t)\, d^2x = \rho_0 \int_{-\infty}^{\infty} \phi(\mathbf{X}(\mathbf{y},t))\, d^2y. \tag{6.38}$$

In order to use the expression (6.38), it remains to find a way to construct the function $\mathbf{x} = \mathbf{X}_w(\mathbf{y},t)$. It can be easily shown that, like in the one-dimensional case, the Lagrangian-to-Eulerian coordinate transformation is given by

$$\mathbf{x} = \mathbf{X}_w(\mathbf{y},t) = -\nabla\bar{\varphi}(\mathbf{y},t), \tag{6.39}$$

where $\bar{\varphi}(\mathbf{y},t)$ is the convex hull of the function

$$\varphi(\mathbf{y},t) = h_0(\mathbf{y})\,t - \frac{y^2}{2}.$$

In this case, in order to obtain the convex hull, it is necessary to pull an elastic film over the surface $\varphi(\mathbf{y},t)$ from above. The surface of the stretched film is the convex hull of the function $\varphi(\mathbf{y},t)$.

Geometrically, the construction of the transformation (6.39) is reduced to finding a plane tangent to the convex hull $z = \bar{\varphi}(\mathbf{y},t)$ at the point with the coordinates $\mathbf{y}$. Let us discuss this precedure in more detail. Let $\mathbf{r}$ be the position vector in a three-dimensional space $(\mathbf{y},z)$. The equation of the tangent plane has the following form:

$$(\mathbf{n}\cdot\mathbf{r} - \mathbf{a}) = 0, \quad \mathbf{a} = \{\mathbf{y},\, \bar{\varphi}(\mathbf{y},t)\}.$$

Here $\mathbf{n}$ is the external normal vector with respect to the convex hull $z = \bar{\varphi}(\mathbf{y},t)$ (if we consider the region under the convex hull its interior). Let the z-component of the normal be everywhere equal to unity: $\mathbf{n}_z = 1$. The projection of the normal onto the plane $\mathbf{y}$ is the sought-for vector $\mathbf{X}_w(\mathbf{y},t)$. In other words, we find the transformation $\mathbf{x} = \mathbf{X}_w(\mathbf{y},t)$, if we determine the normal $\mathbf{n}$ at each point of the plane $z = \bar{\varphi}(\mathbf{y},t)$ and project it onto the plane $\mathbf{y}$.

There three robust (not vanishing under small deviations of the surface) types of tangency of the plane and convex hull defining qualitatively different parts of the transformation (6.39). The Lagrangian $\mathbf{y}$ and Eulerian $\mathbf{x}$ planes are divided into three types of regions corresponding to these tangency types.

Let us list the tangency types and show their mechanical meaning as applied to the density field (6.37) of a substance interacting on overtaking.

1. The plane is tangent to the convex hull at a single point. All such points belong to both the convex hull and the original surface $\varphi(\mathbf{y},t)$. Projections of these points onto the plane $\mathbf{y}$ are the Lagrangian coordinates of those particles of the flow, which have not yet participated in interactions, and their Eulerian coordinates $\mathbf{x} = \mathbf{X}_w(\mathbf{y},t)$ are given by the transformation (6.33) for noninteracting particles.
2. The plane is simultaneously tangent to the original surface $\phi(\mathbf{y},t)$ at two points. Then the whole interval ℓ joining these points belongs to the convex hull $\bar{\phi}(\mathbf{y},t)$. Hence, everywhere within this interval, the vector normal to the convex hull is the same. This means that all points of the projection ℓ_y of the interval ℓ onto the Lagrangian plane $\mathbf{y}$ are transformed into a single point with the same Eulerian coordinates $\mathbf{x} = \mathbf{X}_w(\mathbf{y},t)$. By gliding a tangent plane covered with chalk over the convex hull and making sure that the plane touches the hull at two points simultaneously, let us draw on the latter a bounded region $\mathbb{G}$. All points of its projection $\mathbb{G}_y$ onto the plane $\mathbf{y}$ are projected onto the curve

$$\mathscr{L} = \{\mathbf{x} = \mathbf{X}_w(\mathbf{y},t) : \mathbf{y} \in \mathbb{G}_y\}$$

in the Eulerian plane $\mathbf{x}$, where the entire substance originally occupying the region $\mathbf{y} \in \mathbb{G}$ is concentrated.
3. The plane is tangent to the surface at three points. By joining these points, we obtain a triangle $\mathbb{T}$. All points of the projection $\mathbb{T}_y$ of this triangle onto the Lagrangian plane $\mathbf{y}$ are transformed into a single point

$$x^* = \{\mathbf{x} = \mathbf{X}_w(\mathbf{y},t) : \mathbf{y} \in \mathbb{T}_y\}.$$

Graphs explaining the division of the Lagrangian plane $\mathbf{y}$ into the three types of regions and the features of their mapping onto the Eulerian plane $\mathbf{x}$ are shown in Fig. 6.3. In the appendix to the English edition of book [3] (authors of the appendix are V.I. Arnold, Yu.M. Baryshnikov and I.A Bogaevski) a classification of singu-

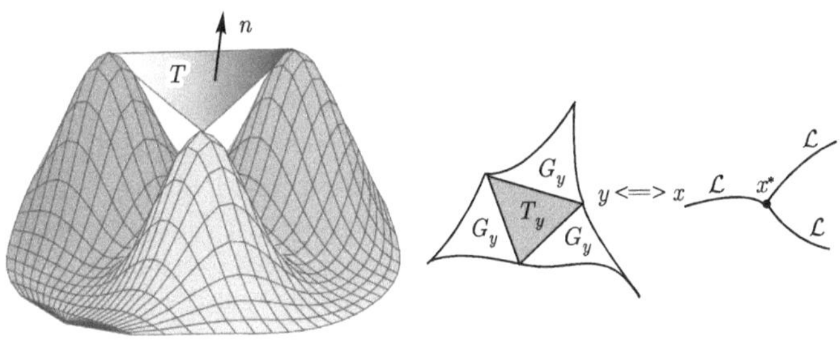

Fig. 6.3 A characteristic fragment of the surface $z = \varphi(\mathbf{y},t)$ with three peaks and the triangle $\mathbb{T}$ whose vertices are the points where the tangent plane touches the surface are shown on the left. The interior of the projection $\mathbb{T}_y$ of this triangle on the Lagrangian plane $\mathbf{y}$ is transformed into a single point of x^* of the Eulerian plane. Grooves bounded by the lines tangent to both the surface and the tangent plane go from the sides of the triangle. They are projected onto the lines $\mathscr{L}$ in the Eulerian plane. Geometry of the above mentioned regions in the Lagrangian and Eulerian planes is depicted on the right-hand side.

larities and their bifurcations for two- and three-dimensional flows is given. The mapping considered above corresponds precisely to such flows.

The three types of mapping listed above define the structure of the generalized density field:

$$\rho(\mathbf{x},t) = \hat{\rho}(\mathbf{x},t) + \sum_i \rho_i \delta_{\mathscr{L}_i} + \sum_j m_j^* \delta(\mathbf{x}_j^* - \mathbf{x}). \tag{6.40}$$

Here the first term

$$\hat{\rho}(\mathbf{x},t) = \left\{ \frac{\rho_0}{J(\mathbf{y}(\mathbf{x},t),t)} \right\}$$

describes the regular density of uniformly moving until the current moment of time t particles. It contains the Jacobian $J(\mathbf{y},t)$ of the Lagrangian-to-Eulerian coordinate transformation (6.33) and also the inverse of it $\mathbf{y}(\mathbf{x},t)$. Curved brackets signify that the expression holds only within the regions of the first type. In the regions of the second and third type, which are of measure zero in the Eulerian plane, the bracketed expression should be supplemented by arbitrary bounded functions.

The last term in (6.40) gives the singular component of the density with the carriers in the points of the third type x^*, where the substance from the triangular regions $\mathbb{T}_y$ of the Lagrangian plane is accumulated. The coefficients of delta functions are equal to the mass of the substance originally found within the triangles $\mathbb{T}_y$. If, as we assume, the initial density of the two-dimensional flow considered here is everywhere the same is equals ρ_0, then

$$m^* = \rho_0 S_{\mathbb{T}},$$

where $S_{\mathbb{T}}$ is the area of the corresponding triangle $\mathbb{T}_y$.

Let us separately discuss the second term on the right-hand side of Eq. (6.40). It is equal a sum of linear delta functions corresponding to the second-type regions $\mathbb{G}_y$. A linear delta function acts on a test function $\phi(\mathbf{y})$ in the following way:

$$\int_{-\infty}^{\infty} \phi(\mathbf{x}) \rho \delta_{\mathscr{L}} d^2x = \int_{\mathscr{L}} \rho(\sigma,t) \phi(\mathbf{x}(\sigma)) d\sigma. \tag{6.41}$$

In other words, the linear delta function $\delta_{\mathscr{L}}$ cuts out of a double integral a curvilinear integral of the first kind along the curve $\mathscr{L}$. The integrand is the product of the linear density ρ of the material line $\mathscr{L}$ and the test function $\phi(\mathbf{x})$. While writing the integral down, we used the parametric equation $\mathbf{x} = \mathbf{x}(\sigma)$ of the curve $\mathscr{L}$. Here σ is a natural parameter, which is equal to the length of the curve measured from some initial point on the curve.

In order to find the linear density $\rho(\sigma,t)$, let us take an infinitesimal interval $[\sigma, \sigma + d\sigma]$ on the curve $\mathscr{L}$. A subregion $d\mathbb{G}_y$ of the region $\mathbb{G}_y$ collapsing into the curve $\mathscr{L}$ of the Eulerian plane is mapped onto it. The subregion $d\mathbb{G}_y$ is bounded by the intervals $\ell_y(\sigma,t)$ and $\ell_y(\sigma + d\sigma,t)$, which are mapped into the ends of the interval $[\sigma, \sigma + d\sigma]$. Therewith the sought-for linear density is equal to

$$\rho(\sigma,t) = \lim_{d\sigma \to 0} \frac{dm(\sigma)}{d\sigma},$$

where $dm(\sigma)$ is the mass of the substance initially contained within the subregion $d\mathbb{G}_y$.

6.2 Multidimensional nonlinear equations of the second order

Until now, we have predominately been discussing solutions of one-dimensional nonlinear partial differential equations. Real nonlinear fields evolve in the three-dimensional space, and the one-dimensional approximations is not always sufficiently adequate. The problem of describing nonlinear fields and waves in multi-dimensional spaces, however, is too vast and rather little studied in order to claim even a brief exposition of it in a single book. Therefore we limit ourselves here only to a brief enumeration of several natural generalizations of the nonlinear equations considered above. First of all these are the generalizations of the KPZ and Burgers equations to the two- and three-dimensional cases. Further information can be found in [8, 11, 13, 14].

6.2.1 The two-dimensional KPZ equation

Let a surface grow with the speed c predominantly along a chosen axis in the three-dimensional space. Let us denote the coordinate along this axis as z, and the coordinates in the orthogonal to the z-axis plane as $\mathbf{x}$. Assuming that the growing surface is one-to-one mapped on the orthogonal plane, let us describe it by the following function:

$$z = ct + h(\mathbf{x},t). \tag{6.42}$$

The first term on the right-hand side describes the growth of a flat surface orthogonal to the z-axis, and the last term takes unevenness of the surface and other effects influencing the rate of its growth along the z-axis into account. As before, let us assign the surface-growth speed to be equal to unity, i.e. everywhere in what follows we set $c \equiv 1$. If the angles between the surface normals and the z are small, the function $h(\mathbf{x},t)$ satisfies, in the small angle approximation, the two-dimensional analogue of Eq. (3.4):

$$\frac{\partial h}{\partial t} = \frac{1}{2}(\nabla h)^2 + \mu \Delta h + F(\mathbf{x},t). \tag{6.43}$$

Here $F(\mathbf{x},t)$ takes the irregularity of sedimentation of particles adhering to the surface into account, and the term proportional to μ does the same for the mobility of the particles along the surface.

The substitution

$$h(\mathbf{x},t) = 2\mu \ln \varphi(\mathbf{x},t) \tag{6.44}$$

reduces Eq. (6.43) to the linear diffusion equation

$$\frac{\partial \varphi}{\partial t} = \mu \Delta \varphi + \frac{1}{2\mu} F(\mathbf{x},t)\varphi, \tag{6.45}$$

which needs to be solved subject to the following initial condition:

$$\varphi(\mathbf{x}, t=0) = \exp\left(\frac{h_0(\mathbf{x})}{2\mu}\right). \tag{6.46}$$

Analysis of the properties of the solution of Eq. (6.45) and the corresponding solution of the KPZ equation is beyond the scope of this book. Here we only show the exact solutions of Eqs. (6.43) and (6.45) in the homogeneous case, when $F(\mathbf{x},t) \equiv 0$. In this case,

$$\varphi(\mathbf{x},t) = \left(\frac{1}{2\sqrt{\pi\mu t}}\right)^n \int \exp\left(\frac{1}{2\mu t}\left[h_0(\mathbf{y})t - \frac{(\mathbf{y}-\mathbf{x})^2}{2}\right]\right) d^n y. \tag{6.47}$$

Here n is the dimensionality of the space $\mathbf{x}$, which in this context equals $n = 2$.

6.2.2 *The three-dimensional Burgers equation*

Let us introduce a vector function of slopes of the surface given by the following equation:

$$\mathbf{v}(\mathbf{x},t) = -\nabla h(\mathbf{x},t). \tag{6.48}$$

It is easy to verify that if $h(\mathbf{x},t)$ satisfies the KPZ equation (6.43), the vector field $\mathbf{v}(\mathbf{x},t)$ obeys the multidimensional Burgers equation:

$$\frac{\partial \mathbf{v}}{\partial t} + (\mathbf{v}\cdot\nabla)\,\mathbf{v} = \mu\Delta\mathbf{v} + \mathbf{f}(\mathbf{x},t), \quad \mathbf{f}(\mathbf{x},t) = -\nabla F(\mathbf{x},t).$$

The analytical solution of the homogeneous KPZ equation, along with Eq. (6.48), gives an exact analytical solution of the homogeneous Burgers equation

$$\frac{\partial \mathbf{v}}{\partial t} + (\mathbf{v}\cdot\nabla)\,\mathbf{v} = \mu\Delta\mathbf{v} \tag{6.49}$$

in the case of a *potential* initial field

$$\mathbf{v}(\mathbf{x}, t=0) = \mathbf{v}_0(\mathbf{x}). \tag{6.50}$$

The potentiality of this field means that there exists a scalar potential $s_0(\mathbf{x})$ such that

$$\mathbf{v}_0(\mathbf{x}) = \nabla s_0(\mathbf{x}). \tag{6.51}$$

At the same time, the solution of the Burgers equation $\mathbf{v}(\mathbf{x},t)$ remains to be potential for all $t>0$ and is described by the expression

$$\mathbf{v}(\mathbf{x},t) = \frac{\mathbf{x} - \{\mathbf{y}\}(\mathbf{x},t)}{t}. \tag{6.52}$$

which follows from (6.47), (6.48). The curved brackets $\{\ldots\}$ here signify a spatial averaging by means of the following function:

$$f(\mathbf{y};\mathbf{x},t) = \frac{\exp\left[-\frac{1}{2\mu t}G(\mathbf{y};\mathbf{x},t)\right]}{\int \exp\left[-\frac{1}{2\mu t}G(\mathbf{y};\mathbf{x},t)\right] d^n y}, \tag{6.53}$$

where

$$G(\mathbf{y};\mathbf{x},t) = s_0(\mathbf{y})t + \frac{(\mathbf{y}-\mathbf{x})^2}{2}. \tag{6.54}$$

Accordingly, the spatial average $\{g(\mathbf{y})\}$ is equal, in a general case, to the n-tuple integral

$$\{g(\mathbf{y})\}(\mathbf{x},t) = \int g(\mathbf{y})\, f(\mathbf{y};\mathbf{x},t)\, d^n y. \tag{6.55}$$

6.2.3 Model density field

As it has already been said, with $n=2$, the solution of the multidimensional Burgers equation (6.49) has a transparent geometric sense: it describes the slopes of a growing surface. On the other hand, with $n=3$, it is appropriate to interpret the Burgers equation as an equation for the velocity field $\mathbf{v}(\mathbf{x},t)$ of a certain moving medium. Let us note, in support of this, that the Burgers equation and its solutions have successfully been used for a model description of evolution of the large-scale matter distribution in the Universe. The latter is quantitatively expressed by the density $\rho(\mathbf{x},t)$ of the matter distribution. Therefore, let us show one of the ways to specify the model density field of a medium whose velocity of motion is described by a solution of the Burgers equation (6.49).

Recall, that in a general case, the density $\rho(\mathbf{x},t)$ of a medium with a known velocity field $\mathbf{v}(\mathbf{x},t)$ may be computed by using the following formula:

$$\rho(\mathbf{x},t) = \rho_0(\mathbf{y}(\mathbf{x},t))J(\mathbf{x},t), \tag{6.56}$$

where $\mathbf{y}(\mathbf{x},t)$ are the Lagrangian coordinates of the moving medium, which satisfy the following equation:

$$\frac{\partial \mathbf{y}}{\partial t} + (\mathbf{v}\cdot\nabla)\mathbf{y} = 0, \quad \mathbf{y}(\mathbf{x},t=0) = \mathbf{x}, \tag{6.57}$$

and $J(\mathbf{x},t)$ is the Jacobian of the Lagrangian-to-Eulerian coordinate mapping

$$J(\mathbf{x},t) = \left| \frac{\partial y_i(\mathbf{x},t)}{\partial x_j} \right|, \quad i,j = 1 \dots n. \tag{6.58}$$

By a direct substitution of the right-hand side of Eq. (6.52) into the Burgers equation, it is easy to verify that the function

$$\{\mathbf{y}\}(\mathbf{x},t) = \mathbf{x} - \mathbf{v}(\mathbf{x},t)\,t \tag{6.59}$$

entering (6.52) satisfies the following, similar to (6.57) equation:

$$\frac{\partial \{\mathbf{y}\}}{\partial t} + (\mathbf{v} \cdot \nabla)\{\mathbf{y}\} = \mu \Delta \{\mathbf{y}\}. \tag{6.60}$$

By substituting in (6.56) and (6.58) for the Lagrangian coordinates $\mathbf{y}(\mathbf{x},t)$ an approximating them (the smaller μ, the better approximation) vector field $\{\mathbf{y}\}(\mathbf{x},t)$, we arrive at the sought-for model density field of a medium whose velocity satisfies the Burgers equation

$$\rho(\mathbf{x},t) = \rho_0(\{\mathbf{y}\}(\mathbf{x},t)) \left| \frac{\partial \{y\}_i(\mathbf{x},t)}{\partial x_j} \right|. \tag{6.61}$$

Another alternative definition of the density is possible, in the framework of which, the trajectories of particles are given by a velocity field satisfying the Burgers equation, and the density is obtained as the Jacobian of the Eulerian-to-Lagrangian coordinate transformation [3]. In the limiting case of a vanishing viscosity, dynamics of such motion is investigated in [15, 16], where, in particular, it is shown that at the singularities of the velocity field the particles behave in a nontrivial way.

6.2.4 Concentration field

Recall, that the nonlinear KPZ equation (6.43) is reduced to the linear parabolic equation (6.45) by means of the substitution (6.44). Such possibility of a reduction of a nonlinear equation to a linear one is believed to be a great stroke of luck, because methods of analytical and numerical analysis of linear equations are developed much better than similar methods of investigation of solutions to nonlinear equations. This is why, from time to time, attempts are made to reduce certain nonlinear equations to more convenient for analysis linear equations. Moreover there are real hunters for solutions of nonlinear equations, who approach the problem from the other end — they take linear equations and by means of various substitutions reduce them to nonlinear ones. Most often, solvable nonlinear equations obtained in this way have little to do with the equations indeed arising in applications. Yet, every now and then, this method brings about astonishing results and generates solutions of important for applications nonlinear equations.

Let us arrange for the reader a little hunt for solvable nonlinear equations by taking guidance from the following "natural" considerations: if the substitution (6.44) reduces the important for applications KPZ equation (6.43) to the linear parabolic equation (6.45), then similar substitutions applied to a *system* of linear parabolic equations will reduce them to more general nonlinear equations possibly applicable to the surface-growth theory and gasodynamics.

Let us take a pair of coupled linear parabolic equations

$$\begin{cases} \dfrac{\partial \varphi}{\partial t} = \mu \Delta \varphi + a\varphi + b\psi, \\ \dfrac{\partial \psi}{\partial t} = \mu \Delta \psi + d\varphi + e\psi. \end{cases} \tag{6.62}$$

Let us apply to the first of these equations the substitution (6.44), which has already proven itself useful. For this, let us multiply the first equation (6.62) by $2\mu/\varphi$. As a results, we arrive at the following equation

$$\frac{\partial h}{\partial t} = \frac{1}{2}(\nabla h)^2 + \mu \Delta h + 2\mu a + 2\mu bC. \tag{6.63}$$

Here we used the following new notation:

$$C(\mathbf{x},t) = \frac{\psi(\mathbf{x},t)}{\varphi(\mathbf{x},t)}. \tag{6.64}$$

Let us find the equation governing the field $C(\mathbf{x},t)$ (6.64). First of all, let us write down the derivative of this field with respect to time

$$\frac{\partial C}{\partial t} = \frac{1}{\varphi}\frac{\partial \psi}{\partial t} - \frac{\psi}{\varphi^2}\frac{\partial \varphi}{\partial t}. \tag{6.65}$$

By substituting here, for the derivatives φ and ψ, the right-hand side parts of Eqs. (6.62), we obtain

$$\frac{\partial C}{\partial t} = \mu\left(\frac{\Delta \psi}{\varphi} - \frac{\psi \Delta \varphi}{\varphi^2}\right) + d + (e-a)C - bC^2. \tag{6.66}$$

In order to finish the task, it remains to express the first term on the right hand side of Eq. (6.66) via C and h. We do this, by noting that an analogous to (6.65) formula exists for the gradient of the field C:

$$\nabla C = \frac{\nabla \psi}{\varphi} - \frac{\psi \nabla \varphi}{\varphi^2}. \tag{6.67}$$

In its turn, by taking the dot product of the del vector operator with both parts of this equation ∇, we obtain

$$\Delta C = \left(\frac{\Delta \psi}{\varphi} - \frac{\psi \Delta \varphi}{\varphi^2}\right) - \frac{2}{\varphi}\left[\frac{(\nabla \varphi \cdot \nabla \psi)}{\varphi} - \frac{\psi(\nabla \varphi \cdot \nabla \varphi)}{\varphi^2}\right]. \tag{6.68}$$

By taking the relation (6.67) and the expression for the gradient of the field h

$$\nabla h = 2\mu \frac{\nabla \varphi}{\varphi},$$

into account, let us rewrite the formula (6.68) in a more convenient for analysis form

$$\frac{\Delta \psi}{\varphi} - \frac{\psi \Delta \varphi}{\varphi^2} = \Delta C + \frac{1}{\mu}(\nabla h \cdot \nabla) C. \tag{6.69}$$

In view of this relation, Eq. (6.66) is transformed into the following form:

$$\frac{\partial C}{\partial t} = \mu \Delta C + (\nabla h \cdot \nabla) C + d + (e - a) C - b C^2, \tag{6.70}$$

containing only the fields h and C.

We arrived at the closed system of nonlinear equations (6.63) and (6.70), whose solution is reduced to solving the linear parabolic equations (6.62). Discussion of possible applications of the obtained nonlinear equations with arbitrary parameters a, b, d, e is beyond the scope of this book. Therefore let us discuss here possible physical meaning of Eqs. (6.63) and (6.70) only in one particular case, when

$$a = e = \frac{1}{2\mu} F(\mathbf{x}, t), \quad b \equiv 0, \quad d = d(\mathbf{x}, t). \tag{6.71}$$

Furthermore let us get from the field h over to the potential vector field $\mathbf{v}(\mathbf{x}, t)$ (6.48) while treating it, as before, as the velocity field of a certain gas. Following from (6.63) and (6.70) corresponding equations for the fields $\mathbf{v}(\mathbf{x}, t)$ and $C(\mathbf{x}, t)$ have the form:

$$\begin{cases} \dfrac{\partial \mathbf{v}}{\partial t} + (\mathbf{v} \cdot \nabla)\, \mathbf{v} = \mu \Delta \mathbf{v} + \mathbf{f}(\mathbf{x}, t), \\ \dfrac{\partial C}{\partial t} + (\mathbf{v} \cdot \nabla) C = \mu \Delta \mathbf{C} + d(\mathbf{x}, t). \end{cases} \tag{6.72}$$

The first of them is well known to us, therefore let us only discuss the physical meaning of the second equation. It describes, for instance, evolution of *concentration* $C(\mathbf{x}, t)$ of a passive admixture moving in a gas with the velocity field $\mathbf{v}(\mathbf{x}, t)$. Recall that concentration is equal to the ratio of the density of the admixture and the density of the medium does not change under compressions or expansions of the medium. For this reason, without taking molecular diffusion into account, the concentration of the passive admixture satisfies the following equation:

$$\frac{DC}{Dt} = 0 \Rightarrow \frac{\partial C}{\partial t} + (\mathbf{v} \cdot \nabla) C = 0$$

Apart from hydrodynamical transport of the passive admixture, the equation for C (6.72) also takes into account change of C due to molecular diffusion with the diffusion coefficient μ, as well as the presence of a source of the admixture described by the function $d(\mathbf{x},t)$. We note that the first equation (6.72) contains the potential vector force field

$$\mathbf{f}(\mathbf{x},t) = -\nabla F(\mathbf{x},t),$$

which influences the motion of the medium.

From the calculations cited above follows that the solution of the pair of equations (6.72) with the initial conditions

$$\mathbf{v}(\mathbf{x},t=0) = \mathbf{v}_0(\mathbf{x}), \quad C(\mathbf{x},t=0) = C_0(\mathbf{x}), \tag{6.73}$$

the substitutions

$$\mathbf{v} = -2\mu\frac{\nabla\varphi}{\varphi}, \quad C = \frac{\psi}{\varphi} \tag{6.74}$$

is reduced to solving the linear equations of the parabolic type

$$\begin{cases} \dfrac{\partial\varphi}{\partial t} = \mu\Delta\varphi + \dfrac{1}{2\mu}F(\mathbf{x},t)\varphi, \\ \dfrac{\partial\psi}{\partial t} = \mu\Delta\psi + \dfrac{1}{2\mu}F(\mathbf{x},t)\psi + d(\mathbf{x},t)\,\varphi \end{cases} \tag{6.75}$$

with the initial conditions

$$\varphi_0(\mathbf{x},t=0) = \exp\left(-\frac{s_0(\mathbf{x})}{2\mu}\right), \quad \psi_0(\mathbf{x}) = C_0(\mathbf{x})\exp\left(-\frac{s_0(\mathbf{x})}{2\mu}\right). \tag{6.76}$$

Here $s_0(\mathbf{x})$ is the potential of the initial velocity field linked to this field by Eq. (6.51).

In particular, under the absence of an external force $\mathbf{f} \equiv 0$ and take on the following from: sources of the passive admixture $d \equiv 0$, solutions of Eqs. (6.72)

$$\mathbf{v}(\mathbf{x},t) = \frac{\mathbf{x} - \{\mathbf{y}\}(\mathbf{x},t)}{t}, \quad C(\mathbf{x},t) = \{C_0(\mathbf{y})\}(\mathbf{x},t). \tag{6.77}$$

Here we used the spatial averaging procedure given by Eqs. (6.53) and (6.55).

6.3 Evolution of the main perturbation types in the KPZ equation and in the multidimensional Burgers equation

It had already been mentioned that the nonlinear diffusion equation

$$\frac{\partial v}{\partial t} + v\frac{\partial v}{\partial x} = \mu\frac{\partial^2 v}{\partial x^2} \tag{6.78}$$

was originally introduced by J.M. Burgers as a model of hydrodynamic turbulence [17, 18]. It has indeed a lot in common with the well-known Navier-Stokes equation: the same type of nonlinearity, common invariants, the same frequency dependence for energy losses, etc. [19]. At the same time, distinctions between the Burgers (6.78) and Navier-Stokes equations are as interesting as their similarities [20]. It is even more so for the multidimensional Burgers equation. The multidimensional Burgers equation with external random forces is widely used as a model of the hydrodynamic Navier-Stokes turbulence without pressure [21–23]. Attention to the study of other possible applications of the multidimensional Burgers equation was renewed in 1986, when Kardar, Parisi and Zhang, for the first time, suggested a nonlinear equation with a random source describing non-equilibrium surface evolution [24], which is now called the KPZ equation. As it will be shown below, a three-dimensional version of Eq. (6.78) along with an equation for the density are used to describe formation of large-scale structures of the Universe at the nonlinear stage of the gravitational instability, when it is possible to neglect pressure forces. This model is known in astrophysics as the adhesion model [3,6,10,25,26]) and describes formation of strongly inhomogeneous structures in the matter distribution starting from a random initial perturbation. Other problems leading to the multidimensional Burgers equation or its variants are the growth of a boundary between two media due to random sedimentation of a substance on a surface and fire-front motion [14]. In these cases the potential ψ ($\mathbf{v} = -\nabla\psi$) corresponds to the surface profile, and the equation describing its evolution is equivalent to the KPZ equation [14, 24, 27]. The mean-square gradient $E(t) = \langle(\nabla\psi(\mathbf{x},t))^2\rangle = \langle\mathbf{v}^2(\mathbf{x},t)\rangle$ therewith characterizes the roughness of the surface.

In this section, we will discuss evolution of the main types of perturbations in the multidimensional Burgers equation on the basis of the results from [3–6].

6.3.1 Asymptotic solutions of the multidimensional Burgers equation and local self-similarity

Let us consider the vector Burgers equation without external forces

$$\frac{\partial\mathbf{v}}{\partial t} + (\mathbf{v}\cdot\nabla)\,\mathbf{v} = \mu\triangle\mathbf{v} \tag{6.79}$$

and look for its potential solutions of the following form:

$$\mathbf{v}(\mathbf{x},t) = -\nabla\psi(\mathbf{x},t). \tag{6.80}$$

As it was shown above, the velocity potential $\psi(\mathbf{x},t)$ satisfies the nonlinear euqation

$$\frac{\partial\psi}{\partial t} = \frac{1}{2}(\nabla\psi)^2 + \mu\triangle\psi, \tag{6.81}$$

identical to the KPZ equation [14, 24, 27], which is usually written with respect to the variables $h = \lambda^{-1}\cdot\psi$. Therewith the parameter λ, which has the dimensionality of velocity, is a local velocity of surface growth, and $h(\mathbf{x},t)$ describes deviation of surface growth from the normal and has the dimension of length. In problems of the growth of an interface between two media, μ has the meaning of the surface-tension coefficient and the last term on the right-hand side describes linear effects of the smoothening of the surface. Surface's roughness is measured by its mean square gradient

$$E(t) = \langle (\nabla\psi(\mathbf{x},t))^2 \rangle = \langle \mathbf{v}^2(\mathbf{x},t) \rangle = \sum_i E_i(t),$$

$$E_i(t) = \left\langle \left(\frac{\partial\psi}{\partial x_i} \right)^2 \right\rangle = \langle v_i^2 \rangle . \tag{6.82}$$

Angular brackets signify an ensemble averaging or spatial integration (for a localized perturbation). In the one-dimensional case, $E(t)$ is the energy of the turbulence, and, in dissipating medium, always decreases with time. Therewith, in a medium with a vanishing viscosity ($\mu \to 0$), the energy $E(t)$ is conserved until the formation of discontinuities in the wave profile and decreases due to dissipation at shock fronts of an infinitesimal width.

At the initial stage of the evolution, before discontinuities are formed, the multidimensional Burgers equation in the limit of vanishing viscosity is equivalent to the free particle motion. In the Lagrangian representation, the particle velocity $\mathbf{V}(t;\mathbf{y})$ is constant and depends only on the initial (Lagrangian) particle coordinate $\mathbf{y}$. In the one-dimensional case, before the formation of discontinuities, a length increase of a single elementary interval in the Eulerian representation $\Delta x = \Delta y + t\Delta V$ is compensated by a length reduction of another neighboring interval $\Delta x = \Delta y - t\Delta V$, and, consequently, the wave energy is conserved. After formation of discontinuities, the energy starts to decrease with time. In a multidimensional case, a change of an elementary volume in the Eulerian representation depends on the initial curvature of a surface perturbation, and a similar compensation of expanding and compressing volumes is not observed. Hence, for $d > 1$, the roughness measure of a surface $E(t)$ (6.82) may both grow and decrease with time [2]. Nevertheless we will call $E(t)$ the "turbulence energy", and $E_i(t)$ — the "energy" of the i-th velocity component.

As in the one-dimensional case, by using the Hopf-Cole substitution [28, 29]

$$\psi(\mathbf{x},t) = 2\mu \ln U(\mathbf{x},t), \quad \mathbf{v}(\mathbf{x},t) = -2\mu\nabla \ln U(\mathbf{x},t), \tag{6.83}$$

it is possibe to reduce the multidimensional nonlinear equation (6.79) to the linear diffusion equation

$$\frac{\partial U}{\partial t} = \mu \Delta U, \tag{6.84}$$

$$U(\mathbf{x},0) = U_0(\mathbf{x}) = \exp\left(\frac{\psi_0(\mathbf{x})}{2\mu} \right) . \tag{6.85}$$

Below we will discuss evolution of regular and random fields at large Reynolds numbers, when effective nonlinear interaction of spatial harmonics of the initial perturbation takes place, and dissipation is substantial only in the region of large wavenumbers. In the spatial language — energy losses occur only in small neighborhoods of discontinuities. Thus, for not so large initial time intervals, it is possible to use the solution of the Eq. (6.79) in the limit of vanishing viscosity. At later stages of evolution, when nonlinear interaction processes become insignificant, development of the field is determined only by linear dissipation and is described by the linearized Hopf-Cole solution.

In the limit of vanishing viscosity $\mu \to 0$, as in the one-dimensional case, the use of the steepest descent method in the Hopf-Cole solution leads to the so-called "maximum method" for the potential velocity field [3, 26, 28]:

$$\psi(\mathbf{x},t) = \max_{\mathbf{y}} \Phi(\mathbf{x},\mathbf{y},t), \quad \Phi(\mathbf{x},\mathbf{y},t) = \psi_0(\mathbf{y}) - \frac{(\mathbf{x}-\mathbf{y})^2}{2t}, \tag{6.86}$$

$$\mathbf{v}(\mathbf{x},t) = \frac{\mathbf{x}-\mathbf{y}(\mathbf{x},t)}{t} = \mathbf{v}_0(\mathbf{y}(\mathbf{x},t)). \tag{6.87}$$

Here $\psi_0(\mathbf{y})$ is the initial potential: $\mathbf{v}_0(\mathbf{x}) = -\nabla\psi_0(\mathbf{x})$. In the expression (6.87), the function $\mathbf{y}(\mathbf{x},t)$ is the Lagrangian coordinates of the point where the function $\Phi(\mathbf{x},\mathbf{y},t)$ at fixed Eulerian coordinate $\mathbf{x}$ and time t achieves its absolute maximum.

Evidently, $\mathbf{y}$ also determines the initial coordinates of the particle which reaches the point $\mathbf{x}$ at the current moment of time t [3].

At sufficiently long times, the parabolic in (6.86) is a much smoother function of the coordinates than the initial potential $\psi_0(\mathbf{y})$. Hence the absolute maximum of the function $\Phi(\mathbf{x},\mathbf{y},t)$ coincides with one the maximum values of $\psi_0(\mathbf{y})$. In a vicinity of a local maximum $\mathbf{y_k}$, the initial potential can be written as

$$\psi_0(\mathbf{x}) = \psi_{0,k}\left(1 - \sum_i \frac{(x_i - y_{i,k})^2}{2L_i^2}\right). \tag{6.88}$$

Here x_i give a basis of a principal axis expansion of a local quadratic form at the point $\mathbf{y_k}$. From the solutions (6.86) and (6.87), respectively, we obtain

$$\psi(\mathbf{x},t) = \psi_{0,k}\left(1 - \sum_i \frac{(x_i - y_{i,k})^2}{2L_i^2(1+\psi_{0,k}t/L_i^2)}\right),$$

$$v_i(\mathbf{x},t) = \frac{\psi_{0,k}(x_i - y_{i,k})}{L_i^2(1+\psi_{0,k}t/L_i^2)}. \tag{6.89}$$

From (6.89), it is easy to see that because of nonlinearity, with time, local isotropization of the velocity field and establishment of local self-similarity in a vicinity of a maximum of $\psi_0(\mathbf{x})$ take place. Therewith the velocity field $\mathbf{v}(\mathbf{x},t)$ will be determined by the particles starting from the points with the coordinates $y_i(\mathbf{x},t)$, which lie in a small neighborhood of the given maximum

$$y_i(\mathbf{x},t) = \frac{(x_i - y_{i,k})}{(1+\psi_{0,k}t/L_i^2)}.$$

Thus, at long times, the Lagrangian coordinate $\mathbf{y}(\mathbf{x},t)$ becomes a discontinuous function of the coordinate $\mathbf{x}$ constant within the region (cell) corresponding to one maximum and having "jumps" at its boundaries [3]. The velocity field $\mathbf{v}(\mathbf{x},t)$ has discontinuities of values, and the potential field $\psi(\mathbf{x},t)$ has discontinuities of the derivative at the cell boundaries. From (6.89), it is seen that inside cells the potential and velocity fields have a universal and self-similar structure

$$\psi(\mathbf{x},t) = \psi_0(\mathbf{y}_k) - \frac{(\mathbf{x}-\mathbf{y}_k)^2}{2t}, \tag{6.90}$$

$$\mathbf{v}(\mathbf{x},t) = \frac{\mathbf{x}-\mathbf{y}_k}{t}. \tag{6.91}$$

The longitudinal component of the velocity vector $\mathbf{v}(\mathbf{x},t)$ consists of a sequence of sawtooth pulses, as in the one-dimensional case. The transverse component of the velocity vector is constant within a cell. By using Eq. (6.89), it is possible to show that such universal behavior of the fields starts to manifest itself sooner in the directions with greater initial gradients (small L_i).

At later stages, the evolution of the velocity and potential fields is defined by the properties of the local maxima of $\psi_0(\mathbf{y}_k)$. In the case of periodic initial perturbations, a periodic universal structure with conserving shape is developed, and the amplitude of the velocity field decreases proportionally to t^{-1}. For random initial perturbations, the structure development is accompanied by continuous changes of the surface shape determined by absorptions of cells (discontinuities in the one-dimensional case) by each other. In the process, the general characteristic scale of the Burgers turbulence $L(t)$ increases as well.

Let us discuss the so-called "late limit" of the solution to the Burgers equation, when, at a given viscosity coefficient $\mu > 0$, time t goes to infinity. Let us consider a class of perturbations with a bounded initial potential $\langle \psi_0(\mathbf{x})^2 \rangle < \infty$ assuming that $\psi_0(\mathbf{x})$ is a periodic structure or a statistically homogeneous random field. For such signals, in a scalar field $U(\mathbf{x},t)$, it is possible to single out the constant component $\bar{U}$

$$U(\mathbf{x},t) = \bar{U} + \tilde{U}(\mathbf{x},t) = \bar{U}(1+u(\mathbf{x},t)) \tag{6.92}$$

and the relative perturbation $u(\mathbf{x},t) = \tilde{U}(\mathbf{x},t)/\bar{U}$ of the field $U(\mathbf{x},t)$. Here it is assumed that $\tilde{U}_0(\mathbf{x})$ and $u_0(\mathbf{x})$ are fields with a zero mean value (over a period or, for a random field, statistically). With time, diffusion smoothens away inhomogeneities of the field $U(\mathbf{x},t)$ in the linear diffusion equation (6.84), which leads to a reduction of the amplitude of the field perturbation $\tilde{U}(\mathbf{x},t)$. At times when $|\tilde{U}| \ll \bar{U}$ ($|u| \ll 1$), the Hopf-Cole solution (6.83) can be linearized by replacing it with

$$\mathbf{v}(\mathbf{x},t) = -2\mu \nabla u(\mathbf{x},t). \tag{6.93}$$

Because both $\tilde{U}(\mathbf{x},t)$ and $u(\mathbf{x},t)$ satisfy the linear diffusion equation, $\mathbf{v}(\mathbf{x},t)$ also is described by a linear equation. The latter is an evidence of the arrival of the linear stage of the evolution. Overall nonlinear effects are present in this solution only due to the nonlinear integral link between the initial velocity field $\mathbf{v}_0(\mathbf{x})$ and the fields

$\tilde{U}(\mathbf{x},0)$ and $\bar{U}$ (see Eqs. (6.80) and (6.85)), and is characterized by the magnitude of the initial Reynolds number $\mathrm{R}_0 \sim |\triangle\psi_0|/\mu$. Here $\triangle\psi_0$ is a characteristic amplitude of ψ_0.

From (6.93), it is easy to obtain the well-known result of the asymptotic behavior of a harmonic perturbation for the one-dimensional Burgers equation (see, e.g., [11, 30] and Problem 4 in Chapter 4). At $\mathrm{R}_0 \gg 1$, a harmonic wave is transformed into a sawtooth one, but due to dissipation the wave, at long times, again takes on a harmonic form, but its amplitude is independent of the initial one. At large initial Reynolds numbers, a statistically homogeneous one-dimensional Gaussian field $v_0(x)$ is also transformed into a sequence of sawtooth pulses and has, during the nonlinear stage, substantially non-Gaussian statistical properties [3]. Nevertheless, at long times, when the linearization (6.93) holds, random fields $\mathbf{v}(\mathbf{x},t)$ with statistically homogeneous initial potentials $\psi_0(\mathbf{x})$ weakly converge to a homogeneous Gaussian field with a zero mean [31]. This stage is known as the Gaussian scenario in the Burgers turbulence. This scenario is also realized for the multidimensional Burgers equation. In the absence of long-range correlations, distributions of the initial potential, the velocity and potential fields have a universal covariant function [3, 31] with an amplitude nonlinearly connected with its initial value and proportional to $\exp(\mathrm{R}_0^2)$. If the initial potential has long-range correlations ($\langle\psi_0(\mathbf{x})\psi_0(0)\rangle = |\mathbf{x}|^{-\alpha}F(\mathbf{x}/x)$, $0<\alpha<3$), then, at the linear stage, both the long-range correlations and anisotropy of the field $F(\mathbf{x}/x)$ are preserved [31].

6.3.2 Evolution of simple localized perturbations

Let us consider evolution of a localized anisotropic perturbation in the multidimensional Burgers equation. For the sake of simplifying the calculation, let us start with the two-dimensional ($d=2$) case, since a generalization for $d>2$ is straightforward in most cases. First, let us start with a particular case, when the initial potential $\psi_0(\mathbf{x})$ is a quadratic function of the coordinates (6.88) ($\gamma_{i,k}=0$) inside a region S_0: $x_1^2/2L_1^2 + x_2^2/2L_2^2 \leqslant 1$, and $\psi_0(\mathbf{x})=0$ outside S_0. Therewith the evolution of the fields of the potential $\psi(\mathbf{x},t)$ and the velocity $\mathbf{v}(\mathbf{x},t)$ inside an expanding ellipse $S(t)$

$$x_1^2/2L_1^2(t) + x_2^2/2L_2^2(t) \leqslant 1,$$

$$L_i(t) = L_i(1+\psi_0 t/L_i^2)^{1/2} = L_i(1+t/t_{nl,i})^{1/2} \tag{6.94}$$

is described by Eqs. (6.89) and $\mathbf{v}=0$, $\psi=0$ outside this region. Here $t_{\mathrm{nl},i} = L_i^2/\psi_0$ is the nonlinearity time of the i-th component of the velocity. In this case, each velocity component $v_i(x_i,t)$ evolves independently and, in particular, $v_2(x_2,t) = \psi_0 x_2/L_2^2(1+\psi_{0,k}t/L_2^2)$ does not depend on the other coordinate x_1. However, the boundaries of the interval $\Delta x_1(x_2,t) = L_1(t)[2(1-x_2^2/2L_2^2(t))]^{1/2}$, expanding along the x_1-axis, where the velocity $v_2(x_2,t)$ does not depend on x_1, are defines as both $L_2(t)$ and $L_1(t)$, and consequently there is a strong interaction between the velocity

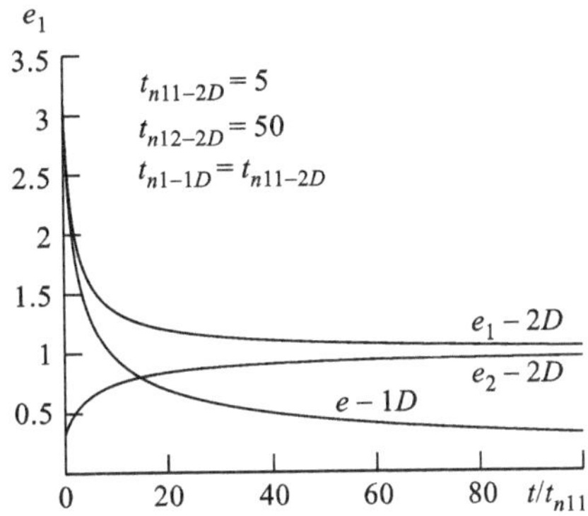

Fig. 6.4 Evolution of the dimensionless energy $e_i - 2D = E_i\psi_0^2/\pi$ of the components of the two-dimensional anisotropic perturbation $(L_2/L_1 = \sqrt{10})$ as a function of the dimensionless time $\tau = t/t_{\text{nl},1}$. Evolution of the energy of the one-dimensional localized perturbation $e - 1D$ is shown for comparison.

components. The energy of each velocity component is determined by the following expressions:

$$E_1(t) = \pi\psi_0^2 L_2(t)/L_1(t), \quad E_2(t) = \pi\psi_0^2 L_1(t)/L_2(t). \tag{6.95}$$

Let us consider evolution of a strongly anisotropic perturbation ($L_1 \ll L_2$). As a measure of anisotropy, let us choose the ratio of the energy components $\kappa(t) = E_1(t)/E_2(t) = L_2^2(t)/L_1^2(t)$. It follows from (6.95) that the energy of the small-scale component $E_1(t)$ monotonously decreases, while the energy of the large-scale component $E_2(t)$ monotonously increases. Accordingly, the anisotropy coeffcient $\kappa(t)$ monotonously decreases from the value $\kappa(0) = L_2^2/L_1^2 \gg 1$ and tends to 1 at $t \gg t_{\text{nl},2}$. At $t_{\text{nl},1} \ll t \ll t_{\text{nl},2}$, when the nonlinear self-action of the large-scale component is not yet substantial, we have for the energies of the components:

$$E_1(t) \simeq \pi\psi_0^2 L_2/(\psi_0 t)^{1/2}, \quad E_2(t) \simeq \pi\psi_0^2(\psi_0 t)^{1/2}/L_2.$$

Thus the energy of the small-scale component monotonously decreases according to the same law as in the one-dimensional case. The energy of the large-scale component increases with time due to the spatial transport of the non-decaying velocity component $v_2(x_2,t) \simeq v_2(x_2,0)$ by the component v_1. At long times, the energies of the entire field $E(t)$ and of each component turn out to be constant. Conservation of energy (of the average surface roughness) at long times is determined by the fact that the decrease of the maximum gradients $v_i(t) \sim t^{-1/2}$ with time is compensated by the increase of the volume $V(t) \sim t^{1/2}$. In Fig. 6.4, evolution of the dimensionless energy $e_i(t) = E_i(t)\psi_0^2/\pi$ of the anisotropic perturbation components $(L_2/L_1 = \sqrt{10})$ is shown as a function of the dimensionless time $\tau = t/t_{\text{nl},1}$.

In the three-dimensional case, it is easy to show that for the initial potential $\psi_0(\mathbf{x})$ described within the corresponding ellipsoid by Eq. (6.88) the energy of the velocity component $v_1(t)$ varies as

$$E_1(t) \sim \psi_0^2 L_2(t)L_3(t)/L_1(t),$$

where $L_i(t)$ is determined by Eq. (6.94). For a strongly anisotropic perturbation, the energy of the field's components at the initial stage ($\min(t_{\mathrm{nl},i}) \ll t \ll \max(t_{\mathrm{nl},i})$) may either grow, decay or remain constant with time, but at $t \gg \max(t_{\mathrm{nl},i})$ the field becomes anisotropic and the energy grows $\sim t^{1/2}$.

Let us assume that the initial anisotropic localized perturbation may be represented in the following form:

$$\psi_0(\mathbf{x}) = \psi_0 f_1(x_1) f_2(x_2),$$

where the function f_i has a maximum at the point $\mathbf{x} = 0$, ($f_1(0) = f_2(0) = 1$) and the characteristic length scales L_i ($L_1 \ll L_2$). For such perturbation, $E_1(0) \gg E_2(0)$. At times $t_{\mathrm{nl},1}/f_2(x_2) \ll t \ll t_{\mathrm{nl},2}$ ($t_{\mathrm{nl},i} = L_i^2/\psi_0$) the small-scale component $v_1(\mathbf{x},t)$ is transformed into an N-shaped pulse, and the self-action of the large-scale component $v_2(\mathbf{x},t)$ is not yet substantial. Therefore, at a fixed x_2, in the spatial interval

$$|x_1| \leqslant L_s(t) = (2\psi_0 f_2(x_2)t)^{1/2}, \tag{6.96}$$

a universal behavior of the filed's components is observed:

$$v_1(\mathbf{x},t) \simeq x_1/t, \quad v_2(\mathbf{x},t) \simeq \psi_0 f_1(0)\frac{\partial f_2(x_2)}{\partial x_2}, \tag{6.97}$$

namely, $v_1(\mathbf{x},t)$ does not depend on x_2 and the initial amplitude of the perturbation, whereas $v_2(\mathbf{x},t)$ does not depend on x_1 and is equal to the initial field on the axis $x_1 = 0$: $v_2(\mathbf{x},t) = v_2(0,x_2,0)$. Hence, from (6.96), (6.97) for the energies of the components, we have

$$E_1(t) \simeq \frac{2^{5/2}\psi_0^{3/2}}{3t^{1/2}} \int f_2^{3/2}(x_2)dx \sim E_1(0)\frac{L_1}{(\psi_0 t)^{1/2}},$$

$$E_2(t) \simeq 2^{3/2}\psi_0^{3/2}t^{1/2} \int f_2^{1/2}(x_2)\left(\frac{\partial f_2(x_2)}{\partial x_2}\right)^2 dx \sim E_2(0)\frac{(\psi_0 t)^{1/2}}{L_1}.$$

Thus, also in this case, attenuation of the small-scale component v_1 and growth of the large-scale component v_2 are observed. At $t \gg t_{\mathrm{nl},2}$, isotropization of the initial perturbation takes place, and the velocity field has in universal structure (6.91) within the region $|\mathbf{x}| < (2\psi_0 t)^{1/2}$.

6.3.3 *Evolution of periodic structures under infinite Reynolds numbers*

The simplest analogue of the one-dimensional harmonic perturbation is the following, periodic along the two coordinates (x_1,x_2) structure:

$$\psi_0(x_1,x_2) = 2\psi_0 \cos(k_2x_2)\cos(k_1x_1) = \\ = \psi_0 \cos(k_1x_1 + k_2x_2) + \psi_0 \cos(k_1x_1 - k_2x_2). \quad (6.98)$$

Here $k_1 = k_0n_1$, $k_2 = k_0n_2$, $\mathbf{n}$ is a unit vector with the components n_1, n_2 and $l_i = 1/2\pi k_i$.

Evolution of such initial conditions may be interpreted as an interaction of plane harmonic waves. Under the interaction of waves with small angles $n_1 \gg n_2$ this initial condition may also be interpreted as plane periodic wave modulated by a large-scale function $M(\mathbf{x})$

$$\psi_0^M(\mathbf{x}) = M(\mathbf{x})\psi_0 \cos(k_1x_1) \ . \quad (6.99)$$

With $M(\mathbf{x}) \equiv 1$, the velocity field has only one component $v_{1,0}(x_1,x_2) = k_1\psi_0 \sin(k_1x_1)$ and with $\mu \to 0$ the harmonic wave is transformed into a sawtooth one with the period $l_1 = 1/2\pi k_1$. Apparently, when $M(\mathbf{x}) = 2\cos(k_2x_2)$, this corresponds to the case of plane wave interaction considered above.

Let us discuss the initial stage of evolution of the modulated plane wave (6.99). If the characteristic length scale of the function $M(\mathbf{x})$ is much greater than l_1, for the initial velocity field we have

$$v_{1,0}(x_1,x_2) \simeq k_1\psi_0 \sin(k_1x_1)M(x_1,x_2),$$

$$v_{2,0}(x_1,x_2) = -\psi_0 \cos(k_1x_1)M'_{x_2}(x_1,x_2),$$

and, accordingly, $v_2 \ll v_1$. In the limit of vanishing viscosity $\mu \to 0$ evolution of the velocity field is described by Eq. (6.87) and $\mathbf{v}(\mathbf{x},t) = \mathbf{v}_0(\mathbf{y}(\mathbf{x},t))$, where $\mathbf{y}(\mathbf{x},t)$ are the Lagrangian coordinate of the point, from which starts the particle ending up at the point $\mathbf{x}$ at the moment of time t. In other words, the velocity is constant along a characteristic. When $L_{M,i} \gg l_1 = 1/2\pi k_1$, $v_2 \ll v_1$ and $t \ll t_{\mathrm{nl},2} = L_{m,2}^2/\psi_0$, it is possible to neglect the particle motion along the x_2-axis. In this case, the expressions for the coordinates have the form

$$X_1(y_1,y_2,t) = y_1 + tk_1\psi_0 \sin(k_1y_1)M(y_1,y_2), \ X_2(y_1,y_2,t) = y_2. \quad (6.100)$$

As long as $t < t_{\mathrm{nl},1} = 1/k_1^2\psi_0$, the solution $\mathbf{v}(\mathbf{x},t) = \mathbf{v}_0(\mathbf{y}(\mathbf{x},t))$ is single-valued, and at $t > t_{\mathrm{nl},1}$ it is necessary to take discontinuities into account. In the quasi-static approximation, one may assume that the evolution of the velocity component $v_1(x_1,x_2,t)$ is equivalent to the evolution of the harmonic perturbation $v_{1,0} = A\sin(k_1x_1)$ in the one-dimensional Burgers equation. The signal's amplitude $A = k_1\psi_0 M(x_{1,m},x_2)$ $(x_{1,m} = l_1 m)$ depends on the coordinate x_2 parametrically and does not depend on x_1 within each separately considered period.

When $t_{\mathrm{nl},1} \ll t \ll t_{\mathrm{nl},2}$, the field component v_1 is transformed into a sawtooth wave. For definitiveness, let $M(x_1,x_2) > 0$. It is easy to see that at $t \gg t_{\mathrm{nl},1}$, which period $l_1(m-1/2) < x_1 < l_1(m+1/2)$ will be filled with particles from a small neighborhood of the point $x_{1,m} = l_1 m$, and the solutions of the equations $x_1 = X(y_1,y_2,t)$, $x_2 = X_2$ can be written as

$$y_1 - x_{1,m} = \frac{x_1 - x_{1,m}}{1 + tk_1^2\psi_0 M(x_{1,m}, x_2)}, \quad y_2 = x_2. \tag{6.101}$$

Discontinuities are situated within the intervals $x_{1,s} = l_1(m+1/2)$. From Eqs. (6.100), (6.101) at $M > 0$ within the intervals $l_1(m-1/2) < x_1 < l_1(m+1/2)$, it is possible to obtain the following expressions for the velocity-field components:

$$v(x_1, x_2, t) = \frac{x_1 - y_{1,m}}{t}\left(1 - \frac{1}{1 + tk_1^2\psi_0 M(x_{1,m}, x_2)}\right),$$

$$v_2(x_1, x_2, t) = -\psi_0 M'_{x_2}(x_{1,m}, x_2)\cos\left(\frac{k_1 x_1}{tk_1^2\psi_0 M(x_{1,m}, x_2)}\right).$$

From the last equation, it is seen that at $t \gg t_{\mathrm{nl},1}$ the velocity-field component $v_1(x_1, x_2, t)$ is transformed into a sawtooth wave $v_1 \simeq (x_1 - y_{1,m})/t$ as in the one-dimensional case. This means that complete suppression of the initial amplitude modulation of this component takes place. The velocity component v_2 loses the periodic modulation along x_1 and is equal to $v_{2,0}(x_1, x_2, t) \simeq -\psi_0 M'_{x_2}(x_1, x_2)$ for a positive M and $v_{2,0}(x_1, x_2, t) \simeq \psi_0 M'_{x_2}(x_1, x_2)$ for a negative M. The energy of this component becomes twice the initial one.

For such wave, the velocity field can also be represented in the form

$$\mathbf{v} = \mathbf{v}_l + \mathbf{v}_s,$$

here $\mathbf{v}_l(\mathbf{x}, t)$ is the large-scale component of the field, and $\mathbf{v}_s(\mathbf{x}, t)$ is its small-scale component. Therewith generation of the large-scale component is determined by the energy gradient of the small-scale component. At $t \gg t_{\mathrm{nl},1}$ and periodic modulation, the energy $E_s(x, t)$ ceases to depend on the initial amplitude. The latter means that with periodic modulation at such times generation of the large-scale component stops. The gradient of the mean potential $\langle\psi(\mathbf{x}, t)\rangle = \psi_0|M(\mathbf{x})| - l_1^2/16t$ at such times does not depend on t and may be represented by

$$\mathbf{v}_l(\mathbf{x}, t) = -\nabla\langle\psi(\mathbf{x}, t)\rangle = -\psi_0\nabla|M(\mathbf{x})|.$$

Consequently, due to nonlinear interaction, the large-scale component is generated. The amplitude of the small-scale component is equal to l_1/t, and the large-scale component is of the order of $\psi_0/L_{M,i}$. Therefore, at $t > L_{M,i}l_1/\psi_0$, the main part of the velocity-field energy is concentrated in the large-scale component. Its nonlinear distortions become discernible at $t > \min(L_{M,i}^2)/\psi_0$. Further evolution of the large-scale component strongly depends on the properties of the modulation function $M(\mathbf{x})$.

Let us return to the problem of interaction of two plane waves in the two-dimensional Burgers equation, which is equivalent to the evolution of the periodic structure (6.98). For a plane wave, the energy of the$i$-th component is equal to $E_{i,p}(t) = E(t)n_i^2$, where $E(t)$ is the plane wave energy initially equal to $E(0) = \psi_0^2 k_0^2/2$. When $\mu \to 0$, the plane wave is transformed at times $t \gg t_{\mathrm{nl}} = 1/k_0^2\psi_0$

into a sawtooth wave with the gradient $\partial v/\partial x = 1/t$, and the energy varies as $E(t) = \pi^2/3k_0^2t^2$.

Interaction of waves at small angles, at $n_1 \gg n_2$, is equivalent to the case when the plane periodic wave $\psi_0 \cos(k_1x_1)$ is modulated by the large-scale function $M(\mathbf{x}) = \cos(k_2x_2)$ (see Eq. (6.99)). The initial perturbation in this case is a periodic structure with periods $l_1 = 2\pi/k_1$, $l_2 = 2\pi/k_2$ and $l_1 \ll l_2$. Before nonlinear distortions of the large-scale component ($t \ll t_{\mathrm{nl},2} = l_2/\psi_0$), the field evolution is similar to the general case of a modulated wave (6.99). The velocity component $v_1(x_1,x_2,t)$ is transformed into a sawtooth wave and complete suppression of the initial amplitude modulation of this component takes place. The velocity component v_2 loses the periodic modulation along x_1 and varies as $v_{2,0}(x_1,x_2,t) \simeq \psi_0|\cos(k_2x_2)|'_{x_2}$. The period of this component is half the initial period, and the energy grows twice the initial value.

In Fig. 6.5, evolution of the velocity components is depicted as functions of the slow coordinate x_2. Energy variation law of the components is plotted in Fig. 6.6.

Let us now consider the asymptotic stage of the evolution of the perturbation, when the velocity field has a universal form in each cell (see Eq. (6.91)), where $\mathbf{y}_k$ are the maxima of the initial potential (6.98). For the chosen initial field, there are two sets of maxima satisfying the conditions $\cos k_1x_1 = \cos k_2x_2 = 1$ and $\cos k_1x_1 =$

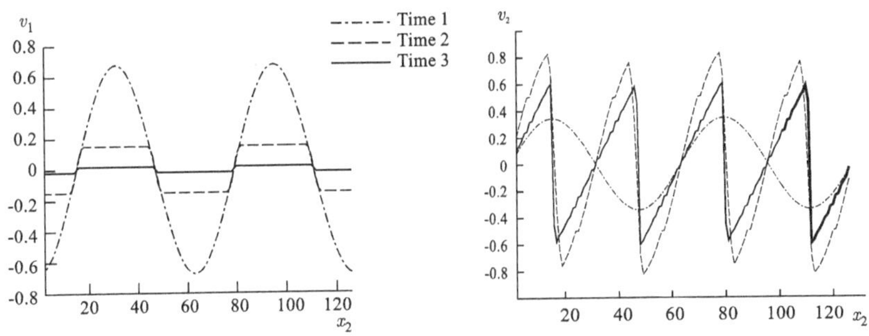

Fig. 6.5 Evolution of the velocity components $v_1(x_1,x_2,t)$ and $v_2(x_1,x_2,t)$ as functions of x_2.

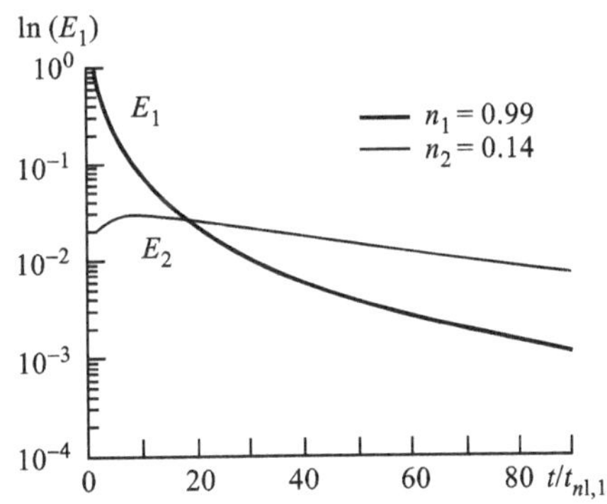

Fig. 6.6 Evolution of the "energy" of the components of the periodic velocity field.

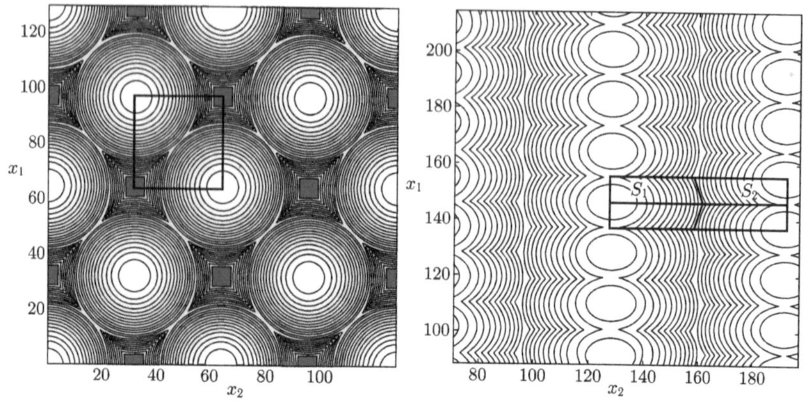

Fig. 6.7 Cellular structure of the field when $k_1 = k_2$ and $k_1 \gg k_2$.

$\cos k_2x_2 = -1$. Lines of velocity-field discontinuities (cell boundaries) are therewith immobile, orthogonal to the vector connecting the centers of neighboring cells and are situated in the middle of the given interval. Due to the symmetry of the initial conditions, the velocity field is symmetric with respect to the point $(l_1/2, l_2/2)$. Let us now assume that $l_1 \leqslant l_2$ and consider the velocity field in the region S: $x_1 \in [0, L_1/2], x_2 \in [0, L_2/2]$ (see Fig. 6.7).

The region S is divided into regions S_1 and S_2 by discontinuities

$$S_1 : 0 \leqslant x_2 \leqslant -\frac{l_1}{l_2}x_1 + \frac{l_1^2 + l_2^2}{4l_2^2}. \tag{6.102}$$

The cell center in the region S_1 is at the point $(x_1 = 0, x_2 = 0)$, while in the region S_2, it is at the point $(x_1 = l_1/2, x_2 = l_2/2)$. Hence for the velocity field we have

$$v_1 = x_1/t, \quad v_2 = x_2/t, \quad \mathbf{x} \in S_1,$$

$$v_1 = (x_1 - l_1/2)/t, \quad v_2 = (x_2 - l_2/2)/t, \quad \mathbf{x} \in S_2. \tag{6.103}$$

From Eqs. (6.102), (6.103) follows that in the case of a strongly anisotropic initial field $(l_1 \ll l_2)$, the velocity component v_1 behaves as the field in the one-dimensional Burgers equation, but the period of the large-scale component is now equal to $L = l_2/2$ instead of $L = l_2$ of the initial perturbation.

For the velocity-component energies, from Eq. (6.103) follows

$$E_1(t) = \frac{l_1^2}{12t^2}\left(1 - \frac{l_1^2}{l_2^2}\right) = \frac{\pi^2}{3k_0^2n_1^2t^2}\left(1 - \frac{n_2^2}{n_1^2}\right),$$

$$E_2(t) = \frac{l_2^2}{48t^2}\left(1 + \frac{l_1^4}{l_2^4}\right) = \frac{\pi^2}{12k_0^2n_2^2t^2}\left(1 + \frac{n_2^4}{n_1^4}\right).$$

Let us now compare energy decay for the periodic structure (6.98), which is a superposition of two plane waves, with energy decay of $E_{i,p}$ of a single plane wave. When $l_1 \ll l_2$, the energy of the small-case component decays as $E_1 \simeq \pi^2/3k_0^2n_1^2t^2 \simeq E_{i,1} = \pi^2n_1^2/3k_0^2t^2$. The energy of the large-scale component varies as $E_2 \simeq \pi^2/12k_0^2n_2^2t^2 \gg E_{i,2} = \pi^2n_2^2/3k_0^2$. Thus nonlinear interaction substantially increases the energy of the large-scale component.

6.3.4 Evolution of the anisotropic Burgers turbulence

If, for a periodic perturbation at the final stage, the field's structure is "frozen" (discontinuities are "frozen"), then, for a random field, continuous absorption of class by each other takes place, and consequently the characteristic length-scale of the field grows. As in the one-dimensional case, for the multidimensional Burgers turbulence with finite variance of the initial potential, it is possible to give an exhaustive description of the turbulence, find one- and two-point probability distributions, spectra and correlation functions of the vector velocity field. (see, e.g., [3, 6]). In a general case, long-time behavior of the turbulence is determined by the "tails" of the initial potential's distribution function [2]. Therewith, depending on the form of the initial potential's distribution, three universal self-similar regimes of turbulence decay ay be realized.

In what follows, we will qualitatively describe evolution of an anisotropic random field and at a physical level of rigor will show that how statistical properties of the multidimensional Burgers turbulence formed in the process are connected with parameters of the initial anisotropic field. Statistical laws of extrema of random fields used here are briefly described in Sect. 6.3.7.

6.3.4.1 Initial stage of field development

Let us first describe the intermediate stage of evolution of the anisotropic two-dimensional Burgers turbulence. We assume that the initial potential $\psi_0(x_1,x_2)$ is a random strongly anisotropic field with spatial scales $l_1 \ll l_2$. The initial energy $E_i(t) = \langle v_i^2 \rangle = \langle (\partial\psi/\partial x_i)^2 \rangle \simeq \sigma_\psi/l_i^2$ of the small-scale component v_1 in this case is much greater than the initial energy of the large-scale component v_2. Let us introduce characteristic times of nonlinear distortions of the i-th component as $t_{\mathrm{nl},i} = l_i^2/\sigma_\psi$. At $t \ll t_{\mathrm{nl},2}$, it is possible to neglect Lagrangian particle motion along the coordinate x_2 and because of this the problem can be considered as a one-dimensional case with an initial potential $\psi_0(y_1,x_2,t)$ letting $y_2 = x_2$ be a parameter in the expression (6.86).

Under the condition $l_1 \ll l_2$, first discontinuities (i.e. points where the Lagrangians coordinate, and, consequently, the velocity and potential fields undergo a jump) appear in those points where the function $\partial\psi/\partial y_1$ has a minimum. In the Eulerian space, the discontinuities are oriented predominantly along the x_2-axis and their length in this direction grows with time. At $t \gg t_{\mathrm{nl},1}$, the velocity field $v_1(x_1,x_2,t)$ is transformed into a sequence of sawtooth pulses

$$v_1(x_1,x_2,t) = \frac{x_1 - y_{1,k}(x_1,x_2,t)}{t}, \quad x^s_{1,k} < x_1 < x^s_{1,k+1}, \tag{6.104}$$

where $y_{1,k}(x_1,x_2,t)$ are the coordinates of the absolute maxima of the function (6.86) with respect to y_1 under the condition $y_2 = x_2$. Discontinuity positions $x^s_{1,k}(x_2,t)$ therewith are equal to

$$x^s_{1,k} = \frac{y_{1,k+1} + y_{1,k}}{2} + v_k t,$$
$$v_k = \frac{\psi_0(y_{1,k}(x_1,x_2),x_2) - \psi_0(y_{1,k+1}(x_1,x_2),x_2)}{y_{1,k+1}(x_1,x_2) - y_{1,k}(x_1,x_2)}. \tag{6.105}$$

The latter means that at a fixed x_2, the interval $x^s_{1,k} < x_1 < x^s_{1,k+1}$ will filled with particles from a small neighborhood of the point with the Lagrangian coordinate $y_{1,k}(x_1,x_2,t)$. For the velocity component v_2, it is possible to obtain

$$v_2(x_1,x_2,t) = -\frac{\partial \psi_0(x_1,x_2)}{\partial x_2}\Big|_{x_1 = y_{1,k}(x_2,t)}, \quad x^s_{1,k} < x < x^s_{1,k+1}. \tag{6.106}$$

It is seen that the magnitude of $v_2(x_1,x_2,t)$ does not depend on x_1 in the interval between discontinuities $x^s_{1,k}(x_2)$ and $x^s_{1,k+1}(x_2)$. Interaction of discontinuities in this case is equivalent to a contact of two boundaries $x^s_{1,k}$ and $x^s_{1,k+1}$ at a point $\mathbf{x}_*$. Therewith, at this point, a new discontinuity line is formed $x^{s,*}_{1,k}(x_2)$ with its length growing with time along the x_2-axis, and, finally, transforming into lines $x^s_{1,k}, x^s_{1,k+1}$. Thus, at $t_{\mathrm{nl},1} \gg t \gg t_{\mathrm{nl},1}$, the velocity field will have a cellular structure. The cell boundaries therewith are described by Eq. (6.105). The field component $v_1(\mathbf{x})$ has the universal structure (6.104), and $v_2(\mathbf{x})$ does not depend on x_1 within the cells and varies along x_2 as v_2 with respect to $x_1 = y_{1,k}(x_2,t)$ (see Eq. (6.106)).

Statistical properties of the component v_1 at this stage of development are similar to the one-dimensional Burgers turbulence (Sect. 5.3.2). The integral length-scale $L_1(t)$ and energy $E_1(t) \sim (L_1(t)/t)^2$ of the component v_1 are described by the expressions

$$L(t) \approx (t\sigma_\psi)^{1/2} \ln^{-1/4}\left(\frac{t}{2\pi t_{\mathrm{nl}}}\right), \; E(t) \simeq t^{-1}\sigma_\psi \ln^{-1/2}\left(\frac{t}{2\pi t_{\mathrm{nl}}}\right), \tag{6.107}$$

where

$$t_{\mathrm{nl}} \equiv L_0^2/\sigma_\psi = L_0/\sigma_v, \quad L_0 \equiv \sigma_\psi/\sigma_v. \tag{6.108}$$

Here σ_ψ is the variance of the initial two-dimensional potential ψ_0, and σ_v^2 is the variance of the velocity component v_1. Due to interaction of discontinuities, the integral length scale if the turbulence with respect to the x_1-axis grows with time as $L_1(t) \sim (t\sigma_\psi)^{1/2}$. Therefore at $t \sim t_{\mathrm{nl},2}$, when relative equalizing of the energies of the components $L_1(t) \simeq l_2$ and $E_1(t) \simeq E_2(0)$ takes place, it is necessary to take nonlinear evolution of the field into account also along the x_2-axis. Mentioned pe-

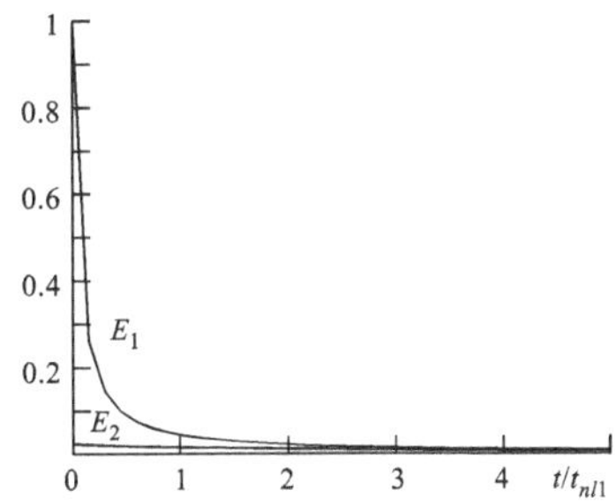

Fig. 6.8 Dependence of the energies E_i of the components of a random anisotropic velocity field on time $t/t_{\mathrm{nl},1}$

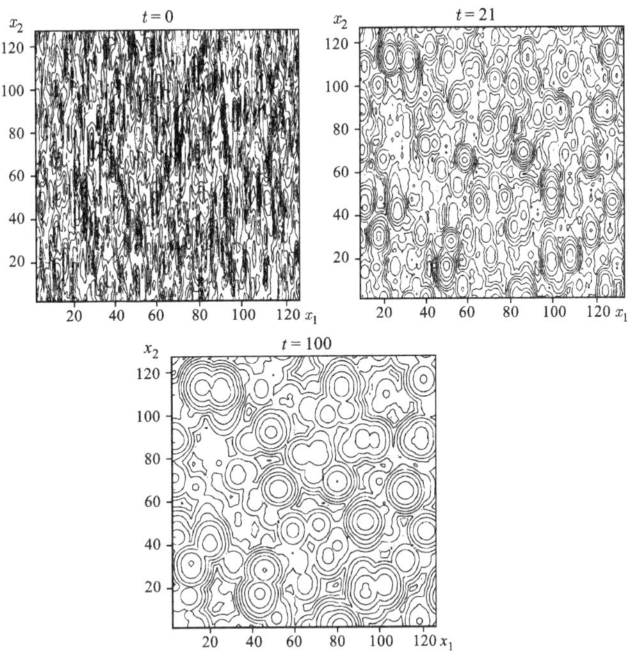

Fig. 6.9 Equipotential lines of $\psi(\mathbf{x},t)$ at $t=0$, $t/t_{\mathrm{nl},1}\sim 1$ and $t/t_{\mathrm{nl},1}\sim 10$.

culiarities of energies $E_1(t)$ and $E_2(t)$ behavior with course of time are seen in Fig. 6.8.

At $t \gg t_{\mathrm{nl},2}$, the fields of the velocity and potential will have a universal isotropic and self-similar structure, which is described by Eqs. (6.91), (6.90) inside cells. The cell boundaries at this stage become degenerate into straight lines (planes, in the three-dimensional case). Multiple changes of the number of cells and their boundaries leads to establishment of statistical self-similarity and isotropization of the field. In Fig. 6.9 equipotential lines of $\psi(\mathbf{x},t)$ at $t=0$, $t/t_{\mathrm{nl},1}\sim 1$ are $t/t_{\mathrm{nl},2}\sim 10$, respectively, are shown.

6.3.4.2 Statistical properties of the multidimensional Burgers turbulence

Let us take as the initial potential $\psi_0(\mathbf{x})$ a random Gaussian field with the correlation function representable in the following form

$$\langle \psi_0(\mathbf{x})\psi_0(\mathbf{x}+\rho)\rangle = B_\psi(\rho) = \sigma_\psi^2 \prod_{i=1}^{d} R_i(\rho_i),$$

$$R_i(\rho_i) = 1 - \frac{\rho_i^2}{2! l_{0,i}^2} + \frac{\rho_i^4}{4! l_{1,i}^4} + \ldots \tag{6.109}$$

Let us also assume that the correlation function sufficiently rapidly decays, $B_\psi(|\rho| > l_{st}) \simeq 0$, and the values of the potential $\psi_0(\mathbf{x})$ at points $|\mathbf{x}_1 - \mathbf{x}_2| > l_{st}$ are statistically independent beyond a certain separation l_{st}. The above corresponds to the so-called case of "near correlations" of the initial potential.

In the limit of vanishing viscosity, in it possible to apply the maximum principle for the initial potential (see Eq. (6.87)) in order to find a solution. In this case, the solution $\mathbf{v}(\mathbf{x},t)$ (6.87) is determined by the coordinates $\mathbf{y}$ of the maximum of the function $\Phi(\mathbf{x},y,t)$. Let us denote by $Q(H,\triangle V_k)$ the integral distribution function equal to the probability of finding the absolute maximum with the value H within an elementary volume V_k. Let us denote the corresponding probability density as $W_{\max}(H,\triangle V_k)$:

$$Q(H,\triangle V_k) = \Pr(\Phi < H, \mathbf{y} \in \triangle V_k), \quad W_{\max}(H,\triangle V_k) = Q_H'(H,\triangle V_k).$$

Here it is assumed that the characteristic size of an elementary volume $\triangle V_k$ is much greater than l_{st}, but much less than the integral length scale of the turbulence $L(t)$. The probability that the value of the absolute maximum lies within the interval between H_1 and $H_1 + \triangle H_1$, and its coordinates are contained in the region $\mathbf{y}(\mathbf{x},t) \in \triangle V_k$, is equal to the probability of the event that the values of all maxima situated outside the volume $\triangle V_k$ (of the region $\overline{\triangle V}_k$), is less than H

$$\Pr(\mathbf{y} \in \triangle V_k, H \in [H_1, H_1 + \triangle H]) = W_{\max}(H,\triangle v_k)\triangle H Q(H,\overline{\triangle V}_k). \tag{6.110}$$

Here it is taken into account that the absolute maxima within the volume $\triangle V_k$ are statistically independent. The probability of finding the coordinates of the absolute maximum $\mathbf{y}(\mathbf{x},t)$ within the volume $\triangle V_k$ regardless of its value may be found by integration (6.110) with respect to H:

$$\Pr(\mathbf{y} \in \triangle V_k) = \int W_{\max}(H,\triangle V_k) Q(H,\overline{\triangle V}_k) dH. \tag{6.111}$$

It is possible to show that for large H, the integral distribution function $Q(H,\triangle V_k)$ is defined by the mean number of extrema $N(H,\triangle V_k)$ with a value greater than H (see (6.147)), $Q(H,\triangle V_k) = e^{-N(H,\triangle V_k)}$. Having integrated Eq. (6.111) by parts, we obtain

$$\Pr(\mathbf{y} \in \triangle V_k) = \int N(H, \triangle V_k) Q'_H(H) dH, \tag{6.112}$$

where $Q(H)$ is the integral distribution function in the entire space. We will analyze the behavior of the turbulence at long times, when the paraboloid $\alpha = (\mathbf{x}-\mathbf{y})^2/2t$ in Eq. (6.86) turns out to be a sufficiently smooth function compared with the initial potential. Then, in order to find the mean number of maxima, it is possible to use the quasistatic approximation

$$Q(H) = e^{-N_\infty(H)}, \quad N_\infty(H) = \int n_{\text{ext}} \left(H + \frac{(\mathbf{x}-\mathbf{y})^2}{2t} \right) d^d\mathbf{y}, \tag{6.113}$$

where $N_\infty(H)$ is the mean number of extrema of the function $\Phi(\mathbf{x}, y, t)$ exceeding the value of H in the entire space. and n_{ext} is the density of the number of extrema of the initial homogeneous field $\psi_0(\mathbf{x}) \equiv S(\mathbf{x})$. When $H \gg \sigma_\psi$, the density is determined by Eq. (6.146) and then

$$\begin{aligned} N_\infty(H) &= \frac{1}{(2\pi)^{(d+1)/2} l_{\text{eff}}^d} \int \left(\frac{H}{\sigma_\psi} \right)^{d-1} e^{-(H+y^2/2t)^2/2\sigma_\psi^2} d^d\mathbf{y} \\ &\simeq \left(\frac{H}{\sigma_\psi} \right)^{d-1} \frac{1}{\sqrt{2\pi}} \left(\frac{\sigma_\psi^2 t}{H l_{\text{eff}}^2} \right)^{d/2} e^{-H/2\sigma_\psi^2}, \end{aligned} \tag{6.114}$$

$$l_{0,\text{eff}}^d = \prod_{i=1}^d l_{0,i}.$$

In Eq. (6.113), the integration is performed over all space, but the most dominant contribution into the integral $(\sigma_\psi^2 t / H l_{\text{eff}}^2)^{d/2}$ is from the region determined by the paraboloid in the expression for n_{ext}. The effective number of local maxima $N_{\max} \sim (\sigma_\psi t / l_{\text{eff}}^2)^{d/2}$ of the initial field grows with time and at $N_{\max} \gg 1$ it is possible to introduce a dimensionless potential h, where $h_0 = H_0 \sigma_\psi$, and H_0 is the solution of the equation $N_\infty(H_0) = 1$:

$$h_0 \simeq d^{1/2} \left(\ln \frac{\sigma_\psi t}{l_{\text{eff}}^2 (2\pi)^{1/d}} \right)^{1/2}, \quad \langle \psi(\mathbf{x}, t) \rangle \simeq \sigma_\psi h_0.$$

This dimensionless potential has a double exponential distribution cosidered in Sect. 6.3. Evidently, at $t \gg t_{\text{nl}} = l_{\text{eff}}^2 / \sigma_\psi$, the integral distribution function is concentrated in a narrow region $\triangle H / H \simeq \sigma_\psi^2 / H_0^2 \ll 1$ in a vicinity of H_0 (see Eq. (6.89)). By using this fact, it is possible to obtain from (6.112) the following expression for the probability density of the maximum's coordinates

$$W(\mathbf{y}, \mathbf{x}, t) = \frac{1}{\sqrt{2\pi L^2(t)}} \exp\left(-\frac{(\mathbf{x}-\mathbf{y})^2}{2L^2(t)} \right), \tag{6.115}$$

where

$$L(t) = \left(\frac{\sigma_\psi t}{h_0}\right)^{1/2} = (\sigma_\psi t)^{1/2} d^{-1/4} \left(\ln \frac{\sigma_\psi t}{l_{\text{eff}}^2 (2\pi)^{1/d}}\right)^{-1/4} \tag{6.116}$$

is the integral length scale of the turbulence. For the energies of all components, we have

$$E_i(t) = \sigma_{v,i}^2 = \frac{L^2(t)}{t^2} = \left(\frac{\sigma_\psi}{t}\right) d^{-1/2} \left(\ln \frac{\sigma_\psi t}{l_{\text{eff}}^2 (2\pi)^{1/d}}\right)^{-1/2}. \tag{6.117}$$

From Eqs. (6.87) and (6.115), it is seen that the velocity field becomes isotropic at long times. Let us show that all statistical characteristics will have a self-similar form.

A two-dimensional probability density for multidimensional turbulence had previously been obtained in [3] within the framework of the so-called "cellular" (discrete) model. In this model, it was assumed that, within different elementary volumes (cells) $\triangle$, random values of the initial potential are Gaussian and statistically independent. In this section, however, we discuss a continuous random field with a given correlation function (6.109). Nevertheless, the procedure for derivation of the two-point distribution function is similar to the one used in the "cellular" model [3]. It is easy to show that in our case, the expression for the two-point probability density will be the same as in [3], but with a cell size $\triangle$ replaced by an effective spatial length scale l_{eff}. It is determined by the length scales $l_{0,i}$ of the initial correlation function (6.114). It follows from this that, at long times, the probability density, correlation function and energy spectrum will have a self-similar form. In particular, for the normalized correlation function of the longitutinal (LL) and transverse (NN) components of the field $\tilde{\mathbf{v}} = \mathbf{v}/\sigma_{v,i}$, it is possible to obtain

$$\tilde{B}_{LL}(\tilde{x}) = \langle \tilde{v}_{1L} \tilde{v}_{2L} \rangle = \frac{d}{d\tilde{x}} \left(\tilde{x} P(\tilde{x})\right),$$

$$\tilde{B}_{NN}(\tilde{x}) = \frac{1}{2} \langle \tilde{v}_{1N} \tilde{v}_{2N} \rangle = P(\tilde{x}),$$

where $\tilde{x} = x/L(t)$ and

$$P(\tilde{x}) = \frac{1}{2} \int_{-\infty}^{\infty} \frac{dz}{g\left(\frac{\tilde{x}+z}{2}\right) \exp\left[\frac{(\tilde{x}+z)^2}{8}\right] + g\left(\frac{\tilde{x}-z}{2}\right) \exp\left[\frac{(\tilde{x}-z)^2}{8}\right]},$$

$$g(z) \equiv \int_{-\infty}^{z} e^{-s^2/2} ds.$$

It is possible to show that $P(\tilde{x})$ also is the probability of absence of discontinuities within an Eulerian interval of length $\tilde{x}L(t)$. Since we consider potential isotropic fields, the normalized energy spectrum $e(k)$ is expressed via the one-dimensional spectrum $e_{NN}(k)$ of the transverse component.

The spectral density $E_v(k,t)$ is also isotropic and self-similar

$$E(k,t) = \frac{L^3(t)}{t^2}\tilde{E}(kL(t)). \tag{6.118}$$

At large wavenumbers k, formation of discontinuities (small-scale jumps) leads to appearance of the power-law asymptotic dependence $e(k) \sim k^{-2}$. At small wavenumbers in the three-dimensional case, the spectrum is also characterized by a universal behavior

$$E(k,t) = k^{d+1}\frac{L^{4+d}(t)}{t^2} \sim k^{d+1}t^{d/2},$$

which signifies nonlinear generation of the large-scale component corresponding to small wavenumbers. So in the case of the tree-dimensional Burger turbulence $E(k,t) \sim k^4 t^{3/2}$. For large but finite Reynolds numbers, discontinuities have a finite width $\delta \sim \mu t/L(t)$ and grow with time compared with the integral length scale as $\delta/L(t) \sim \left(\ln(\sigma_\psi t/l_{\text{eff}}^2)\right)^{1/2}$. Due to this, at very large times, evolution enters its linear stage.

6.3.5 Evolution of perturbations with complex internal structure

In this section we discuss evolution of localized multidimensional perturbations generally having a small-scale structure. This problem appear, e.g., in a surface-growth analysis or fire-front evolution in a bounded domain. [14,32].

From the solution of the Burgers equation (6.87) follows that the asymptotic solution (6.91)

$$\mathbf{v}(\mathbf{x},t) = (\mathbf{x} - \mathbf{y}_k)/t, \ \ |\mathbf{x} - \mathbf{y}_k| < L_s(t) = (2Ht)^{1/2} \tag{6.119}$$

take place for any initial localized perturbation with the only maximum $H = \psi_0(\mathbf{y}_k)$ situated at the point $\mathbf{y} = \mathbf{y}_k$. During this stage, the field "energy" in a d-dimensional case is given by the following expression:

$$E(t) = \frac{2^{(d+4)/2}H^{(d+2)/2}t^{(d-2)/2}}{\Gamma(d/2)(d+2)}, \tag{6.120}$$

where $\Gamma(z)$ is the gamma function. From (6.120) It is seen that for $d = 1$, the energy $E(t)$ decreases with time; in the two-dimensional case, $E(t)$ turns out to be constant; and at $d \geqslant 3$, the energy $E(t)$ grows with time. Recall that in a multidimensional case, $E(t) = \langle(\nabla\psi(\mathbf{x},t))^2\rangle = \langle\mathbf{v}^2(\mathbf{x},t)\rangle$ represents the mean square gradient of a surface and characterizes its roughness.

If an initially localized perturbation has a complex internal structure, the process of isotropization may exhibit different stages. Let us discuss evolution of multi-scale localized initial perturbation assuming that its initial potential is representable in the form

$$\psi_0^M(\mathbf{x}) = M(\mathbf{x})\psi_0(\mathbf{x}), \ \ M(\mathbf{x}) = 1 - \Sigma x_i^2/2L_{M,i}^2 + \ldots, \tag{6.121}$$

here $\psi_0(\mathbf{x})$ is a random Gaussian statistically homogeneous field with the correlation function (6.109). The envelope function $M(\mathbf{x})$ has a maximum at the point $\mathbf{x}=0$, and the characteristic length scales $L_{M,i}$ are much greater than the scales of the internal structure l_{0i}.

In the previous section, it was shown that for a statistically homogeneous initial field $\psi_0(\mathbf{x})$ at sufficiently long times $t \gg \max(l_{0,i})^2/\sigma_\psi$, isotropization of the fields of the velocity $v(\mathbf{x},t)$ and potential $\psi(\mathbf{x},t)$ takes place. Accordingly, all statistical properties of the turbulence become self-similar and are characterized by the integral length scale $L_{M,i}$

$$L(t) = (\sigma_\psi t)^{1/2} d^{-1/4} \left(\ln \frac{\sigma_\psi t}{l_{\rm eff}^2 (2\pi)^{1/d}} \right)^{-1/4},$$

where $l_{0,\rm eff}^d = \prod_{i=1}^d l_{0,i}$ is an effective spatial scale of the initial field. For the energy of each velocity component and the energy of the turbulence, we have

$$E_i(t) = \frac{L^2(t)}{t^2} = \frac{\sigma_\psi}{t\sqrt{d}} \left(\ln \frac{\sigma_\psi t}{l_{\rm eff}^2 (2\pi)^{1/d}} \right)^{-1/2}, \quad E(t) = \sum_i E_i(t).$$

The mean potential (average height of the surface) therewith grows logarithmically

$$\langle \psi(\mathbf{x},t) \rangle = d^{1/2} \left(\ln \frac{\sigma_\psi t}{l_{\rm eff}^2 (2\pi)^{1/d}} \right)^{1/2}. \tag{6.122}$$

For a statistically inhomogeneous field (6.121) at the stage when the integral length scale of the turbulence $L(t)$ is much less than the scale of modulation $L_{M,i}$, it is possible to use the quasistatic approximation. In this approximation, at times $\min(L_{0,i})^2/\sigma_\psi \gg t \gg \max(l_{0,i})^2/\sigma_\psi$, the integral length scale $L(\mathbf{x},t)$ and energy $E(\mathbf{x},t)$ of the turbulence are as before described by Eqs. (6.116), (6.117), but the variance of the initial potential becomes a slow function of the coordinate $\sigma_\psi^2 = \sigma_\psi^2 M^2(\mathbf{x})$. The latter means that local isotropization of the internal structure takes place. At the same time, the integral length scale grows faster in regions of larger amplitude of the field $L(\mathbf{x},t) \simeq (\sigma_\psi M(\mathbf{x})t)^{1/2}$, and nonlinear effects lead to a partial suppression of modulation $E(\mathbf{x},t) \simeq \sigma_\psi M(\mathbf{x}) t^{-1}$, whereas for the initial perturbation $E(\mathbf{x},0) = \sigma_\psi^2 M^2(\mathbf{x})$.

At this stage, the velocity field has a cellular structure with the universal behavior (6.91) within each cell. Cell boundaries are determined from the condition of contact of two local maxima $\mathbf{y}_k$ and $\mathbf{y}_m$ of the function $\psi_0(\mathbf{x})$, and they form planes orthogonal to the vector $\Delta\mathbf{y}_{k,m} = \mathbf{y}_k - \mathbf{y}_m$. The velocity of boundary motion is constant and is directed along the vector $\Delta\mathbf{y}_{k,m}$, whose magnitude is proportional to the potential difference $\psi(\mathbf{y}_k) - \psi(\mathbf{y}_m)$ of two neighboring maxima and directed towards the cell with the smaller maximum. For a statistically inhomogeneous field (6.121), the mean value of a local maximum slowly grows from the center of the perturbation Hence the boundary velocity and the velocity field itself $\mathbf{v}(\mathbf{x})$ will have a certain mean component directed from the point $\mathbf{x}=0$. The boundaries of the localized perturbation will therewith have a "bubbly" structure. The boundary cells have flat boundaries at contacts with the internal cells and spherical boundaries $|\mathbf{x}-\mathbf{y}_k| < (2\psi_0(\mathbf{y}_k)t)^{1/2}$ at the surface of the perturbation. Pointed out above typical cells configuration cleary seen in Figs. 6.10 and 6.11.

Let us represent the velocity field as the sum of the large-scale $\mathbf{v}_l$ and small-scale $\mathbf{v}_s$ components

$$\mathbf{v}(\mathbf{x},t) = \mathbf{v}_l(\mathbf{x},t) + \mathbf{v}_s(\mathbf{x},t), \quad \mathbf{v}_l(\mathbf{x},t) = \langle \mathbf{v}(\mathbf{x},t) \rangle. \tag{6.123}$$

Here the angular brackets signify statistical averaging. Let us write down the Burgers equation for a potential field in the form

$$\frac{\partial \mathbf{v}}{\partial t} = -\frac{1}{2}(\nabla \mathbf{v})^2 + \mu \triangle \mathbf{v}. \tag{6.124}$$

Let us assume that evolution of the small-scale component $\mathbf{v}_s$ may be described in a quasistatic approximation. By neglecting nonlinear distortions and dissipation of the large-scale component, after averaging (6.124), we obtain

$$\frac{\partial \mathbf{v}_l(\mathbf{x},t)}{\partial t} = -\frac{1}{2}\nabla \langle \mathbf{v}_s^2(\mathbf{x},t) \rangle = -\frac{1}{2}\nabla E_s(\mathbf{x},t).$$

From here, it is seen that an inhomogeneous random field is characterized by generation of a regular large-scale component with a non-zero mean value. Until development of nonlinear distortions of the small-scale component ($t \ll t_{\mathrm{nl},s} = \min l_{1,i}^2/\sigma_\psi$), the regular component is determined by the initial energy of the velocity field: $\mathbf{v}_l(\mathbf{x},t) = (t\sigma_v^2/2)\nabla M^2(\mathbf{x})$. At strongly nonlinear stage of development, when local isotropization of the internal structure takes place, from Eqs. (6.123), (6.122),

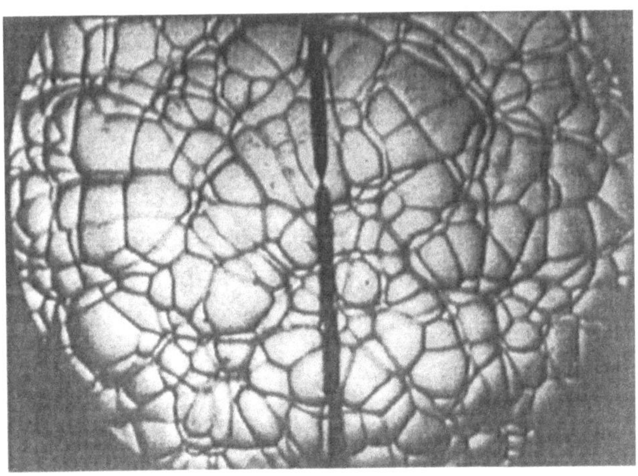

Fig. 6.10 Experimental snapshot of propagation of a spherical fire front. The cellular structure of the front is clearly seen. Black line in the center is electrodes causing a flash.

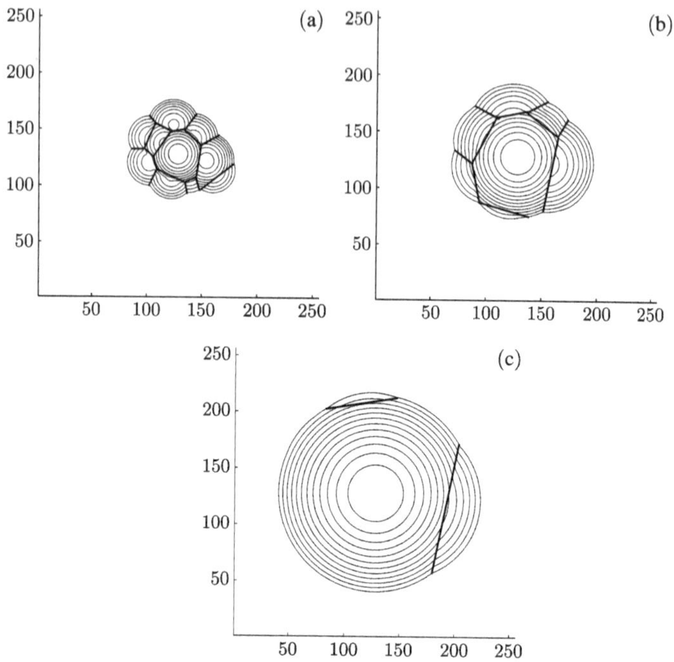

Fig. 6.11 Equipotential lines of a two-dimensional localized perturbation at $t/t_{\rm nl}=10$, $t/t_{\rm nl}=30$ and $t/t_{\rm nl}=80$.

we have a logarithmic growth of the large-scale component:

$$\mathbf{v}_l(\mathbf{x},t) = -\nabla\langle\psi(\mathbf{x},t)\rangle \simeq -\nabla|M(\mathbf{x})|\sigma_\psi d^{1/2}\left(\ln\frac{\sigma_\psi t}{l_{\rm eff}^2}\right)^{1/2}.$$

In the case of an anisotropic function $M(\mathbf{x})$, the mean velocity field at this stage also turns out to be anisotropic. As soon as the length scale of the internal structure $L(\mathbf{x},t)$ becomes of the order of the scale of the modulation function $M(\mathbf{x})$, it is necessary to take nonlinear distortions of the regular component $\mathbf{v}_l(\mathbf{x},t)$ into account. Finally, interaction (mergence) of cells leads to isotropization of the velocity and potential fields. At long times, the cells with the absolutely maximum value of the potential will absorb all other cells and the asymptotic solution will be described by Eq. (6.119). The boundaries $L_s(t)$ (6.119) and energy $E(t)$ (6.120) of such a structure are only determined by the absolute maximum H of the initial potential $\psi_0^M(\mathbf{x})$ (6.121).

Let us consider statistical properties of the absolute maximum magnitude H for perturbation with complex internal structure assuming that the characteristic scale of the the internal structure is much less than the scale of the envelope. It is possible to show that in this case the integral function $Q(H,V)$ of probability of finding the absolute maximum within a certain volume V is expressed via the average number

$N(H;V)$ of maxima of the potential ψ_0 exceeding the level H (see Eq. (6.147)):

$$Q(H;V) = e^{-N(H;V)}. \tag{6.125}$$

For a homogeneous field, the density of maxima n is determined from Eq. (6.146). For an inhomogeneous field $\psi_0^M(\mathbf{x}) = M(\mathbf{x})\psi_0(\mathbf{x})$ (6.121) at $L_{M,i} \gg l_i$, it is possible to introduce a local density $n_{\text{loc}}(\mathbf{x})$ described by the same equation, but with the following substitution $\sigma_s = M(\mathbf{x})\sigma_\psi$. Therewith for the average number $N_\infty(H)$ of maxima of the potential ψ_0^M in all space, we have

$$N_\infty(H) = \frac{1}{(2\pi)^{(d+1)/2} l_{\text{eff}}^d} \int \left(\frac{H}{M(\mathbf{x})\sigma_\psi}\right)^{d-1} \exp\left(-\frac{H^2}{2M^2(\mathbf{x})\sigma_\psi^2}\right) d^d\mathbf{x}. \tag{6.126}$$

For large H, by using the Laplace method, from Eqs. (6.121), (6.126), we obtain

$$N_\infty(H) = \frac{1}{(2\pi)^{1/2}} \left(\frac{H}{\sigma_\psi}\right)^{d-1} \left(\frac{L_{\text{eff}}^M}{l_{\text{eff}}}\right)^d \exp\left(-\frac{H^2}{2\sigma_\psi^2}\right), \tag{6.127}$$

where

$$l_{0,\text{eff}}^d = \prod_{i=1}^d l_{0,i} \quad \text{and} \quad (L_{\text{eff}}^M)^d = \prod_{i=1}^d L_{M,i}.$$

In Eq. (6.127) the ration $(L_{\text{eff}}^M/l_{\text{eff}})^d = N_{\max}$ is equal to the number of independent local maxima of the initial perturbation (6.121). In our case ($N_{\max} \gg 1$), it is possible to introduce a dimensionless potential h

$$h = \frac{H}{\sigma_\psi} = h_0(1 + z/h_0^2),$$

where $h_0 = H_0/\sigma_\psi$, and H_0 is the solution of the equation $N_\infty(H_0) = 1$:

$$H_0 \simeq \sigma_\psi \left[d^2 \ln\left(\frac{L_{\text{eff}}^M}{l_{\text{eff}}}\right)\right]^{1/2}. \tag{6.128}$$

The dimensionless potential h has a double exponential distribution

$$Q(z) = \exp(-e^{-z}), \quad Q_h(h) = \exp(-e^{-(h-h_0)h_0}). \tag{6.129}$$

At $N_{\max} \gg 1$, the integral function (6.125) of distribution of the absolute maximum is concentrated in a narrow neighborhood $\triangle H/H \simeq 1/h_0^2 \ll 1$ of the point $H_0 = h_0\sigma_\psi$. Therefore, from Eqs. 6.119), (6.120) follows that relative fluctuation of the spatial scale $\triangle L_s(t)/L_s(t) \simeq 1/2h_0^2$ and energy $\triangle E(t)/E(t) \simeq (d+2)/2h_0^2$ of an isotropic field are rather small. Derivations similar to those listed above show that the density of parobability of coordinates $\mathbf{y}_k$ of the isotropic field (6.119) turns out to be Gaussian with a quadratic mean, which equals $\langle y_{k,i}^2\rangle = L_{M,i}^2/h_0^2$. At times when the length scales of the structure is $L_s(t) \gg L_{M,i}$, field variations are determined only

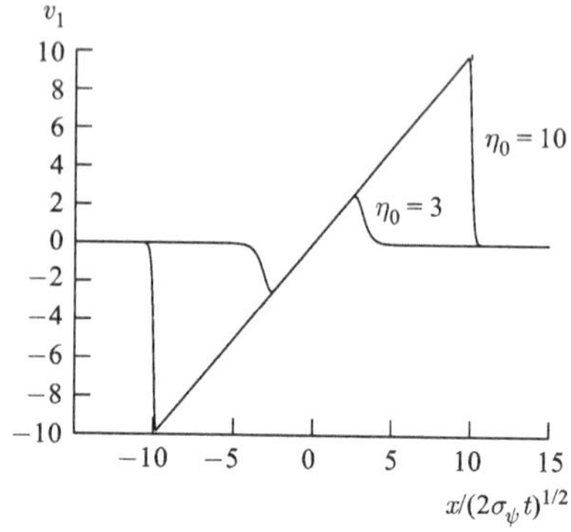

Fig. 6.12 Dimensionless self-similar mean field $\mathbf{V}_l(x)$ at $h_0 = 3$ and $h_0 = 10$.

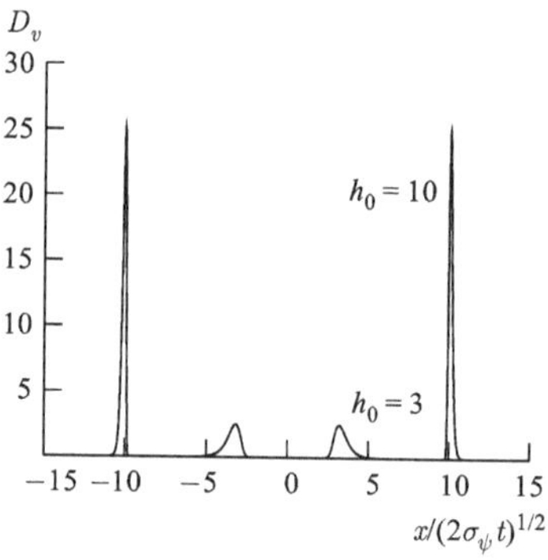

Fig. 6.13 Dimensionless self-similar variance $D_\mathbf{v}(x)$ at $h_0 = 3$ and $h_0 = 10$.

by changes in the positions of discontinuities $L_s(t)$, which are sufficiently small. For the mean velocity $\mathbf{v}_l(\mathbf{x},t)$ (see (6.123)) and variance $\sigma_\mathbf{v}^2(\mathbf{x},t) = \langle \mathbf{v}_s^2(\mathbf{x},t)\rangle$ from (6.119) and (6.128) follows:

$$\mathbf{v}_l(\mathbf{x},t) = \langle \mathbf{v}(\mathbf{x},t)\rangle = \frac{\mathbf{x}}{t}\left(1 - Q_h\left(\frac{\mathbf{x}^2}{2\sigma_\psi t}\right)\right),$$

$$\sigma_\mathbf{v}^2(\mathbf{x},t) = \frac{\mathbf{x}^2}{t^2} Q_h\left(\frac{\mathbf{x}^2}{2\sigma_\psi t}\right)\left(1 - Q_h\left(\frac{\mathbf{x}^2}{2\sigma_\psi t}\right)\right). \tag{6.130}$$

From these expressions it is seen that the mean field and variance are self-similar functions: $\mathbf{v}_l(\mathbf{x},t) = (2\sigma_\psi t)^{1/2}\mathbf{V}_l(\mathbf{x}/(2\sigma_\psi t)^{1/2})$; $\sigma_\mathbf{v}^2(\mathbf{x},t) = 2\sigma_\psi t D_\mathbf{v}(\mathbf{x}/(2\sigma_\psi t)^{1/2})$, whose shape is determined by a single parameter $h_0 = H_0/\sigma_\psi$ (6.128).

When the ratio of the characteristic length scale of the perturbation to the scale of the internal structure increases, the mean field tends to an N-wave, and the variance is localized in neighborhoods of discontinuities as is seen from Figs. 6.12 and 6.13.

As follows from (6.129), at $N_{\max} \gg 1$, the energy of the regular component $\mathbf{v}_l(\mathbf{x},t)$ is described by Eq. (6.120), where $H = h_0\sigma_\psi$. The variance $\sigma_\mathbf{v}^2(\mathbf{x},t)$ is not equal to zero in a narrow neighborhood $\triangle L_s(t)/L_s(t) \simeq 1/2h_0^2$ of the discontinuity coordinate $L_s(t) = (2\sigma_\psi h_0 t)^{1/2}$. The energy of the random component $E_s(t)$ is much less than the energy $E_l(t)$ of the mean component of the field $\mathbf{v}_l(\mathbf{x},t)$

$$E_s(t)/E_l(t) \simeq (d+2)/h_0^2 \simeq \left[\frac{d+2}{d}\right]\left[2\ln\left(\frac{L_{\rm eff}^M}{l_{\rm eff}}\right)\right]^{-1} \ll 1 \ .$$

Thus, in a medium with vanishing viscosity, nonlinear effects lead to generation of a practically deterministic large-scale isotropic structure.

6.3.6 Asymptotic long-time behavior of a localized perturbation

In order to analyze behavior of the field at large, but finite Reynolds numbers, we will use the Hopf-Cole solution. When the scale of Green's function of the linear diffusion equation (6.84) is much greater than the scale of the initial localized perturbation, from Eqs. (6.84), (6.85), we obtain

$$U(\mathbf{x},t) = 1 + \frac{B}{(4\pi\mu t)^{d/2}} \exp\left(-\frac{\mathbf{x}^2}{4\mu t}\right), \tag{6.131}$$

where the constant B is equal

$$B = \int \left[\exp\left(\frac{\psi_0(\mathbf{y})}{2\mu}\right) - 1\right] d^d\mathbf{y}. \tag{6.132}$$

For large initial Reynolds numbers $\mathrm{R}_0 \sim H/2\mu$, where H is the global maximum of the function $\psi_0(y)$, B can be represented as

$$B = L_{\rm eff}^d \exp(H/2\mu), \tag{6.133}$$

where $L_{\rm eff}$ is a certain effective scale of the integrand in (6.132). Therewith Eq. (6.131) crosses over to

$$U(\mathbf{x},t) = 1 + \exp\left[-\frac{1}{2\mu}\left(\frac{\mathbf{x}^2}{2t} - H + \mu d \ln\frac{4\pi\mu t}{L_{\rm eff}^2}\right)\right]. \tag{6.134}$$

At small viscosity ($\mu \to 0$), from Eqs. (6.83), (6.134), we obtain the solution (6.119). But at finite Reynolds numbers, Eq. (6.119) holds only within a limited time interval. For finite t and for sufficiently small values of x, we as before have the solution(6.119) inside the "d-sphere":

$$|\mathbf{x}| \leqslant L_s(t) = \left[2t\left(H - d\mu\ln\frac{4\pi\mu t}{L_{\rm eff}^2}\right)\right]^{1/2}. \tag{6.135}$$

At finite Reynolds numbers, a shock front has a finite width $\delta \sim t^{1/2}$. But it is more relevant that due to a logarithmic correction to the position of the discontinuity (6.119), the ration of the discontinuity width to the position of the shock front $\delta(t)/L_s(t)$ grows with time. This leads to a decrease of the effective Reynilds number and to consequent decay of the nonlinear structure. At long times, when

$B/(4\pi\mu t)^{d/2} \ll 1$,, the linear solution is asymptotically valid, and for the velocity field from (6.93), (6.131) we have

$$\mathbf{v}(\mathbf{x},t) \simeq -\frac{B}{(4\pi\mu t)^{d/2}} \nabla \exp\left(-\frac{\mathbf{x}^2}{4\mu t}\right). \tag{6.136}$$

At long times, evolution of the surface (of the potential $\psi(\mathbf{x},t)$) is described by the linear diffusion equation, and the surface itself has a Gaussian shape with the height $B(4\pi\mu t)^{-d/2}$ and spatial scale $(2\mu t)^{1/2}$.

If the potential of the initial perturbation has one maximum and is representable in its neighborhood in the form (6.88), then, as it follows from Eq. (6.133),

$$B = (4\pi\mu/\psi_0)^{(d+1)/2} \prod_{i=1}^{d} L_i \exp(\psi_0/2\mu).$$

If the initial localized random perturbation is Gaussian and can be represented in the form (6.121), then for the mean value of B from Eq. (6.132) we obtain

$$\langle B \rangle = \int \left[\exp\left(\frac{\mathrm{R}_0^2 M^2(\mathbf{y})}{2} \right) - 1 \right] d^d\mathbf{y}, \quad \mathrm{R}_0 = \frac{\sigma_\psi}{2\mu}.$$

From the last expression follows that the mean value $\langle B \rangle$ does not depend on the internal structure of the potential $\psi_0(\mathbf{x})$ and is always positive, which is For the variance $\sigma_B^2 = \langle (B - \langle B \rangle)^2 \rangle$ we have

$$\sigma_B^2 = \iint \exp\left(\frac{\sigma_\psi^2 (M^2(\mathbf{y}) + M^2(\mathbf{y}'))}{8\mu^2} \right) \times \\ \times \left[\exp\left(\frac{B_\psi(\mathbf{y}-\mathbf{y}') M(\mathbf{y}) M(\mathbf{y}')}{4\mu^2} \right) - 1 \right] d^d\mathbf{y} d^d\mathbf{y}'. \tag{6.137}$$

Here $B_\psi(\mathbf{z})$ is the correlation function of the homogeneous initial potential $\psi_0(\mathbf{x})$. At large Reynolds numbers R_0 for the mean value of B it is easy to obtain

$$\langle B \rangle \simeq (2\pi/\mathrm{R}_0)^{(d+1)/2} \prod_{i=1}^{d} L_{M,i} \exp\left(\mathrm{R}_0^2/2\right) \sim (L_{\text{eff}}^M/\mathrm{R}_0^{1/2})^d \exp\left(\mathrm{R}_0^2/2\right).$$

Accordingly, for the variance, the following expression holds

$$\sigma_B^2 \sim (l_{\text{eff}} L_{\text{eff}}^M/\mathrm{R}_0)^d \exp\left(\mathrm{R}_0^2\right).$$

Thus, at the linear stage of evolution, the field has the universal structure (6.136) with a random amplitude B. Therewith the ratio of energies of the random and regular fields is determined by the magnitude of relative fluctuations of B

$$E_s(t)/E_l(t) = \sigma_B^2/\langle B \rangle^2 \sim (l_{\text{eff}}/L_{\text{eff}}^M)^d \exp\left(\mathrm{R}_0^2\right).$$

These fluctuations, at the linear stage of development, are approximately exp $\left(\mathrm{R}_0^2\right)$ times greater than similar fluctuations at the nonlinear stage. Nevertheless, at $(l_{\mathrm{eff}}/L_{\mathrm{eff}}^M)^d \ll \exp(-\mathrm{R}_0^2)$ there is only relatively small spread in B, and, with increasing ratio $(l_{\mathrm{eff}}/L_{\mathrm{eff}}^M)^d$, the distribution of B gradually tends to the normal one. Such behavior is similar to properties of the statistically homogeneous field at the late stage of development [31].

In conclusion, let us briefly describe how a localized perturbation with a complex internal structure evolves. In the limit of vanishing viscosity, nonlinear effects lead to appearance of local self-similarity of the velocity and potential fields, when a random perturbation is broken into cells with a universal behavior of the fields inside each of them. Because of mutual absorption of cells by each other, at long times, only one cell with the maximum value of the initial potential survives. At this stage, inside a d-dimensional sphere, the surface has a quadratic form, the height of which H and its radius L_s are determined by the magnitude of the maximum potential of the initial localized perturbation H. Therewith the velocity field undergoes a discontinuity, and the shock front amplitude decreases with time. If the scale of the complex internal structure is substantially less than the scale of localization, the parameters of the asymptotic structure H and L_s little change during a transition from one random realization to another. This means that a practically deterministic coherent structure is generated from a random complex localized perturbation with zero mean. At the late stage, we have self-similar evolution of the mean field and the variance field.

At bounded Reynolds numbers, a strongly nonlinear stage of evolution is in the end followed by a linear stage. At not so long times, a shock front has a finite width $\delta \sim t^{1/2}$. However, it is more important that due to a logarithmic correction to the discontinuity position, the ratio of the discontinuity width to the position of the shock front $\delta(t)/L_s(t)$ grows with time. This leads to a decrease of the effective Reynolds number and to subsequent decay of nonlinear structure. At long times, surface evolution is described by the linear diffusion equation, and the surface itself has a Gaussian shape with the height $B(4\pi\mu t)^{-d/2}$, whereas the mean value $\langle B\rangle$ does not depend on the internal structure of the potential $\psi_0(\mathbf{x})$ and is always positive. This effect appears due to mean field generation at the nonlinear stage. At the linear stage, fluctuations of the height significantly grow in comparison with the nonlinear stage. This is due to the fact that the time of transition from the nonlinear stage to the linear one in different realization exponentially depends on the maximum height of the initial perturbation.

6.3.7 Appendix to Section 6.3. Statistical properties of maxima of inhomogeneous random Gaussian fields

As it follows from the solution of the Burgers equation, asymptotic behavior of the field at long times is determined by the maxima of the random field ψ_0, whose amplitude significantly exceeds the variance of the initial potential σ_ψ. Therefore it is possible to use a number of results from the theory of extrema of random processes [3, 33, 34].

The problem of statistics of peaks of a Gaussian field has been studied sufficiently well in the isotropic and statistically homogeneous cases (see [35]). But for an analysis of the Burgers turbulence, it is necessary to investigate statistical properties of absolute maxima of an anisotropic and statistically inhomogeneous field $\boldsymbol{\Phi}(\mathbf{x},\mathbf{y},t)$. Let us first consider statistics of maxima of a statistically homogeneous field $S(\mathbf{x})$. Evidently, for relatively smooth fields, the number of peaks above a certain level asymptotically tends to the number of of maxima and extrema, whose magnitude is above this level. Therefore let us discuss properties of extrema of the field $S(\mathbf{x})$. Assuming that the equation $\nabla S(\mathbf{x}) = 0$ has only one root $\mathbf{x}_r$, it is possible to write down the following expression for the integral of a multidimensional delta function (see Appendix):

$$\int \delta(\nabla S(\mathbf{x}))d\mathbf{x} = 1/|J(\mathbf{x}_r)|, \tag{6.138}$$

where J is the Jacobian of the transformation

$$J = J(a_{ij}) = \det(a_{ij}), \quad a_{ij} = \frac{\partial S(\mathbf{x})}{\partial x_i \partial x_j}.$$

By using the delta function properties, it is possible to obtain the following relationship for the mean number $N(H) = \langle N_{ext}(H)\rangle$ of extrema within a volume V and exceeding a value of H:

$$N(H) = \left\langle \int_V \delta(\nabla S)|J(a_{ij})|E(S-H)d\mathbf{x} \right\rangle. \tag{6.139}$$

Here $E(S)$ is the unit function. By using the conditional probability density $W_{\text{cond}}(a_{ij}|S) = W(a_{ij},S)/W(S)$, we obtain

$$n = W_v(0) \int_H^\infty W_S(S)\,dS \int J(a_{ij}) W_{\text{cond}}(a_{ij}|S) da_{ij}. \tag{6.140}$$

For a statistically homegeneous field, spatial density of extrema $n(H) = N(H)/V = \langle N_{ext}\rangle/V$ is determined by the integral probability-density function (depending on S) of the components of the gradient $v_i = \partial S/\partial x_i$ and the tensor $a_{ij} = \partial^2 S/\partial x_i \partial x_j$. For a statistically homegeneous Gaussian field, it holds

$$W_{S,v_i,a_{ij}} = W_v(v_i) W_{S,a_{ij}}(S,a_{ij}). \tag{6.141}$$

From Eqs. (6.140), (6.141), for $n(H)$ we obtain

$$n(H) = W_v(0) \int_H^\infty \int dS J(a_{ij}) W_S(S,a_{ij}) da_{ij}. \tag{6.142}$$

Let us assume that the correlation function of the field $S(\mathbf{x})$ may be represented in the following way

$$B_S(\rho) = \langle S(\mathbf{x})S(\mathbf{x}+\rho)\rangle = \sigma_S^2 \prod_{i=1}^{d} R_i(\rho_i),$$

$$R_i(\rho_i) = 1 - \frac{\rho_i^2}{2! l_{0,i}^2} + \frac{\rho_i^4}{4! l_{1,i}^4} + \ldots \tag{6.143}$$

The Gaussian distribution in (6.142) in this case will be determined by the set of constants

$$\langle a_{ij}\rangle_S = S\langle a_{ij}S\rangle/\sigma_s^2, \quad \langle a_{ij}S\rangle = -\delta_{ij}\sigma_S^2/l_{0,i},$$
$$\langle a_{ij}^2\rangle = \sigma_S^2/l_{0,i}^2 l_{0,j}^2, \quad i \neq j, \quad \langle a_{ii}^2\rangle = \sigma_S^2/l_{1,i}^4,$$
$$W_v(0) = (l_{0,\text{eff}}^2/2\pi\sigma_\psi^2)^{d/2}, \quad l_{0,\text{eff}}^d = \prod_{i=1}^{d} l_{0,i}. \tag{6.144}$$

Here we have introduced an effective length $l_{0,\text{eff}}$.

For the asymptotic of $n(H)$ at large values of H, the following approximation is valid

$$\langle J(a_{ij})\rangle_S \simeq J(\langle a_{ij}\rangle_S) \simeq \prod_{i=1}^{d} \langle a_{ii}\rangle_S = \frac{S^d}{l_{0,\text{eff}}^{2d}}. \tag{6.145}$$

Finally, for the density of extrema, from Eqs. (6.140)–(6.145) we have

$$\begin{aligned} n_{\text{ext}}(H) &= W_v(0)\int_H^\infty W_S(S)\frac{S^d}{l_{\text{eff}}^2 d} dS \\ &= \frac{1}{(2\pi)^{(d+1)/2} l_{\text{eff}}^d}\int_{H/\sigma_S}^\infty S^d e^{-S^2/2} dS \simeq \left(\frac{H}{\sigma_S}\right)^{d-1} \frac{1}{(2\pi)^{(d+1)/2} l_{\text{eff}}^d} e^{-H^2/2\sigma_S^2}. \end{aligned} \tag{6.146}$$

From the latter expression, it follows that the mean number of extrema of the anisotropic field $S(x)$ depends on an effective spatial scale l_{eff}, which is a geometric average of the values of $l_{0,i}$ (see Eq. (6.144)). For a relatively large H, the extremum density (6.146) is equivalent to the density of events describing overshoots of the value of H by the random field $S(\mathbf{x})$.

The probability density of finding the absolute maximum of S in a region V is found by a method similar to the one-dimensional case [3]. For a fixed volume V and large values of H, it is possible to neglect a possibility of more than one overshoot of H by $S(\mathbf{x})$ and assume such an extremum to be the only one in the given region. Thus it is possible to obtain for the mean number $\langle N(H,V)\rangle$ of overshoots of the value of H by the field $S(\mathbf{x})$ or for the mean number of extrema $\langle N_{\text{ext}}(H,V)\rangle$ greater than H the following expression:

$$\langle N(H,V)\rangle \simeq \langle N_{\text{ext}}(H,V)\rangle \simeq P(1,H,V),$$

where $P(M;H,V)$ is the probability of the event that the number of events $S > H$ in the volume V is equal to M.

Assuming that $V \gg l_{\mathrm{st}}^d$, where l_{st}^d is a characteristic distance at which the values of $S(\mathbf{x})$ become statistically independent, the volume V may be broken into physically small volumes dV_k ($l_{\mathrm{st}}^d \simeq dV_k$). The probability of the event that, within a given volume dV_k, the function $S(\mathbf{x})$ does not exceed H, may be expressed as

$$dP_k = 1 - P(1; H, dV_k) = 1 - \langle N(H, dV_k) \rangle,$$

where $\langle N(H, dV_k) \rangle \ll 1$. Under the condition $l_{\mathrm{st}}^d \simeq dV_k$, events in each interval dV_k are statistically independent. Hence, for the integral distribution function of the absolute maximu of the function $S(\mathbf{x})$ within the volume V, we obtain

$$\begin{aligned} Q(H,V) &= P(S(\mathbf{x}) < H, \mathbf{x} \in V) = \\ &= \prod_k dP_k = \prod_k (1 - \langle N(H, dV_k) \rangle) = e^{-N(H,V)}. \end{aligned} \tag{6.147}$$

The function $Q(H,V)$ is equivalent to the joint probability of the event that, within a given volume V, there are no overshoots $S(x) > H$ and, for large H, there are no extrema greater than H. Eq. (6.147) reflects the known fact the extremum theory about the Poisson distribution of maxima [33]. At large H, for a uniform field, it ensues $N(H,V) = Vn(H)$, where n is given by Eq. (6.146).

For nonuniform fields, even in the one-dimensional case, the expression for N is much more complex. But if we suppose that nonuniform fields $\boldsymbol{\Phi}(\mathbf{x}) = S(\mathbf{x}) - \alpha(\mathbf{x})$ and $\alpha(\mathbf{x})$ are sufficiently smooth functions (on the scale of $S(\mathbf{x})$), then in the quasistatic approximation it is easy to obtain the following equation for the mean number $N(H,V)$ of events $\boldsymbol{\Phi}(\mathbf{x}) > H$ within a volume V

$$N(H,V) = \int_V n_{\mathrm{ext}}(H + \alpha(\mathbf{x})) dV, \tag{6.148}$$

where n is determined by Eq. (6.146) and is equal to the density of extrema of a uniform function $S(\mathbf{x})$.

6.4 Model description of evolution of the large-scale structure of the Universe

The multidimensional Burgers equation appears in cosmology in description of the large-scale structure of the Universe, where it is closely related to a known astrophysical model — the Zeldovich approximation.

6.4.1 Gravitational instability in an expanding Universe

Before turning to an investigation of special features of matter distribution in the Universe, let us briefly describe the modern outlook of formation of the large-scale structure of the Universe (scales of tens to hundreds of Megaparsecs). Elements of this structure are objects with a higher concentration of galaxies — galaxy groups and clusters, filaments (fiber-like groups of galaxies connecting galaxy clusters) and "walls". It is believed that the large-scale formations existing today were formed from small initial density perturbations due to gravitational instability. Statistical information of these perturbations is contained in thermal fluctuations of cosmic microwave radiation (CMB — Cosmic Microwave Background), which also carry plentiful information on the composition, history of development of the Universe and on the process of structure formation in the Universe.

Several recent experiments on investigation of the structure of the Universe (see, e.g., [36]) showed that the Universe consists of ordinary matter (atoms of various substances) (4%), cold dark matter of an unknown physical nature (23%) and mystical dark energy (73%), which plays an antigravitational role in the process of formation of the Universe. The first two components were detected from observed dynamics of cosmic objects quite a long time ago [37], while the dark energy was discovered relatively recently during observations of supernovae lying at the boundary of the observable Universe.

The new portrait of the Cosmos after the so-called Big Bang was obtained by NASA scientists by means of the Wilkinson Microwave Anisotropy Probe (WMAP) [36], which conducts observations of CMB over all skies starting from mid-2001. In the radiation structure, which we now observe as the cosmic microwave background, there are very small thermal fluctuations bearing an imprint of what later formed galaxy groups and clusters. WMAP is able to track minute temperature fluctuations at levels finer than a millionth of a degree.

The expanding Universe theory makes it possible to link the CMB parameters of temperature fluctuations with characteristics of density perturbations.

Baryonic matter in the early Universe was entirely ionized, which ensured a close link with CMB radiation. While expanding, the Universe cooled down, which lead to proton and electron recombination, and after that baryonic matter practically ceased to interact with the radiation. Immediately after separation of baryonic matter from radiation, the Universe was filled with a mixture of neutral hydrogen (with a small admixture of helium) and dark matter, which interact exclusively by gravitation. The density of the dark matter is 6–7 times greater than the density of baryons, and therefore the growth of inhomogeneities is determined mainly by the dark matter. Precisely this growth of inhomogeneities in the dark matter is responsible for the formation of the large-scale structures. Baryonic component simply followed the dark matter evolution under gravity.

The scenario of development of small initial perturbations into large-scale structures essentially is a problem of classical gravitational physics, where all is determined by a choice of initial conditions and description of the expansion process. But even such a problem is far from trivial. The principal difficulty consists in that a self-gravitating medium does not have any ground state and its dynamics are not ergodic. In the hydrodynamic formulation of this problem, solution for the velocity field is reduced to the Euler–Poisson equations (see, e.g., [7, 37]). Numerical simulation therewith becomes one of the main investigation methods of this problem. Never-

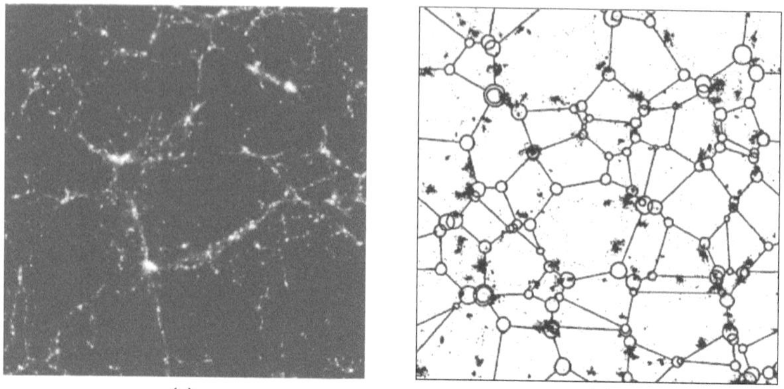

(a) (b)

Fig. 6.14 **(a)** projection of a matter distribution in two-dimensional cross-section obtained numerically by the Virgo consortium group. **(b)** comparison of the results of direct numerical simulation of a gas of gravitationally interacting particles with a skeleton of the large-scale structure obtained in the adhesion approximation.

theless simpler and more visual approximate analytical methods — the Zeldovich and adhesion approximations — are also frequently used in astrophysics [10].

The linear theory of gravitational instability predicts growth with time of the potential mode of initially weak density fluctuations. In appropriate coordinates, particle motion is therewith equivalent to free inertial motion. In 1970, Zeldovich [12] suggested to extend this solution to the case of finite density fluctuation as well. In this approximation, features in the matter-density distribution appear naturally, which are similar to caustics of optic waves behind a phase screen.

But results of direct numerical simulation show that the large-scale structure of the matter distribution in the Universe is much simpler than a system of random caustics. Matter is concentrated in thin layers, lines and clusters (see Fig. 6.14, (a)). In Refs. [6,25] (see also [3,10,26,38,39]), it has been shown that similar structures are well approximated by a model where particles do not penetrate each other, but coalesce. Despite of the fact that this mechanism is not collisional, but gravitational, this effect may be modeled by introducing a viscous, diffusive term into the Euler-Poisson equation. This respectively leads to the use of the three-dimensional Burgers equation in cosmological applications. The model itself is commonly known as the adhesion model.

6.4.2 From the Vlasov-Poisson equation to the Zeldovich approximation and adhesion model

Evolution of collision-less matter in a three dimensional expanding Universe is described by the kinetic Vlasov-Poisson equation. If $\mathbf{r}$ is the coordinate of a certain point, in cosmology, it is conventional to introduce the following comoving coordinate **x** [7]:

$$\mathbf{r} = a(t)\mathbf{x}, \tag{6.149}$$

where the scaling factor $a(t)$ is a function of world time and describes expansion of the Universe. For an Einstein-de Sitter Universe (which is a good approximation of a real model of the Universe):

$$a = \left(\frac{t}{t_0}\right)^{2/3} \tag{6.150}$$

and $t_0^{-2} = 6\pi G\rho(t_0)$, where $\rho(t_0)$ is the mean density of matter at time t_0 [7, 37], and G is the gravitational constant. In such coordinate system, the Vlasov-Poisson is written as:

$$\begin{cases} \partial_t f + \dfrac{\mathbf{p}}{ma^2} \cdot \nabla_x f - \nabla_x \psi \cdot \nabla_p f = 0, \\ \nabla^2 \psi = 4\pi G a^2 (\rho - \rho_b), \end{cases} \tag{6.151}$$

p is the variable conjugate to **x**; $f(\mathbf{x}, \mathbf{p}, t)$ is a distribution function in the six-dimensional space $(\mathbf{x}, \mathbf{p})$; ψ is the gravitational potential; ρ_b is the mean density of matter distribution. The densities of particles $\rho(\mathbf{x}, t)$ and velocity $\mathbf{u}(\mathbf{x}, t)$ are defined via $f(\mathbf{x}, \mathbf{p}, t)$ as:

$$\rho(\mathbf{x}, t) = \frac{m}{a^3} \int_{-\infty}^{\infty} f(\mathbf{x}, \mathbf{p}, t) d\mathbf{p}, \tag{6.152}$$

$$\rho(\mathbf{x}, t)\mathbf{u}(\mathbf{x}, t) = \frac{1}{a^4} \int \mathbf{p} f(\mathbf{x}, \mathbf{p}, t) d\mathbf{p}. \tag{6.153}$$

It is well known that there is a special solution of these equations [26]:

$$f(\mathbf{x}, \mathbf{p}, t) = \frac{a^3 \rho(\mathbf{x}, t)}{m} \delta^d(\mathbf{p} - ma\mathbf{u}(\mathbf{x}, t)), \tag{6.154}$$

where d is a spatial dimensionality, and $\delta^d(\ldots)$ is the d-dimensional delta function. Solutions of this class are called single-velocity solutions, because to each given point $(\mathbf{x}, t)$ corresponds a single velocity **u**. Assuming that the condition (6.154) is satisfied, from Eqs. (6.152), (6.153) we obtain

$$\begin{cases} \partial_t \rho + 3\dfrac{\dot{a}}{a}\rho + \dfrac{1}{a}\nabla \cdot (\rho \mathbf{u}) = 0, \\ \partial_t \mathbf{u} + \dfrac{\dot{a}}{a}\mathbf{u} + \dfrac{1}{a}(\mathbf{u} \cdot \nabla)\mathbf{u} = \mathbf{g}, \\ \nabla \cdot \mathbf{g} = -4\pi G a(\rho - \rho_b). \end{cases} \tag{6.155}$$

Here we introduced $\mathbf{g} = -\nabla\psi/a$ so that $\nabla \times \mathbf{g} = 0$. Note that the use of an expanding coordinate system lead to the fact that the mean density ρ_b entered the Poisson equation. It should be emphasized that the system of equations (6.155) is only valid if the distribution function $f(\mathbf{x}, \mathbf{u})$ may be represented in the form (6.154).

After formation of caustics, when fast particles overtake slow one, the solution becomes a multistream one and the system of equations (6.155) is no longer applicable.

The system (6.155) describes gravitational instability of a gas of collision-less particles in an expanding Universe. Linearized solutions of these equations are superpositions of two modes — growing and decaying ones. In the growing mode, the peculiar velocity is a potential field parallel to the acceleration field [7, 26, 42]:

$$\mathbf{g} = F(t)\,\mathbf{u}, \tag{6.156}$$

where $F(t)$ is a proportionality coefficient equal to

$$F(t) = 4\pi G\rho_b b/\dot{b}. \tag{6.157}$$

Here b is the coefficient of growth of the amplitude of density perturbations in the growing mode, and for an Einstein-de Sitter Universe $b \sim t^{2/3}$.

Zeldovich [12] suggested that the particle motion remains the same as in the linear theory and at the stage when density fluctuations are not small. This means that the conditions of parallelism are satisfied also at the nonlinear stage. Then, introducing a new velocity $\mathbf{v} = \mathbf{u}/(a\dot{b})$ [25] and considering only the growing mode, it is possible to reduce the system (6.155) to the following equations for the velocity and potential [26]:

$$\begin{cases} \partial_b \mathbf{v} + (\mathbf{v}\cdot\nabla)\mathbf{v} = 0, \\ \mathbf{v} = -\nabla\tilde{\psi}, \\ \partial_b \rho + \nabla\cdot(\rho\mathbf{v}) = 0, \end{cases} \tag{6.158}$$

having excluded the Poisson equation. Here $\tilde{\psi} = \psi/(\dot{b}F(t))$.

The first equation describes free motion of particles and is the Eulerian form of the famous Zeldovich approximation. This equation is approximate for two reasons. Firstly, it takes only the growing mode into account, and secondly, it assumes that the parallelism conditions are satisfied also at the nonlinear stage, when density perturbations already are not small. Note that for one-dimensional perturbations, the latter condition is always satisfied, and for the growing mode, the solution of the equations is exact until the formation of multistreamness. As it has been already mentioned, in the two-dimensional case these equations are equivalent to the equations for tilt angles of the wave front and intensity of an optic wave behind a phase screen. Therewith the variable t in these equations plays the role of the distance from the phase screen. And bright structures of caustics at the bottom of a swimming pool with a rough surface on a sunny day (see Fig. 6.15) reproduce the matter-density distribution in the two-dimensional case [43].

In the Lagrangian representation, the Zeldovich approximation (6.158) describes free motion of particles

$$\mathbf{X}(\mathbf{y},t) = \mathbf{y} + t\mathbf{v}_0(\mathbf{y}). \tag{6.159}$$

Fig. 6.15 Caustic patterns at the bottom of a swimming pool.

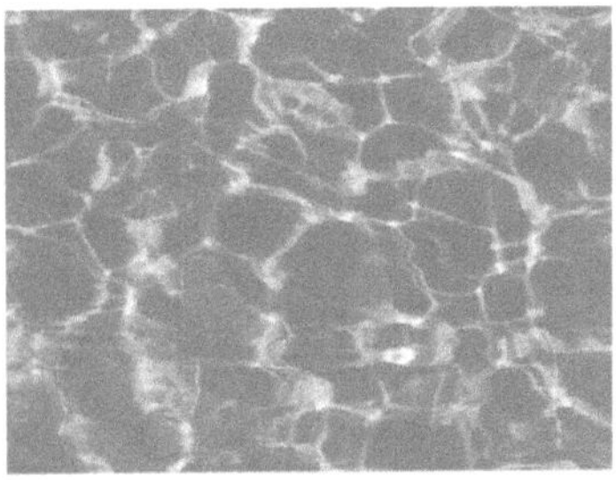

From the mass-conservation law, for the matter density $\rho(t,\mathbf{y})$ in the Lagrangian representation, we have

$$\rho(t,\mathbf{y}) = \frac{\rho_0}{J(t,\mathbf{y})}, \tag{6.160}$$

where J is the Jacobian of the Eulerian-to-Lagrangian coordinate transformation

$$J(t,\mathbf{y}) = \det(\delta_{ij} - t a_{ij}(\mathbf{y})), \quad a_{ij}(\mathbf{y}) = \frac{\partial \tilde{\psi}_0(\mathbf{y})}{\partial y_i \partial y_j}. \tag{6.161}$$

Here $\tilde{\psi}_0(\mathbf{y})$ is the potential of the initial velocity field. At each point, the matrix $a_{ij}(\mathbf{y})$ may be reduced to the diagonal form, and then, for the density, we have

$$\rho(t,\mathbf{y}) = \frac{\rho_0}{(1-t\beta_1(\mathbf{y}))(1-t\beta_2(\mathbf{y}))(1-t\beta_3(\mathbf{y}))}. \tag{6.162}$$

Here β_i are eigenvalues of the matrix $a_{ij}(\mathbf{y})$. When one of the factors in (6.162) becomes zero, the matter density tends to infinity, i.e. density singularities (for optic waves — caustics) are formed. In astrophysical applications, the initial potential $\tilde{\psi}_0(\mathbf{y})$ is a random Gaussian field. For such fields, the probability of the event that all three eigenvalues β_i coincide is zero, and therefore matter compression is the fastest along one of the axes. First, in the Zeldovich approximation, strongly anisotropic density singularities appear, which have a much smaller length scale along one of the axes. Therefore this approximation is often called the Zeldovich pancake theory. With time, caustics (singularities) expand, overlap and, in the Zeldovich approximation, there appears a complex multistream structure of matter distribution.

However, results of direct numerical simulation show that after appearance of singularities their width grows much slower than it follows from the Zeldovich theory. This is due to the fact that, because of an increased matter density at singularities, particles passing a singularity are subject to a restoring force, which causes the particles to oscillate in a vicinity of the singularity. For a qualitative description of the effect of the transition from the large-scale motion of matter to small-scale oscillations around singularities, it was suggested to introduce a diffusive term $\mu\nabla^2\mathbf{v}$ into the equation of motion [6, 25] (see also [3, 10, 26]). This term should, in an averaged way, describe the effect of gravitational "adhesion" around the singularities. That is why in cosmology this model is called the adhesion model. As a result, in the system of equations (6.158), the equation of free motion of particles is replaced by the three dimensional Burgers equation

$$\partial_b \mathbf{v} + (\mathbf{v}\cdot\nabla)\mathbf{v} = \mu\nabla^2\mathbf{v}. \tag{6.163}$$

In order for the diffusive term to have averaging action only in a vicinity of discontinuities, the viscosity coefficient μ must be sufficiently small. Frequently, the limit $\mu \to 0$ is also considered, which corresponds to gravitational "coalescence" of particles into infinitesimally thin singularities. In this case, the Burgers equation describes a "skeleton" of the large-scale matter distribution. As it follows from the properties of the three-dimensional Burgers equation, at long times, there appears a cellular structure of matter: regions with a density much smaller that the mean density, surfaces with an elevated concentration of matter separating these dark regions, surface intersections — lines and, finally, line intersections — clusters.

Naturally, the adhesion model does not describe therewith the internal structure of singularities [44]. Numerical experiments directly simulating a gas of gravitationally interacting particles showed a sufficiently good agreement with the adhesion model (see, e.g., [38,39,41]). But, in spite of this, the question of a link between the original equations and the model still remains open (see, e.g., [45]).

In contract to the Navier-Stokes equation, the Burgers equation does not contain a density and, accordingly, there is no law of conservation of momentum for this equation in a general case. Only for one-dimensional perturbations and for a constant initial density the Burgers equation with a vanishing viscosity describes a gas of coalescing particles satisfying the momentum-conservation law. Therewith positions of density singularities (heavy particles), formed as a result of light particle adhesion, coincide with velocity discontinuities in the Burgers equation. As it has been shown above (Chapter 2), positions of singularities of the density of coalesced particles at a non-constant initial density behave according to laws other than discontinuities of the velocity field of the Burgers equation. In the multidimensional Burgers equation, formation of singularities also does not depend on a density distribution. However, even at a constant initial density, singularities do not satisfy the momentum-conservation law because of the fact that adhesion of particles with non-flat geometry is, from the viewpoint of the momentum-conservation law, equivalent to a medium with a non-constant density. Moreover, for the spherically symmetrical case, from the formal definition of the coordinates of the coalesced according to the Burgers equation particles follows that in the three-dimensional case the energy of the system as a result of adhesion grows [46]!

Thus a relatively good agreement is very nontrivial and its explanation is, most likely, in a random character of initial perturbations. Indeed, conditions of applicability of the Zeldovich model are exactly satisfied only for the growing mode and for one-dimensional perturbations. Therewith positions of singularities as a result of particle adhesion, is predicted correctly on the basis of the Burgers equation also only for one-dimensional perturbations. Precisely such quasi-one-dimensional perturbations are realized with a random character of the initial conditions.

References

1. A.G. Doroshkevich, E.V. Kotok, I.D. Novikov, A.N. Polyudov, S.F. Shandarin, Y.S. Sigov, Two dimensional simulation of the gravitational system dynamics and formation of the large-scale structure of the Universe, Mon. Not. R. Astron. Soc. **192**, 321–337 (1980)
2. S.N. Gurbatov, Universality classes for self-similarity of noiseless multidimensional Burgers turbulence and interface growth, Phys. Rev. E. **61**, 2595–2604 (2000)
3. S.N. Gurbatov, A.N. Malakhov, A.I. Saichev, *Nonlinear Random Waves and Turbulence in Nondispersive Media: Waves, Rays and Particles.* (Manchester University Press, 1991)
4. S.N. Gurbatov, A.Y. Moshkov, Generation of large-scale coherent structures in the KPZ equation and multidimensional Burgers turbulence, JETP **97**, 1186–1200 (2003)
5. S.N. Gurbatov, A.Y. Moshkov, A. Noullez, Evolution of anisotropic structures and turbulence in the multidimensional Burgers equation, Phys. Rev. E **81**(4), 046,312 (2010)
6. S.N. Gurbatov, A.I. Saichev, Probability distribution and spectra of potential hydrodynamic turbulence, Radiophys. Quantum Electron. **27**, 303–315 (1984)
7. P.J.E. Peebles, *Large-Scale Structure of the Universe* (Princeton University Press, 1980)
8. B.L. Rozhdestvenskii, N.N. Yanenko, *Systems of Quasilinear Equations* (Nauka, Moscow, 1978). In Russian
9. A.I. Saichev, W.A. Woyczynski, in *The IMA Volumes in Mathematics and its Applications*, vol. 77 (Springer, New York, 1996), pp. 167–192
10. S.F. Shandarin, Y.B. Zeldovich, The large-scale structure of the Universe: turbulence, intermittency, structures in a self-gravitating medium, Rev. Mod. Phys. **61**, 185–220 (1989)
11. G.B. Whitham, *Linear and Nonlinear Waves* (Wiley, New York, 1974)
12. Y.B. Zeldovich, Gravitational instability: an approximate theory for large density perturbations, Astron. Astrophys. **5**, 84–89 (1970)
13. Y.B. Zeldovich, *Elements of Mathematical Physics* (Nauka, Moscow, 1973). In Russian
14. A.L. Barabási, H.E. Stanley, *Fractal Concepts in Surface Growth* (Cambridge University Press, 1995)
15. I.A. Bogaevsky. Matter evolution in Burgulence. eprint arXiv:math-ph/0407073 (2004)
16. K. Khanin, A. Sobolevski, Particle dynamics inside shocks in Hamilton-Jacobi equations, Philos.Trans. R. Soc. A. **368**(1916), 1579–1593 (2010)
17. J.M. Burgers, Mathematical examples illustrating relations occurring in the theory of turbulent fluid motion, Kon. Ned. Akad. Wet. Verh. **17**, 1–53 (1939)
18. J.M. Burgers, *The Nonlinear Diffusion Equation* (D. Reidel, Dordrecht, 1974)
19. U. Frisch, *Turbulence: the Legacy of A.N. Kolmogorov* (Cambridge University Press, 1995)
20. R. Kraichnan, Small-scale structure of a scalar field convected by turbulence, Phys. Fluids Mech. **11**, 945–953 (1968)
21. A. Cheklov, V. Yakhot, Kolmogorov turbulence in a random-force-driven Burgers equation: anomalous scaling and probability functions, Phys. Rev. E. **52**, 5681 (1995)
22. J. Davoudi, A.A. Masoudi, M.R. Tabar, A.R. Rastegar, F. Shahbazi, Statistical theory for the Kardar-Parisi-Zhang equation in 1+1 dimension, Phys. Rev. E. **63**, 6308 (2001)
23. W. E, K. Khanin, A. Mazel, Y.G. Sinai, Probability distribution functions for the random forced Burgers equation, Phys. Rev. Lett. **78**, 1904 (1997)
24. M. Kardar, G. Parisi, Y.C. Zhang, Dynamical scaling of growing interfaces, Phys. Rev. Lett. **56**, 889–892 (1986)
25. S.N. Gurbatov, A.I. Saichev, S.F. Shandarin, The large-scale structure of the Universe in the frame of the model equation of non-linear diffusion, Mon. Not. R. Astron. Soc. **236**, 385–402 (1989)
26. M. Vergassola, B. Dubrulle, U. Frisch, A. Noullez, Burgers' equation, Devil's staircases and the mass distribution for large-scale structures, Astron. Astrophys. **289**, 325–356 (1994)
27. W.A. Woyczynski, *Burgers-KPZ Turbulence. Gottingen Lectures* (Springer, Berlin, 1998)
28. E. Hopf, The partial differential equation $u_t + uu_x = u_{xx}$, Comm. Pure Appl. Mech. **3**, 201–230 (1950)

29. J.D. Cole, On a quasi-linear parabolic equation occurring in aerodynamics, Quart. Appl. Math. **9**, 225–236 (1951)
30. O.V. Rudenko, S.I. Soluyan, *Theoretical Foundations of Nonlinear Acoustics* (Plenum, New York, 1977)
31. S. Albeverio, A.A. Molchanov, D. Surgailis, Stratified structure of the Universe and Burgers' equation — a probabilistic approach, Prob. Theory Relat. Fields. **100**, 457–484 (1994)
32. E.A. Kuznetzov, S.S. Minaev, Formation and propagation of cracks on the flame surface, Phys. Let. A. **221**, 187 (1996)
33. M.R. Leadbetter, G. Lindgren, H. Rootzen, *Extremes and Related Properties of Random Sequences and Processes* (Springer, Berlin, 1983)
34. S.A. Molchanov, D. Surgailis, W.A. Woyczynski, Hyperbolic asymptotics in Burgers' turbulence and extremal processes, Comm. Math. Phys. **168**, 209–226 (1995)
35. J.M. Bardeen, J.R. Bond, N. Kaiser, A.S. Szalay, Cosmic fluctuation spectra with large-scale power, Astrophys. J. **304**, 15–61 (1986)
36. WMAP Mission: Results. URL http://map.gsfc.nasa.gov
37. S. Weinberg, *Gravitation and Cosmology* (Wiley, New York, 1972)
38. D. Weinberg, J. Gunn, Large-scale structure and the adhesion approximation, MNRAS **247**, 260 (1990)
39. A.L. Mellot, S.F. Shandarin, D.H. Weinberg, A test of the adhesion approximation for gravitational clustering, Astrophys. J. **352**, 28 (1994)
40. A. Jenkins, C.S. Frenk, F.R. Pearce, P.A. Thomas, J.M. Colberg, S.D. White, H.M. Couchman, J.A. Peacock, G. Efstathiou, A.H. Nelson, Evolution of structure in cold dark matter Universes, Astrophys. J. **499**, 20–40 (1998)
41. L. Kofman, D. Pogosyan, S. Shandarin, A. Melott, Coherent structures in the Universe and the adhesion model, Astrophys. J. **393**, 437–449 (1992)
42. T. Buchert, A. Dominguez, J. Perez-Mercader, Extending the scope of models for large-scale structure formation in the Universe, Astron. Astrophys. **349**, 343–353 (1999)
43. Y.B. Zeldovich, A.V. Mamaev, S.F. Shandarin, Laboratory observation of caustics, optical simulation of the motion of particles, and cosmology, Sov. Phys. Usp. **26**, 77–83 (1983)
44. E. Aurell, D. Fanelli, S.N. Gurbatov, A.Y. Moshkov, The inner structure of Zeldovich' pancakes, Phys. D **186**, 171–184 (2003)
45. D. Fanelli, E. Aurell, Asymptotic behavior of a planar perturbation in a three-dimensional expanding Universe, Astron. Astrophys. **395**, 399 (2002)
46. A.A. Andrievskii, S.N. Gurbatov, A.N. Sobolevskii, Ballistic aggregation in symmetric and nonsymmetric flows, JETP **104**, 887–896 (2007)

Part II
Mathematical Models and Physical Phenomena in Nonlinear Acoustics

Chapter 7
Model Equations and Methods of Finding Their Exact Solutions

7.1 Introduction

The first part of this book has a very general character. It is devoted to nonlinear waves and wave structures (such as shock fronts, solitary waves, cellular multidimensional structures and some others) considered from the position of the general nonlinear wave theory. This approach is especially important for familiarization with the material of a big area of nonlinear physics — the theory of propagation of nondispersive and weakly dispersive waves, and also related to it fields of science united by similar mathematical models and methods of their analysis. Hence Part I may be used for educational purposes.

However, along with the general point of view, it is of interest to turn to an expanded treatment of the models and ideas of Part I as applied to specific physical situations. As it is known, one of the most important (from the viewpoint of applications) areas of physics of waves in nondispersive media is nonlinear acoustics or physics of powerful acoustic fields [1–4]. A detailed description of the relevant theory and particularization of the material from Part I as applied to nonlinear acoustics are given in Part II of this book.

7.1.1 *Facts from the linear theory*

Let us begin with the general information on the linear theory of acoustic waves [2,4], which is necessary for the consequent analysis of nonlinear problems.

The system of equations describing motion of liquids and gases, while taking their shear η and bulk ς viscosities into account, consists of the equation of motion in the Navier-Stokes form

$$\rho\left[\frac{\partial \mathbf{u}}{\partial t}+(\mathbf{u}\nabla)\mathbf{u}\right]=-\nabla p+\eta\,\Delta\mathbf{u}+\left(\varsigma+\frac{\eta}{3}\right)\operatorname{grad}\operatorname{div}\mathbf{u}, \tag{7.1}$$

the continuity equation

$$\frac{\partial \rho}{\partial t} + \operatorname{div}(\rho\,\mathbf{u}) = 0 \tag{7.2}$$

and the equation of state, which, for acoustic waves, may be taken in the form of the Poisson adiabat

$$p = p(\rho) = p_0\,(\rho/\rho_0)^{\gamma}. \tag{7.3}$$

In writing the system (7.1)–(7.3), we used Euler's approach towards a description of continuous medium motion. Within the framework of this approach, all variables — pressure p, density ρ and velocity $\mathbf{u}$ — are considered to be functions of coordinates in a stationary reference frame, as well as of time t. Often, especially in one-dimensional problems, Lagrange's approach is used. Within the Lagrangian description of continuous medium motion, instead of the coordinates of a stationary reference frame, coordinates of liquid particles of the medium, measured at a certain fixed (initial) moment of time, are used. Lagrange's approach is the main one in the solid state elasticity theory, when relative displacements of different inner volume domains of a body, responsible for appearance of mechanical stresses and deformations, and not the translations of the body as a whole, are of interest.

Let the unperturbed state of a medium be $\rho = \rho_0$, $p = p_0$, $\mathbf{u} = 0$. Let us denote perturbations of parameters connected with a wave by primed letters and assign in the system (7.1)–(7.3)

$$p = p_0 + p', \quad \rho = \rho_0 + \rho'. \tag{7.4}$$

We consider the perturbation to be small:

$$\frac{p'}{p_0} \sim \frac{\rho'}{\rho_0} \sim \frac{|\mathbf{u}|}{c_0} \sim \mu \ll 1. \tag{7.5}$$

Here μ is the small parameter, whose powers will be used in order to expand equations into series,

$$c_0 = \sqrt{(\partial p/\partial \rho)_{\rho=\rho_0}} = \sqrt{\gamma p_0/\rho_0} \tag{7.6}$$

is the equilibrium speed of sound. The ratio of the velocity of liquid's particle motion to the sound speed $|\mathbf{u}|/c_0$ is called the acoustic Mach number M. From Eq. (7.5), it is seen that the small parameter μ has the same order of smallness as the acoustic Mach number.

By substituting (7.4) into the system of Eqs. (7.1)–(7.3), it is reduced to the following form:

$$\rho_0 \frac{\partial \mathbf{u}}{\partial t} + \nabla p' - \eta\,\Delta\mathbf{u} - \left(\varsigma + \frac{\eta}{3}\right) \operatorname{grad}\operatorname{div}\mathbf{u} = -\rho' \frac{\partial \mathbf{u}}{\partial t} - (\rho_0 + \rho')(\mathbf{u}\nabla)\mathbf{u}, \tag{7.7}$$

$$\frac{\partial \rho'}{\partial t} + \rho_0 \operatorname{div}\mathbf{u} = -\operatorname{div}(\rho'\mathbf{u}), \tag{7.8}$$

$$p' = c_0^2 \rho' + \frac{1}{2}\left(\frac{\partial^2 p}{\partial \rho^2}\right)\rho'^2 + \cdots \equiv C_1 \frac{\rho'}{\rho_0} + \frac{1}{2} C_2 \left(\frac{\rho'}{\rho_0}\right)^2 + \cdots \tag{7.9}$$

In Eqs. (7.7) and (7.8), the linear terms are collected on the left-hand sides, and the nonlinear ones are grouped on the right-hand sides. The nonlinear terms contain powers and products of variables describing perturbations of the medium. By retaining only the linear terms, the system (7.7)–(7.9) is reduced to the following form:

$$\rho_0 \frac{\partial \mathbf{u}}{\partial t} + \nabla p' - \eta \Delta \mathbf{u} - \left(\varsigma + \frac{\eta}{3}\right) \operatorname{grad} \operatorname{div} \mathbf{u} = 0, \tag{7.10}$$

$$\frac{\partial \rho'}{\partial t} + \rho_0 \operatorname{div} \mathbf{u} = 0, \tag{7.11}$$

$$p' = c_0^2 \rho'. \tag{7.12}$$

The density perturbation in Eq. (7.11) is eliminated by means of Eq. (7.12). As a result, a system of two equations is obtained: the continuity equation

$$\frac{\partial p'}{\partial t} + c_0^2 \rho_0 \operatorname{div} \mathbf{u} = 0 \tag{7.13}$$

and the equation of motion (7.10), which connect two variables: p' and $\mathbf{u}$.

According to the Helmholtz theorem, any vector field (in our case — the velocity field) may be represented as a sum of the potential and vortical components:

$$\mathbf{u} = \mathbf{u}_l + \mathbf{u}_t, \quad \mathbf{u}_l = \nabla \varphi, \quad \mathbf{u}_t = \operatorname{rot} \mathbf{A}. \tag{7.14}$$

The function φ is called the scalar or acoustic potential, and the function $\mathbf{A}$ is called the vector potential. By substituting Eq. (7.14) into Eq. (7.13) while taking the identity $\operatorname{div} \operatorname{rot} \mathbf{A} = 0$ into account, we obtain

$$\frac{\partial p'}{\partial t} + c_0^2 \rho_0 \operatorname{div} \mathbf{u}_l = 0. \tag{7.15}$$

It is seen from here that variation of the pressure (and also density (7.12)) of a medium is connected only with the potential (acoustic) component of the velocity field. The vortical component describes shear motion, at which the the medium behaves as an incompressible fluid. Shear motion, as it follows from Eq. (7.10), is described by the diffusion equation

$$\frac{\partial \mathbf{u}_t}{\partial t} = \frac{\eta}{\rho_0} \Delta \mathbf{u}_t. \tag{7.16}$$

For the second (potential) mode of eigen-motions of the medium, from Eq. (7.10), the following equation is obtained:

$$\rho_0 \frac{\partial \mathbf{u}_l}{\partial t} + \nabla p' = b \Delta \mathbf{u}_l, \quad b \equiv \varsigma + \frac{4}{3} \eta. \tag{7.17}$$

Let us apply the gradient operation to Eq. (7.15), then differentiate Eq. (7.17) with respect to time and subtract the second resultant equation from the first one. As a result of these simple transformations, we have managed to exclude the pressure perturbation p' and to obtain a single equation for the potential component — oscillatory velocity $\mathbf{u}_l$:

$$\frac{\partial^2 \mathbf{u}_l}{\partial t^2} - c_0^2 \Delta \mathbf{u}_l = \frac{b}{\rho_0} \frac{\partial}{\partial t} \Delta \mathbf{u}_l. \tag{7.18}$$

Let us now consider a plane wave, in which all characteristics depend on one of the coordinates (say, x) and time t. From the potentiality condition, it follows that the velocity vector has the only nonzero component — the projection onto the x-axis, which we denote as u. Thus, an acoustic wave is a longitudinal one, i.e. the particles of the medium oscillate in this wave along the direction of its propagation. For such a wave, Eq. (7.18) takes on the following form:

$$\frac{\partial^2 u}{\partial t^2} - c_0^2 \frac{\partial^2 u}{\partial x^2} = \frac{b}{\rho_0} \frac{\partial^3 u}{\partial t\, \partial x^2}. \tag{7.19}$$

Let a monochromatic wave propagate along the x-axis:

$$u(x,t) = A \exp(-i\omega t + ikx), \tag{7.20}$$

where k, ω are the wavenumber and frequency, respectively. By substituting Eq. (7.20) into (7.19), we find the law of dispersion:

$$k^2 = \frac{\omega^2}{c_0^2} \left(1 - i\frac{b\omega}{c_0^2 \rho_0}\right)^{-1}, \quad k = \pm \frac{\omega}{c_0} \left(1 - i\frac{b\omega}{c_0^2 \rho_0}\right)^{-1/2}. \tag{7.21}$$

The sign "plus" in the second formula (7.21) corresponds to the wave propagating in the positive direction of the x-axis, and the sign "minus" to the same in the opposite direction. Let us assume that the dimensionless combination of parameters in the parentheses in (7.21), containing the coefficient of effective viscosity b, is small, i.e.

$$\frac{b\omega}{c_0^2 \rho_0} \ll 1. \tag{7.22}$$

In this case, for the wave propagating towards the right-hand side, the dispersion relation (7.21) assumes the following form:

$$k = \frac{\omega}{c_0} + i\frac{b\omega^2}{2c_0^3 \rho_0}. \tag{7.23}$$

By substituting (7.23) into (7.20), we find

$$u(x,t) = A \exp\left(-\frac{b\omega^2}{2c_0^3 \rho_0} x\right) \exp\left(-i\omega t + i\frac{\omega}{c_0} x\right). \tag{7.24}$$

It is seen that the wave amplitude decreases according to the following law:

$$A(x) = A \exp(-\alpha x), \quad \alpha \equiv \frac{b\omega^2}{2c_0^3 \rho_0}. \tag{7.25}$$

The combination of parameters α (7.25) has the meaning of the attenuation coefficient of the wave. If attenuation on a wavelength is small, i.e.

$$\alpha\lambda = \frac{b\omega^2}{2c_0^3\rho_0}\frac{2\pi c_0}{\omega} = \pi\frac{b\omega}{c_0^2\rho_0} \ll 1, \tag{7.26}$$

then the assumption (7.22) is justified. Indeed, the term "wave" is usually used in order to denote a process, which transports energy at long distances, far greater than the wavelength λ. Thus, the typical and most interesting case corresponds precisely to the fulfillment of the inequality (7.26).

If the viscosity of a medium (wave attenuation) may be neglected, from Eqs. (7.12), (7.15) and (7.17), the following linear relationships are obtained for acoustic excitations of an equilibrium state of the medium propagating in the positive direction along the x-axis :

$$\frac{p'}{c_0^2\rho_0} = \frac{\rho'}{\rho_0} = \frac{u}{c_0}. \tag{7.27}$$

For a wave propagating in the negative direction, the sing "minus" should be inserted in front of the oscillatory velocity in Eq. (7.27). Thus, any of the excitations (of the pressure, density or velocity) is described by the wave equation.

It is possible to obtain a more simple equation, if we limit ourselves by taking into account only one wave propagating in one (e.g., positive) direction. By replacing in the corresponding dispersion relation (7.23) the wavenumber and frequency by the operators of differentiation with respect to the coordinate and time, in according with Eq. (7.20):

$$k \to -i\frac{\partial}{\partial x}, \quad \omega \to i\frac{\partial}{\partial t}, \tag{7.28}$$

we obtain an equation not of the third order (as (7.19)), but of the second order:

$$\frac{\partial u}{\partial x} + \frac{1}{c_0}\frac{\partial u}{\partial t} = \frac{b}{2c_0^3\rho_0}\frac{\partial^2 u}{\partial t^2}. \tag{7.29}$$

It is convenient instead of the variables x, t to use new variables

$$x, \ \tau = t - x/c_0. \tag{7.30}$$

By measuring time in the coordinate system (7.30) moving together with the wave propagating with the sound speed c_0, we exclude from consideration "fast" process of propagation and monitor only "slow" distortions (wave evolution) caused by the weak influence of viscosity. In the coordinate system "co-moving" with the wave, Eq. (7.29) assumes the form of the ordinary diffusion equation:

$$\frac{\partial u}{\partial x} = \frac{b}{2c_0^3\rho_0}\frac{\partial^2 u}{\partial \tau^2}. \tag{7.31}$$

Generalization of this equation onto the nonlinear case, when it is necessary to take the nonlinear terms in Eqs. (7.7)–(7.9) into account, leads to the Burgers equation:

$$\frac{\partial u}{\partial x}=\frac{\varepsilon}{c_0^2}u\frac{\partial u}{\partial \tau}+\frac{b}{2c_0^3\rho_0}\frac{\partial^2 u}{\partial \tau^2}. \tag{7.32}$$

Here

$$\varepsilon=(\gamma+1)/2, \quad \varepsilon=1+C_2/2C_1 \tag{7.33}$$

is the so-called nonlinear acoustic parameter. The first of the formulas (7.33) is valid for a gas (7.3), and the second one — for the more general equation of state given near it (7.9), which is often used for condensed media, in this case the coefficients C_1, C_2 are determined from experimental data.

By using the approach described above, we obtain another important linear equation, which describes evolution of spatial bounded wave beams. The dispersion equation for the three-dimensional wave equation (here we do not take absorption into account) has the following form:

$$\omega^2/c_0^2=k^2\equiv k_x^2+k_y^2+k_z^2. \tag{7.34}$$

Here k_x, k_y, k_z are projections of the wave vector onto the x-, y-, z- axes, respectively. We assume that the wave beam propagates along the x-axis and, simultaneously, weakly converges or diverges. This means that the projections k_y, k_z are small in comparison with k_x, and the following approximate relationship holds:

$$\frac{\omega}{c_0}=k_x\sqrt{1+\frac{k_y^2+k_z^2}{k_x^2}}\approx k_x+\frac{k_y^2+k_z^2}{2k_x}, \quad k_x(\omega-c_0k_x)=\frac{c_0}{2}\left(k_y^2+k_z^2\right). \tag{7.35}$$

By substituting in the second relationship from (7.35) for the wave-vector components and frequency the operators (in analogy with Eq. (7.28))

$$k_x\to -i\frac{\partial}{\partial x}, \quad k_y\to -i\frac{\partial}{\partial y}, \quad k_z\to -i\frac{\partial}{\partial z}, \quad \omega\to i\frac{\partial}{\partial t}, \tag{7.36}$$

we obtain

$$\frac{\partial}{\partial x}\left(\frac{\partial u}{\partial t}+c_0\frac{\partial u}{\partial x}\right)=\frac{c_0}{2}\left(\frac{\partial^2 u}{\partial y^2}+\frac{\partial^2 u}{\partial z^2}\right). \tag{7.37}$$

By transforming to the "co-moving" coordinate system (7.30), we arrive at the evolution equation:

$$\frac{\partial^2 u}{\partial x\partial \tau}=\frac{c_0}{2}\Delta_\perp u, \quad \Delta_\perp\equiv\frac{\partial^2}{\partial y^2}+\frac{\partial^2}{\partial z^2}. \tag{7.38}$$

Generalization of this equation onto the nonlinear case leads to the Khokhlov-Zabolotskaya (KZ) equation [1]:

$$\frac{\partial}{\partial \tau}\left[\frac{\partial u}{\partial x}-\frac{\varepsilon}{c_0^2}u\frac{\partial u}{\partial \tau}\right]=\frac{c_0}{2}\Delta_\perp u. \tag{7.39}$$

7.1.2 How to add nonlinear terms to simplified equations

Let us now clarify as to why generalization of Eq. (7.31) onto the nonlinear case leads to Eq. (7.32) and, similarly, Eq. (7.38) assumes the form (7.39). To this end, we consider a model nonlinear wave equation [4] for the acoustic pressure p (here and everywhere below the prime over the variable present in Eqs. (7.4)–(7.17), (7.27) is omitted):

$$\Delta p - \frac{1}{c_0^2}\frac{\partial^2 p}{\partial t^2} = -\frac{\varepsilon}{c_0^4\rho_0}\frac{\partial^2 p^2}{\partial t^2}. \tag{7.40}$$

Equation (7.40) contains only one nonlinear term $\sim \varepsilon$, unlike the original system of the equations of hydrodynamics (7.1)–(7.3) or its "weakly nonlinear" variant (7.7)–(7.9). Apart from that, Eq. (7.40) does not contain "viscous" terms. Therefore, the derivation will be extremely simple.

In nonlinear acoustics, the main method of simplification is the "method of a slowly varying profile", introduced into practice by R.V. Khokhlov [1–4].

Let us illustrate the idea of this method by using Eq. (7.40) as an example. When the nonlinear term is absent, the solution of this equation is the sum of two plane counter-propagating waves with arbitrary profiles:

$$p(x,t) = \Phi(t - x/c_0) + \Psi(t + x/c_0).$$

Evidently, the wave with the profile Φ propagates in the positive direction along the x-axis, and the wave Ψ — in the negative direction. Suppose that we deliberately limit ourselves to consideration of particular problems connected with nonlinear distortion and interaction of waves propagating strictly in one direction — along the x-axis. In this case, one of the waves will be the "generating" solution of the linear problem, *viz.*:

$$p(x,t) = \Phi(t - x/c_0).$$

When there is weak nonlinearity, the acoustic Mach number $M = p/c_0^2\rho_0$ is nonzero, but small. While taking the nonlinear term in the model (7.40) into account, the profile of the propagating wave ceases to be constant. It will be distorted the stronger, the larger the distance travelled by the wave. At weak nonlinearity (small M), distortions develop slowly. The wave needs to propagate at a distance multiple of many wavelengths in order for its shape to be noticeably distorted. Hence, along with the "fast" dependence of the wave profile on the "co-moving" time $\tau = t - x/c_0$, there must appear a "slow" dependence on the x coordinate. In other words, the "perturbed" solution should be sought for in the following form:

$$p(x,\tau) = \Phi(\tau = t - x/c_0,\ x_1 = \mu x). \tag{7.41}$$

Here μ is a dimensionless small parameter being in this problem of the order of the Mach number M.

By performing in Eq. (7.40) the transformation to new variables, we obtain the following expression:

$$\mu^2\frac{\partial^2 p}{\partial x_1^2}-\frac{2}{c_0}\mu\frac{\partial^2 p}{\partial x_1\partial\tau}+\frac{1}{c_0^2}\frac{\partial^2 p}{\partial\tau^2}=\frac{1}{c_0^2}\frac{\partial^2}{\partial\tau^2}\left[p\left(1-\frac{\varepsilon}{c_0^2\rho_0}p\right)\right]. \qquad (7.42)$$

The terms of the zeroth order of smallness μ^0 on the right and left-hand sides of Eq. (7.42). are mutually cancelled, because the generating solution has been chosen correctly. We neglect the only term of the order of μ^2 (the first term on the left-hand side) — it is too small for our purposes. The remaining two terms have the same — the first order of smallness. They form the following equation:

$$\frac{2}{c_0}\mu\frac{\partial^2 p}{\partial x_1\partial\tau}=\frac{\varepsilon}{c_0^4\rho_0}\frac{\partial^2 p^2}{\partial\tau^2}.$$

By returning now formally from x_1 to the coordinate x and by integrating with respect to the variable τ, we arrive at the equation for simple (Riemann) waves:

$$\frac{\partial p}{\partial x}=\frac{\varepsilon}{c_0^3\rho_0}p\frac{\partial p}{\partial\tau},\quad \frac{\partial u}{\partial x}=\frac{\varepsilon}{c_0^2}u\frac{\partial u}{\partial\tau}. \qquad (7.43)$$

Note that the transformation from the pressure perturbation to the vibration velocity in the evolution equations of nonlinear acoustics is performed according to the linear formulas (7.27): $p=c_0\rho_0 u$. The structure of the nonlinear term is given by the right-hand side of Eq. (7.43). The form of the dissipative term is given by the right-hand side of the other evolution equation (7.31). If it is necessary simultaneously to take both nonlinearity and dissipation into account, it is evidently necessary to write down on the right-hand side of the evolution equation the sum of these terms. Indeed, in the original equations (7.7)–(7.9), the small nonlinear and dissipative terms are present additively, as separate terms. In the process of simplification, obviously, this additivity must be preserved. By proceeding as stated, we obtain from Eqs. (7.31) and (7.43) the Burgers equation (7.32).

R.V. Khokhlov devised a generalization of the simplification method described above, which allows one to solve not only one-dimensional problems, but also related to them "nearly" one-dimensional ones [1–4]. Suppose that a wave beam is generated in a medium, which either weakly diverges or gets weakly focused, i.e. the wave is "nearly one-dimensional". In these cases, the basic equation (7.40) is simplified on the grounds of the assumptions of slowness of the field variation not only along the beam axis coinciding with the x-axis, but also in the cross section:

$$p(x,y,z,t)=\Phi(\tau=t-x/c_0,\ x_1=\mu x, y_1=\sqrt{\mu}y,\ z_1=\sqrt{\mu}z). \qquad (7.44)$$

By transforming in Eq. (7.40) from x, y, z, t to new variables x_1, y_1, z_1, τ:

$$\mu^2\frac{\partial^2 p}{\partial x_1^2}+\mu\frac{\partial^2 p}{\partial y_1^2}+\mu\frac{\partial^2 p}{\partial z_1^2}-\frac{2\mu}{c_0}\frac{\partial^2 p}{\partial x_1\partial\tau}=-\frac{\varepsilon}{c_0^4\rho_0}\frac{\partial^2 p^2}{\partial\tau^2}$$

and by neglecting the terms of the order of μ^2, we obtain the KZ equation (7.39). By adding to it the dissipative term, we obtain the KZK (Khokhlov-Zabolotskaya-

Kuznetsov) equation:

$$\frac{\partial}{\partial \tau}\left[\frac{\partial p}{\partial x}-\frac{\varepsilon}{c_0^3\rho_0}p\frac{\partial p}{\partial \tau}-\frac{b}{2c_0^3\rho_0}\frac{\partial^2 p}{\partial \tau^2}\right]=\frac{c_0}{2}\Delta_\perp p. \tag{7.45}$$

7.1.3 More general evolution equations

The number of mathematical models used to date while solving nonlinear acoustics problems is very large. In Introduction, it makes sense to point out only the simplest, "basic" model equations with the goal of drawing one's attention to their specifics, and also their connection with other models used in nonlinear wave physics. More complex and particular models are given below in other sections while discussing specific acoustic problems. Here only most important evolution equations generalizing the Burgers and KZ equations are shown.

The general one-dimensional equation describing propagation of diverging and converging waves (horns, concentrators, ray tubes in the approximation of nonlinear geometrical acoustics) has the following form [5]:

$$\frac{\partial p}{\partial x}+\frac{p}{2}\frac{d}{dx}\ln S(x)-\frac{\varepsilon}{c_0^3\rho_0}p\frac{\partial p}{\partial \tau}-\frac{b}{2c_0^3\rho_0}\frac{\partial^2 p}{\partial \tau^2}=0. \tag{7.46}$$

Here $S(x)$ is the area of the cross section of the tube and $\tau=t-x/c_0$.

Important particular cases: at $S=const$, this equation is transformed into the Burgers equation for plane waves; $S\sim x$ corresponds to cylindrically, and $S\sim x^2$ — to spherically symmetric waves. Dissipation (the second derivative) it related to the effects of viscosity and heat transfer. In order take losses due to scattering at small inhomogeneities into account, a similar equation with the fourth derivative is used [6].

The integro-differential equation [3]

$$\frac{\partial p}{\partial x}-\frac{\varepsilon}{c_0^3\rho_0}p\frac{\partial p}{\partial \tau}-\frac{m}{2c_0}\frac{\partial}{\partial \tau}\int_{-\infty}^{\tau}K(\tau-\tau')\frac{\partial p}{\partial \tau'}d\tau'=0 \tag{7.47}$$

describes nonlinear waves in hereditary media (media "with memory"). The important case of $K(t)=\exp(-t/T)$ corresponds to a relaxing medium, while power-law kernels are used for soft biological tissues, and models with several relaxation times are used for melts and strongly viscous fluids.

The basic equation for intense acoustic beams is the KZ equation (7.39). The general construction of an equation for diffracting, focusing or diverging beams, however, is as follows:

$$\frac{\partial}{\partial \tau}\left[\hat{\Pi}(p)\right]=\frac{c_0}{2}\Delta_\perp p. \tag{7.48}$$

Here $\hat{\Pi}(p) = 0$ is the corresponding equation for plane waves (e.g., any of Eqs. (7.46), (7.47)). Naturally, in all equations, the quadratic nonlinearity may be replaced with a nonlinear term of a more general form $\gamma \partial f(p)/\partial \tau$ and even with an integral nonlinear term taking retarded nonlinearity into account.

7.1.4 Two types of evolution equations

A natural question arises as to why, everywhere in Part I of this book, time has been used as the "slow" (evolution) variable, but, in Part II, it is the coordinate? This difference is connected only with a choice of the way to describe the problem, which depends on the problem formulation and convenience for result analysis.

In Part I, among other problems, there have been considered: a model of one-dimensional turbulence, a model of a flow of noninteracting particles and other problems, which are described by the simple (Riemann) wave equation or the Burgers equation. For turbulence, for instance, the problem is posed as follows (see (5.1)): at the initial moment of time $t = 0$, a distribution of the velocity field in space $v(t = 0, x) = v_0(x)$ is given, and with growing time $t > 0$, the solution $v(t, x)$ is sought. In a corresponding experiment, sensors measuring the velocity field are placed in various locations, and the measurement itself is made by all sensors at the same moment of time t_1. These results determine the spatial structure of the field $v(t_1, x)$. Then similar measurements performed at t_2, give the field profile $v(t_2, x)$. By repeating measurements in this way, we trace the field evolution with time.

When propagating waves are of interest, the experiment is done in a different way. The only sensor placed at the position x_1 measures the variation of the signal with time: $v(x_1, \tau)$. Then the sensor is moved to another point of the field $x_2 > x_1$, and the signal $v(x_2, \tau)$ is measured. By moving the sensor of the oscillatory velocity (or the acoustic pressure) farther and farther from the source of radiation, we trace the evolution of the form of the wave profile as the wave propagates. In a real experiment, when the wave gets distorted at distances of the order of a thousand wavelengths, and, for a good reconstruction of the wave profile within its each length λ, it is necessary to place no fewer than ten sensors, the method of the "slow time" is very inconvenient. It is outright impossible in those cases, when the wave profile contains shock fronts, whose extent is very small, e.g., $10^{-4}\lambda$.

But in a number of acoustic problems, e.g. that of standing waves in a resonator, it is, nevertheless, convenient to transform back from the "slow coordinate" to the "slow time". It is clear that the resonator has a limited length and, by measuring the field at the lowest modes, it is quite realistic to place several sensors along the length of the resonator and perform simultaneous measurement with them at various moments of time. Precisely such approach is used in Chapter 11.

Let us show by using Eq. (7.40) as an example that mathematically both approaches are equivalent. Assuming that the field rapidly varies along the coordinate $\xi = x - c_0 t$, which moves together with the wave at the sound speed, and thereby the wave varies slowly with time, let us seek the solution of Eq. (7.40) instead of

(7.41) in the following form:

$$p(x,\tau) = \Phi(\xi = x - c_0 t, t_1 = \mu t). \tag{7.49}$$

By transforming the variables in Eq. (7.40) according to (7.49) and by neglecting small terms, we obtain

$$\frac{\partial p}{\partial t} + \frac{\varepsilon}{c_0 \rho_0} p \frac{\partial p}{\partial \xi} = 0. \tag{7.50}$$

It is seen that Eq. (7.50) differs from the equation for Riemann waves (7.43) only by notation.

7.2 Lie groups and some exact solutions

It is often said that regular methods for finding exact solutions of nonlinear equations do not exist. This is not quite so. There is a regular method based on the use of symmetries of differential equations found by means of the group theory. This method was invented by a great Norwegian mathematician Sophus Lie and further developed by Russian mathematicians L.V. Ovsyannikov, N.H. Ibragimov and their disciples. Another thing is that this method not always allows one to find physically interesting solutions and, of course, does not allow us, as a rule, to obtain the general solution (even if the theorems of existence and uniqueness have been proved) and satisfy necessary initial and boundary conditions. The latter problem may sometimes be solved by using the renormgroup theory developed by N.N. Bogolyubov and D.V. Shirkov and applied by V.F. Kovalev et al. to solving a number of physical problems [7].

In this section, we discuss some problems of nonlinear acoustics, which are of interest for other branches of nonlinear wave physics as well. We provide exact solutions having a physical meaning. We describe some methods of finding or guessing these solutions. By using some examples, we show a connection of "non-rigorous" approaches with correct mathematical analysis of nonlinear models based on their symmetries. We discuss the meaning of the *a-priori*-symmetry-use principle.

7.2.1 Exact solutions of the Burgers equation

Let us begin with the "basic" model of nonlinear acoustics, *viz.* the Burgers equation (BE) describing nondispersive waves in dissipative media:

$$\frac{\partial V}{\partial z} - V\frac{\partial V}{\partial \theta} = \Gamma \frac{\partial^2 V}{\partial \theta^2}. \tag{7.51}$$

Here we used reduced variables:

$$V=\frac{u}{u_0},\ \theta=\omega\left(t-\frac{x}{c_0}\right),\ z=\frac{x}{x_{SH}}=\frac{\varepsilon\omega u_0}{c_0^2}x,\ \Gamma=\alpha x_{SH}=\frac{b\omega}{2\varepsilon c_0\rho_0 u_0}. \quad (7.52)$$

Here V is the field variable (vibration velocity or acoustic pressure) normalized by u_0 — "amplitude" (for a periodic signal) ot "peak" (for a pulse) value. Time θ is measured in the coordinate system "co-moving" with the wave at the sound speed, it is normalized by the characteristic duration (inverse frequency ω^{-1}) of the signal. The distance z is measured in units of sock-formation lengths x_{SH}; Γ is the reciprocal acoustic Reynolds number (Goldberg number) — the ratio of the characteristic "nonlinear" x_{SH} to "dissipative" α^{-1} lengths [3].

The general solution of the BE (7.51) has a complex structure and is not always convenient for analysis of particular problems. Apart from trivial particular solutions obtained from the stationary solution

$$\partial V/\partial z=0,\quad V=\tanh\left[(\theta-\theta_0)/2\Gamma\right] \quad (7.53)$$

(this is a shock wave with a finite front width) by translations along z, θ, V; other, "nontrivial" exact solutions turned out to be useful.

The "Khokhlov solution" [4]

$$V=\frac{1}{1+z}\left[-\theta+\pi\tanh\frac{\pi\theta}{2\Gamma(1+z)}\right],\quad -\pi<\theta<\pi \quad (7.54)$$

describes one period of a sawtooth wave in the region of existence of developed shock fronts. This formula was in fact "guessed" in 1960. It is also obtained by the method of matched asymptotic expansions, thereby the first approximation gives an exact solution.

The self-similar solution of the BE [4,8]

$$V=\sqrt{\frac{4\Gamma}{\pi z}}\frac{\exp\left(-\theta^2/4\Gamma z\right)}{C+\operatorname{erf}\left(\theta/\sqrt{4\Gamma z}\right)} \quad (7.55)$$

describes a unidirectional pulse with a steep leading front; it is obtained from the invariance of Eq. (7.51) with respect to the transformation

$$V\to V/C,\quad z\to C^2 z,\quad \theta\to C\theta. \quad (7.56)$$

Accordingly, by constructing the following substitution:

$$V=z^{-1/2}Q(z^{-1/2}\theta), \quad (7.57)$$

which is invariant with respect to (7.56), it is possible to reduce (7.51) to an ordinary differential equation and find the solution (7.54). Another nontrivial transformation has been guessed by S.N. Gurbatov [9]: if the function $V=\Phi(z,\theta)$ is an exact solution of the BE, then the following expression will also be an exact solution:

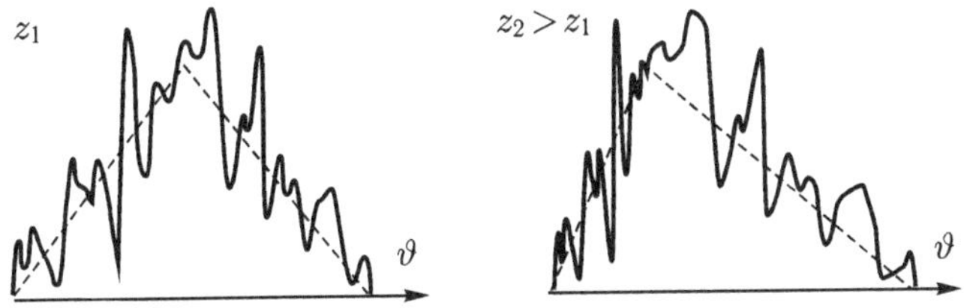

Fig. 7.1 Interaction of high-frequency noise (solid curves) and a regular wave with a triangular profile (dashed intervals of straight lines) described by the solution (7.58).

$$V = \frac{1}{1-z/z_0}\Phi\left(\frac{z}{1-z/z_0}, \frac{\theta}{1-z/z_0}\right) + \frac{\theta/z_0}{1-z/z_0}. \tag{7.58}$$

This formula describes, for instance, interaction of high-frequency noise and a low-frequency signal [10]. With growing distance z, the frequency of noise at the leading front of a regular wave is growing, and at the tail front, it is decreasing (Fig. 7.1). In more detail, this interaction is considered in Sect. 9.8.

This story of "guessing" the exact results, however, indicates that the methods of the Lie group theory as applied to solving differential equations are not sufficiently widely known [11–13].

7.2.2 Finding exact solutions of the Burgers equation by using the group-theory methods

Let us show how the results of Sect. 7.2.1 can be obtained by using regular methods. By changing the normalization of the variables, let us write the BE (7.51) in the simplest form

$$u_x = uu_t + u_{tt}. \tag{7.59}$$

Infinitesimal symmetries of the BE [14–17] form a 5-dimensional Lie algebra spanned by the following linearly independent operators:

$$\begin{aligned} &X_1 = \frac{\partial}{\partial x}, \quad X_2 = \frac{\partial}{\partial t}, \quad X_3 = x\frac{\partial}{\partial t} - \frac{\partial}{\partial u}, \\ &X_4 = 2x\frac{\partial}{\partial x} + t\frac{\partial}{\partial t} - u\frac{\partial}{\partial u}, \quad X_5 = x^2\frac{\partial}{\partial x} + tx\frac{\partial}{\partial t} - (t+xu)\frac{\partial}{\partial u}. \end{aligned} \tag{7.60}$$

The technique of finding the operators (7.60) is a standard one; even computer programs for computing them exist.

If the symmetry is known, the invariant solution of the BE is obtained as follows. Two independent invariants as derived as solution of the equation $X(J) = 0$: $J_1 = \lambda(t,x)$, $J_2 = \mu(t,x,u)$. Then one of the invariants is expressed as a function of the other, $\mu = \phi(\lambda)$. Next, the expression solved with respect to u is substituted into the BE. As a result, an equation for a function of one variable $\phi(\lambda)$ is obtained. This procedure reduces the number of independent variables by one. Solutions invariant with respect to the extension group generated by the operator X_4 are often called self-similar.

In this case, the equation $X(J) = 0$ has the following form:

$$X_4(J) = 2x\frac{\partial J}{\partial x} + t\frac{\partial J}{\partial t} - u\frac{\partial J}{\partial u} = 0. \tag{7.61}$$

Its characteristic system and invariants are:

$$\frac{dx}{2x} = \frac{dt}{t} = -\frac{du}{u}; \quad \lambda = \frac{t}{\sqrt{x}}, \quad \mu = \sqrt{x}u. \tag{7.62}$$

Hence the invariant solution needs to be sought in the following form:

$$u = x^{-1/2}\Phi(\lambda), \quad \lambda = x^{-1/2}t. \tag{7.63}$$

By substituting (7.63) into (7.59), we obtain the ordinary differential equation

$$\Phi'' + \Phi\Phi' + 0.5\left(\lambda\Phi' + \Phi\right) = 0 \tag{7.64}$$

and find its exact solution

$$u = \frac{2}{\sqrt{\pi x}}\frac{\exp\left(-t^2/4x\right)}{C + \operatorname{erf}(t/2\sqrt{x})}, \quad \operatorname{erf}(z) = \frac{2}{\sqrt{\pi}}\int_0^z \exp\left(-s^2\right)ds. \tag{7.65}$$

Eq. (7.65) coincides with (7.55). For the generalized BE (whose coefficients depend on coordinates) self-similar solutions are found in Ref. [5].

For the projective group generated by the operator X_5, we obtain

$$X_5(J) = x^2\frac{\partial J}{\partial x} + tx\frac{\partial J}{\partial t} - (t + xu)\frac{\partial J}{\partial u} = 0. \tag{7.66}$$

The characteristic system and two invariants have the following form:

$$\frac{dx}{x^2} = \frac{dt}{tx} = -\frac{du}{t + xu}; \quad \lambda = \frac{t}{x}, \quad \mu = t + xu. \tag{7.67}$$

Hence the invariant solution needs to be sought in the following form:

$$u = -\frac{t}{x} + \frac{1}{x}\Phi(\lambda), \quad \lambda = \frac{t}{x}. \tag{7.68}$$

By substituting this expression into the BE, for $\Phi(\lambda)$, we obtain the equation $\Phi'' + \Phi\Phi' = 0$, from which we immediately find the Khokhlov solution (7.54):

$$u = \frac{1}{x}\left[-t + \pi\tanh\left(C + \frac{\pi t}{2x}\right)\right]. \tag{7.69}$$

By using the projective transformation, from a known solution $u = \Phi(t,x)$ for the BE, it is possible to obtain the following one-parameter family of new solutions:

$$u = \frac{ax}{1-at} + \frac{1}{1-at}\Phi\left(\frac{t}{1-at}, \frac{x}{1-at}\right). \tag{7.70}$$

Eq. (7.70) differs from (7.58) only by notation. If we apply the transformation (7.70) to the stationary solution of the BE, we obtain a number of new non-stationary solutions, with Eq. (7.69) being among them [17].

Solutions can be found not only from main symmetries (7.60), but also from their linear combinations. Let us consider, for example, the operator

$$X_1 + X_5 = \left(1+x^2\right)\frac{\partial}{\partial x} + tx\frac{\partial}{\partial t} - (t+xu)\frac{\partial}{\partial u}. \tag{7.71}$$

By solving the characteristic equation, we find the invariant form

$$u = -\frac{tx}{1+t^2} + \frac{1}{\sqrt{1+t^2}}\Phi(\lambda), \quad \lambda = \frac{x}{\sqrt{1+t^2}} \tag{7.72}$$

and the corresponding new exact solution of the BE [17]:

$$\Phi = 2\frac{d}{d\lambda}\ln\left[\sqrt{\lambda}J_{1/4}\left(\frac{\lambda^2}{4}\right) + C\sqrt{\lambda}Y_{1/4}\left(\frac{\lambda^2}{4}\right)\right]. \tag{7.73}$$

7.2.3 *Some methods of finding exact solutions*

Despite the power of the group-theory methods, their use in a number of cases is connected with difficulties while finding exact solutions, which are easier to obtain by other methods [18]. Such a situation is typical for equations with low symmetry.

Sometimes it is possible to find exact solutions of such equations by reducing their order. Let us give some examples.

Example 1. Nonlinear equation of the second order (7.40) for propagating plane waves

$$\frac{\partial^2 p}{\partial x^2} = \frac{1}{c^2}\frac{\partial^2}{\partial t^2}\left(p - \frac{\varepsilon}{c^2\rho}p^2\right) \tag{7.74}$$

is exactly reduced to a pair of first order equations:

$$\frac{\partial p}{\partial x} = \pm\frac{1}{c}\sqrt{1 - \frac{2\varepsilon}{c^2\rho}p}\,\frac{\partial p}{\partial t}. \tag{7.75}$$

This can be easily verified. By differentiating Eq. (7.75) with respect to x and replacing the derivatives with respect to x on the right-hand side by the derivatives with respect to time, we obtain the original equation (7.74). Solving (7.75) is much simpler than solving (7.74). Its solution computed by means of the method of characteristics has the following form:

$$p = \Phi\left(t \pm \frac{x}{c}\sqrt{1 - \frac{2\varepsilon}{c^2\rho}p}\right). \tag{7.76}$$

This is a special solution of Eq. (7.74). It describes nonlinear waves propagating to the right or left (depending on the sign) along the x-axis. ∎

Example 2. Let us now consider the following equation of the fourth order [6]:

$$\frac{\partial V}{\partial z} - V\frac{\partial V}{\partial \theta} = -R\frac{\partial^4 V}{\partial \theta^4}, \tag{7.77}$$

which continues the series of the following remarkable equations: the BE (7.51) — the second order, the Korteweg-de Vries (KdV) equation — the third order. For waves in a scattering medium,

$$R = \frac{x_{SH}}{x_{SCATT}} = \frac{8\langle\mu^2\rangle a^3}{c^4}\frac{\omega_0^3 c^3 \rho}{\varepsilon p_0} \tag{7.78}$$

is the ratio of characteristic scales of nonlinearity and scattering, $\langle\mu^2\rangle$ is the mean square of fluctuations of the refractive index, a is the correlation radius, ε is the nonlinear parameter and p_0 is the pressure-wave amplitude. The equation for stationary waves and one of its solutions have the following form:

$$R\frac{d^4 V}{d\theta^4} = V\frac{dV}{d\theta}, \quad \theta = \left(\frac{40}{9}R\right)^{1/3}\int_0^V \frac{dy}{(1-y^2)^{2/3}}. \tag{7.79}$$

Eq. (7.79) is obtained as follows. A first order equation $dV/d\theta = f(V)$, the right-hand side of which is unknown, was put into correspondence with a fourth-order equation. Through a chain of transformations, a fourth-order equation was found, from which the function $f(V)$ was determined. It is not difficult to repeat these transformations, if $f(V)$ known:

$$\frac{dV}{d\theta} = \left(\frac{9}{40R}\right)^{1/3}(1-V^2)^{2/3},$$

$$\frac{d^2V}{d\theta^2} = -\frac{4}{3}\left(\frac{9}{40R}\right)^{2/3}V(1-V^2)^{1/3},$$

$$\frac{d^3V}{d\theta^3} = \cdots$$

Another solution, *viz.* a bounded stationary wave, describes a shock front with rapidly damped oscillations [6]. As opposed to the oscillations at the front of the Korteweg-de Vries-Burgers (KdVB) solution linked to dispersion, here the oscillations are caused by the "Fourier phenomenon", i.e. the "cutting-off" the higher harmonics forming the front. ∎

Another method, known by the example of the BE, is the finding of a linearizing change of variables. These substitutions are frequently "guessed", but also are found by means of the Lie group theory methods. Examples of such, generally exclusive, models are given below.

Example 3. Inhomogeneous Burgers Equation

$$\frac{\partial U}{\partial T}+\Delta\frac{\partial U}{\partial \xi}-\pi\varepsilon U\frac{\partial U}{\partial \xi}-D\frac{\partial^2 U}{\partial \xi^2}=F(\xi) \tag{7.80}$$

is used in various problems, e.g. for describing a laser excitation of intense hypersound [19], transonic gas flow past bodies and heated domains [20], nonlinear standing waves [21]. In this problem, T is the "slow" time describing evolution of the field, ξ is the "fast" time describing oscillations, D is the dissipation parameter, Δ is the resonance detuning, $F(\xi)$ gives oscillations of one of the walls of the resonator. Eq. (7.80) is linearized by the same Hopf-Cole (Florin) substitution as the regular BE (7.51):

$$U=\frac{2D}{\pi\varepsilon}\frac{\partial}{\partial \xi}\ln W, \quad \frac{\partial W}{\partial T}+\Delta\frac{\partial W}{\partial \xi}-D\frac{\partial^2 W}{\partial \xi^2}=\frac{1}{2}qD\cos\xi\cdot W. \tag{7.81}$$

Here, for definitiveness, $F=-(M/2)\sin\xi$.

Interestingly, the wave intensity averaged over a period is expressed via the eigenvalue λ_0 of the Mathieu function ce_0 [19]:

$$\overline{U^2}=-\left(\frac{D}{\pi\varepsilon}\right)^2\cdot\lambda_0\left(q=\frac{\pi\varepsilon M}{2D^2}\right), \quad U=\frac{2D}{\pi\varepsilon}\frac{d}{d\xi}\ln ce_0\left(\frac{\xi}{2},q\right). \tag{7.82}$$

The resonance curve for the positive peak pressure in the wave profile has a finite (because of nonlinear attenuation) maximum shifted into the region $\Delta>0$ by a value of the order of $\sqrt{M}$ (see Chap. 11). In the same way, under nonlinear streamlining of bodies, the maximum of the resistance coefficient happens to be finite and shifted into the supersonic domain [20]. ∎

Example 4. Equation for wave beams in cubically nonlinear nondispersive media [22]

$$\frac{\partial}{\partial \tau}\left[\frac{\partial p}{\partial x}+\gamma p^2\frac{\partial p}{\partial \tau}-\beta\frac{\partial^2 p}{\partial \tau^2}\right]=\frac{c}{2}\Delta_\perp p \tag{7.83}$$

is used, in particular, for description of diffraction of strongly distorted waves and their self-focusing (SF) (see Chap. 10). If diffraction is weak, a harmonic wave turns into a sawtooth wave, whose each period has a trapezoidal shape and contains two shock fronts: compression and rarefaction. In the approximation of nonlinear geometric acoustics and for a parabolic wave front, from Eq. (7.83), a solution for mean (averaged over a period) intensity is obtained

$$I = \frac{1}{f^2(x)} I_0\left(\frac{r}{af}\right)\left[1 + \alpha\,\omega\gamma I_0\left(\frac{r}{af}\right)\int_0^x \frac{dx'}{f^2(x')}\right]^{-1}. \tag{7.84}$$

Here α is a certain constant. The function f, which describes variation of the wave amplitude and beam width, satisfies the following complex integro-differential nonlinear equation

$$f^3 \frac{d^2 f}{dx^2} + \frac{1}{2x_d x_{SH}}\left[1 + \frac{\alpha}{x_{SH}}\int_0^x \frac{dx'}{f^2(x')}\right]^{-2} = \frac{1}{x_d^2}. \tag{7.85}$$

Here $x_{SH} = \left(\omega\gamma p_0^2\right)$ is the shock-formation distance and $x_d = \omega a^2/2c$ is the diffraction length. The boundary conditions at $x = 0$: $f = 1$, $df/dx = R^{-1}$, where R is the curvature radius of the front. If the right-hand side of (7.85) is equal to zero, this Cauchy problem has the following exact solution

$$f(x) = \left(1 + \frac{x}{R} + \delta_1 \frac{x}{x_{SH}}\right)^{\frac{\delta_2}{\delta_1+\delta_2}} \cdot \left(1 + \frac{x}{R} - \delta_2 \frac{x}{x_{SH}}\right)^{\frac{\delta_1}{\delta_1+\delta_2}},$$
$$\delta_{1,2} = \frac{\sqrt{\alpha^2 + 2x_{SH}/x_d} \pm \alpha}{2}. \tag{7.86}$$

It is obtained as follows. First, an exact particular solution $f = \exp(-x/\alpha x_d)$ was guessed, which then was generalized (7.86) by means of the "lens transformation" using the symmetry property of Eq. (7.83). A shortcoming of the solution (7.86) is in that the beam described by it self-focuses into a point at a distance of $x_{SF} = (\delta_2/x_{SH} - 1/R)^{-1}$. In order to remove the singularity, it is necessary to take diffraction, i.e. the right-hand side of (7.85), into account. Surprisingly, also in this case there is an exact solution, It can be found by linearizing (7.85) using the following change of variables:

$$q = \frac{1}{f},\; \xi x_d = x_{SH}/\alpha + \int_0^x \frac{dx'}{f^2(x')},\; \frac{d^2 q}{d\xi^2} + \left(1 - \frac{x_{SH}/x_d}{\alpha^2 \xi^2}\right)\cdot q = 0. \tag{7.87}$$

The solution of the linear equation is given by the cylindrical functions

$$f(\xi) = \frac{\xi^{-1/2}}{C_1 J_\nu(\xi) + C_2 Y_\nu(\xi)},\quad \nu = \frac{1}{2}\sqrt{1 + \frac{2x_{SH}}{\alpha^2 x_d}}. \tag{7.88}$$

This solution is depicted in Fig. 10.12. From this figure, it is seen that, at weak diffraction, the beam is appreciably narrowed (curves 1 and 2), and at strong diffraction SF does not manifest itself (curves 3 and 4). Without dispersion, SF does not lead to a strong growth of the amplitude, as is the case at laser-beam self-focusing.

Let us now discuss models, which can be not linearized, but substantially simplified and for which exact solutions can be obtained. ∎

Example 5. Let us consider an ensemble of weak shock waves (Fig. 7.2) having random positions and "amplitudes". We associate each "step" with a particle, whose

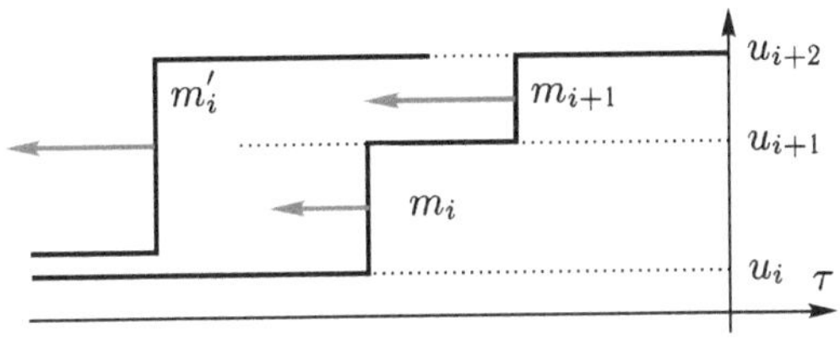

Fig. 7.2 Illustration of the process of pairwise collision and merging of two weak shock waves.

mass and velocity are given by the following formulas:

$$m_i = u_{i+1} - u_i, \quad v_i = -(\varepsilon/c^2)\cdot(u_{i+1}+u_i)\,. \tag{7.89}$$

On the merging of the two steps, the third one is formed, while the "mass" and "momentum" are conserved:

$$m_i' = m_i + m_{i+1}, \quad m_i'v_i' = m_i v_i + m_{i+1}v_{i+1}\,. \tag{7.90}$$

The analogy with nonelastic particles allows us to obtain the following kinetic equation [23]:

$$\frac{\partial G}{\partial x} - \frac{\varepsilon}{2c^2}(m+\langle m\rangle)\frac{\partial G}{\partial t} = \frac{\varepsilon}{2c^2}\left[m\int_0^m G(x,t,\xi)G(x,0,m-\xi)d\xi \right.$$
$$\left. -(m-\langle m\rangle)G\int_0^\infty G(x,0,\xi)d\xi\right]. \tag{7.91}$$

Here G is the probability of the event that the time interval between the two neighboring shocks is equal to t and the magnitude of the second of them is equal to m. The nonlinear terms of (7.91) form the collision integral. By making a change of variable and by Laplace transforming the new function

$$G = \frac{1}{t_0}\exp\left(-\frac{t}{t_0} - \frac{\varepsilon x}{c^2 t_0}m\right)\cdot F(x,t,m), \quad f = \int_0^\infty F\exp(-sm)\,dm, \tag{7.92}$$

we obtain the equation of the simple wave type

$$\frac{\partial f}{\partial x} + \frac{\varepsilon}{c^2 t_0} f\frac{\partial f}{\partial s} = 0, \tag{7.93}$$

which is exactly solvable (see Sect. 9.7). A similar approach is applicable to a sawtooth wave, i.e. an ensemble of triangular pulses with random peak values and durations [24]. Nonlinear attenuation is equivalent to "evaporation" ("mass" losses) of particles between their collisions. ∎

Example 6. The system of equations of nonlinear geometric acoustics

$$\frac{\partial u}{\partial x}-\frac{\varepsilon}{c_0^2}u\frac{\partial u}{\partial T}+\alpha\frac{\partial u}{\partial y}+\beta\frac{\partial u}{\partial z}+\left(\frac{\partial \alpha}{\partial y}+\frac{\partial \beta}{\partial z}\right)\frac{u}{2}=0, \tag{7.94}$$

$$\frac{\partial \alpha}{\partial x}+\alpha\frac{\partial \alpha}{\partial y}+\beta\frac{\partial \alpha}{\partial z}=0, \quad \frac{\partial \beta}{\partial x}+\alpha\frac{\partial \beta}{\partial y}+\beta\frac{\partial \beta}{\partial z}=0, \tag{7.95}$$

where $\alpha=\partial\psi/\partial y$, $\beta=\partial\psi/\partial z$ are ray angles, can be reduced to the exactly solvable simple wave equation [25]

$$\frac{\partial u}{\partial x}+\frac{u}{2}\frac{d}{dx}\ln S-\frac{\varepsilon}{c_0^2}u\frac{\partial u}{\partial T}=0 \tag{7.96}$$

by means of the transformation to the Lagrangian coordinates $\xi=y-\alpha x$, $\eta=z-\beta x$, where S is the Jacobian. Thereby the variables ξ and η are parameters: there are no derivatives with respect to them. Note also that time can be eliminated from the transfer equation (7.94) assuming a sawtooth profile. After this, it can be linearized. ∎

Example 7. In a nonlinear resonator, it is necessary to consider two counter-directional, undergoing distortion and interacting waves. But for periodic in time excitations, it is possible to limit oneself by the superposition: take "self-action" into account, but neglect "cross-interactions" (non-resonant ones) [21]. Thereby the field in the resonator is described by the following nonlinear functional equation:

$$F\left[\omega t+kL-\frac{\varepsilon}{c}kLF\right]-F\left[\omega t-kL+\frac{\varepsilon}{c}kLF\right]=A\sin(\omega t), \tag{7.97}$$

in which F is an unknown function. Nevertheless, in the case of interest in practice, when the length of the resonator is small compared with the nonlinear length, the frequency is close to the frequency of one of the modes, and attenuation over the length L of the resonator is small, (7.97) is reduced to the exactly solvable equation (7.80). ∎

7.3 The *a priori* symmetry method

In conclusion, let us discuss an approach to solving nonlinear equation by the means of "immersion" into a class of more general (and complex) models [17]. Experience, it would seem, contradicts the idea of further complication: "In order to simplify a problem, we should, up to certain limits, idealize the system's properties, make a number of simplifying assumptions..." [26]. But behind the exterior differences hides the unity of these two approaches. It is clear that a more symmetrical model must have more exact solutions. How to achieve a greater symmetry? It is possible to follow the traditional path of simplification by "cutting off" elements of a model violating its symmetry (by neglecting some term of an equation or by modifying them in some way). On the other hand, it is possible to "upgrade" the model up to a more symmetrical one by means of its further complication. If the complex model permits a suitable exact solution, necessary simplifications may be performed in the final formulas.

Example 1. Let us consider the following equation:

$$\frac{\partial}{\partial t}\left[\frac{\partial u}{\partial x}-u\frac{\partial u}{\partial t}\right]=-\beta u, \tag{7.98}$$

which models nonlinear processes with low-frequency dispersion (with diffracting beams being among them). This equations admits a three-dimensional Lie algebra with the basis

$$X_1=\frac{\partial}{\partial t},\quad X_2=\frac{\partial}{\partial x},\quad X_3=t\frac{\partial}{\partial t}-x\frac{\partial}{\partial x}+2u\frac{\partial}{\partial u}. \tag{7.99}$$

The class of group-invariant solutions is limited to propagating waves (they are constructed by means of the transfer generators X_1, X_2) and to self-similar solutions (stretching generator X_3). Therefore, by using the idea of immersion, we consider the generalizing model

$$\frac{\partial}{\partial t}\left[\frac{\partial u}{\partial x}-Q(x,u)\frac{\partial u}{\partial t}\right]=F(x,u). \tag{7.100}$$

In order to determine the functional form of Q and F, at which Eq. (7.100) is enriched by symmetries and, consequently, by nontrivial exact solutions, it is necessary to use the notion of the equivalence algebra, perform computations using the infinitesimal Lie technique (thereby Q and F are considered to be independent variables along with the physical variables t, x, u). By means of N.H. Ibragimov's theorem of projections, the specific form (7.100) was found:

$$\frac{\partial}{\partial t}\left[\frac{\partial u}{\partial x}-\Phi_1\left(\frac{u}{x-k}\right)\frac{\partial u}{\partial t}\right]=\frac{1}{x-k}\Phi_2\left(\frac{u}{x-k}\right) \tag{7.101}$$

and shown that (7.101) admits, along with the obvious transfer generator with respect to time, an additional operator

$$X'=t\frac{\partial}{\partial t}+(x-k)\frac{\partial}{\partial x}+u\frac{\partial}{\partial u}. \tag{7.102}$$

A particular case of linear functions Φ_1 and Φ_2 gives an exact solution for focused wave beams in a quadratically nonlinear medium. ∎

Example 2. Earnshow equation

$$\frac{\partial^2 v}{\partial t^2}-c^2\left(1+\frac{\partial v}{\partial \xi}\right)^{-2\varepsilon}\frac{\partial^2 v}{\partial \xi^2}=0 \tag{7.103}$$

in the Lagrangian representation describes one-dimensional motion of a compressible gas. It is linearized by the hodograph transformation $x = v_\xi, y = v_t, \xi = X(x,y)$, $t = u(x,y)$; now the coordinate and time are functions of new independent variables, *viz.* the first derivatives of the sought-for function. The linear equation and its simplified (for small Mach numbers) version have the following form:

$$\frac{\partial^2 u}{\partial x^2} = c^2 (1+x)^{-2\varepsilon} \frac{\partial^2 u}{\partial y^2} \approx c^2 [1 - 2\varepsilon x] \frac{\partial^2 u}{\partial y^2}. \tag{7.104}$$

But Eq. (7.104) is not rich with symmetries and is not exactly solvable. Whereas the more general equation

$$\frac{\partial^2 u}{\partial x^2} - c^2 \psi^2(x) \frac{\partial^2 u}{\partial y^2} = 0 \tag{7.105}$$

has the maximally wide symmetry group at $\psi = [l + sx]^{-2}$. By solving (7.105), assuming that $l = 1$, $s = \varepsilon/2$ and expanding in a series with respect to small x, we find the exact solution of Eq. (7.104) (see [17]). ∎

References

1. B.K. Novikov, O.V. Rudenko, V.I. Timoshenko, *Nonlinear Underwater Acoustics* (Am. Inst. of Phys., New York, 1987)
2. O.V. Rudenko, S.N. Gurbatov, C.M. Hedberg, *Nonlinear Acoustics through Problems and Examples* (Trafford, 2010)
3. O.V. Rudenko, S.I. Soluyan, *Theoretical Foundations of Nonlinear Acoustics* (Plenum, New York, 1977)
4. M.B. Vinogradova, O.V. Rudenko, A.P. Sukhorukov, *Theory of Waves*, 2nd edn. (Nauka, Moscow, 1990). In Russian
5. B.O. Enflo, O.V. Rudenko, To the theory of generalized Burgers' equations, Acta Acustica **88**, 155–162 (2002)
6. O.V. Rudenko, V.A. Robsman, Equation of nonlinear waves in a scattering medium, Dokl. Phys. **47**, 443–446 (2002)
7. V.F. Kovalev, D.V. Shirkov, in *Nonlinear Waves — 2006*, ed. by A.V. Gaponov-Grekhov, V.I. Nekorkin (IAP RAS, Nizhny Novgorod, 2007), pp. 433–446. In Russian
8. O.V. Rudenko, S.I. Soluyan, Some nonstationary problems in the theory of waves of finite amplitude in dissipative media, Sov. Phys. Dokl. **15**, 114–117 (1970)
9. S.N. Gurbatov, A.I. Saichev, I. Yakushkin, Nonlinear waves and one-dimensional turbulence in nondispersive media, Sov. Phys. Usp. **26**, 857–876 (1983)
10. O.V. Rudenko, Interactions of intense noise waves, Sov. Phys. Usp. **29**, 620–641 (1986)
11. N.H. Ibragimov, *Transformation Groups Applied to Mathematical Physics* (D. Reidel, Dordrecht, 1985)
12. N.H. Ibragimov, *ABC of Group Analysis*. No. 8 in Mathematics, Cybernetics (Znanie, Moscow, 1989). In Russian
13. N.H. Ibragimov, *Experience of Group Analysis of Ordinary Differential Equations*. No. 7 in Mathematics, Cybernetics (Znanie, Moscow, 1991). In Russian
14. N.H. Ibragimov (ed.), *Symmetries, Exact Solutions and Conservation Laws, CRC Handbook of Lie Group Analysis of Differential Equations*, vol. 1 (CRC Press, Boca Raton, 1994)

15. N.H. Ibragimov (ed.), *Applications in Engineering and Physical Sciences, CRC Handbook of Lie Group Analysis of Differential Equations*, vol. 2 (CRC Press, Boca Raton, 1995)
16. N.H. Ibragimov (ed.), *New Trends in Theoretical Developments and Computational Methods, CRC Handbook of Lie Group Analysis of Differential Equations*, vol. 3 (CRC Press, Boca Raton, 1996)
17. N.H. Ibragimov, O.V. Rudenko, Principle of an *a priori* use of symmetries in the theory of nonlinear waves, Acoust. Phys. **50**, 406–419 (2004)
18. O.V. Rudenko, in *Nonlinear Waves — 2006*, ed. by A.V. Gaponov-Grekhov, V.I. Nekorkin (IAP RAS, Nizhny Novgorod, 2007), pp. 139–150. In Russian
19. O.V. Rudenko, Feasibility of generation of high-power hypersound with the aid of laser radiation, JETP Lett. **20**, 203–206 (1974)
20. A.A. Karabutov, O.V. Rudenko, The modified khokhlov method for investigation of nonsteady transonic flows of a compressed gas, Sov. Phys. Dokl. **24**, 835–838 (1979)
21. B.O. Enflo, C.M. Hedberg, O.V. Rudenko, Resonant properties of a nonlinear dissipative layer excited by a vibrating boundary: Q-factor and frequency response, J. Acoust. Soc. Am. **117**, 601–612 (2005)
22. O.V. Rudenko, O.A. Sapozhnikov, Wave beams in cubically nonlinear nondispersive media., JETP **79**, 220–229 (1994)
23. O.V. Rudenko, V.A. Khokhlova, Kinetic approach to the description of one-dimensional acoustic turbulence, Sov. Phys. Acoust. **34**, 289–293 (1988)
24. O.V. Rudenko, V.A. Khokhlova, Kinetics of one-dimensional sawtooth waves, Sov. Phys. Acoust. **37**, 90–93 (1991)
25. V.A. Gusev, O.V. Rudenko, Statistical characteristics of an intense wave behind a two-dimensional phase screen, Acoust. Phys. **52**, 24–35 (2006)
26. A.A. Andronov, A.A. Vitt, S.E. Khaikin, *Theory of Oscillators* (Pergamon, Oxford, 1966)

Chapter 8
Types of Acoustic Nonlinearities and Methods of Nonlinear Acoustic Diagnostics

8.1 Introduction

Chapter 8 describes basic concepts of the mechanisms of acoustic nonlinearity. It emphasizes the role of anomalously large nonlinearities of multiphase, defective and structurally inhomogeneous media. It also reviews methods of nonlinear diagnostics — an application area, which has been intensively developing in recent years, as well as spheres of their applications.

Nonlinear elastic properties of condensed media and nonlinear waves in such media have been extensively studied since the 1950s [1–3]. Recently, there has been an increasing interest in similar studies covering multiphase systems (gas-liquid medium, granulated and fluid-saturated porous media, geological structures, gels, and composites), as well as solid bodies with defects and inhomogeneities on a mesoscopic (supramolecular) scale. It is of interest due to the unusually large values of nonlinear elastic moduli of such media, where it is often possible to observe strongly expressed nonlinear phenomena at moderate intensities of sound. This opens up possibilities for the development of highly sensitive methods for nonlinear diagnostics, as well as other applications.

8.1.1 Physical and geometric nonlinearities

As it was thought previously, the macroscopic elastic properties are formally determined by the power-series expansion of the internal energy of a weakly deformed medium in terms of the invariants of the strain tensor [4]; coefficients of the quadratic terms of the expansion are linear elastic moduli and those of the cubic terms are Landau nonlinear moduli (or third order moduli). This nonlinearity is commonly called "physical" [5] as it relates to the nonlinearity of intermolecular forces in condensed medium and, naturally, differs for various specific media. Alongside with the effects of acoustic wave interaction, this nonlinearity is responsible for many well-known phenomena such as thermal expansion, deviations from the Dulong-Petit law at high temperatures, sound attenuation as a result of the interaction of coherent phonons with thermal noise (Landau–Rumer mechanism) [6], and others.

Nonlinearity of the second type is determined by the nonlinear relationship between the strain-tensor components and the derivatives of the displacement-vector components with respect to the coordinates. This relationship does not depend on the physical properties of the deformable body and called "geometric" [5] nonlinearity.

Recall how to allocate physical and geometric nonlinearity in hydrodynamic Eqs. (7.1)–(7.3). Assuming that perturbations of the equilibrium state of the medium, associated with the wave field, are small (see, e.g., (7.5)), we arrive at Eqs. (7.7)–(7.9). The left hand sides of the equation of motion (7.7) and the continuity equation (7.8) contained the linear terms, while the nonlinear terms of these equations are gathered on the right hand sides. The appearance of the latest ones are caused by the nonlinearity of the initial equations, but not by the properties of the medium. For this reason such nonlinearity is known as "geometric". On the contrary, in the series expansion of the equation of state (7.9), nonlinear terms appear in the relation connecting the pressure and density increments, i.e. this is a physical nonlinearity, which is determined by the nonlinear character of interaction between molecules.

For isotropic solids, the equation of motion and the relationship between the stress σ_{ik} and strain e_{ik} tensor have the form

$$\rho_0\frac{\partial^2 U_i}{\partial t^2}=\frac{\partial}{\partial x_k}\sigma_{ik},\ \sigma_{ik}=Ke_{ll}\delta_{ik}+2\mu\left(e_{ik}-\frac{1}{3}\delta_{ik}e_{ll}\right)+O(e_{ik}^2). \tag{8.1}$$

Here, U_i is a displacement vector; K, μ are the bulk compression and shear moduli [4] correspondingly; the strain tensor is defined as

$$e_{ik}=\frac{1}{2}\left(\frac{\partial U_i}{\partial x_k}+\frac{\partial U_k}{\partial x_i}+\frac{\partial U_l}{\partial x_k}\frac{\partial U_l}{\partial x_i}\right). \tag{8.2}$$

The group of nonlinear terms is denoted by $O(e_{ik}^2)$:

$$\begin{aligned}O(e_{ik}^2)=&\left(\mu+\frac{A}{4}\right)\left(\frac{\partial U_l}{\partial x_i}\frac{\partial U_l}{\partial x_k}+\frac{\partial U_i}{\partial x_l}\frac{\partial U_k}{\partial x_l}+\frac{\partial U_l}{\partial x_k}\frac{\partial U_i}{\partial x_l}\right)\\&+\frac{1}{2}\left(K-\frac{2}{3}\mu+B\right)\left(\frac{\partial U_l}{\partial x_m}\frac{\partial U_l}{\partial x_m}\delta_{ik}+2\frac{\partial U_i}{\partial x_k}\frac{\partial U_l}{\partial x_l}\right)+\frac{A}{4}\frac{\partial U_k}{\partial x_l}\frac{\partial U_l}{\partial x_i}\\&+B\left(\frac{\partial U_l}{\partial x_m}\frac{\partial U_m}{\partial x_l}\delta_{ik}+2\frac{\partial U_k}{\partial x_i}\frac{\partial U_l}{\partial x_l}\right)+C\frac{\partial U_l}{\partial x_l}\frac{\partial U_l}{\partial x_l}\delta_{ik},\end{aligned} \tag{8.3}$$

describing the deviations from the Hooke law. Here, A, B and C are the nonlinear elastic moduli of the third order (nonlinear Landau coefficients [5] in the expansion of the internal energy in powers of the strain tensor):

$$E = \mu e_{ik}^2 + \left(\frac{K}{2} - \frac{\mu}{3}\right) e_{ll}^2 + \frac{A}{3} e_{ik} e_{il} e_{kl} + B e_{ik}^2 e_{ll} + \frac{C}{3} e_{ll}^3. \quad (8.4)$$

Evidently, geometric nonlinearity appears in the relation between the strain tensor and displacement-vector components (8.2), and physical nonlinearity is represented by all terms in the expression for $O(e_{ik}^2)$ (8.3).

For liquids and gases, the coefficient of physical nonlinearity is usually introduced on the basis of expansion (7.9): $\varepsilon_p = C_2/2C_1$. The coefficient of geometric nonlinearity is $\varepsilon_g = 1$. The sum of these quantities

$$\varepsilon = \varepsilon_g + \varepsilon_p = 1 + \frac{C_2}{2C_1} \quad (8.5)$$

is simply called the coefficient of acoustic nonlinearity. For gases, this coefficient is expressed through the adiabatic index $\gamma = c_p/c_v$ as follows:

$$\varepsilon = (\gamma + 1)/2. \quad (8.6)$$

Apparently, for air, the coefficient (8.6) is equal 1.2, since

$$\gamma = (i+2)/i = 1.4,$$

where the degrees of freedom for diatomic molecules of air are $i = 5$. In the case of liquids, the coefficient ε is measured experimentally, e.g., from the generation of the second harmonic [1]. Typical values at 20°C: $\varepsilon = 3.5$ (distilled water), $\varepsilon = 5.6$ (acetone), $\varepsilon = 6.3$ (alcohol).

Note, that the coefficient ε introduced by Eqs (8.5) and (8.6) is present in basic mathematical models describing the propagation of nonlinear waves in liquids and gases, e.g., in Riemann wave equations, Burgers and Khokhlov–Zabolotskaya equations, as well as in their various modifications (see, e.g., Sect. 7.1).

The presence of quadratically nonlinear terms in these equations is associated with the appearance of a characteristic parameter — the nonlinear length or length of shock formation

$$x_{SH} = \frac{c_0^3 \rho_0}{\varepsilon \omega p_0'} = \frac{c_0^2}{\varepsilon \omega u_0} = \frac{\lambda}{2\pi \varepsilon M_\omega}, \quad (8.7)$$

where λ is the wavelength, and $M_\omega = p_0'/c_0^2 \rho_0 = u_0/c_0$ is the acoustic Mach number for a wave with frequency ω. Ideally, i.e., when nonlinearity is free from attenuation, diffraction and other competitive factors, a discontinuity (the shock front) occurs in the initial plane harmonic wave at the distance x_{SH} from the input of the medium. For instance, for a wave with an acoustic pressure amplitude of $p_0' = 5.5 \times 10^5$ Pa (an intensity of 10 W cm $^{-2}$) and a frequency of 1 MHz in water, this length is equal to $x_{SH} \approx 25$ cm.

The amplitude p_2 of the second harmonic, without taking redistribution of its energy in higher harmonics [7] into account, would increase linearly with increasing x and would be as large as $0.5 p_0'$ at a distance $x = x_{SH}$, but in reality it only reaches $J_2(2) p_0' (\approx 0.35 p_0')$. Thus, the simplest way to estimate the nonlinear parameter ε is to determine the nonlinear length or to measure the amplitude of the second harmonic p_2 at small distances $x \leqslant 0.5x_{SH}$:

$$\varepsilon = \frac{2c_0^3\rho_0}{\omega x}\frac{p_2}{p_0'^2} = \frac{1}{\pi N}\frac{M_{2\omega}}{M_\omega^2}, \tag{8.8}$$

where $N = x/\lambda$ is the number of the wavelengths along the distance x. There are many other methods for estimating ε based on the measurements of spatio-temporal and spectral characteristics of traveling waves and resonance phenomena (see, e.g., [1–3,8–10]). The resonance methods have found extensive use in biomedical research [11] that require high-precision measurements of physical nonlinearity for the correct diagnosis of tissue, organs and biological solutions.

In solids, waves of different types can interact, which accounts for the lack of universal expression (8.6) for the nonlinear coefficient. In the particular case, when plane longitudinal waves propagating in isotropic medium [1] the nonlinear coefficient has the following form:

$$\varepsilon = -\frac{3}{2} - \frac{1}{c_0^2\rho_0}(A + 3B + C). \tag{8.9}$$

As shown by measurements, that for homogeneous bodies, ε (8.9) has the same order of magnitude as that for liquids (e.g., $\varepsilon = 7.2$ for aluminium) and rarely exceeds 10.

However, there are many experiments in structurally inhomogeneous media, where observed values of the nonlinearity parameter reaching $\varepsilon \sim 10^2 - 10^3$. The causes of such large values differ from those discussed above in connection with the physical and geometric nonlinearities. This provides the basis for the allocation nonlinearity of the third type, called "structural" nonlinearity.

8.2 Classification of types of acoustic nonlinearity

It follows from the previous section, that it is convenient to consider three types of nonlinearity, viz. geometric, physical and structural, each being either distributed in the volume of the medium or concentrated in a spatial domain that is small compared with the wavelength [12]. Effects of bulk nonlinearities are able to accumulate as the wave propagates (if competing processes, such as attenuation, diffraction, dispersion, etc. are sufficiently weak). These effects tend to manifest themselves more strongly the longer distance traveled by the wave and can be strongly pronounced even for the weak nonlinearity. In contrast, the effects of boundary nonlinearity are able to accumulate only in case of repetitive wave influence on the nonlinear element (boundary), e.g., if the item is enclosed in the resonator.

8.2.1 Boundary nonlinearities

Let us discuss examples of boundary nonlinearities: geometric, physical and structural.

Example 1. refers to the geometric boundary nonlinearity. Let us consider a flat piston oscillating along the normal (coincident with the x-axis) to its surface and exciting traveling wave in an elastic half-space $x > 0$. A piston displacement from the mean position $x = 0$ is described by the law $x = X(t)$. The piston generates a running wave, in which the velocity of particles in the medium varies as $u = u_0\Phi\,(t - x/c)$. Since the speed of the piston surface is equal to the speed of medium particles on this surface, for unknown Φ we obtain the functional equation:

$$\frac{dX}{dt} = u_0\Phi\,(t - X(t)/c)\,, \tag{8.10}$$

the solution of which [13] nonlinearly depends on the known function $X(t)$:

$$\Phi(t) = \frac{1}{2\pi i}\int_{-\infty}^{\infty} \exp(i\omega t)\frac{d\omega}{\omega}\int_{-\infty}^{\infty} \frac{d^2X}{d\xi^2} \exp\left[i\frac{\omega}{c}X(\xi) - i\omega\xi\right] d\xi\,. \tag{8.11}$$

In particular, if the piston moves according harmonic law $X(t) = -X_0 \cos\omega t$, Eq. (8.10) for function Φ takes the form

$$\frac{u}{u_0} = \Phi\left(\omega t + \frac{u_0}{c}\cos\omega t\right) = \sin\omega t, \quad u_0 = \omega X_0. \tag{8.12}$$

Evidently, in the case of the harmonic dependence $X(t)$, shape of the traveling wave $\Phi(t)$ contains both a constant component and higher harmonics. The difference between $X'(t)$ and $\Phi(t)$ increases with increasing the Mach number $M = u_0/c$ and becomes especially noticeable at the speeds of piston's motion comparable with the speed of sound. Such a situation may arise in liquids containing gas bubbles, in which the speed of sound can be very low; and also in resonators, where effects of boundary nonlinearity can accumulate with time. Since the nonlinearity of relation (8.10) does not depend on the properties of the medium, it would be worthwhile to call this nonlinearity geometric. In the case of small Mach numbers, the shape of the wave (8.12) is close to sinusoidal, while for finite M its positive and negative "half-periods" are distorted differently: the phase of positive values of u shortened in length and has a higher maximum than the absolute value of the maximum phase of negative values of u. Spectral components of this wave are defined by the Fourier series expansion:

$$\frac{u}{u_0} = \Phi(\omega t) = \sum_{n=0}^{\infty}\frac{i^{-n}}{n}J'(nM)e^{in\omega t} = \sum_{n=0}^{\infty}(A_n\cos n\omega t + B_n \sin n\omega t). \tag{8.13}$$

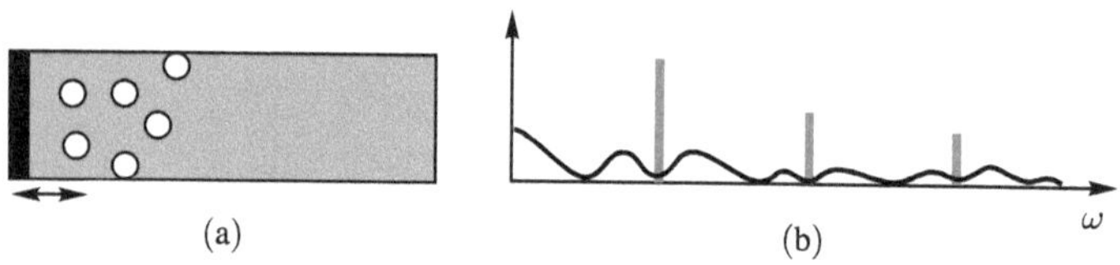

Fig. 8.1 Broadening of the spectrum of cavitation noise in the interaction with oscillating boundary.

Specifically, for the constant component and amplitudes of the first two harmonics, we have

$$A_0 = -\frac{M}{2},\ B_1 = J_0(M) - J_2(M),\ A_2 = -\frac{1}{2}[J_1(2M) - J_3(2M)]. \tag{8.14}$$

The constant component of the velocity is directed toward the piston. Its appearance is connected with the representation of the oscillating boundary in the form of an infinite plane; due to equal pressure in any direction orthogonal to x (in contrast to the piston of finite size), liquid cannot flow to the axis (see, e.g., [14], Sect. 101, problem 4).

Thus, the manifestations of the geometric boundary nonlinearity do not depend on the properties of the medium or the distance traveled by the wave; they become stronger with increasing the Mach number M.

This nonlinearity can become noticeable when a cloud of cavitation bubbles in the liquid arises close to the high-intensity ultrasonic transducer. Speed of sound in such medium sometimes goes down to 30–40 m/s. The bubbles oscillate, collapse, and radiate broadband noise. This noise interacts with boundary oscillations and its spectrum is reproduced in the "bottom" of discrete spectral components, i.e., higher harmonics of the main frequency (Fig. 8.1). As a result, the noise becomes stronger, and the spectrum effectively expands [13]. Described phenomenon complements the known mechanisms [6] of broadening of the spectra under the influence of bulk nonlinearity. ∎

Other problems that require to take into account the finite displacement of the border are related to the accumulation of nonlinear distortion in high-Q resonators. Since the shape of intense "standing" waves is strongly distorted, their saturation occurs when using the harmonic pumping. Hence, in order the "pumping" energy process into resonator to be continued the shape of the boundary oscillations needs to be altered [13] (in analogy with increasing the time interval between pushes in the child's rocking swing to keep it pumping). The required form of motion of the wall (one period) in order to maintain resonant excitation is shown in Fig. 11.12. It is interesting, that the resonance in a system with a boundary nonlinearity is observed not at certain discrete eigenfrequencies, but in frequency bands whose width increases with increasing the amplitude of boundary oscillations of the border (see Sect. 11.7).

Example 2. is devoted to the nonlinearity of the same type as the Example 1 (geometric boundary nonlinearity), but it is interesting because of the connection with the well-known devices such as resonance sound-absorbers. The device is used to reduce noise indoors and usually appears in the form of a perforated panel which is attached to a wall leaving a small gap. Such a device is equivalent to a system of coupled Helmholtz resonators, where each hole is functioning as the "neck" of a resonator, and the air gap situated behind it is a nearly immovable compressible volume. Vibrations of air in the holes are damped out due to friction against the hole walls or nets and a special fibrous material enclosed in them. Proper selection of parameters at a particular frequency allows to achieve complete absorption of the incident wave (the coefficient $K = 1$). Nonlinearity may reduce K for the absorber tuned to be resonant with certain linear parameters, or, vice versa, improve sound absorption by a poorly tuned system by setting it closer to the exact resonance [15]. Thus, in the construction of absorbers for intensive sounds one needs to bear in mind the effects of boundary nonlinearity. The nature of this nonlinearity has a general character and manifests itself when an oscillating stream flows around a sharp-edges body. In such a case, gradients of the flow are on the order $u/\max(r_0, \delta)$, where $\delta = \sqrt{\nu/\omega}$ is the thickness of the acoustic boundary layer, r_0 is minimum radius of curvature constraint, ν is the kinematic viscosity. For sharp edges thickness δ is paramount. Nonlinearity is essential when the Reynolds number Re$\sim$1 is proportional to the ratio of the terms in the equation of motion (7.1), which can be estimated as

$$\mathrm{Re} \sim \left| (\mathbf{u}\nabla)\,\mathbf{u} \left(\frac{\partial \mathbf{u}}{\partial t} \right)^{-1} \right| \sim \frac{u}{\sqrt{\omega \nu}} = \sqrt{\frac{2I}{c\omega\eta}}. \tag{8.15}$$

According to (8.15), in the air ($\eta = 0.018 \cdot 10^3$ Pa·s) at the frequency 500 Hz nonlinearity manifests itself in levels of sound $\sim$120 dB [15]. This estimate is consistent with the experimental data, but if vortices form at the edges of the holes, nonlinear phenomena manifests themselves already starting from 90 dB [15]. ∎

Example 3. refers to the physical boundary nonlinearity. In many problems, it is the force $F(t)$ applied to the piston that should be considered known, rather than the law of displacement of the piston $x = X(t)$ as in Example 1. For instance, when an alternating voltage V is fed to an electromechanical transducer, it is the law $V(t)$ that is known and consequently $F(t)$. The equation of oscillations of a piston of a mass m and the surface area S

$$m\frac{d^2X}{dt^2} = F(t) - p_a S \tag{8.16}$$

takes into account the response of the pressure p_a creating by running away acoustic wave. The pressure is linked with the oscillation velocity u by the nonlinear relationship $p_a = p_a(u)$ known from the theory of Riemann waves [14]. Since at the piston surface we must set $p_a = p_a(dX/dt)$ in Eq.(8.16). If the nonlinearity is weak, we may restrict ourselves to a quadratic nonlinear relationship and Eq. (8.16) takes the form

$$\frac{d^2X}{dt^2} + \frac{c\rho S}{m}\frac{dX}{dt}\left(1 + \frac{\varepsilon}{2c}\frac{dX}{dt}\right) = \frac{1}{m}F(t). \tag{8.17}$$

It is clear that the response of the running away wave to the action of the piston is also nonlinear. If $F(t)$ varies according to the harmonic law then the function $X(t)$ contains higher harmonics. The nonlinearity manifests itself more strongly the greater the product of the nonlinear parameter of the medium and the Mach number, i.e., εM. The nonlinear response is due to the nonlinear dependence of pressure on the velocity or the perturbation of medium density (in solids, we can speak of nonlinear stress-strain dependence), and therefore, it makes sense to call the described nonlinearity "physical". ∎

Example 4. refers to the structural boundary nonlinearity. Fig. 8.2 shows a system of two plates, one of each (bottom) is polished, and the other is rough. Evidently, the larger pressing force P, the more "teeth" (i.e. microscopic asperities at the contact sites) undergo distortion and the rigidity of the contact increases.

Structural nonlinearity is observed in a simple experiment [16] schematically represented in Fig. 8.3. In this case, structural nonlinearity can be used to estimate the quality of two rough surfaces which are in contact with each other [17]. If $P \to 0$, the incident wave with frequency ω is almost entirely reflected from the interface. Conversely, if $P \to \infty$, the wave passes through the interface due to ideal acoustic contact. In both cases, there is no reflected wave at the frequency 2ω. The second harmonic arises at intermediate values of P, and the dependence of the amplitude of the displacement $U_{2\omega}$ on P has a maximum. Interestingly, the profile $U_{2\omega}(P)$ represents the statistical distribution of microasperity heights [17] (in the framework of the model shown in Fig. 8.2(b)).

Nonlinearity of contacts [18] has already been exploited for measurements and realization of interactions between various types of bulk and surface waves (in particular, as applied to acoustoelectronic devices for signal processing). There now exists the term CAN (contact acoustic nonlinearity). These issues are described in detail in the review [19].

The magnitude of the signal generated as a result of the reflection from a nonlinear element depends on a variety of parameters. Therefore, one should be cautious

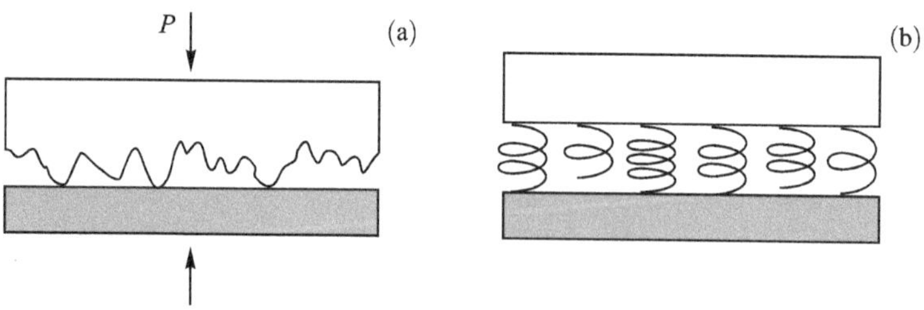

Fig. 8.2 Schematic representation of a rough surface **(a)**, and model of rough surface in the form of an ensemble of springs of different lengths, but the same stiffness **(b)**.

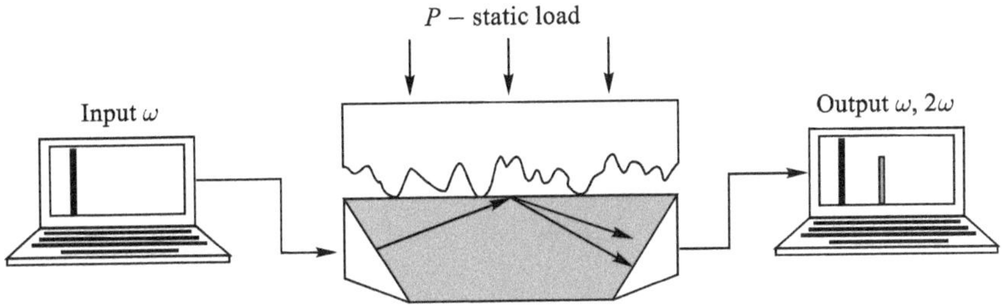

Fig. 8.3 Schematic depiction of rough surface diagnostics due to structural nonlinearity.

when speaking of "giant medium nonlinearities". As an example, let us discuss the problem of acoustic wave reflection in the simplest one-dimensional formulation. Let the displacement $X(t)$ of an element at point $x = 0$ under the action of acoustic pressure be described by the equation $\hat{L}(X) = p_a(t)$, where the pressure field is the sum of the incident (from $-\infty$) and reflected waves:

$$p_a(x,t) = p_+(t - x/c) + p_-(t + x/c).$$

To find the reflected wave the following system is needed

$$\rho c\, dX/dt + \hat{L}(X) = 2p_+(t), \quad p_- = p_+ - \rho c\, dX/dt.$$

Specifically, for a harmonic incident wave and a weak zero-delay quadratic nonlinearity $\hat{L}(X) = E\,(1 + \varepsilon X/h)X/h$ (where E is the Young modulus, ε is the coefficient of the material nonlinearity and h is the thickness of the nonlinear layer) we obtain the following relations:

$$\frac{M_{2\omega}}{M_\omega^2} = 4\varepsilon\frac{c^2\rho}{E}\frac{G}{1+G^2}\frac{1}{\sqrt{1+4G^2}}, \qquad G = \frac{\omega}{c}h\frac{c^2\rho}{E}. \tag{8.18}$$

It is seen that the ratio of the Mach number of the second harmonic to the square of the Mach number of the first harmonic can increase not only with the growth of the nonlinear parameter ε but also with increasing compressibility ratio $c^2\rho/E$ of the nonlinear material and the "buffer" medium in which the incident signal is excited and the reflected signal is registered.

Comparison of Eq. (8.18) in the limit of low frequencies with the analogous expression (8.8) for bulk nonlinearity, it is seen that the coefficient of ε in Eq. (8.18) instead of the number πN of wavelengths contains the product of the small wave layer thickness at the square of the ratio of compressibility $4(kh)\,\left(c^2\rho/E\right)^2$. If the nonlinear element has a Young's modulus smaller than the modulus for the "buffer" medium, then it is more appropriate to speak about the strong manifestation of weak nonlinearity rather than of strong nonlinearity. The response of a thin layer of gas (ρ_G, c_G) located in a liquid (ρ_L, c_L) medium (Fig. 8.4) can serve as an example. The exact solution of the problem [20] for reflection of harmonic signal from the layer, whose density dependence on acoustic pressure is modeled by the expression

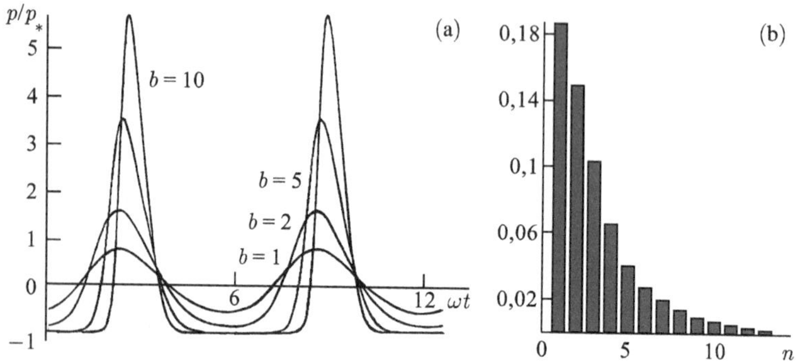

Fig. 8.4 **(a)** The shape of a time-periodic, strongly nonlinear response of the layer, **(b)** and its spectrum for the value $b = 10$.

$c^2\rho/p_* = \ln(1 + p/p_*)$, has the form

$$\frac{p}{p_*} = \frac{\exp\left(-\frac{\varsigma}{\Delta}\cos\omega t\right)}{I_0\left(\frac{\varsigma}{\Delta}b\right) + 2\sum\limits_{n=1}^{\infty}(-1)^n I_n\left(\frac{\varsigma}{\Delta}b\right)\frac{\varsigma}{\sqrt{\varsigma^2+n^2\Delta^2}}\cos\left(n\omega t - \arctan\frac{\varsigma}{\Delta}\right)} - 1. \quad (8.19)$$

This relationship contains the ratio of two small parameters $\varsigma = \rho_G c_G/\rho_L c_L$ and $\Delta = \omega h/2c_L$. The profiles in Fig. 8.4(a) constructed for the ratio $\varsigma/\Delta = 1$ and the values of the parameter $b = P_0/p_*$, equal to 1, 2, 5 and 10. It is seen that with increasing b nonlinear distortions become stronger. At $b = 10$ in Fig. 8.4(b), the reflected spectrum contains about ten harmonics of the incident wave frequency. As is shown in [20], by processing the wide spectrum of the reflected signal the inverse problem, reconstruction of the state equation of the layer, can be solved. ∎

As distinct from a separate weakly nonlinear element, which forms the strong nonlinear response, a distributed system composed of such elements can be appropriately described in such terms as a system having "strong" and even "giant" nonlinearity. In this case, effective elastic characteristics of a structurally inhomogeneous medium are involved. This does not apply to individual elements that reveal strongly nonlinear behavior even under weak acoustic influence. The examples are nonlinearities inherent in systems with couplings and constraints (see Sect. 8.3.2 for "clapping" nonlinearity) as well as in systems subjected to shocks or containing singularities in the equation of state. In such systems, as is known, the linear regime can be completely absent even when an arbitrary small deviation from equilibrium exists. If the medium contains an ensemble of such strongly nonlinear elements, the term "giant" nonlinearity applied to it with more reason.

8.3 Some mechanisms of bulk structural nonlinearity

Let us discuss here possible reasons leading to the appearance of large bulk nonlinearities in structurally inhomogeneous media.

In liquids, this type of nonlinearity arises if strongly compressible inclusions are introduced (e.g., gas bubbles); it is known that the nonlinear parameter of aerated water may by two or three orders of magnitude higher than the nonlinearity of each component of the mixture: gas ($\varepsilon = 1.2$) and water ($\varepsilon = 3.5$). Such nonlinearities have many times been observed and used for implementation of various acoustic interactions in liquids (see, for instance [21–23]. Large nonlinearities of vapor-liquid and gas-liquid systems are important for a variety of wave problems in mechanics and thermal physics [24, 25].

In structurally inhomogeneous solid media (granulated, fluid-saturated, cracked, porous, etc), the amplification coefficient of the nonlinearity K (compared with a homogeneous defect-free medium of the same material), according to many experiments, may also be as large as 10^2–10^4. The increase in K often serves as an indicator of the presence of defects and is used in nonlinear acoustic diagnostics.

8.3.1 Nonlinearity of media with strongly compressible inclusions

Giant nonlinearity of liquids containing gas bubbles opened up the possibility of detecting a small number of bubbles and even individual ones to detect the path of a ship, to monitor fermentation processes or the start of boiling of a coolant in nuclear reactors, to diagnose caisson disease during decompression or in other various industrial processes. These works were carried intensively in the 1980s [26, 27]. At present, medical diagnostic technologies based on the injection into blood vessels of special contrast agents are widely adopted. Nonlinear contrast agents are suspensions of stable microbubbles (see below in Sect. 8.5.1).

Significant growth of nonlinearity in the medium containing strongly compressible inclusion can be explained by a simple example. Let a thin layer of a light compressible medium be surrounded by a denser medium with a high value of the speed of sound (for instance, a thin layer of air in water or in aqueous gel). Here, there are two small parameters: the ratio of acoustic impedances $\rho_G c_G / \rho_L c_L \ll 1$ and the wave thickness of the layer $\omega h / c_G \ll 1$. The solution of the problem of wave propagation through this layer [20] indicates that the second harmonic at the output is in $K \gg 1$ times stronger when the light layer is surrounded by a dense medium (compared with the case in the absence of a dense media). The magnitude of "growth" of nonlinearity required for the generation of the second harmonic, comes out to

$$K = \frac{P_2^{inh}}{P_2^{hg}} = \frac{2}{3}\frac{\varepsilon_G}{\varepsilon_L}\left(\frac{c_L^2 \rho_L}{c_G^2 \rho_G}\right)^2. \tag{8.20}$$

For the air layer in water $K \approx 5.5 \cdot 10^7$. If the layer consists of water with bubbles, the volume concentration of which is about 10^{-4}, the increase in nonlinearity will be around 5000.

Explanation of the giant enhancement of nonlinearity is very simple. Let a wave propagate in a layer of water with a characteristic pressure of a few atmospheres.

Such a wave is weak because the internal pressure $c_L^2\rho_L$ of the water is of the 23,000 atmospheres order. However, when such pressure begins to act on the layer of air, it changes its volume several times and these strong deformations lead to harmonic generation.

Despite the simplicity of this phenomenon, so far there was no quantitative assessment of the maximum possible value of the nonlinearity of gas-liquid media. Formula (8.20) is obtained from very simplified model and gives, of course, only an upper bound. Following [22], it is possible to consider the dynamics of a single bubble and then move on to a liquid containing an ensemble of bubbles (nonlinear oscillators). The equation for bubble oscillations in the field of acoustic pressure in liquid $p(t)$ is derived from the Rayleigh equation [14] and, with allowance for gas compressibility inside the bubble, has the form

$$\frac{d^2w}{dt^2}-\frac{1}{6}\left[2w\frac{d^2w}{dt^2}+\left(\frac{dw}{dt}\right)^2\right]+\omega_0^2w(1-\varepsilon_Gw)=-\omega_0^2\frac{p(t)}{c_G^2\rho_G}. \tag{8.21}$$

Here, w, ω_0^2 are the relative perturbation of the bubble volume and the square of eigenfrequency of its linear vibrations:

$$w=\frac{V'}{V_0},\quad \omega_0^2=\frac{3c_G^2}{R_0^2}\frac{\rho_G}{\rho_L}, \tag{8.22}$$

where V_0, R_0 are the equilibrium volume of a spherical bubble and its radius, and ε_G is the nonlinear parameter of gas. In accordance with formulas (8.22), the resonance wavelength is much larger than the radius of the bubble, since the oscillator is strongly compressible (gas) and has a large virtual mass of the cooscillating fluid.

Thus, the wavelength in water at a frequency of 1 MHz is 1.5 mm, while the radius of "resonant" bubble is only 4 μm. Equation (8.21) contains both the geometric nonlinearity (the term in square brackets appeared in the Rayleigh equation because of the nonlinearity of the Euler equation), and physical nonlinearity which is proportional to ε_G. Their ratio is a value on the order of $\omega^2/(2\varepsilon_G\omega_0^2)$, where ω is the frequency of acoustic vibrations. Thus, the physical nonlinearity for low-frequency (nonresonant) bubbles is substantially superior the geometric one; therefore, the latter may be neglected. Apparently, a large nonlinear response at low frequencies associated with the strong compressibility of the gas in the bubble is the basis for nonlinear diagnostics of individual microbubbles. As the frequency approaches the resonance one, the linear scattering becomes predominant; and the resonance scattering cross-section exceeds the cross-section of the bubble in $4/(kR_0)^2$ times (the relative increase for a bubble in water is on the order of $2\cdot10^4$ [28]). By keeping only the nonlinear term $\sim\varepsilon_G$ in Eq. (8.21) and supplementing it by the wave equation for acoustic pressure, which is derived from the linearized equations of hydrodynamics for a liquid with the effective density $\rho=\rho_L(p)(1-nV(p))$, where n is the number of bubbles per unit volume, it is possible to obtain the system of equations [22]

$$\frac{d^2w}{dt^2} + \omega_0^2 w\,(1-\varepsilon_G w) = -\omega_0^2 \frac{p(t)}{c_G^2 \rho_G}, \tag{8.23}$$

$$\Delta p - \frac{1}{c_L^2}\frac{\partial^2 p}{\partial t^2} = -\rho_L n V_0 \frac{\partial^2 w}{\partial t^2}. \tag{8.24}$$

System (8.23), (8.24) coincides with the equations used in nonlinear optics of dielectrics [29], where p is the electric field, and w is the polarization of the medium in the Drude–Lorentz type model. This system is useful for solving the problem of maximum possible nonlinearities.

Without paying attention to resonance phenomena, let us neglect the second derivative in Eq. (8.23). In this case, the effective low-frequency speed of sound

$$c_{ef}^2 = \frac{c_L^2}{1+nV_0\eta}, \qquad \eta = \frac{c_L^2 \rho_L}{c_G^2 \rho_G} \tag{8.25}$$

decreases with both growing gas content nV_0 and growing compressibility ratio η of the medium. The system (8.23), (8.24) is weakly dispersive and can be reduced to the Riemann wave equation by the method of slowly changing profile [29]:

$$\frac{\partial p}{\partial x} - \frac{\varepsilon_{ef}}{c_{ef}^3 \rho_{ef}} p \frac{\partial p}{\partial \tau} = 0, \qquad \frac{\varepsilon_{ef}}{c_{ef}^3 \rho_{ef}} \equiv \varepsilon_G c_{ef} \frac{\rho_L n V_0}{\left(c_G^2 \rho_G\right)^2}, \tag{8.26}$$

where $\tau = t - x/c_{ef}$ is the time in the coordinate system "co-moving" with the wave. Whence, the effective nonlinearity coefficient is defined as

$$\frac{\varepsilon_{ef}}{\varepsilon_G} = \frac{\eta^2 n V_0\,(1-nV_0)}{(1+\eta n V_0)^2}. \tag{8.27}$$

It can be seen that the maximum nonlinearity

$$\varepsilon_{ef} = \varepsilon_G \frac{\eta^2}{4(\eta+1)} \tag{8.28}$$

is achieved at a gas content $nV_0 = (\eta+2)^{-1}$.

Estimates for a two-phase system consisting of air bubbles in water, show that the effective nonlinearity may increase by $K = \varepsilon_{ef}/\varepsilon_G \approx 3900$ times compared with that of a diatomic gas and reach a maximum value of $\varepsilon_{ef} \approx 4700$ at a relative bulk content of the gas as small as $0.7 \cdot 10^{-4}$.

The above values are consistent with the assessments of many measurements as well as evaluation obtained from the formula (8.20). At the same time, things are far from completely clear. In a previous consideration, the bubble was regarded as an oscillator free from losses, deformations were assumed to be finite but small, while scattering and some other factors were disregarded. It would seem, that the issue of maximum ε_{ef} could be solved in principle by considering one-dimensional problem of periodically alternating plane-parallel layers of two media, $\rho_G c_G$, $\rho_L c_L$

of thickness h_G, h_L. In the linear formulation, such problem has long been solved (see, e.g., [29,30]). The corresponding dispersion equation

$$\cos(k_{ef}(h_G+h_L)) = \cos k_G h_G \cdot \cos k_L h_L - \frac{1}{2}\left(\frac{k_G}{k_L}+\frac{k_L}{k_G}\right) \sin k_G h_G \cdot \sin k_L h_L \quad (8.29)$$

results from joining the solutions of the wave equation at the boundaries for each layer. In the long-wave approximation, it follows from Eq. (8.29) that

$$\frac{h_G+h_L}{c_{ef}^2} = \frac{h_G}{c_G^2} + \frac{h_L}{c_L^2}. \quad (8.30)$$

For $c_G^2 \ll c_L^2$, the formula (8.30) yields an incorrect result being in conflict with the experimental data. Thus, with water and air layers of equal thickness there are small speeds of sound (30 - 100 m/s), but according to Eq. (8.30) that speed is 235 m/s. The fact is that the classical theory (8.30) does not take into account the displacement of boundaries that are essential in the case of high compressibility of air, i.e., the boundary nonlinearity (see Example 1.1 in Sect. 8.2.1). The correct result is obtained in the framework of the quasi-static approach (Mallock's formula [25]) is given by

$$\frac{(h_G+h_L)^2}{h_G h_L} \frac{1}{c_{ef}^2} = \frac{\rho_L}{\rho_G} \frac{1}{c_G^2} + \frac{\rho_G}{\rho_L} \frac{1}{c_L^2}; \quad (8.31)$$

it shows that in the case of identical layer thicknesses $h_G = h_L$, we obtain the minimum possible speed rate of $c_{ef} = 23.8$ m/s, which is much lower than the speed of sound in either water or air. One order of magnitude difference between the linear problem solution and the real data due to disregarding boundary displacements demonstrates the difficulties of a strict solution of the problem in the "nonlinear" formulation.

In addition to the lack of a clear and definite answer to the question concerning how large can be the magnitude of nonlinear moduli, there is an equally important question of how large the acoustic Reynolds numbers [1,3] that characterize the relative contributions of nonlinear effects and competing with them damping effects (due to wave dissipation, reflection, scattering, etc.) may be. The growth of nonlinearity is often accompanied by even greater losses, which makes it more difficult to take the measurements.

8.3.2 *Nonlinearity of solid structurally inhomogeneous media*

A granular system is an example of a medium with strong nonlinear properties. The area of contact between grains depends on the applied stress, i.e. the system is deformed as an ensemble of nonlinear springs. An example is provided by the classical contact problem of the theory of elasticity, viz., the problem of two spheres (the Hertz contact [4], see Fig. 8.5). The force by which two spheres of radii R_1

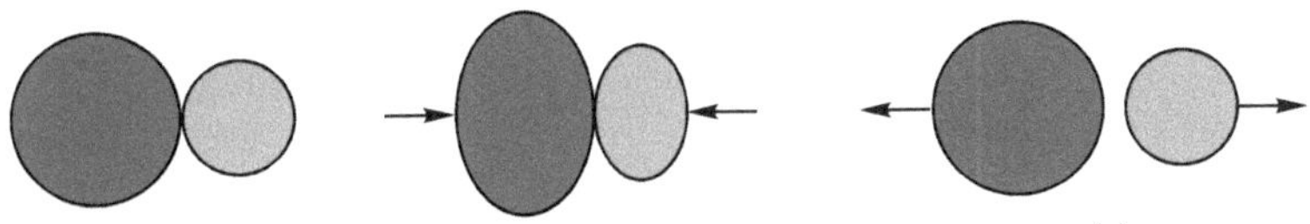

Fig. 8.5 Nonlinear Hertz contact.

and R_2 are repeled from each other nonlinearly depends on the difference between the displacements of their centers $(\xi_2 - \xi_1)$ appeared as a result of deformation:

$$F = E\sqrt{\frac{R_1 R_2}{R_1 + R_2}}\,(\xi_2 - \xi_1)^{3/2}\,\Theta\,(\xi_2 - \xi_1)\,. \tag{8.32}$$

Here, Θ is the Heaviside function, and E is the effective modulus dependent on the Young moduli of the materials constituting the spheres and their Poisson coefficients.When the difference of displacement $(\xi_2 - \xi_1)$ has a negative value, the spheres are repulsed undistorted and force is equal to zero. When the same difference is positive, the force depends on it as $(\xi_2 - \xi_1)^{3/2}$.

Obviously, when the system of two spheres vibrates under the influence of a periodic external force, the nonlinearity is essential only if the contact area between the two bodies changes substantially. If contact additionally compressed by large static force, the nonlinearity decreases. In the case of a weak compression, when the stretching forces can break the contact, in the compression phase, the granules collide; then, such a mechanism is referred to as a "clapping" nonlinearity. The model of a system in which compressive and stretching strains are described by the linear Hooke's law, but with different moduli of elasticity is called "bimodular". It is evident that a system with "clapping" contacts is a particular case of a bimodular system, which lacks resistance with respect to elastic stretching.

Properties of the Hertz contacts are used to describe the nonlinear dynamics of granular media (see [31]), nonlinear contact between rough surfaces [17] and some other systems.

Another important example of media characterized by large structural nonlinearity is fractured media (see Fig. 8.6). It is known that the stress σ applied to a specimen of such a medium increases at the tip of a sharp crack ($\sigma^* = K\sigma$) where it is increased by $K = 1 + 2\sqrt{l/2r_0}$ times, where l is the crack length, and r_0 is the radius of curvature at the top of the notch (see, e.g., [32]). At $r_0 \to 0$, the enhancement is $K \to \infty$. High stresses nearby the tip of a crack usually cause plastic strain of the adjacent medium and r_0 takes a finite value.

Let an alternating stress be applied to a solid sample with internal cracks (Fig. 8.6, (a)), for instance, by irradiating it with a wave of frequency ω or a pair of waves at frequencies ω, Ω. The homogeneous volume deforms linearly, but crack tips generate the second harmonic 2ω or combination frequencies $\omega + \Omega$ and $\omega - \Omega$ (Fig. 8.6, (b)). With the increase of the number of cracks, the level of the nonlinear response must grow.

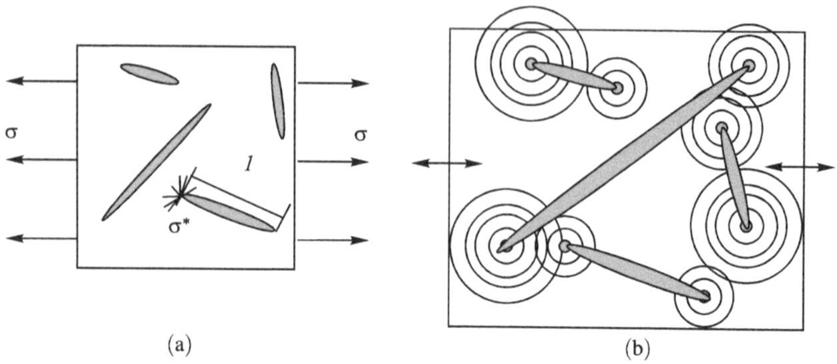

Fig. 8.6 **(a)** The stress applied near the sharp crack tip is increased by $K \gg 1$ times; **(b)** the crack tips emit harmonics and combination frequencies of the spectrum of the incident wave.

The influence of structural defects on the nonlinearity of concrete deformation is observed in the ultrasonic and tensometric strain gauge measurements [33–35].

It is found that water-saturated samples have pseudoelastic properties, and their nonlinearity increases upon evaporation of moisture (the drying of cracks). The dependence of nonlinear effects on the frequency and different hysteretic phenomena have been observed.

Direct confirmation of amplification of nonlinear properties of the medium with an increase in the number of cracks is given in [36, 37] (see Fig. 8.7). A growing static load has been applied to a concrete beam placed in test desk right up to the destruction of the beam. The number of cracks has been increasing with growth of load, as well as the structural nonlinearity of the medium. Amplification of nonlinear wave interactions are observed at the same beam length (6 m) and the same level of the initial signal. As an example, Fig. 8.7 illustrates the interaction of a narrow spectral line of the acoustic signal with a broad noise-like spectrum produced by the shock (*cf.* Fig. 8.1). The processes of generating higher harmonics and appearance of the broad "pedestals" in each spectral line are expressed stronger under greater loads. It has been noted that acoustic emission signals, generated due to the formation of new cracks, have also interacted. Immediately prior to the abrupt destruction of the specimen, the spectrum has become very complex; its constant component ("white noise") has noticeably been growing. Evidently, as the system of cracks develops, the material's strength decreases, therefore the amplification of nonlinear effects in a defective medium may serve as a strength-loss criterion.

In recent years many works on nonlinear acoustics of media with hereditary properties, including hysteretic ones, have been published. These works are still poorly connected with a long research on the mechanics of hereditary media, inaugurated by Boltzmann (1876), Rayleigh (1887), and Volterra (1913). The authors of "mechanical" works prefer the term "constitutive equations" to the former term "equations of state" containing the physical nonlinearity.

Even Volterra used for construction of the nonlinear theory of hereditary elasticity the Frechét representation for the functional in the form of multiple integral

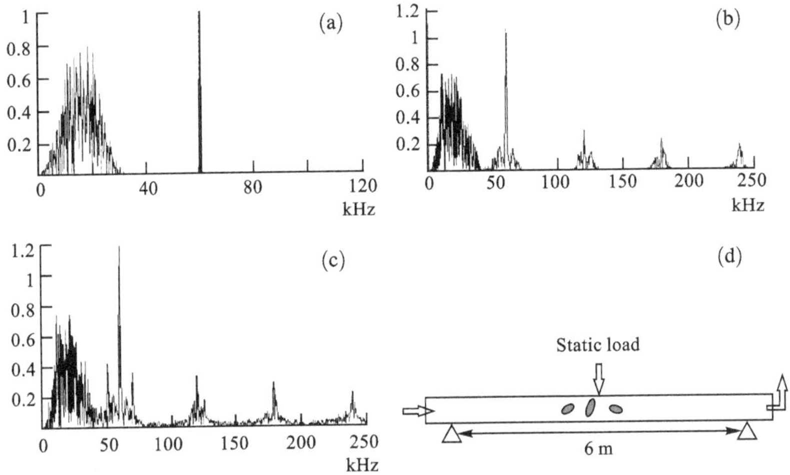

Fig. 8.7 Nonlinear interactions of broadband noise and monochromatic wave in a reinforced concrete beam at different stages of crack formation.

series generalizing the Taylor series. For one-dimensional case, the scalar version of the Volterra-Freshét expansion has the form

$$\sigma(t) = \int_{-\infty}^{t} G_1(t-\tau)de(\tau) + \int_{-\infty}^{t}\int_{-\infty}^{t} G_2(t-\tau_1, t-\tau_2)de(\tau_1)de(\tau_2) + \ldots,$$
$$e(t) = \int_{-\infty}^{t} J_1(t-\tau)d\sigma(\tau) + \int_{-\infty}^{t}\int_{-\infty}^{t} J_2(t-\tau_1, t-\tau_2)d\sigma(\tau_1)d\sigma(\tau_2) + \ldots, \tag{8.33}$$

where σ, e are the stress and the strain, and G_n, J_n are the relaxation and creep functions, respectively [38]. Sometimes the model expansions are used, e.g., the Rabotnov equation

$$\varphi[e(t)] = \sigma(t) + \int_{-\infty}^{t} K(t-\tau)\sigma(\tau)d\tau \tag{8.34}$$

or the Linderman-Rozovsky equation

$$e(t) = \psi[\sigma(t)] + \int_{-\infty}^{t} K(t-\tau)\chi[\sigma(t)]d\tau, \tag{8.35}$$

where $\varphi(e)$, $\psi(\sigma)$ are certain functions; here, functional series (8.33) are assumed to be partly summed. In mechanics, these functions, as well as the kernels under the integral (8.33), are selected on the basis of large amounts of experimental data for a given particular material [38]. In acoustics, where the frequency range is wider and the structure of the kernel (or their spectrum) is much more complicated, the experimental data are scarce. Such data could be obtained on the basis of nonlinear spectroscopy by analogy with optics (see, e.g., [39]), however we have no information on development in this field nor on the conducting of such measurements. In acoustics, the term "nonlinear spectroscopy" is used in quite a different sense; for example, the term "nonlinear resonance spectroscopy" is taken to mean a simple measurement of the amplitude-dependent frequency of resonator oscillations [40].

Volterra type theories are concerned with retarded processes, but reversible in the sense that the profiles of instantaneous deformation (in the stress-strain dependence) coincide under loading and unloading. In hysteretic media, the situation may be different. For example, nonlinearity in metals is associated with the accumulation of essentially irreversible plastic deformation and the unloading law is close to linear. For a material with a destructive pseudoplasticity (e.g., reinforced plastics with concentration of stresses on the fibre bends, cracks), the unloading result is the "closure" of some cracks and the unloading graph approaches the origin of coordinates $\sigma = e = 0$ [38]. Crack "healing" in the process of deformation is observed in the concrete. The phenomenon of birth–disappearance of the defect has been observed recently in metal on the generation of higher harmonics [41]. For cyclic processes, the suitable model of the stress–strain relationship is in the form of the Rayleigh.

Such a hysteresis loop in Fig. 8.8 is defined by the following formulas (for sections $A'B'A$, ABA')

$$\sigma = (E + be_m)e + \frac{b}{2}(e^2 - e_m^2), \quad \sigma = (E + be_m)e - \frac{b}{2}(e^2 - e_m^2),$$

and $\sigma = Ee - be^2$ (section $0A'$). Residual stresses and hysteresis losses (per cycle) are given by the following expressions

$$\sigma^* = \frac{b}{2}e_m^2, \quad W = \oint e \cdot d\sigma = \frac{4}{3}e_m^3.$$

This model is, however, valid only for quasi-stationary processes. It is evident that, with rapid changes in the applied acoustic pressure, the internal restructuring of the medium will not keep up with the pressure, and at very high frequencies the internal processes will get completely "frozen". Hysteresis loss defined by the area of the "loop" in Fig. 8.8 must decrease with increasing frequency. Overall, the picture resembles the one described by the Mandelshtam–Leontovich relaxation

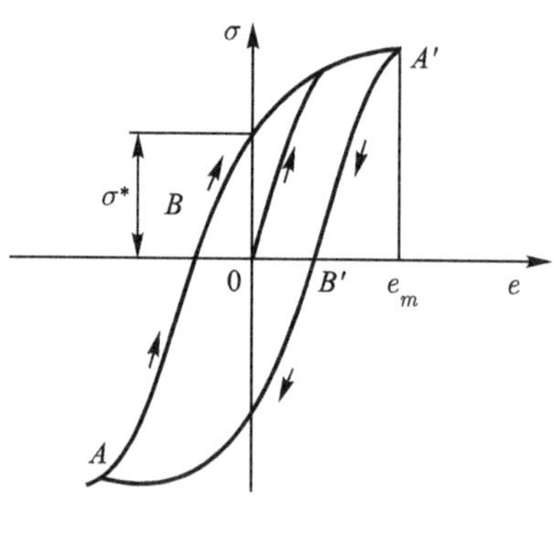

Fig. 8.8 Rayleigh hysteresis.

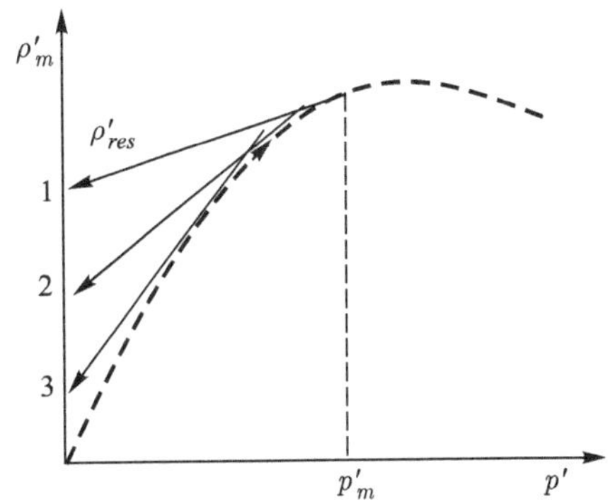

Fig. 8.9 The wave-induced densification process of the medium: the dashed curve follows the loading process, the unloading is shown by the straight lines 1–3.

theory [14]. In this theory, however, a linear internal parameter (concentration of one of the chemically reactive components of the vibrationally excited molecules, etc.) undergoes relaxation, approaching the equilibrium value with its own characteristic time T; as a result, "linear memory" appears in the dependence of medium density perturbation on acoustic pressure [3]:

$$\rho' = \frac{p}{c^2} - \frac{\varepsilon}{c^4\rho}p^2 + \frac{m}{c^2\rho T}\int_{-\infty}^{t}\frac{\partial p(x,t')}{\partial t'}\exp\left(-\frac{t-t'}{T}\right)dt'. \tag{8.36}$$

Despite the additional loss ("second viscosity" [14]) contributed by internal motion, the response is reversible and after the passage of the wave the medium returns to its equilibrium state. In contrast, in hysteretic media after unloading occurs "nonlinear memory": irreversible deformations and residual stresses.

The authors of [42] described a soil type medium compacted by a single loading (Fig. 8.9); the unloading process, however, may follow different ways depending on its speed. The straight line 1 in Fig. 8.9 corresponds to the slow process; thereby the residual strains attain a maximum. In the rapid cycle, the straight line 3 is close to the under loading curve. In contrast to (8.36), the internal dynamics here is described by the nonlinear integral term:

$$\rho' = \frac{p}{c^2} - \frac{\varepsilon}{c^4\rho}p^2 + \frac{\varepsilon}{c^4\rho}\frac{1}{T}\int_{t_m}^{t}\left[p(x,t') - p_m(x)\right]^2\exp\left(-\frac{t-t'}{T}\right)dt'. \tag{8.37}$$

The wave equation of evolution type for these cases look different. For constitutive equation (8.36), the wave equation has the form [3]:

$$\left(\frac{\partial}{\partial\tau} + \frac{1}{T}\right)\left[\frac{\partial p}{\partial x} - \frac{\varepsilon}{c^3\rho}p\frac{\partial p}{\partial\tau}\right] = \frac{m}{2c}\frac{\partial^2 p}{\partial\tau^2},$$

for the case described by Eq. (8.37), it is written down [42] as

$$\left(\frac{\partial}{\partial\tau} + \frac{1}{T}\right)\left[\frac{\partial p}{\partial x} - \frac{\varepsilon}{c^3\rho}p\frac{\partial p}{\partial\tau}\right] = -\frac{\varepsilon}{2c^3\rho T}\frac{\partial}{\partial\tau}\left[p - p_m(x)\right]^2.$$

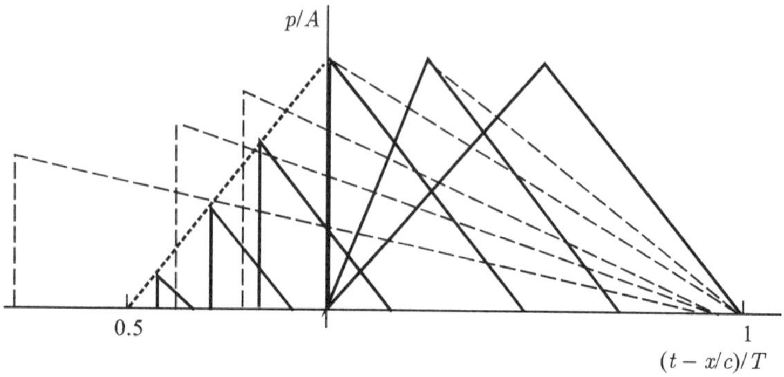

Fig. 8.10 The profile distortion of the unipolar pulse propagating in the hysteretic medium (solid lines) and in an ordinary nonlinear medium (dashed lines).

In Fig. 8.10 is shown the process of transformation of a unipolar pulse in the ordinary nonlinear medium and in medium with residual deformations. It is possible to see the following fundamental differences: (1) in the normal medium pulse area is constant, and in irreversibly-deformable medium it decreases with the propagation; (2) the speed of the trailing edge is greater than the speed of sound, since it moves through the medium compacted by the leading edge; (3) the trailing and leading edges are getting closer and the pulse starts to "collapse"; (4) in the ordinary medium, the pulse asymptotically decays as $x \to \infty$, but losses on residual strains lead to its disappearance over a finite distance.

Apparently, the analysis of direct and inverse wave problems is of greatest interest in this area, for nonlinear diagnostics purposes among other things. However, most acoustic studies of the hereditary media are rather from the field of materials science and are descriptive in character. As shown in Fig. 8.10, waves in such media behave differently than in the case of the ordinary stress-strain algebraic dependence. For "relaxing" (in the sense of the Mandelshtam–Leontovich concept) dependencies between the parameters, nonlinear waves are studied in detail [3]; but these results are insufficient to characterize hysteretic media [42].

8.4 Nonlinear diagnostics

At the core of the usual acoustic diagnostics is the ability of acoustic waves to penetrate media opaque for other types of radiation. It is known that low-frequency waves can propagate thousands of kilometers underwater and underground, while high-frequency waves are focused on any internal organ of the human body to produce its ultrasounic image. That is why acoustic diagnostics finds such wide applications in geophysics, medicine, and industry. Linear methods allow us selected objects to be examined by varying the frequency, phase, polarization, and direction of wave propagation. With the use of the nonlinearity appears the dependence of the phenomena on the signal amplitude (intensity). Thus, in a variety of methods and schemes of acoustic diagnostics appears a "new dimension". In principle, any of the existing methods can be generalized and extended to a nonlinear case, and number of such modifications can be very large. So it makes sense to discuss only those schemes in which nonlinearity has already opened up new interesting opportunities.

Ideas, that lie in the basis of nonlinear methods of diagnostics and nondestructive testing, are well known. The growth of wave amplitudes (intensity) leads to the violation of the superposition principle: strong waves intersecting in time and space start to interact and exchange their energies. In this process, each wave can "memorize" both individual characteristics of their "partners" and material characteristics of the medium (in the region where the interaction occurred). This information may be "delivered" to the receiver by the original waves themselves, which have undergone cross-modulation, and this information may also be radiated directly from the interaction region in the form of new spectral components, which have been absent in the initial wave spectrum.

In Fig. 8.11, the region of intersection of two wave beams with frequencies ω, Ω is shown. This region can emit harmonics and combination frequency waves, which amplitudes depend on both the initial wave amplitudes and the parameters of the medium. By processing the signals, it is possible to obtain information about linear and nonlinear properties of the medium in the interaction region. Moreover, each beam at the exit of this region gets modulated with the spectrum of another beam. In the basis of these phenomena is the effect of "sound-by-sound scattering" [43] (for more details, see also [44, 45]).

Device that implement nonlinear "storage" of the signal serves as an example of a "parametric" sound receiver [44, 46] used in hydroacoustics (see Fig. 8.12). The role of the receiving antenna is here played by a water column of a length of tens and hundreds of meters, in which an intense high-frequency beam ω is localized. Parametric devices operating in the air have also started to be used for remote diagnostics of objects [47].

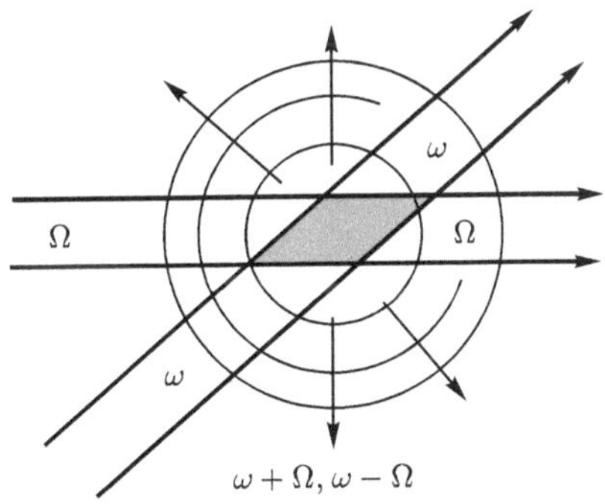

Fig. 8.11 Sound-by-sound scattering and cross modulation in intense wave beams.

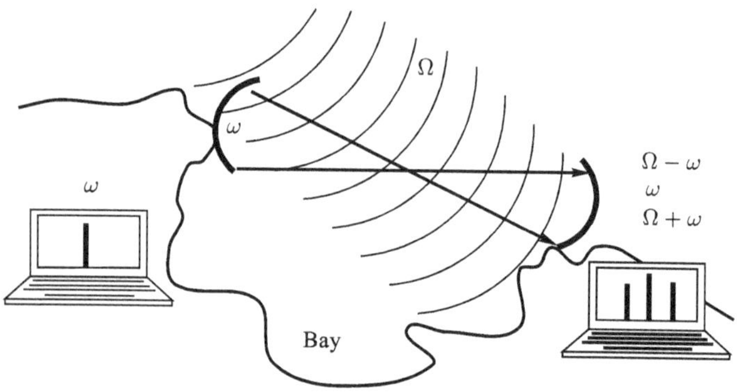

Fig. 8.12 The principle of operation of a receiving "parametric" antenna: the strong wave ω can "store" the parameters of a weak signal.

8.4.1 Inverse problems of nonlinear diagnostics

Strictly speaking, the condition of synchronous (resonant) interaction between three waves at quadratic nonlinearity

$$\omega_3 = \omega_1 + \omega_2, \quad \mathbf{k}_3 = \mathbf{k}_1 + \mathbf{k}_2$$

in acoustic media with weak dispersion is fulfilled only for small angles of beam intersection. In particular, the directivity pattern of the receiver shown in Fig. 8.12 has a sharp peak in the direction of radiation of the reference beam that forms "immaterial" or "virtual" receiving antenna [46]. In experiments, however, without much difficulty the effect of nonresonant scattering can be measured at any angle of beam intersection. Therefore, to measure the distribution of medium characteristics, the intersection region can be moved in space. It was even possible to implement an acoustic tomography scheme based on the use of colliding beams, when the length of synchronous wave interaction is minimal [48]; scanning the space was performed by means of delayed pulse signals, due to which the pulses are encountered and interacted in different places.

For the most complete information on the spatial distribution of the nonlinear parameter $\varepsilon(\mathbf{r})$, one should use methods of diffraction reconstructive tomography. The simplest scheme has been described in [49]. Let a nonlinear region (e.g., a cloud of bubbles in water or in biological tissue, or a network of cracks in a solid) be irradiated by waves ω_1, ω_2 with directions given by unit vectors $\mathbf{n}_1$, $\mathbf{n}_2$. The parameter measured is the difference frequency $\omega_3 = \omega_1 - \omega_2$ in the $\mathbf{n}_3$ direction. The solution of the wave Eq. (7.40) with dependent on coordinates the nonlinear parameter

$$\frac{\partial^2 p}{\partial t^2} - c^2 \Delta p = \frac{\varepsilon(\mathbf{r})}{c^2 \rho} \frac{\partial^2 p^2}{\partial t^2}$$

in the Born approximation for the amplitude of the difference signal in the far field has the form

$$P_3 = \frac{\pi^2 \omega_3^2}{c^2 \rho} \frac{\exp\left(i \frac{\omega_3}{c} r\right)}{r} P_1 P_2^* \cdot \tilde{\varepsilon}\left(\frac{\omega_3}{c}\mathbf{n}_3 - \frac{\omega_1}{c}\mathbf{n}_1 + \frac{\omega_2}{c}\mathbf{n}_2\right), \tag{8.38}$$

$$\tilde{\varepsilon} = \tilde{\varepsilon}\left(\frac{\omega_3}{c}(\mathbf{n}_3 - \mathbf{n}_1)\right), \tag{8.39}$$

i.e., the vectors $\mathbf{n}_3$, the ends of which are located on a sphere of unit radius, can be measured for each direction of irradiation. Thus, we determine the values of the argument of the Fourier transform (8.39) on a sphere of radius ω_3/c. By varying the values of the difference frequency or using different combinations of the directions of irradiation and reception, it is possible to fill with measurement data the inside of the corresponding sphere in the $\mathbf{k}$ — space. Then, the $\varepsilon(\mathbf{r})$ distribution is reconstructed by numerical methods that implement the inverse Fourier transform.

The ability of the nonlinear wave to "store" the properties of the track is used in scheme for the diagnostics of waveguides with variable cross section [50]. If function $S(x)$ describing cross section changes is unknown, it can be found by solving Eq. (7.46) for the second harmonic, represented in the form of the Fredholm integral equation

$$\frac{2c_0^3\rho_0}{\varepsilon\omega}\frac{P_2(x)}{P_1^2(x)} = \int_0^x \left[\frac{S(x)}{S(z)}\right]^{1/2} \exp\left[\frac{b\omega^2}{c_0^3\rho_0}(z-x)\right] dz.$$

The channel profile can be reconstructed using the values of amplitudes of both harmonics measured at distance x and at different frequencies of the initial signal.

In Ref. [51], it has been proposed to use a different effect for channel profiling, *viz.* the phenomenon of self-reflection of a wave after the formation of shock fronts in this wave [3].

By varying the amplitude of the initial wave, it is possible to change the distance at which the shock-wave discontinuity occurs, this distance being also integrally dependent on the channel cross section. By measuring the arrival time of the self-reflected signal [52, 53], the leading edge of which is delayed for a period of time $2x_{SH}/c_0$ (see (8.7)) with regard to the probing pulse, makes it possible to form a data array for the solution of the inverse problem.

Thus, the general approach to the reconstruction of the boundaries and the internal structure of nonlinear scatterers should be based on the methods for the solution of inverse problems i.e. by nonlinear acoustic tomography. However, even the simplest diagnostic method based on the generation of harmonics and combination frequencies is highly efficient, especially when the medium contains strongly nonlinear inclusions like bubbles or cracks. In fact, any analytical solution of the direct nonlinear problem includes parameters (nonlinear moduli, wave amplitudes, and geometric characteristics), which can be found experimentally by measuring the nonlinearly distorted wave field or its spectrum.

8.4.2 Peculiarities of nonlinear diagnostics problems

Let us consider some basically essential features of nonlinear diagnostics.

The dependence on the amplitude (intensity) of the probing wave can be used to detect internal damages in a medium when there is no prior information about the influence of defects on the variation of the response. For example, if a batch of details is to be checked by an ordinary (linear) method, an "acoustic certificate" of an ideal (intact) item is needed. The degree of damage can be estimated by comparing the responses of the defective and intact product. On the contrary, no comparison is needed if the defect is a nonlinear scatterer. It is enough to perform a series of measurements for different intensities of sound excitation in every detail (Fig. 8.13). If it turns out that the time response stops to grow linearly with increasing amplitude of excitation, i.e., in the response acquires new features or in its spectrum displays new spectral components, these findings can be the reason for the rejection of a defective part. The simplest method of diagnostic based on the excitation of sound by a stroke has long been used for examining the wheel-pairs at train-stops as well as for examining crystal ware by the sound of their clinking when tapped. It should be noted, that the stroke may induce a pulse signal with pronounced nonlinear behavior, which is able to interact with a rather weak wave that lacks nonlinearity in itself. These days, such interactions are frequently used for diagnostic purposes (see, e.g., Fig. 8.7).

The difference between the linear and nonlinear responses found application in many measuring schemes. For instance, the "method of inverted pulses" is used in medicine. First, one pulsed probing signal $p_1(t)$ is sent into the volume that is being probed, and then another, identical, but with the inverted pressure $p_2(t) = -p_1(t)$, signal follows. The scattered signals are recorded by one receiver and then summed. The linear scatterer produces a zero difference, while nonlinearity leads to a nonzero difference. The advantages of this approach in the fact that probing signals can be focused in the desired region of space and thereby increasing the nonlinear response by K^2 times (where K is the amplification coefficient of the probing signals at the focus) as well as detune away from interference created by reflections from the surface (skin) and bulk inhomogeneities.

Medical diagnostic uses nonlinear way to control the absorption of ultrasound energy in order to enhance the localization process of heating of biological tissues or excite radiation forces in it. It is known that excessive absorption of intense waves may substantially exceed the usual dissipative losses [1,3]; this phenomenon is pronounced for strongly distorted waves containing shock fronts [7]. At ultrasound intensities of several kW/cm^2 reached in the focal regions of modern medical devices, the nonlinear absorption coefficient is one order of magnitude higher than the linear one [11,54,55]. Evidently, the task is to deliver the acoustic energy to a given region of the medium with minimal losses and to ensure its complete absorption over there.

To arrange such transportation, a preliminary distortion needed to be introduced into the emitted wave, such that in the process of nonlinear-difractional evolution of the wave profile the shock fronts would be formed directly in the focus. In order to

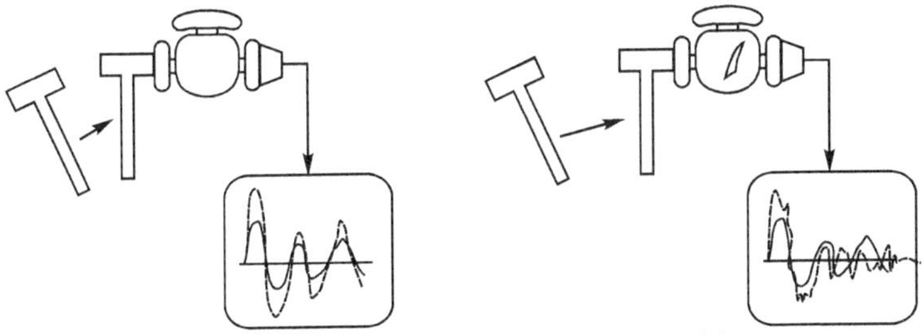

Fig. 8.13 **(a)** Response of an intact part increases linearly with increasing impact force; **(b)** in the time and spectral responses of a defective part appear new features.

calculate the shape of the wave evolving in such way, the nonlinear inverse problem must be solved [54].

The concentration of energy at the focus is employed in acoustic hyperthermia (thermal destruction of malignant neoplasms), in ultrasound hemostasis (the stopping of internal bleeding by noninvasive vascular coagulation) [56], the destruction of intracellular structures in order to trigger an immune response to cancer [57], etc.

Let us consider a diagnostic procedure by means of pulsed radiation forces, which are created inside an object under study by focused ultrasound. Radiation pressure, described by Rayleigh more than 100 years ago, is a strong effect markedly superior the pressure of light. For instance, by focusing ultrasound on the water surface, a water jet can be formed about 10 cm height (see, Fig. 8.14). Absorption of ultrasound or its reflection from inhomogeneities in the medium creates a field of forces, which has vortex character. Formally, these forces appear due to the presence of nonlinear terms in the equations of hydrodynamics (7.1)–(7.3) and the theory of elasticity (8.1)–(8.3), by averaging them over the rapid oscillations [3]. Therefore, flows are formed in liquids ("acoustic wind"), while in biological tissues the stresses are formed. When ultrasound is modulated at low frequencies, far away from the boundaries, the alternating force field excites shear waves. These waves can be detected [58] and their speed of propagation used to estimate a shear elasticity that is highly responsive to pathological changes in the tissues [59]: it increases by 2 or 3 orders of magnitude in tumor tissue, whereas the variation of other parameters (medium density, speed of sound) does not exceed a several percent. This fact allows to propose a new method of diagnostic (SWEI), which stated below in Sect. 8.5.2.

Shear waves are sensitive to structural inhomogeneities, which are responsible for large nonlinearities [19]. Therefore, the method of remote excitation of shear waves may be used to test constructions materials in not easily accessible areas, for example, in the analysis of fatigue strength changes at the wing and fuselage joints of aircraft. This problem is currently discussed in connection with the implementation of new diagnostic schemes.

The use of acoustic resonators has opened up new opportunities for the measurements of nonlinear medium parameters. Usual values of the Q factor for these devices are $10^2 - 10^4$. The amplitude of oscillations in the cavity of a resonator is as

Fig. 8.14 Water jet formation under the effect of radiation pressure. (Photograph courtesy of O. A. Sapozhnikov).

many times larger than the amplitude of oscillations at their boundaries. It implies the possibility of using in experiments substantially less powerful sources than in measurements performed with the use of traveling waves.

Record-breaking values of the Q factor (10^8–10^9) were obtained by Braginsky's group [60] when they developed detectors of gravitational waves. Possibilities for the improvement of the quality factor with regard to strong manifestations of nonlinearity were analyzed in Ref. [61]. In acoustic, measurements of nonlinear parameters of various media in acoustic resonators were initiated by Zarembo and co-workers in the 1960s [1]. In Ref. [33], the problem of assessing the strength of concrete based on acoustic data has been discussed. The authors demonstrated that ultimate strength in compression and tension are determined simultaneously by coefficients of quadratic and cubic nonlinearities. The cubic nonlinearity is measured from the downward shift of eigenfrequency of resonator; when the acoustic strain amplitude increased from 10^{-7} to 7×10^{-6}, the eigenfrequency of a concrete block decreased by $\Delta f / f_0 = 5 \times 10^{-3}$ from the initial value $f_0 = 6.033$ kHz. Strength estimated from measurements of the nonlinearity is in consistent with the previously known data. Latter, the measurements in resonators are being carried out in other laboratories (see, for instance, Refs. [10, 40]).

It is also worthwhile mentioning the methods and equipment that use the stretching signal, the reversing of it in time and amplification for subsequent increases in the density of acoustic energy inside the medium that is being examined [40]. It also uses the signals with reversed front [62].

8.5 Applications of nonlinear diagnostics methods

In the early 1990's there was a noticeable increase in the number of publications on nonlinear inhomogeneous media, various materials, industrial goods, building constructions, and geological structures, as well as methods for nonlinear diagnostic of these objects. A large group of European scientists has held regular conferences on nonlinear methods of nondestructive testing and together with Airbus Industry developed research on aviation diagnostics. Similar work in the USA were linked to the geology, the safety of nuclear energy and industry. Apart from the obvious applied purpose of this work, an interest in this problem is stimulated also by fundamental problems of nonlinear physics and materials science, some of which have not yet been resolved. The applications discussed below are some examples of the diagnostic usage of nonlinear phenomena.

8.5.1 Detection of bubbles in a liquid and cracks in a solid

The possibility of detecting individual gas bubbles or their aggregates in a liquid, as referred to in Sect. 8.3.1, has found an unexpected for Russian specialists application in medicine.

Among the specific achievements in this field the following should be included: the creation of contrast agents such as "Albunex" for the purposes of visualization of blood flow and medical diagnostics. The extent of this work is illustrated by the fact that American and European companies have already invested millions of dollars in the development and clinical testing of these agents. Albunex is a stable suspension of micrometer-sized micro-bubbles, with each bubble being enclosed by a biologically inert membrane (Fig. 8.15). The bubbles are injected intravascularly

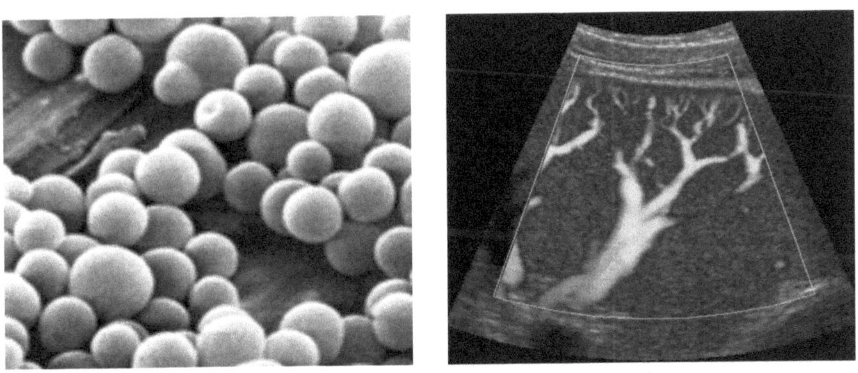

(a) (b)

Fig. 8.15 **(a)** Bubbles in an acoustically contrasted medication, **(b)** and a vascular bed segment visualized by means of this agent. (Photograph courtesy of V. A. Khokhlova).

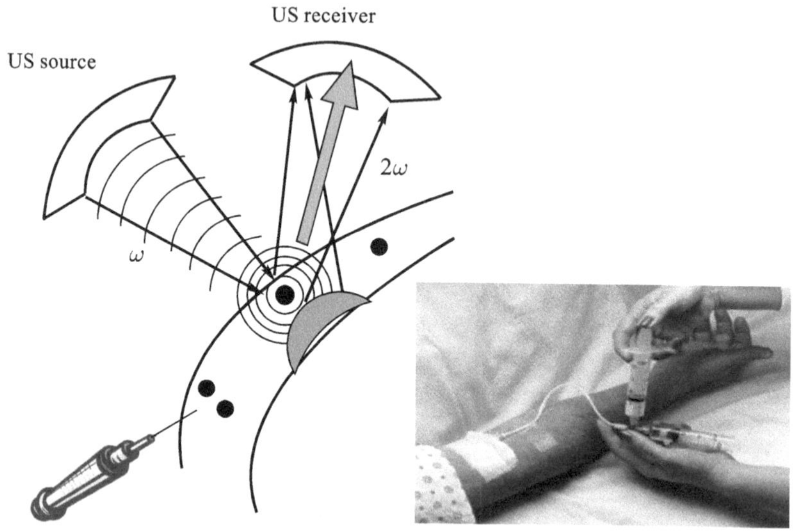

Fig. 8.16 Diagram illustrating the use of bubble-containing medication for blood flow visualization.

and their transport with the blood flow is registered from the usual sound scattering as well as based on the second harmonic or combination frequency (Fig. 8.16). Large local nonlinearity and absence of interference from linear scatterers at the higher harmonics allow one to monitor either a single bubble or a small group of them, or a displacement of a bubble-cloud front, or a part of a vascular bed as a whole.

A similar problem is solved at the detection of defects (cracks) in the amount of solid articles. Large nonlinearity of the cracks allows to get their images on higher harmonics. As an example, Fig. 8.17(a) shows a plate surface vibrating at a frequency of 20 kHz; the relief of surface displacements visualized by laser vibrometer. At this frequency, the signal from the crack is invisible in the background of a strong signal from the surface, which acts as a noise in given case. However, when recording the signal at higher harmonic frequencies the crack is clearly visible (b); the harmonic (in this experiment, the seventh one) is born mainly from vibrations of the crack and the surface does not introduce the interference at that frequencies.

An interesting nonlinear dynamics of a single defect in a solid is observed in experiment [41] (Fig. 8.18). The authors excited different vibrational modes of a metal disk and records the distribution of surface acoustic displacements by vibrometer "Polytec". The displacement pattern of one of the modes is shown in Fig. 8.18(a). The spectrum of modes is not equidistant, and the first few harmonics of the fundamental mode do not match the frequencies of higher modes. For this reason, the excitation of the disk at the second – fourth harmonics produces small surface displacements, but vibrations of the internal defect (most likely a crack) are detected (b). The signal was unstable, which appears to be indicative of "self-healing" of the crack after a few oscillations and opening of it again. The signal is observable when

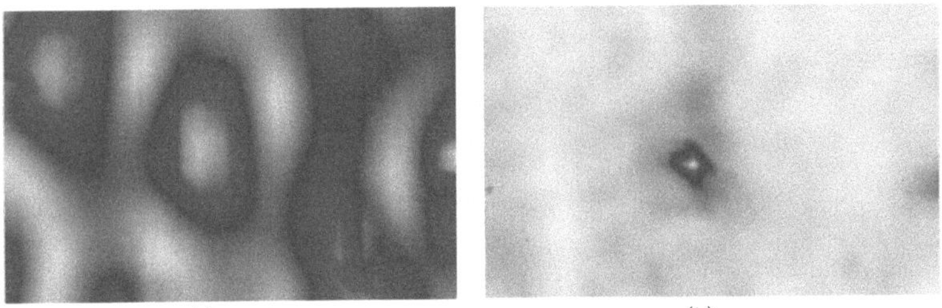

(a) (b)

Fig. 8.17 **(a)** Images of the plate surface region vibrating at a frequency of 20 kHz, **(b)** and of the defect localized under the surface, obtained at the seventh harmonic (140 kHz). (Images courtesy of I. Y. Solodov).

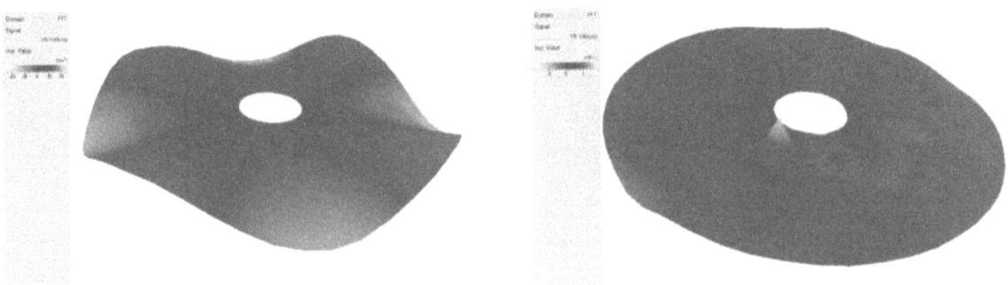

(a) (b)

Fig. 8.18 **(a)** Vibrational eigenmode of a metal disk, **(b)** and vibrations of the defect at the third harmonic of the fundamental mode. Results provided by A. I. Korobov and M. Y. Izosimova.

the displacements at the first harmonic reached 10^{-5} m and exists in the narrow dynamic range of about 10^{-6} m. The maximum displacements at frequencies of 2nd, 3rd, and 4th harmonics are estimated as $(2;1.2;0.2)\times 10^{-7}$ m.

8.5.2 Measurements based on the use of radiation pressure

The SWEI (shear wave elasticity imaging) method proposed by Sarvazyan [59] is based on the remote excitation of shear waves within an object by pulsed radiation pressure generated by an intense beam of modulated and focused ultrasound. The idea is to use ultrasound by analogy with the surgeon's finger (see Fig. 8.14) for "palpation" of internal organs and tissues of the human body. Since the area in which radiation forces are concentrated extending along the axis of the focal region [55], it emits a cylindrical shear wave which diverges from the axis (Fig. 8.19). The speed of wave propagation is low compared with the speed of sound and can vary in the range from a few to hundreds of meters per second, depending on the condition of the tissue. This speed has been measured by an optical method (in a transparent phantom [58]), as well as by MRI (magnetic resonance imaging) and Doppler frequency shift of the probing ultrasound beam [59]. Thus, one can measure, precisely that parameter (shear modulus), which is most sensitive to pathologies. Note that when one is feeling a tumor and speaking of a local "hardening", one is inaccu-

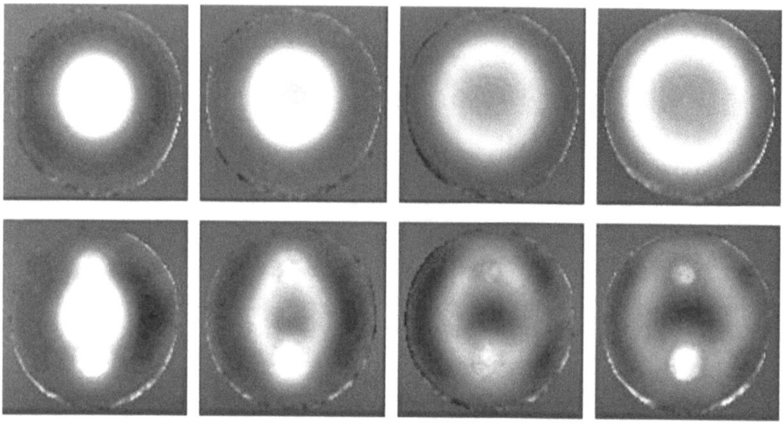

Fig. 8.19 Consecutive positions of the shear wave front in a homogeneous phantom of biological tissue (top row). Inhomogeneous medium with two inclusions simulating a tumor (lower row). (Photographs courtesy of A. P. Sarvazyan).

rate. The inhomogeneity, which is subjectively perceived as a hardening is actually a region with a higher shear modulus.

Currently, work is underway to modify SWEI [59] for the diagnosis of bone and joint disorders. In this case, ultrasound penetrates soft tissues and produces a radiation pressure on the bone, exciting various types of waves. The propagation speed contains information about deficient calcium content, and the analysis of the output signal spectrum provides data on other abnormalities. Evidently, the idea of using radiation pressure is equally promising for diagnostics of complex constructions since the described method may be used for the contactless excitation of vibrations of an isolated element inside a construction and for analyzing its response.

8.5.3 Nonlinear acoustic diagnostics in construction industry

Among the Russian achievements, it is necessary to emphasize the results of nonlinear diagnostics in the construction industry. This activity relates to the late 1980s. A group headed by V. A. Robsman from Research Institute of Transport Construction worked in Armenia in connection with the construction of the Sevan – Arpa tunnel, when a devastating earthquake leveled the city of Spitak, caused severe damage and numerous victims. The group has been asked to diagnose the buildings been damaged and give an opinion on what buildings can be restored and which should be destroyed for security reasons. In the process of ultrasound–"raying" the key elements (beams, load-bearing walls, span panels, etc.) has been found that the greater the damage of constructions, the stronger the distortion of the acoustic spectrum. Later, on the basis of the experiments (see Fig. 8.7) and theoretical studies [36, 37] the empirical criteria has been explained; and now "nonlinear" predictions have become quite ralistic.

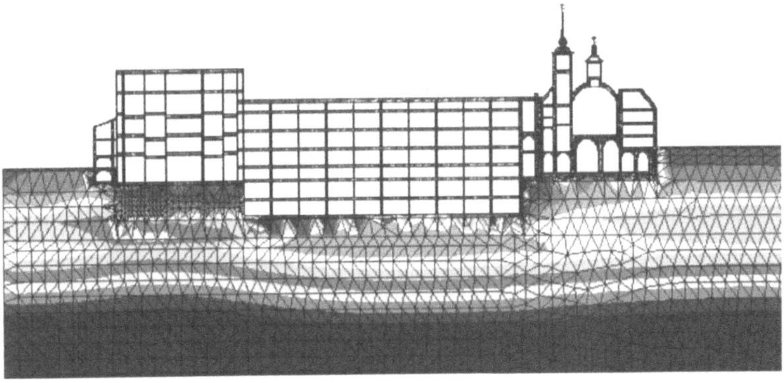

Fig. 8.20 Computer model for the calculation of force interactions between a new building and an old church in Moscow. Data on characteristics of the church building were obtained by acoustic diagnostic techniques. The construction project has not been realized. (Drawing courtesy of V. A. Robsman).

Developed methods of diagnostic have been successfully used in the construction of the Third Ring Road in Moscow (see, for instance, [42]), the renovation and restoration of architectural and historical monuments (Fig. 8.20), the construction of subways, inspection of power–supply units with a view to strengthening their structures and improving seismic resistance, and diagnostics of defects in the piers of large bridges and other long-span structures (over 30 in number) for assessing their actual load capacity and the elaboration of projects of their reconstruction.

8.6 Non-typical nonlinear phenomena in structurally inhomogeneous media

In addition to giant nonlinearity causing high sensitivity of nonlinear methods of measurements, structurally inhomogeneous media are also of interest because of the unusual nonlinear phenomena observed in them.

One of them is the presence of a “dominant” frequency in media such as wet sand, clay, fractured rocks. Regardless of the excitation frequency of vibrations in such media, at its output the “dominant” signal is recorded, while other spectral components, including the initial frequency, turned out to be weak [63–66]. A typical value of this frequency for gravel are 8 – 10 Hz, sea sand 25 Hz, clay 40 Hz, and eroded granite 100 Hz [63, 66]. Interestingly, under the influence of vibrations of the dominant frequency 12 Hz on irrigated oil-bearing stratum the share of oil in the total debit approximately doubled [67]. The cause of the appearance of the dominant frequencies is the presence of internal resonance properties of fragmented soils and rocks, as well as their strong nonlinearity which is responsible for the energy transfer of vibrations into these frequencies.

Among "common" nonlinear phenomena, the processes of the generation of higher harmonics, subharmonics, and combinational frequencies may be considered. From this point of view, the generation of very high (e.g., the one-hundredth) harmonic, avoiding all intermediate cascade of lower harmonics, looks unusual. Similarly, the generation of a low-frequency spectrum with the characteristic frequencies which are many times lower than the pump frequency, at first glance, is also rather exotic phenomenon. However, these processes are observed and can be quite simply explained.

Let us consider an ensemble of granules immersed in a liquid. The system of granules by itself has a strong structural nonlinearity due to boundary contacts. When an oscillating fluid is present, an additional inertial nonlinearity arises caused by the accelerated motion of particles [31]. The forces of attraction appear between particles streamlining by the fluid and the Hertzian repulsion (8.32) arises during the deformation of colliding granules (see Fig. 8.5). Here, large spatial force gradients are due to the marked nonuniformity of the mass distribution. The linear eigenfrequency of vibrations of an elementary oscillator in such a medium is given by

$$f_{lin} = \frac{1}{2\pi}\sqrt{\frac{3a}{2}}\left(E^2 F_0 \frac{R_1 R_2}{R_1+R_2}\right)^{1/6}, \tag{8.40}$$

where a is a coefficient dependent on the volumes and densities of two neighboring spherically shaped particles, F_0 is the static pressing force, and the remaining notations are the same as in Eq. (8.32). However, for the vibration amplitudes A close to the granule diameter, the nonlinear frequency

$$f_{nonl} = \frac{a^{1/2} F_0^{5/6}}{2AE^{1/3}} \frac{R_1+R_2}{R_1 R_2} \tag{8.41}$$

turns out to be 2 – 3 orders of magnitude smaller. When an acoustic wave propagates through the liquid containing granules, it makes the granules attract, collide, and then slightly diverge while moving almost freely within the liquid. After each new collision, the granules turn out to be farther apart from each other. Since the relative velocities of neighboring granules at the moment of collision have become random, thus a pattern of random fluctuations is formed (Fig. 8.21, (a)). The average

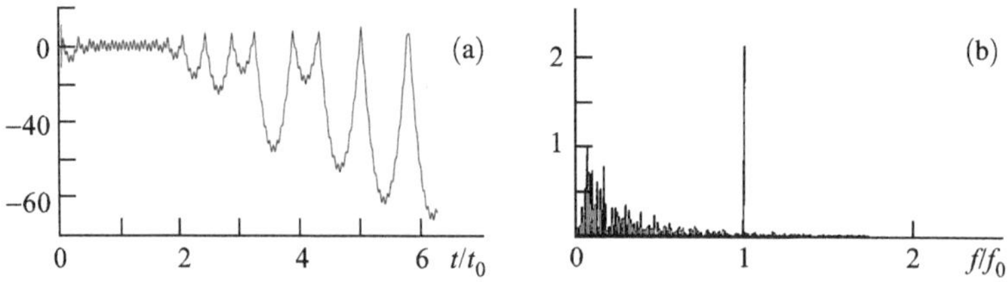

Fig. 8.21 **(a)** Dependence of the distance between the centers of neighboring granules on time, **(b)** and steady-state spectrum of these vibrations.

amplitude of the vibrations increases over time, while the spectrum is shifted to the low-frequency region (b).

The described behavior of granules has a lot of analogies. The same pattern is observed in the field of gravity force when a ball elastically rebounds off a horizontal plate oscillating along the normal to its surface. After the oscillations are initiated the ball experiences collisions with the plate at random time, bouncing higher and higher, as long as the influx of energy is not compensated by losses. This process is observed in the 1920s by N. N. Andreev [68], one of the founders of acoustic studies in Russia, so the phenomenon is called "Andreev's hammer" (see Ref [69]). Stochastic acceleration of the particles (Fermi acceleration) is invoked for explaining many phenomena; in the simplest model, this process is described by the Ulam point transformation [70].

Let us now turn to the generation of high-frequency spectra. Suppose that a limited volume of a medium contains a violation of continuity in the form of loosely pressed to each other or free blocks. A geostructure with "weakly consolidated units" (see Fig. 8.22, (a)) can serve as an example. When an acoustic wave propagates through the medium with a wavelength grater than the size of an inhomogeneity, it causes the appearance of quasi-static deformations due to inertia of separate structural units (blocks). Let the periodic change in pressure accelerate the rigid boundary of the volume under consideration in the positive direction (b), while the separate blocks are shifted and packed. Change of the sign of acceleration leads to the repacking (b). At each collision of the blocks with each other, as well as with the boundaries of the consolidated medium, a high-frequency pulse is generated with a frequency of the order of the reciprocal of the time it takes for sound to propagate through a block. Another characteristic frequency is determined by the number of collisions for the period (i.e., the number of blocks in the bulk). Since the acoustic spectrum of each such impact lies much higher than the frequency of the incident wave, as shown in Fig. 8.22 the structure generates a high-frequency noise.

The output spectrum contains, in addition to the initial low-frequency harmonic, harmonics of the characteristic collision frequency and the set of eigenfrequencies ("ringing") of separate blocks (Fig. 8.23).

A similar transformation takes place in the acoustic spectrum of Afro-Latin-American musical instrument known as a shaker or maraca. When shaking a vessel with granules, the vibration frequency of the order of 1 Hz is converted into the audi-

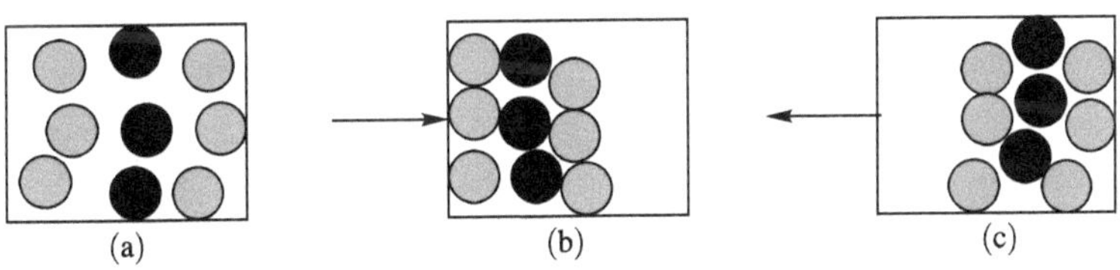

Fig. 8.22 **(a)** Schematic representation of structural changes in a volume with weakly consolidated blocks: steady-state system; **(b)** rigid boundary of the volume is accelerated by a wave to the right; **(c)** a change in wave polarity causes the repacking of blocks.

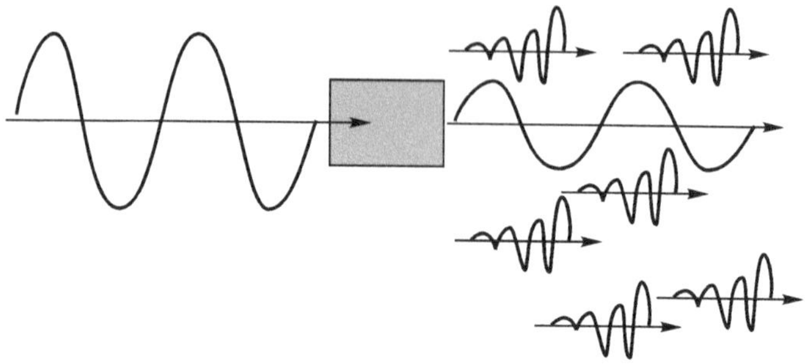

Fig. 8.23 Input and output signals in the structure shown in Fig. 8.22.

ble range. In case of geostructure, its blocks, of course, are shifted by distance much smaller than their own size.

The presence of mechanisms that transfer the vibrational energy down (see Fig. 8.21) and up (Fig. 8.23) the spectrum, means that the received signal, that has passed through the real structurally inhomogeneous medium, carries information not only about the source, but to a large extent, about the track of its propagation. Significant changes in the spectra have been observed when the break has been intersected by an earthquake-induced seismic wave [66]. This means that the signals from distant earthquakes can be used for the purpose of nonlinear diagnostics of localized geostructures by measuring the incident and scattered signals [71].

In conclusion, it should be noted that the number of publications on giant nonlinearities and nonlinear diagnostics continues to grow in both Russian and foreign scientific literature. Thus, in addition to the above-cited publications, there are some recent ones devoted to nonlinear diagnostics of metals [72], granulated media [73, 74], gas bubbles in biological tissues [75]. A supplementary issue of the Acoustical Physics has been out in 2005 with articles on the related problems of acoustics and geophysics. The Session of the Division of Physical Sciences of RAS has been held on this issue [76]. Large amounts of information can be found in the abstracts and proceedings of numerous conferences held since the year 2000.

References

1. L.K. Zarembo, V.A. Krasil'nikov, *Introduction to Nonlinear Acoustics* (Nauka, Moscow, 1966). In Russian
2. K.A. Naugolnykh, L.A. Ostrovsky, *Nonlinear Wave Processes in Acoustics* (Cambridge University Press, 1998)
3. O.V. Rudenko, S.I. Soluyan, *Theoretical Foundations of Nonlinear Acoustics* (Plenum, New York, 1977)
4. L.D. Landau, E.M. Lifshitz, *Theory of Elasticity*, 3rd edn. (Butterworth-Heinemann, Oxford, 1986)
5. L.K. Zarembo, V.A. Krasil'nikov, Nonlinear phenomena in the propagation of elastic waves in solids, Sov. Phys. Usp. **13**, 778–797 (1971)
6. O.V. Rudenko, Interactions of intense noise waves, Phys. Usp. **29**, 620–641 (1986)

7. O.V. Rudenko, Nonlinear sawtooth-shaped waves, Phys. Usp. **38**, 965–989 (1995)
8. O.V. Rudenko, Nonlinear methods in acoustic diagnostics, Russ. J. Nondestructive Testing **29**(8), 583–588 (1993)
9. R.A. Guyer, P.A. Johnson, Nonlinear mesoscopic elasticity: Evidence for a new class of materials, Physics Today **52**, 30–36 (1999)
10. L.A. Ostrovsky, P.A. Johnson, Dynamic nonlinear elasticity in geomaterials, La Rivista del Nuovo Cimento **24**, 1–47 (2001)
11. O.V. Rudenko, A.P. Sarvazyan, Nonlinear acoustics and biomedical applications, Critical Rev. Biomed. Eng. **3**, 6–19 (2000)
12. O.V. Rudenko, in *Nonlinear Waves — 2004*, ed. by A.V. Gaponov-Grekhov, V.I. Nekorkin (IAP RAS, Nizhny Novgorod, 2005), pp. 70–88. In Russian
13. O.V. Rudenko, Nonlinear oscillations of linearly deformed medium in a closed resonator excited by finite displacements of its boundary, Acoust. Phys. **45**, 351–356 (1999)
14. L.D. Landau, E.M. Lifshitz, *Fluid Mechanics*, 2nd edn. (Butterworth-Heinemann, Oxford, 1987)
15. O.V. Rudenko, K.L. Khirnykh, Model of Helmholtz resonator for absorption of intense sound, Acoust. Phys. **36**, 293–297 (1990)
16. F.M. Severin, I.Y. Solodov, Y.N. Shkulanov, Experimental observation of sound nonlinearity in the reflection from an interface between solids, Moscow Univ. Phys. Bull. Ser. 3 Phys. Astron. **43**(4), 105–107 (1988)
17. O.V. Rudenko, C.A. Wu, Nonlinear acoustic properties of a rough surface contact and acoustiodiagnostics of a roughness height distribution, Acoust. Phys. **40**, 593–596 (1994)
18. T. Richardson, Harmonic generation at an unbounded interface, Intern. J. Eng. Sci. **17**, 73–85 (1979)
19. Y. Zheng, R.G. Maev, I. Solodov, Nonlinear acoustic applications for material characterization, Canadian J. Phys. **77**, 927–967 (1999)
20. C.M. Hedberg, O.V. Rudenko, Pulse response of a nonlinear layer, J. Acoust. Soc. Am. **110**, 2340–2350 (2001)
21. G.A. Druzhinin, A.A. Mikhailov, A.C. Tokman, Experimental determination of the concentration of free and dissolved gas in liquid, Sov. Phys. Acoust. **34**, 176–178 (1988)
22. E.A. Zabolotskaya, S.I. Soluyan, A possible approach to the amplification of sound waves, Sov. Phys. Acoust. **13**, 254–256 (1967)
23. G.A. Ostroumov, G.A. Druzhinin, B.M. Kryachko, A.S. Tokman, in *Proc. of the 6th Intern. Symp. on Nonlinear Acoustics* (MGU, Moscow, 1976), pp. 209–219
24. G.M. Lyakhov, *Principles of Dynamics of Blast Waves in Grounds and Bed-Rocks* (Nedra, Moscow, 1974). In Russian
25. V.E. Nakoryakov, B.G. Pokusaev, I.R. Shreiber, *Wave Propagation in Gas-Liquid Media*, 2nd edn. (CRC Press, USA, 1993)
26. A.D. Mansfel'd, A.M. Reiman, in *Ultrasound Diagnostics*, ed. by M.T. Grekhova (IAP RAS, Gorky, 1983), pp. 151–161. In Russian
27. L.A. Ostrovskii, A.M. Sutin, in *Ultrasound Diagnostics*, ed. by M.T. Grekhova (IAP RAS, Gorky, 1983), pp. 139–150. In Russian
28. M.A. Isakovich, *General Acoustics* (Nauka, Moscow, 1973). In Russian
29. M.B. Vinogradova, O.V. Rudenko, A.P. Sukhorukov, *Theory of Waves*, 2nd edn. (Nauka, Moscow, 1990). In Russian
30. L.M. Brekhovskikh, *Waves in Layered Media* (Academic Press, New York, 1960)
31. O.V. Rudenko, C.M. Hedberg, Nonlinear dynamics of grains in a liquid-saturated soil, Nonlinear Dynamics **35**, 187–200 (2004)
32. V.Z. Parton, *Fracture Mechanics: From Theory to Practice*, 1st edn. (Gordon and Breach Science Publishers, Amsterdam, 1992)
33. L.K. Zarembo, V.A. Krasil'nikov, I.E. Shkol'nik, Nonlinear acoustics in a problem of diagnosing the strength of solids, Defectoskopiya [Sov. J. Nondestructive Testing] **10**(1), 16–22 (1989). In Russian

34. Y.A. Nilender, G.Y. Pochtovik, I.E. Shkolnik, The relation of the velocity of elastic wave propagation on internal energy losses in concrete under loading, Concrete and Ferroconcrete **7**, 7–8 (1969). In Russian
35. I. Shkolnik, L. Zarembo, V. Krasilnikov, in *Frontiers of Nonlinear Acoustics*, ed. by M.F. Hamilton, D.T. Blackstock (Elsevier, London, 1990), pp. 589–594
36. V.A. Robsman, Nonlinear transformation of noise spectra in nondestructive testing of concrete structures, Acoust. Phys. **37**, 1038–1040 (1991)
37. V.A. Robsman, Transformation of acoustic spectra in inhomogeneous solid media under nonlinear deformation, Acoust. Phys. **38**, 129–143 (1992)
38. Y.N. Rabotnov, *Elements of Hereditary Solid Mechanics* (Mir, Moscow, 1980)
39. S.A. Akhmanov, N.I. Koroteev, Spectroscopy of light scattering and nonlinear optics. Nonlinear-optical methods of active spectroscopy of Raman and Rayleigh scattering, Sov. Phys. Usp. **20**(11), 899–936 (1977)
40. P.A. Johnson, A.M. Sutin, in *Review of Quantitative Nondestructive Evaluation*, vol. 24, ed. by D.O. Thompson, D.E. Chimenti (AIP, New York, 2005), p. 377
41. A.I. Korobov, M.Y. Izosimova, Nonlinear lamb waves in a metal plate with defects, Acoust. Phys. **52**, 589–597 (2006)
42. O.V. Rudenko, V.A. Robsman, Nonlinear processes in media with an acoustic hysteresis and the problems of dynamic interaction between piles and earth foundation, Acoust. Phys. **50**, 725–731 (2004)
43. P.J. Westervelt, Scattering of sound by sound, J. Acoust. Soc. Am. **29**, 934–939 (1957)
44. V.A. Zverev, How the idea of a parametric acoustic array was conceived, Acoust. Phys. **45**, 611–618 (1999)
45. R.T. Beyer, *Nonlinear Acoustics* (Acoust. Soc. of Am., New York, 1997)
46. B.K. Novikov, O.V. Rudenko, V.I. Timoshenko, *Nonlinear Underwater Acoustics* (AIP, New York, 1987)
47. N.S. Vinogradov, M.S. Dorofeev, A.I. Korobov, S.G. Mikhailov, O.V. Rudenko, A.V. Shanin, A.O. Shilkin, Nonlinear generation of airborne sound by waves of ultrasonic frequencies, Acoust. Phys. **51**, 147–151 (2005)
48. T. Sato, in *Frontiers of Nonlinear Acoustics*, ed. by M.F. Hamilton, D.T. Blackstock (Elsevier, London, 1990), pp. 98–112
49. V.A. Burov, I.E. Gurinovich, O.V. Rudenko, E.Y. Tagunov, Reconstruction of the spatial distribution of the nonlinearity parameter and sound velocity in acoustic nonlinear tomography, Acoust. Phys. **40**, 816–823 (1994)
50. Y.R. Lapidus, O.V. Rudenko, Nonlinear generation of higher harmonics as a technique for mapping the profile of channels, Sov. Phys. Acoust. **36**, 589–591 (1990)
51. O.V. Rudenko, S.I. Soluyan, Self-reflection of a wave at discontinuities as a nonlinear diagnostic technique, Sov. Phys. Dokl. **33**, 83–84 (1988)
52. K.I. Volyak, *Nonlinear Waves in the Ocean. Selected Works* (Nauka, Moscow, 2002). In Russian
53. K.I. Volyak, A.S. Gorshkov, O.V. Rudenko, On the back-traveling wave appearance in homogeneous nonlinear media, Moscow Univ. Phys. Bull. Ser. 3 Phys. Astron. **16**(1), 32–36 (1975). In Russian
54. O.V. Rudenko, Powerful focused ultrasound: nonlinear effects, excitation of shear waves and medical diagnostics, Moscow Univ. Phys. Bull. **37**(6), 12–24 (1996)
55. O.V. Rudenko, A.P. Sarvazyan, S. Emelianov, Acoustic radiation force and streaming induced by focused nonlinear ultrasound in a dissipative medium, J. Acoust. Soc. Am. **99**, 2791–2798 (1996)
56. O.V. Rudenko, Nonlinear waves: some biomedical applications, Phys. Usp. **50**, 359–367 (2007)
57. V.A. Burov, N.P. Dmitrieva, O.V. Rudenko, Nonlinear ultrasound: Breakdown of microscopic biological structures and non-thermal impact on a malignant tumor, Sov. Phys. Dokl. [Biochemistry and Biophysics] **383**(3), 101–104 (2002)

58. V.G. Andreev, V.N. Dmitriev, Y.A. Pishchal'Nikov, O.V. Rudenko, O.A. Sapozhnikov, A. Sarvazyan, Observation of shear waves excited by focused ultrasound in a rubber-like medium, Acoust. Phys. **43**, 123–128 (1997)
59. A. Sarvazyan, O. Rudenko, S. Swanson, J. Fowlkes, S. Emelianov, Shear wave elasticity imaging: a new ultrasonic technology of medical diagnostics, Ultrasound in Medicine and Biology **24**, 1419–1435 (1998)
60. V.B. Braginsky, V.P. Mitrofanov, V.I. Panov, *Systems with Small Dissipation* (University of Chicago Press, Chicago, 1986)
61. O.V. Rudenko, C.M. Hedberg, B.O. Enflo, Resonant properties of a nonlinear dissipative layer excited by a vibrating boundary: Q-factor and frequency response, J. Acoust. Soc. Am. **117**, 601–612 (2005)
62. A.P. Brysev, L.M. Krutyansky, P. Pernod, V.L. Preobazhensky, Nonlinear ultrasonic phase-conjugate beams and their application in ultrasonic imaging, Acoust. Phys. **50**, 623–640 (2004)
63. N.A. Vil'chinskaya, The remodeling wave in sand and acoustic emission, Sov. Phys. Dokl. **262**(3) (1982)
64. O.Y. Dinariev, V.N. Nikolaevskii, High-q oscillations in a layered elastic medium, Acoust. Phys. **51**, 533–537 (2005)
65. N.N. Kochina, P.Y. Kochina, V.N. Nikolaevskii, *The World of Groundwater* (Earth Physics. Institute, Moscow, 1994). In Russian
66. V.N. Nikolaevskii, *Geomechanics and Fluidodynamics* (Barnet & Noble, 1996)
67. M.A. Sadovskii, A.V. Nikolaev, *Seismic Vibrations at Oil Fields* (Schmidt Inst. Phys. Earth RAS, Moscow, 1993). In Russian
68. N.N. Andreev, J. Appl. Physics USSR **2**(1–2), 205 (1925). In Russian
69. L.I. Mandelshtam, *Lectures on Oscillations. Collected Works*, vol. 4 (Akad. Nauk SSSR, Moscow, 1955). In Russian
70. N.V. Karlov, N.A. Kirichenko, *Oscillations, Waves, Structures* (Fizmatlit, Moscow, 2001). In Russian
71. A.L. Sobisevich, O.V. Rudenko, Resonance properties of magmatic structures, Acoust. Phys. **51**, 149–155 (2005)
72. A.I. Korobov, Y.A. Brazhkin, W. Ning, Nonlinear elasticity in structurally inhomogeneous materials: An experimental study, Acoust. Phys. **51**, 571–577 (2005)
73. K.A. Naugolnykh, I. B.Esipov, The propagation of a nonlinear sound wave in an unconsolidated granular medium, Acoust. Phys. **51**, 713–718 (2005)
74. V. Tournat, V.Y. Zaitsev, V. Nazarov, V.E. Gusev, B. Castagnéde, Experimental study of nonlinear acoustic effects in a granular medium, Acoust. Phys. **51**, 543–553 (2005)
75. A.D. Mansfel'd, D.A. Mansfel'd, A.M. Reiman, Abilities of nonlinear acoustic methods in locating gas bubbles in biological tissues, Acoust. Phys. **51**, 209–217 (2005)
76. I.B. Esipov, "Nonlinear Acoustic Diagnostics" — the Scientific Session of the Physical Science Division of the Russian Academy of Sciences, Acoust. Phys. **52**, 366–366 (2006)

Chapter 9
Nonlinear Sawtooth Waves

9.1 Sawtooth waves

This chapter discusses interactions of strongly distorted waves containing shock fronts. Such sawtooth-shaped perturbations are formed in the course of wave propagation through media where nonlinearity predominates over competitive factors like dispersion, diffraction and absorption. Specific character of nonlinear processes in the fields of sawtooth waves is particularly emphasized. We describe experimentally observed phenomena, as well as present-day applied trends.

Sawtooth waves are peculiar objects that may exist in distributed systems of diverse physical nature. Much experimental data on the nonlinear dynamics of sawtooth waves has been obtained in nonlinear acoustics. That is why it is convenient to discuss most of the nonlinear phenomena associated with the propagation and interaction of such waves by using the example of high-intensity acoustic waves.

Nonlinear acoustics is often referred to not only as the modern division of acoustics, but also as a principal part of nonlinear wave physics. Interactions of disturbances of acoustic media, where the dispersion of sound velocity is very weak or altogether absent, have many distinctive properties. Essentially all virtual energy-exchange processes between waves of different frequencies are resonant and evolve with comparable efficiency. As a result, avalanche-like growth of the number of spectral components of the wave field occurs, which, in space-time terms, corresponds to formation of discontinuities in the wave profile (or, when accounting for the dissipative properties of a medium, of weak shock waves with a short length of the front) [1].

From the standpoint of nonlinear wave physics, perturbations with a sawtooth-shaped wave profile are the most typical and, therefore, interesting objects of study in nonlinear acoustics. Sawtooth waves are propagating perturbations, whose time profile contains both discontinuities and smooth sections. In a nondispersive medium, any periodic perturbation turns into a "saw" at long distance. In this case, in media with the quadratic nonlinearity, a plane waves assumes the shape of a "saw" with triangular "teeth". Each period contains a discontinuity (shock) and a rectilinear segment of the profile.

Fig. 9.1 (a) shows the transformation process of a periodic signal into a "saw". As the distance x travelled by the wave grows, fine features of the initial time profile gradually vanish. At moving away from the source of the order of several characteristic nonlinear lengths ($x = x_2$ in Fig. 9.1), the profiles are the same for both a harmonic initial perturbation (curve 1) and a more complex signal (curve 2).

A single (localized in time) perturbation in a quadratically nonlinear medium at long distance turns into an N-wave (Fig. 9.1 (b)). The integral of the function describing the profile tends to zero at $x \to \infty$ because of diffraction, since real perturbations are always bounded in space.

In a cubically nonlinear medium, the "saw teeth" have a trapezoidal shape (Fig. 9.1 (c)), thereby each of the periods contains two shock fronts: of compression and of rarefaction.

In media with more complex nonlinear, dissipative and dispersive properties, sawtooth waves of other types may exist. Nevertheless, the perturbations shown in Fig. 9.1 are the most typical ones.

It is important to note that these shapes of the time profiles are asymptotically universal for a wide class of initial perturbations. Once formed, these waves remain quasi-stable. Afterwards, only some parameters vary: for periodic "saws", that is the peak magnitude of the perturbations; for single pulses, these are the peak magnitudes and duration of the signal. The wave profile is quite stable and little

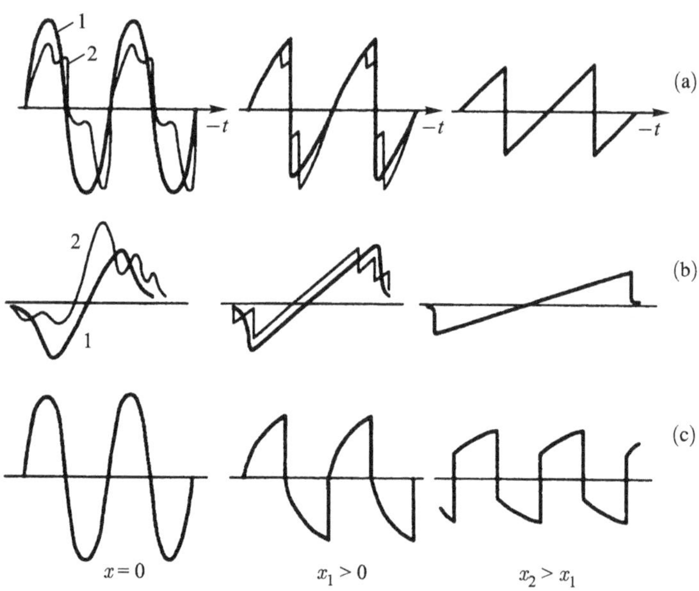

Fig. 9.1 Sawtooth-wave formation: (1) a harmonic or bipolar perturbation with a simple shape, (2) similar signals of a complex form.

changes both at an interaction of the "saws" with each other and at a weak influence of additional factors: diffraction, dispersion, low-frequency modulation, etc. Thus a sawtooth wave represents a universal object, whose stability is connected with a strong manifestation of nonlinear properties of a medium.

In the physics of nonlinear waves, another object with strongly expressed nonlinear properties, whose stability is supported by the competition between dispersion and nonlinearity, is more familiar. This is a soliton. But, strictly speaking, a soliton is stable only in idealized conservative media, whereas the quasi-stability of "saws" takes place in real dissipative systems.

When speaking about interactions of solitons (or sawtooth waves) with each other, it is possible to draw an analogy with the theories of hydrodynamic turbulence. As it is known, in the physics of nonlinear waves, it is possible to identify two groups of phenomena: 1) those, which are explained by a weak manifestation of nonlinear effects (e.g, the behavior of a phonon gas in a solid while accounting for the anharmonicity of the lattice); 2) those connected with a strong manifestation of nonlinearity.

Similarly to this, there are two points of view at the turbulent motion: 1) as an ensemble of interacting quasi-harmonic perturbations; 2) as a superposition of interacting vortex structures, each of which by itself is a substantially nonlinear object. Precisely this second point of view at the turbulence is similar to the problem of interaction of wave objects with strongly manifested nonlinear properties, such as sawtooth waves and solitons. But, while the physics of soliton interactions is exhaustively described in monographs and review articles, the sawtooth perturbations have received much less attention.

The classical studies of sawtooth-wave formation, nonlinear absorption and saturation effects had been performed in the late 1950s [2–6].

Later, new phenomena had been experimentally observed and explained, such as: the self-focusing of sawtooth waves [7–13], self-refraction of pulses [14, 15], existence of a physical limit for the peak acoustic pressure in a focus [16] and a number of others. Furthermore, many well-known effects (the parametric interaction, damping and amplification of signals, collisions of localized waves, etc) proceed for sawtooth waves quite differently than for quasi-harmonic perturbations or solitons. By virtue of their specific character, these phenomena have been studied in detail relatively recently. For a description of the sawtooth waves, an original mathematical apparatus has been developed, which is different from the methods used in other branches of the nonlinear wave theory.

The interest towards these phenomena is related to their use for solving many applied problems. We note the nonlinear methods of nondestructive control and diagnostics in industry [17]; medical applications, e.g, destruction of kidney stones and other bio-concrements [18, 19]); sonic boom and intense aeroacoustic noise [20, 21] (their ecological consequences are currently intensively investigated in connection with the prospect of designing a new generation of supersonic passenger aircraft [22, 23]).

9.2 Field and spectral approaches in the theory of nonlinear waves

It is well known that different approaches are used in order to describe nonlinear waves in media with weak and strong frequency dispersion. When dispersion is weak or altogether absent, i.e. the velocities of different spectral components of a wave are nearly the same or coincide, collinear harmonics interact in a resonant way and efficiently exchange energy with each other. This leads to an avalanche-like multiplication of harmonics and to spectral broadening. In other words, any virtual perturbation, whose generation is permitted by the nonlinearity type of the medium, is realized in the process of interaction and starts affecting the energy exchange. Here the following two possibilities present themselves: to describe the wave field in terms of space and time or to introduce complex amplitudes for each quasi-harmonic spectral component and to monitor spatial variations of these amplitudes.

9.2.1 General remarks

Evidently, the second (spectral) method is inconvenient, when there are many harmonics or the spectrum is continuous. In the case of analytic calculations, it is effective only for dispersive media (if the dependencies of the wave's phase velocity on the frequency are strictly defined and consistent with the spectrum of the initial signal), when a small number of harmonics interact. Classical problems of nonlinear optics [24] may serve as examples. So, in order to achieve efficient generation of the second harmonic in a medium with the quadratic nonlinearity, a birefringent crystal is chosen, which has a "synchronism direction". The harmonics with frequencies ω and 2ω, propagating in that direction, have close phase velocities and exchange energy. At the same time, the virtual higher harmonics with frequencies $3\omega, 4\omega, \ldots$, whose generation is possible as a result of cascade processes in a medium with the quadratic nonlinearity, have strongly differing velocities. Therefore they cannot grow up to the magnitudes, which ensure their participation in the redistribution of the wave energy over the spectrum.

The correct scheme for application of the spectral approach is basically as follows. First, the problem is formulated (e.g., to organize a resonant triplet $\omega_3 = \omega_1 + \omega_2$ in order to transform the energy of the pump wave with the frequency ω_3 into the energy of lower harmonics with the frequencies ω_1 and ω_2). Next, conditions are found (a medium with necessary dispersive characteristics), under which such an interaction could be realized. Finally, as applied to the real situation, "truncated" equations are derived for the complex amplitudes A_1, A_2, A_3 of this triplet.

A reverse scheme of actions is surely possible. Suppose that there is a medium with known dispersive characteristics. By analyzing the form of these characteristics, it is possible to understand, which interactions are resonant and if they exist in this medium at all. Then the spectrum of the initial signal is determined, and the corresponding equations are written down for the amplitudes of wave participating in resonant interactions.

In many studies, however, the authors artificially limit the wave spectrum (the number of interacting harmonics) regardless of the dispersive characteristics of a medium. In doing that, the conditions of evolution are "forced" upon the nonlinear processes, with these conditions being sometimes different from the real ones. Then solvable equations are derived, which are much simpler than the correct, more general field equations. The results obtained may be of interest for the mathematical theory. As far physical consequences are concerned, they, as a rule, unrealistic.

Correct understanding of the possibilities of the field and spectral approaches is useful for solving problems of wave interactions (acoustic, gravitational in shallow water, in plasma, in particle flows, etc.), where both approaches are traditionally used on equal footing. Moreover, the necessity has appeared to apply the novel for optics field approach for describing broadband signals — femtosecond laser pulses [25]. On the contrary, acoustic analogues of nonlinear optic processes [26], it seems, require using the spectral approach. Obviously, active exchange of ideas and methods between different fields of the nonlinear wave physics must be conducted while accounting for the specifics of the phenomena under investigation.

Further on in this chapter, examples of nonlinear processes are given, which are described in the frameworks of the field and spectral approaches. It is interesting to compare the results obtained by these two different methods and to verify their agreement with the physical experimental data.

9.2.2 Generation of harmonics

Propagation of plane waves in a nonlinear medium without dispersion and dissipation is described by the equation of Riemann waves (7.43), which, for definitiveness, contains the vibration velocity as the variable

$$\frac{\partial u}{\partial x} = \frac{\varepsilon}{c_0^2} u \frac{\partial u}{\partial \tau}. \tag{9.1}$$

The field equation (9.1) correctly describes such observed phenomena as the steepening of the leading front of a wave all the way until the formation of a discontinuity, generation of harmonics, combinational frequencies, etc. In particular, when at the input $x = 0$ the harmonic signal $u = u_0 \sin \omega t$ is given, from (9.1) follows the Bessel-Fubini solution for the amplitude of the harmonics with the frequencies $n\omega$ $(n = 1, 2, 3, \ldots)$

$$B_n(x) = u_0 \frac{2J_n(nz)}{nz}, \quad z = \frac{x}{x_{SH}} = \frac{\varepsilon}{c_0^2} \omega u_0 x, \tag{9.2}$$

which gives a good quantitive agreement with the results of measurements. In the solution (9.2), $J_n(nz)$ are the ordinary (at $z < 1$) or incomplete (at $z > 1$) Bessel

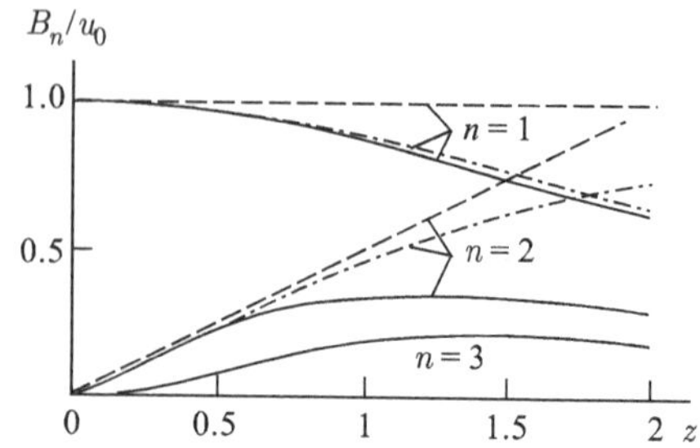

Fig. 9.2 Amplitudes of the harmonics calculated by the method of successive approximations (dashed lines) and on the basis of the truncated equations (9.3) (dash-dotted lines). Solid lines show the exact solution (9.2).

functions [27]. If the spectrum is artificially limited by the first two harmonics, i.e. the solution (9.1) is sought in the form

$$u = B_1(x)\sin\omega\tau + B_2(x)\sin 2\omega\tau,$$

we obtain the following pair of truncated equations:

$$\frac{dB_1}{dx} = -\frac{\varepsilon\omega}{2c_0^2}B_1B_2, \quad \frac{dB_2}{dx} = \frac{\varepsilon\omega}{2c_0^2}B_1^2. \tag{9.3}$$

The solution of Eqs. (9.3)

$$B_1 = \frac{u_0}{\cosh(z/2)}, \quad B_2 = u_0\tanh\frac{z}{2} \tag{9.4}$$

corresponds to the correct result (9.2) only at short distances $z \ll 1$. But at $z \ll 1$, it makes no sense at all to use the truncated equations, since the correct result can be obtained from (9.1) by the method of successive approximations, while assuming that the amplitude of the first harmonic $B_1 = u_0$ is constant. In the region $z \geqslant 1$, where the truncated equations (9.3) could, in principle, give new information, they describe the interactions incorrectly. The behavior of the amplitudes of the first two harmonics is described approximately, and the generation of the higher harmonics is not taken into account at all (see Fig. 9.2).

9.2.3 Degenerate parametric interaction

In order to illustrate the peculiarity of nonlinear processes in sawtooth-wave fields, let us consider an interesting and instructive example related to degenerate parametric interaction. As is known, a quasi-harmonic signal, whose frequency and wave vector are connected by a dispersive relation, is a stable formation in a strongly dispersive medium. If the form of the dispersion law is specially chosen, it is sometimes possible to create conditions for an effective energy exchange only between two waves: the pump wave with the frequency ω_0 and the subharmonic of the half-frequency $\omega_0/2$. Such conditions are realized, e.g., in nonlinear optic crystals for laser beams. Synchronous interaction of the intense pump wave with the frequency ω_0 and a weak signal with the frequency $\omega_0/2$ (Fig. 9.3 (a)) is a phase-sensitive effect. When the phase shift is optimal, it is possible to achieve essentially total energy concentration in the signal wave, having thus realized large coefficients of parametric amplification $K \gg 1$ [1].

It would seem that, while calculating interactions of the waves with the frequencies ω_0 and $\omega_0/2$ in a nondispersive medium, it would be sufficient to take into account energy losses of the pump wave spent to generate its own higher harmonics. Indeed, "parasitic" channels of energy outflow $\omega_0 \to 2\omega_0 \to 3\omega_0 \to \ldots$ considerably weaken the useful process $\omega_0 \to \omega_0/2$ (Fig. 9.3 (b)). As was shown in Ref. [28], the coefficient K, in this case, does not exceed the value of $K = \Gamma^{-1/2}$. Here Γ is the reciprocal of the acoustic Reynolds number (the Goldberg number (7.52)), which is equal to the ratio of the characteristic length scale of shock (discontinuity) formation $x_{SH} = c_0^2/(\varepsilon\omega u_0)$ to the absorption length $x_{abs} = \alpha^{-1} = 2c_0^3\rho_0/(b\omega^2)$, where b is the effective dissipation parameter (7.17). It implies that, e.g., at values of $\Gamma \sim 10^{-2}$ easily attainable in laboratory experiments, amplification may still be significant: $K \sim 10$.

Nevertheless, this conclusion is incorrect, which seems surprising, since in the calculations [28] there have been taken into account an infinite number of interacting waves — the multiple harmonics $n\omega_0$ ($n = 1,2,3,\ldots$), and also the signal $\omega_0/2$.

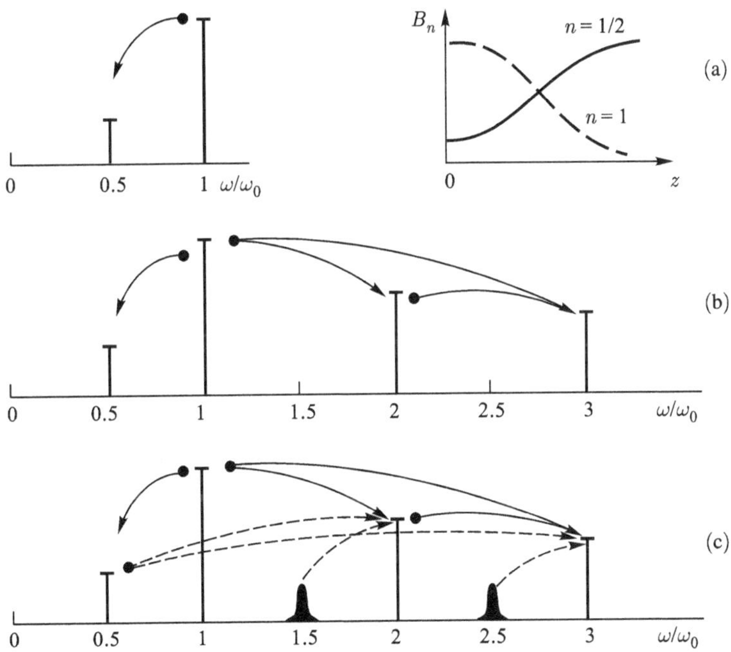

Fig. 9.3 Directions of the main energy flows during interaction of the pump and subharmonic waves **(a)**, with the higher harmonics of the pump wave **(b)**, and higher subharmonics, **(c)** being taken into account.

It turns out, that in order to obtain the correct result, it is necessary to take into account the higher subharmonic components with the frequencies $3\omega_0/2$, $5\omega_0/2$, ... Each of these waves has a small amplitude (compared with the harmonics of the pump wave with the frequencies $(n\omega_0)$, and losses spent to generate them are insignificant. The higher subharmonics, however, open up new channels for energy transfer from the main subharmonic with the frequency $\omega_0/2$ (the signal, which should be amplified) up the spectrum. As a result of these processes, which are shown in Fig. 9.3 (c) by the dashed lines, there is essentially no amplification and the amplification coefficient $K = 4/\pi \approx 1.28$ [29] is only just above unity. The latter fact is well-known for nonlinear waves in long electric lines [30].

The picture of interaction of a large number of harmonics and subharmonics is very tangled, because the spectral language is not expedient for describing nonlinear waves in nondispersive media. If we trace how the profile gets distorted during the propagation of the wave, everything becomes much clearer. Fig. 9.4 (curve 1) shows the initial profile of the wave

$$\frac{u}{u_0} = \sin \omega_0 t + 0.2 \sin\left(\frac{\omega_0 t}{2} + \frac{\pi}{2}\right), \tag{9.5}$$

which represents the sum of the pump wave and half-frequency signal. The phase shift is assigned a value of $\pi/2$, at which amplification is optimal. Curves 1–11 in Fig. 9.4 correspond to the growing distances $z = x/x_{SH} = 0, 0.5, 1, 1.5, 2, 3, 4, 6, 10, 15, 30$. As the wave propagates, nonlinear distortions are accumulated, which leads to the shock formation. The jumps (shocks) are asymmetric with respect to the zero level. Therefore they move towards each other, collide according to the collision law of absolutely inelastic particles and coalesce [1]. As a result, there forms the wave (curve 11 in Fig. 9.4) with the period twice as large as the pump-wave period. Thus the parametric division of the frequency by 2 is observed.

Now, if the profiles distorted during wave propagation [31] are Fourier expanded, it is possible to obtain the full spectrum of the wave field (Fig. 9.5). It is seen that all half-integer subharmonics have amplitudes, whose absolute values are comparable,

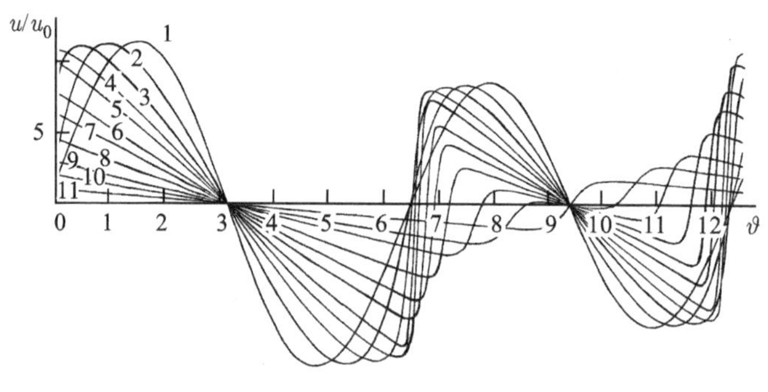

Fig. 9.4 Profile of a wave during degenerate parametric interaction.

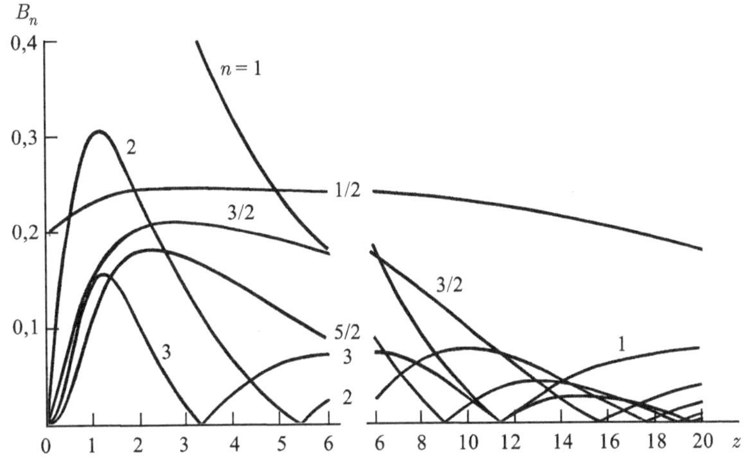

Fig. 9.5 Spectrum of a wave filed during degenerate parametric interaction.

and the main signal with the frequency $\omega_0/2$ is slightly amplified in comparison with its initial value, whereas the amplification is manifested in a limited distance interval.

Nevertheless, the above-said does not mean that, in nondispersive media, it is at all impossible to achieve an appreciable amplification. It is clear that generation of higher subharmonics in a medium is possible only when there is a signal with the frequency $\omega_0/2$ at the input. There are many such subharmonics. Therefore, by summing their intensities (for that, special processing methods are needed), it is possible to obtain a considerable effect [32].

Fig. 9.6 shows a possible experimental setup [31]. The pump wave with the frequency ω_0 propagates isolated in the reference channel 2, and also in the receiving (open) channel 1, where it interacts with the signal wave with the frequency $\omega_0/2$. At the exit of channel 2, a profile is formed as a symmetric "saw", whose spectrum contains only integer harmonics with the frequencies $n\omega_0$. At the exit of channel 1, a "saw" is formed with pairwise asymmetric fronts, displaced towards each other, its spectrum contains both the harmonics and half-integral subharmonic components. By subtracting the output signals at the exits of channels 1 and 2, we obtain the difference signal in the form of two (on each period) peaks of different polarity. The magnitude of these peaks reaches the amplitude of the pump wave, i.e. a considerable amplification is achieved.

This example shows how specific is the picture of interaction in a nondispersive medium and how it is difficult to understand it without an analysis of the behavior of the wave profiles, by limiting ourselves from the very beginning just to the consideration of the spectra.

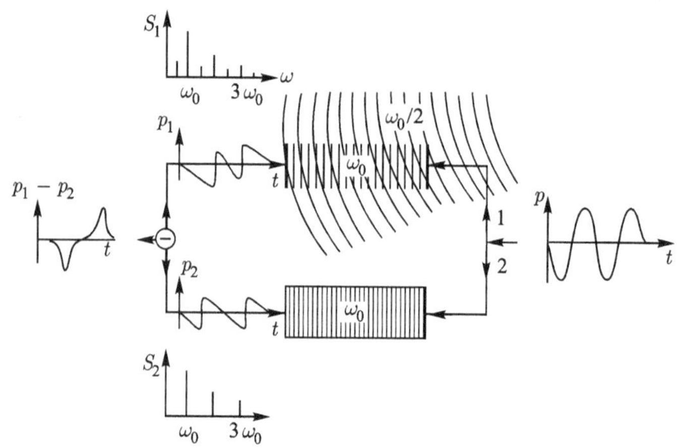

Fig. 9.6 Experimental setup, which realizes a significant amplification in a nondispersive medium.

9.3 Diffracting beams of sawtooth waves

Studying wave interactions in nondispersive media until the early 1970s had been based on an analysis of simple theoretical models. Mainly plane or other one-dimensional (spherically and cylindrically symmetric) waves were considered. But in reality, one has to deal with beams, whose evolution is affected by diffraction, and this idealization is often too coarse.

Peculiarities in the behavior of bounded nonlinear beams had been noted in early experiments [2–5]. But systematic studies had been performed later [33, 34], after an adequate theory was created, for its verification.

Fig. 9.7 shows the profile of the initial harmonic signal measured [33] at different distances from the source of ultrasound in water. A piezo-ceramic disk of a diameter of 30 mm with a resonance frequency of 1 MHz has been used as the source of ultrasound. The signal has been registered by a broadband hydrophone (an x-section piezo-quartz platelet) of a diameter 10 mm with a resonance frequency of 14.ultrasound at a frequency of. It is seen that, at short distances, the signal is close to a harmonic one. Then the front gets steeper and there appears asymmetry in distortions of the compression and rarefaction half-periods. At a distance of approximately 25 cm, a discontinuity forms in the wave profile, which leads to oscillations behind the front that are connected with the resonant excitation of the hydrophone. During further propagation, nonlinear attenuation of the wave is observed, but the asymmetry of the half-wave distortions is sharply pronounced as before: the negative half-period is rounded and stretched, and the positive one is shortened and sharpened.

In a number of experiments (see, e.g., [35]), the "smoothing" of the transverse distribution of the field in a beam has been observed. Since a shock wave forms faster near the axis, it starts strongly to decay. At the same time, the shocks do not yet exist in regions distant from the axis and the wave amplitude is constant. So, the stronger absorption near the axis leads to the broadening of the beam, and

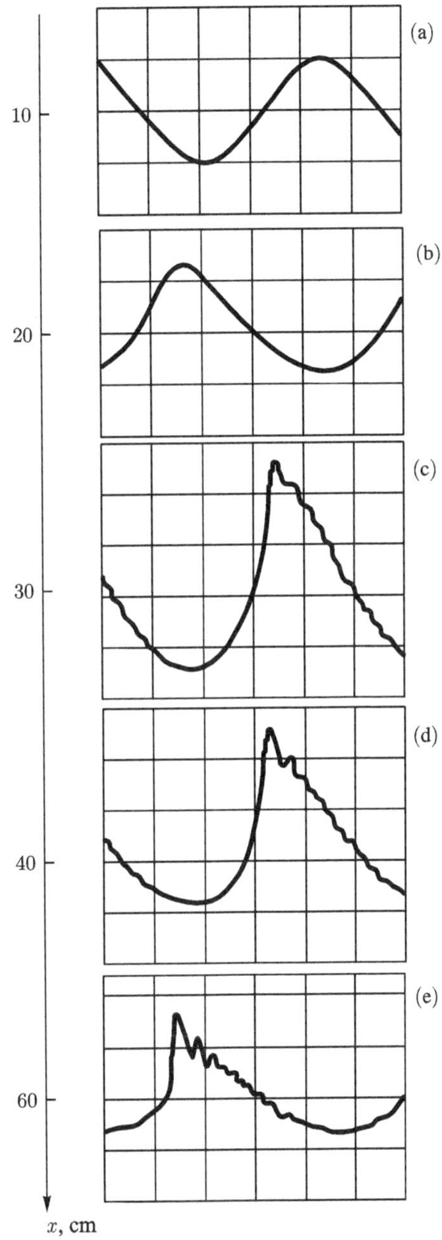

Fig. 9.7 Nonlinear distortion of the wave profile at the beam axis as a function of growing distance x from the source of radiation. Here $I = 0.9$ W/cm^2, $N \approx 0.2$, the scanning rate is 0.2 μs/division, the vertical scale is (**a, b**) — 2.8 atm/division, (**c–e**) — 1.1 atm/division.

the wave gradually transforms into a plane wave of a small amplitude, i.e. the radial distribution becomes more homogeneous [36]. This phenomenon is similar to the process of nonlinear "smoothing" of directivity patterns of high-power acoustic transducers [37].

The processes of non-symmetric distortion of diffracting nonlinear waves have been studied in detail in numerical experiments [38], where it has also been observed that the positive peak pressure exceeds its initial value.

Theoretical investigations of nonlinear effects, which take diffraction into account, have been started after R.V. Khokhlov has suggested to supplement the method of slowly varying profile [39] with the quasi-optic approximation, whose ideas originate in the 1940s works by M.A. Leontovich and V.A. Fok on radio-wave propagation along the Earth's surface. After simplifying, it has been possible to reduce the system of equations describing the mechanics of compressible media to a single equation (7.39) [40], which we proposed to name the Khokhlov-Zabolotskaya (KZ) equation. At present, this name is commonly used. The history of the derivation of KZ and KZK equations as well as of preceding and connected studies is given by recent review [41].

Later, modifications of this equation have been suggested. A dissipative term containing the second derivative of the field in the brackets in Eq. (7.45) has been taken into account [42]. A dispersive term with the third derivative, which has made it possible to describe spatially bounded solitons, has also been taken into account [43]. An integral term [44] has been added, whose kernel can be reconstructed for any frequency dependencies of absorption and dispersion [45,46].

Presently, over a hundred papers are known, which are devoted to calculations on the basis of the KZ equation or its modifications. These mainly are either results of numerical integration [38] or data on harmonics and combination frequencies under a weakly expressed nonlinearity [47–49]. The latter works, despite the simplicity of the theory, have an important applied significance, since they are connected with calculations of parametric devices in hydroacoustics [49,50].

This chapter, however, is devoted to sawtooth waves, and nonlinear effects are strongly expressed in beams of such waves. Because of mathematical difficulties of analytical and numerical solutions of such problems, there are not so many works on this topic.

In [51], an approximate method of the analysis of the KZ equation (7.39) has been developed, which is based on the expansion of the solution into a series, whose small parameter is the ratio of the current value of the radial coordinate r to the initial beam width a. For the acoustic pressure, the expansion has the following form:

$$p(x,r,\tau) = p_0(x,\tau) + \frac{r^2}{2a^2} p_2(x,\tau) + \frac{r^4}{4a^4} p_4(x,\tau) + \ldots . \tag{9.6}$$

Such an approach is similar to the paraxial approximation in the theory of laser self-focusing [52]. The difference is in that here, instead of a system of ordinary differential equation, an infinite chain of nonlinear partial differential equations is obtained. But limiting it to the first two equations, $p_4 = p_6 = \ldots = 0$, we arrive at the canonical and exactly solvable system containing a nonlinear operator with the common principal part [53]:

$$\left(\frac{\partial}{\partial x} - \frac{\varepsilon}{c_0^3 \rho_0} p \frac{\partial}{\partial \tau}\right) \binom{p}{F} = \binom{F}{g(x)}, \; F = \frac{N}{2} \int p_2(x,\tau) d(\omega\tau). \tag{9.7}$$

Here $p \equiv p_0(x,\tau)$ is the field at the beam axis, $g(x)$ is the function determined from the condition of momentum conservation during wave propagation, N is the number (the only similarity criterion in the KZ equation) equal to the ratio of the length of sock formation to the diffraction length:

$$N = \frac{x_{SH}}{x_d} = \frac{c_0^3 \rho_0}{\varepsilon \omega p_0'} \cdot \frac{2c_0}{\omega a^2}. \tag{9.8}$$

In the dimensionless notation

$$V = \frac{p}{p_0'}, \quad \theta = \omega\tau, \quad z = \frac{x}{x_{SH}}, \quad R = \frac{r}{a}, \tag{9.9}$$

the KZ equation assumes the following form:

$$\frac{\partial}{\partial\theta}\left(\frac{\partial V}{\partial z} - V\frac{\partial V}{\partial\theta}\right) = \frac{N}{4}\left(\frac{\partial^2 V}{\partial R^2} + \frac{1}{R}\frac{\partial V}{\partial R}\right). \tag{9.10}$$

Fig. 9.8 shows wave profiles at the beam axis constructed on the basis of the exact solution of the system (9.7) at $N = 0.4$. Curve 1 shows the wave profile at $z = 0$. If the wave were plane, nonlinear effects would lead to a distortion of the profile shown by curves 2′ ($z = 1$) and 3′ ($z = 2$). In the presence of diffraction, the wave behaves in a different way: the positive half-period decreases in length, while the negative one increases. Since the areas of the half-periods must be equal, in a certain region of the values of x near x_{SH}, the amplitude of the positive pressure exceeds the initial value (curve 2, $z = 1$). In the discontinuous region $x > x_{SH}$, this overshoot is "cut off" by the moving front, but unlike the plane wave (curves 3 and 3′), it is manifested even at a greater extent.

These phenomena are not related, as it is sometimes stated, to the effects of self-action [52] or to a more intense generation of harmonics in the beam [54]. They can be easily explained by the difference of the diffraction phase shifts or propagation velocities of the fundamental and higher harmonics [46]. Similar shifts in open resonators, e.g., lead to a difference in the frequencies of different transverse modes [46].

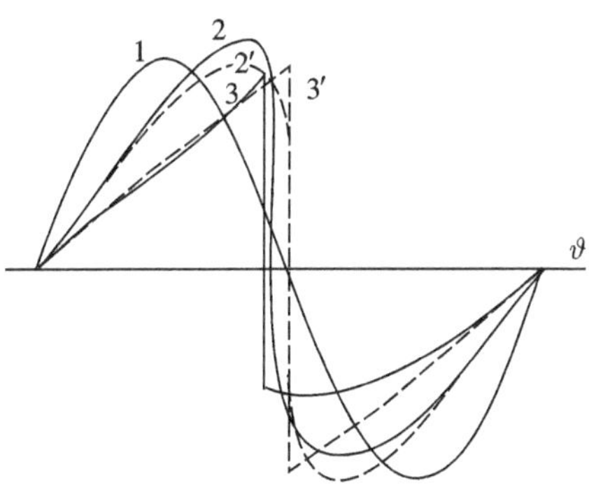

Fig. 9.8 Influence of diffraction phase shifts on the change of wave behavior in a beam (solid curves) in comparison with a plane wave (dashed curves) at $N = 0.4$.

The direct series expansion (9.6) in the transverse coordinate with only two terms (9.7) retained, however, leads to substantial limitations in the applicability of the results. It so happens that the solutions describe well the processes near the axis, but only at small distances in comparison with the diffraction length.

In order to remove this drawback, the method [51] has been modified [55] in the following way. The solution of Eq. (9.10) has been sought in the form

$$V = V\left(z, R, T = \theta - \Psi(z, R)\right), \tag{9.11}$$

where Ψ is an unknown function describing the curving of the phase front. Instead of the KZ equation, the following system has been obtained:

$$\frac{\partial}{\partial T}\left[\frac{\partial V}{\partial z} - V\frac{\partial V}{\partial T} + \frac{N}{4}\left(V\Delta_\perp \Psi + 2\frac{\partial V}{\partial R}\frac{\partial \Psi}{\partial R}\right) - \frac{N}{4}\frac{\partial V}{\partial T}Q\right] = \frac{N}{4}\Delta_\perp V, \tag{9.12}$$

$$\frac{\partial \Psi}{\partial z} + \frac{N}{4}\left(\frac{\partial \Psi}{\partial R}\right)^2 = \frac{N}{4}Q(z, R). \tag{9.13}$$

Here Q is an arbitrary function. By choosing Q based on simplicity considerations (e.g., as in the linear quasi-optic theory of diffraction [46]) and using the paraxial expansion (9.6) for V, and also for Ψ, we obtain the solution at the beam axis in the parametric form $V = V(T_0)$, $T = T(T_0)$:

$$V = \frac{1}{f}\sin(T_0 + \eta) + \frac{1}{2Nf}\int_0^\eta f(y)\sin(\eta - y)\,dy, \tag{9.14}$$

$$T = T_0 - \frac{1}{N}\int_0^\eta f(y)\sin(T_0 + y)\,dy - \frac{1}{2N^2}\int_0^\eta f(y)\,dy\int_0^y f(y')\sin(y - y')\,dy'.$$

Here T_0 is the parameter, $f = \cos^{-1}\eta$, $\eta = \arctan(Nz)$.

The process of sawtooth-wave formation calculated according to Eqs. (9.14) is qualitatively similar to the one shown in Fig. 9.8. A comparison has shown [55] that both the wave profile (9.14) and the spatial distribution of harmonics agree well with the results of numerical integration at any distances from the source of radiation.

But in those cases, when one needs to know the beam structure outside the paraxial region, the approaches [51, 55] are not applicable. A simple asymptotic theory, which takes into account the effect of diffraction and nonlinearity on Gaussian beams, has been developed in [56]. Here a transformation to the implicit "Riemann" variable $T = \theta + zV$, which contains an unknown function V, has been used. Then the resultant nonlinear equations have been solved by means of the method of perturbations for diffracting beams. It turns out that both limiting cases (linear beams with diffraction and non-diffracting nonlinear waves) already in the first approximation are described by this method quite accurately. In the intermediate region (for $N \sim 1$), errors are possible at distances, where shock formation is accompanied by a transformation of a plane wave into a spherically diverging one.

Later, this method [56] has been corrected by taking into account higher approximations [57]. The theory of beams with non-Gaussian (polynomial or uniform) cross-section has been developed in [58]. Unlike [56], it has used the method of perturbations along with the renormalization procedure not only with respect to the time variable, but also with respect to the transverse coordinates of the beam. Good accuracy has been achieved in [59], where the renormalization, which has allowed one to describe sawtooth waves, has been performed on the basis of the first three approximations of the quasilinear perturbation theory.

In conclusion of this section, let us point out the works [60,61], where an analysis of the applicability of the approach based on the KZ equation is given and its adequate agreement with laboratory experiments is demonstrated. Recall that in those situations, when nonlinear effects are weakly expressed and there are not shock fronts, the accuracy of the KZ equation is also confirmed by large-scale hydroacoustic experiments and calculations of real parametric devices [50].

Dozens of papers on the KZ equation and various modifications of field equations of this kind appear annually. Therefore it is worth mentioning that along with the above-described development history of these studies, whose origin is in the classical works on the wave theory, there apparently is an independent second line of events. It originates in the works by L. Prandtl (see, e.g., [62]) on hydrodynamics. Indeed, the ideas of deriving the equations of the laminar boundary layer (1904) are similar to the ideas of the quasi-optic approximation. The development of these ideas in mechanics has lead to appearance of works, which are close in their meaning to the works on the wave theory, but practically have had no effect on it. So, as far back as in 1948, an equation [63], which formally coincides with the KZ equation, has been obtained, but there the physical meaning of the variables and the formulation of the problem are different. Instead of the shape of the wave profile and the shape of the beam at the surface of the source, in the problem of body streamlining the shape of the body and the condition of zero normal component of the velocity at its surface are given. In [64], a similar approach has been used in order to calculate the transonic streamlining of a wing. A known "trace" [63] exists in the book [62] (Chap. 13, Sect. 126), where a stationary variant of an equation of the KZ type is used in order to obtain the T. von Karman law of trans-sonic similarity.

Continuation of the "mechanical line of events" has lead to appearance of purely "wave" works, where the KZ equation is derived anew. These works are on the theory of weak shock waves — the features of their focusing [65] and stability with respect to transverse modulation [66] (see also [62], (Chap. 9, Sect. 93, footnote)). It is expedient to know of all these studies, since many of them contain important mathematical results and physical conclusions, which may be transferred onto other objects of investigation.

9.4 Waves in inhomogeneous media and nonlinear geometric acoustics

The tendencies of investigation development and applications of the theory of nonlinear sawtooth waves have lead to appearance of works on wave propagation in inhomogeneous media. For instance, important topics are: sonic boom pulses from supersonic jet planes [67, 68], shock waves in the atmosphere and ocean [69], continuous acoustic radiation from powerful sources of sound, etc.

The problems appearing here can conditionally be split into three groups. These are problems connected with information transmission (an example is shock signals in an underwater sonic channel), problems of formation of intense impact and environment protection from them (sonic boom), and also inverse problems on nonlinear remote sensing and noninvasive diagnostics (reconstruction of the parameters of a source, scatterers, signal-propagation path).

In order to describe sawtooth waves it is necessary to determine correctly the position and profile of the shock front, as well as the magnitude of perturbations in the transition across the shock front. For this purpose, the gas dynamic methods are used, which are simplified by taking into consideration the small acoustic Mach numbers [70–72]. However, to have an information only on the wave front, of course, is not enough. The wave should be considered as a signal of complex spectral composition carrying the information about the source and its propagation path. For example, during propagation in the atmosphere, ground or ocean, the wave continuously interacts with inhomogeneities, which acting as scatterers, natural waveguides, lenses, filters and having pronounced frequency-selective properties. It is therefore necessary to follow the distortion of the wave spectrum. In terms of spatiotemporal characteristics of the perturbation, this means that, along with the dynamics of shock fronts, it is necessary to describe the evolution of smooth sections of their profiles and interactions of the shocks with each other. This complex problem can be effectively solved only in the nonlinear acoustic approximation by using the results based on the linear theory of wave propagation through inhomogeneous media [73–75] and the theory of nonlinear nondispersive waves [1, 70–72].

Approximations of nonlinear geometric acoustics type have been developed and applied to the waves in smoothly-inhomogeneous media (see, e.g., [76–78]). In Refs. [79, 80], for inhomogeneous media, the evolution equations of KZ-type has been derived that make it possible to take into account the diffraction of beams. However, despite the simplification, these problems are still difficult, which explains fewness of concrete results obtained here.

In order to simplify the original equations, which made it possible to solve various nonlinear problems, it makes sense to distinguish two ways. The first approach is based on approximation of nonlinear geometric acoustics and applied in the case of beams with large rays divergence. However, it is not valid in aberration area, where the rays intersect each other. The second approach is based on quasi-optical approximation and applicable only to beams with narrow angular spectrum, but it allows to describe fields in the vicinity of foci and caustics.

By means of the second approach in [21], the evolution equation has been derived:

$$\frac{\partial}{\partial \tau}\left[\frac{\partial p}{\partial s}-\frac{p}{2}\frac{\partial}{\partial s}\ln(\rho c)-\frac{\varepsilon}{c^3\rho}p\frac{\partial p}{\partial \tau}\right]-\frac{1}{2c^2}\left[(\boldsymbol{\xi}\nabla_\perp)^2 c\right]_{\boldsymbol{\xi}=0}=\frac{\rho}{2}\nabla_\perp\left(\frac{c}{\rho}\nabla_\perp p\right). \tag{9.15}$$

In order to describe the acoustic pressure field p in the vicinity of an arbitrarily selected ray, the curvilinear coordinates are used here. The distance s is measured along the ray from some fixed point, and the coordinates $\boldsymbol{\xi} = (\xi, \eta)$ introduced in the cross section in a special way: the basis of this system is turned relative to the Frenet trihedral through an angle defined by the curvilinear integral of the ray torsion [21]. Parameters of the medium, i.e. sound velocity c, density ρ and nonlinearity ε in Eq. (9.15) depend on space coordinates. Note that using the approach [44] allowed us to generalize Eq. (9.15) for dissipative, relaxing and other media with arbitrary frequency dependences of their linear properties (as done in Ref. [44] for homogeneous media).

For a periodic waves with a strongly distorted profile, in the nonlinear geometric acoustics approximation, the following equations have been obtained:

$$(\nabla\Psi)^2 = \frac{c_0^2}{c^2} = n^2, \tag{9.16}$$

$$\nabla p \nabla\Psi + \frac{p}{2}\Delta\Psi - \frac{p}{2}\nabla \ln\rho\nabla\Psi - \frac{\varepsilon n}{c^3\rho} p\frac{\partial p}{\partial\tau} = 0, \tag{9.17}$$

where $p = p(\mathbf{r}, \tau = t - \Psi(\mathbf{r})/c_0)$. Note that the eikonal equation (9.16) here is the same as in the linear problem. The validity of this coincidence is evident for periodic signals. Indeed, for the fundamental frequency signal the diffraction can be neglected, it is even more true for the higher harmonics. The situation is different for modulated signals, where during the propagation low frequency spectral components are generated, and for intense pulses that already contain low frequencies at the input of the nonlinear medium. In some cases, it is convenient to modify the eikonal equation by including nonlinear terms; it is so done while calculating the effects of self action in a cubic nonlinear nondispersive medium [11] and when the motion of the shock front [14, 15] in the accompanying coordinate system is taken into account.

Let us consider, for example, the two-dimensional problem, taking the eikonal Ψ and the parameter α, "enumerating" rays on the straight line $x = 0$, as independent variables (Fig. 9.9). In this case the system of Eqs. (9.16), (9.17) can be reduced to the equation [81]

$$\frac{\partial p}{\partial\Psi} + \frac{p}{2}\frac{\partial}{\partial\Psi}\ln\left[\frac{D(\alpha,\Psi)}{c^2\rho}\right] - \frac{\varepsilon}{c_0 c^2\rho} p\frac{\partial p}{\partial\tau} = 0, \tag{9.18}$$

where $D = \partial(x,z)/\partial(\alpha,\Psi)$ is a Jacobian of the transformation from the Cartesian coordinates x, z into the curvilinear coordinates α, Ψ. For a stratified medium, which parameters depend only on coordinate z, the solution of the eikonal Eq. (9.16) can be written in a convenient parametric form:

$$\Psi(\alpha,z) = \Psi_0(\alpha) + \int_0^z \frac{n^2(y)\,dy}{\sqrt{n^2(y) - a^2(\alpha)}}, \tag{9.19}$$

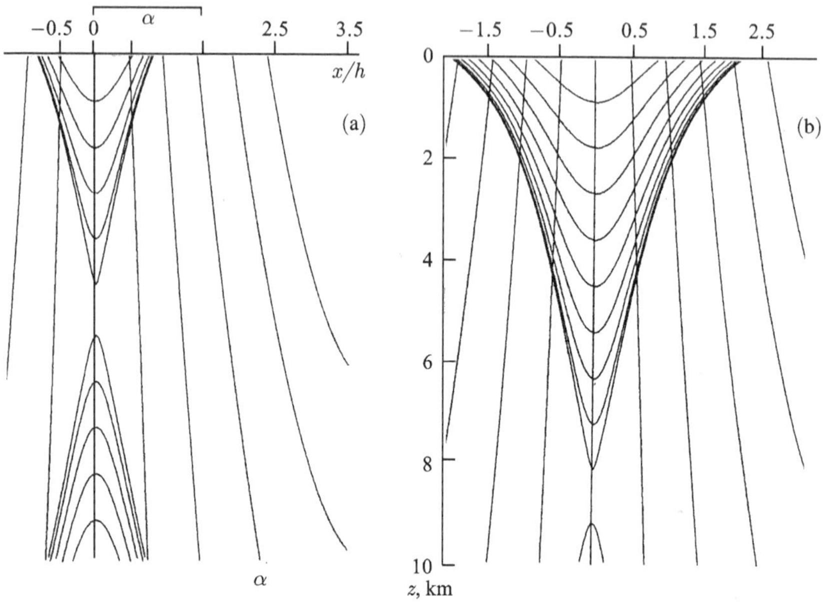

Fig. 9.9 **(a)** Rays and lines of equal levels of peak pressure for a single pulse, **(b)** and periodic "saw".

$$x(\alpha,z)=\alpha+a(\alpha)\int_0^z\frac{n^2(y)\,dy}{\sqrt{n^2(y)-a^2(\alpha)}},\tag{9.20}$$

where the function

$$a(\alpha)=\left(\frac{\partial\Psi}{\partial x}\right)_{z=0}=n_0\cos\theta_0=\frac{\partial\Psi}{\partial x}=n\cos\theta=const\,(\alpha)\tag{9.21}$$

describes the slope of the ray with the number α to the x-axis; θ is the angle between direction of x-axis and the tangent to the ray. By specifying the function $a(\alpha)$ (9.21), we thus fix the angle of departure for each ray. Formula (9.19) allows at $z=0$ define an arbitrary phase front at the "fan" of formed system of rays. In this case the Jacobian is given by [81]

$$D=\frac{\sqrt{n^2(z)-a^2(\alpha)}}{n^2(z)}\left[1+\frac{da}{d\alpha}\int_0^z\frac{n^2(y)\,dy}{\left[n^2(y)-a^2(\alpha)\right]^{3/2}}\right].\tag{9.22}$$

Let us now turn to the transport Eqs. (9.17), (9.18). In contrast to the linear case they contain an additional time variable τ. This variable can be eliminated in linear problems by the transition from p to the complex amplitude A: $p=A(\mathbf{r})\exp(-i\omega\tau)$. However, the Eqs. (9.17), (9.18) can describe an essentially non-harmonic wave with a wide spectrum of interacting Fourier components; generally speaking, it is not possible to eliminate τ for such waves.

Nevertheless, in the most interesting case, when nonlinear effects are expressed strongly and the wave profile has the sawtooth-shaped form (see Fig. 9.1, a), one can put

$$p(\tau,\mathbf{r}) = -2f\tau A(\mathbf{r}) \tag{9.23}$$

and go from Eqs. (9.17), (9.18) to the equations for the peak values A of the field p:

$$\nabla A \nabla \Psi + \frac{A}{2}\Delta\Psi - \frac{A}{2}\nabla \ln\rho \nabla\Psi + \frac{2\varepsilon n f}{c^3\rho}A^2 = 0, \tag{9.24}$$

$$\frac{\partial A}{\partial \Psi} + \frac{A}{2}\frac{\partial}{\partial \Psi}\ln\left[\frac{D(\alpha,\Psi)}{c^2\rho}\right] + \frac{2\varepsilon f}{c_0 c^2\rho}A^2 = 0. \tag{9.25}$$

Formula (9.23) describes the straight line intervals (on τ) of the periodic "saw" profile; in this formula f is fundamental frequency in the spectrum of "saw". Shock fronts are located at $2f\tau_n = \pi(2n+1)$, $n = 0, \pm1, \pm2, \ldots$, and not displaced from those points in the process of wave propagation. Eqs. (9.24), (9.25) can be linearized by the substitution $A = B^{-1}$ and easily solved.

For a bipolar N-pulse (Fig. 9.1, (b)) one can also use Eqs.(9.24), (9.25). However, in this case the variable A (9.23) has a sense of inclination of straight line sections of the wave profile, and both fronts will be shifted during the propagation taking of the positions $\tau = \pm T(\Psi)$. In order to take into account these differences we use the condition of conservation of momentum (it follows from Eq. (9.18) evidently) and the connection between "amplitudes" of N-wave (A_N) and "saw" (A_s) (the last follows from Eq. (9.23)):

$$\left(\frac{D}{c^2\rho}\right)^{1/2} A_N(\Psi)T(\Psi) = const, \quad A_N = 2fTA_s. \tag{9.26}$$

By solving (9.25) for $A = A_s$ and using the conditions (9.26), we obtain an analogous result for A_N.

For the stratified medium whose parameters depend only on z, these solutions have a form [81]

$$A_{s,N}(\alpha,z) = \frac{A_0(\alpha)}{n}\sqrt{\frac{D_0\rho}{D\rho_0}}\left[1+\frac{1}{x_{SH}}\frac{A_0(\alpha)}{p_0'}\int_0^z\left(\frac{D_0\rho_0\varepsilon^2}{D\rho\varepsilon_0^2}\frac{n^6}{n^2-a^2(\alpha)}\right)^{1/2}_{z=z_1}\right]^m. \tag{9.27}$$

In formula (9.27), $m = -1$ corresponds to a periodic "saw", but $m = -1/2$ to an N-wave. In case of bipolar N-pulse here is convenient to put $f = (2T_0)^{-1}$, where T_0 is the initial duration of the compression (or rarefaction) phase.

The solution (9.27) can be used, for example, for the acoustic field calculation [81] in an atmosphere stratified with respect to the density and sound velocity:

$$\rho(z) = \rho_0 \exp(z/H), \quad c = c_0(1+kz).$$

The plane $z = 0$ is located at a height of 10 km, z-axis is directed downward along the vertical; $H = 8$ km, $k = 1.3\times10^{-2}$ km^{-1}, $c_0 = 300$ m s^{-1}, $\rho_0 = 0.37$ kg m^{-3}. At

$z = 0$ the curved phase front have been given as well as the nonuniform distribution of the amplitude:

$$\Psi_0(x = \alpha) = h\left(1 + \frac{\alpha^2}{h^2}\right)^{1/2}, \quad A_0(\alpha) = p_0'\left(1 + \frac{\alpha^2}{h^2}\right)^{-1/2}, \tag{9.28}$$

where h is the height (over the plane $z = 0$) at which lies the focus of a cylindrical diverging wave ($h < 0$ corresponds to the converging wave), and α is the current value of the abscissa fixing the point of ray departure. The shock formation length is set at $x_{SH} = 2.3$ km, which corresponds, for example, to the N-pulse with characteristic duration $T_0 = 0.05$ s and peak pressure of $p_0' = 180$ Pa.

In Fig. 9.9, the ray pattern (9.20) for the diverging beam ($h = 21.3$ km) as well as lines of equal levels of the peak pressure for a single pulse (Fig. 9.9, (a)) and for a periodic "saw" (Fig. 9.9, (b)) are shown. As the distance traveled by the wave increases, the acoustic pressure decreases due to nonlinear damping and divergence of rays. Then the wave penetrates into more dense layers of the atmosphere and the pressure starts to grow. As a result, the spatial distributions of peak pressures have a saddle point; it is located for the pulse at a height of about 5 km, but for the periodic "saw" (which decays more strongly) at the distance 1 km from the Earth's surface.

The amplitude behavior is determined by the combined effect of refraction, the change in parameters of the medium along each ray, as well as by the nonlinear damping. To highlight the role of nonlinear damping, let us consider the converging wave in a homogeneous medium, where Eqs. (9.22) and (9.20) in terms of the first formula (9.28) take the form

$$D = \left(1 - \frac{z}{h}\right)\left(1 + \frac{\alpha^2}{h^2}\right)^{-1/2}, \quad x = \alpha\left(1 - \frac{z}{h}\right). \tag{9.29}$$

The obvious fact follows from formulas (9.29) that the decrease in ray tube cross section is proportional to D happens in homogeneous media only due to the convergence of the initial beam of rays. Thereby the rays $x(z)$ are straight lines. Peak pressure on the beam-axis decreases at first because of the nonlinear damping, but then increases indefinitely as it approaches the focus. Beam width, on the contrary, grows as a result of a stronger damping in the near axial region. But at the point $z = h$ the beams "collapse" and their width goes to zero.

The simplest phenomena described above have a significant impact on the complex picture of the sawtooth wave field in an inhomogeneous medium.

9.5 The focusing of discontinuous waves

To create strong wave fields, focusing devices can be used which have a wide application in many ultrasonic technologies and medical devices. A concentration of the wave energy occurs during the focusing, and the importance of nonlinear effects increases significantly. In addition, the linear dissipative properties of the medium are essential, but in the focal region the diffraction is of basic importance.

Let us consider, at first, the role of the indicated phenomena separately. The solution of the linearized KZ equation (7.39) for Gaussian beams at the axis ($r=0$) has the form [46, 50]

$$p=\int_{-\infty}^{\infty}\frac{\tilde{p}_0(\omega)\sin(\omega\tau+\varphi)}{\sqrt{(1-x/x_0)^2+x^2/x_d^2}}d\omega,\ \varphi=\arctan\frac{x/x_d}{1-x/x_0}+\pi\Theta(x-x_0). \quad (9.30)$$

Here, $x_d=\omega a^2/2c_0$ is the diffraction length, Θ is the Heaviside unit step-function, $\tilde{p}_0(\omega)$ is the initial spectrum of the signal. At the geometric focus $x=x_0$ the solution (9.30) takes the form

$$p=\int_{-\infty}^{\infty}\frac{x_d}{x_0}\tilde{p}_0(\omega)\sin\left(\omega\tau+\frac{\pi}{2}\right)d\omega=\frac{a^2}{2c_0x_0}\frac{\partial}{\partial\tau}\int_{-\infty}^{\infty}\tilde{p}_0(\omega)\sin(\omega\tau)d\omega. \quad (9.31)$$

Thus, the form of the profile at the focus is the time derivative of the initial (at $x=0$) form of the signal. If the signal is a harmonic one, the maximum of its amplitude is achieved at the point $x_{\max}<x_0$ (which is located between source and geometric focus) and the maximum amplification factor is large, $K\gg 1$ (for weak influence of diffraction). According to Eq. (9.30) these quantities are

$$x_{\max}=\frac{x_0}{1+x_0^2/x_d^2},\qquad K=\sqrt{1+\frac{x_d^2}{x_0^2}}. \quad (9.32)$$

In Ref. [15, 82] the distortion process is described for a unipolar pulse signal $p=p_0'\exp(-|\tau|/T_0)$. During the propagation a "tail" of negative polarity appears due to diffraction. As the wave tends to the focus, the "amplitude" increases for both compression and rarefaction phases, and the signal becomes differentiated with respect to time. Behind the focus these peaks decrease due to divergence; the pulse profile tends to assume a shape inverted with respect to the initial one.

Now we neglect the diffraction and consider the behavior of a nonlinear spherically converging wave. The corresponding solution of Eq. (9.10) with an added dissipative term (or the modified Burgers equation for converging waves [83]) written in dimensionless variables (9.9) has the form [31]

$$V=A(z)\left[-\theta+\pi\tanh\left(\pi A(z)\frac{\theta}{2\Gamma}\right)\right], \quad (9.33)$$

$$A(z)=\frac{z_0}{z}\left(1+z_0\ln\frac{z_0}{z}\right)^{-1}. \quad (9.34)$$

The solution (9.33) at small numbers $\Gamma=x_{SH}/x_a$ describes one period ($-\pi<\theta<\pi$) of the sawtooth wave. It was obtained for the signal which is harmonic at the source (at $x=x_0$ or $z=x_0/x_{SH}=z_0$). The signal propagates towards the centre ($x=z=0$), i.e. dimensionless distance decreases from z_0 to 0.

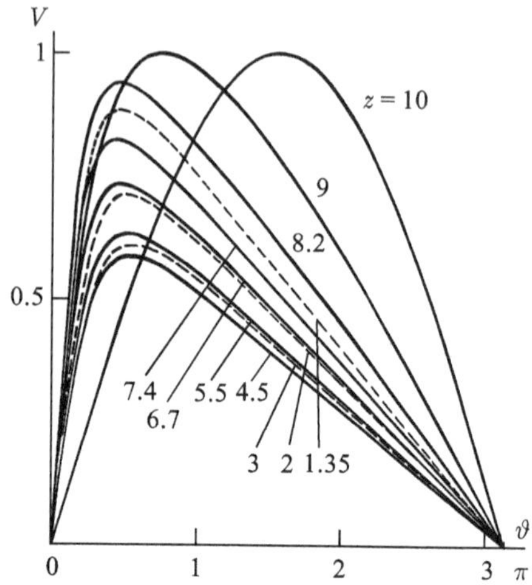

Fig. 9.10 Distortion of the half-period of a spherical wave at its convergence to the focus. Number $\Gamma = 0.1$. By the numbers on profiles, the dimensionless distance $z = x/x_{SH}$, is indicated from the current position of the front to the focus.

Figure 9.10 shows one half-period of the wave for $z_0 = 10$; for the case when the distance between the initial spherical surface and the focus significantly exceeds the length of the shock formation. In this case an interesting phenomenon can be observed, namely, the double formation of the shock front [31, 83]. Fig. 9.10 shows how the initial ($z = z_0 = 10$) harmonic wave is distorted during the process of convergence towards the focus. On the curve $z = 8.2$ the steep leading edge is already clearly visible. Thereafter, the maximum perturbation in the wave decreases while its front expands up to the curve $z = 4.5$. The width of the shock front reaches a maximum value at the point $z_{\max} = z_0 \exp(1/z_0 - 1)$; in its vicinity the process of nonlinear damping of the "saw" is weakened. However, closer to the focus the disturbance begins to grow again (convergence prevails over dissipation), and the front becomes steep again.

Evidently, that the nonlinear damping of the "saw" leads to a decrease in the amplification factor during the focusing [5]. According the solution (9.33), the ratio between the nonlinear K_N and linear K_L amplification coefficients is equal to

$$\frac{K_N}{K_L} = \frac{2\Gamma}{\pi}\frac{z}{z_0}e^{\Gamma(z_0-z)}\left[\sqrt{y(y-1)} - \operatorname{arcosh}\sqrt{y}\right], \; y = \frac{\pi A^2}{2\Gamma}, \tag{9.35}$$

where A is given by the formula (9.34). The dependences of the amplification factors K_N, K_L and their relationship (9.35) on z are shown in Fig. 9.11 (curves 1, 2 and 3 respectively). The dashed curves correspond to the case of vanishingly small dissipation, $\Gamma \to 0$, and solid curves to $\Gamma = 0.1$. The nonlinear amplification factor K_N has a minimum in the region between the source of radiation and the focal point, where the "smearing" of the shock front is observed (see Fig. 9.10). At the approach to the focus both coefficients K_N, K_L increase, but their ratio tends to zero (curves 3 in Fig. 9.11).

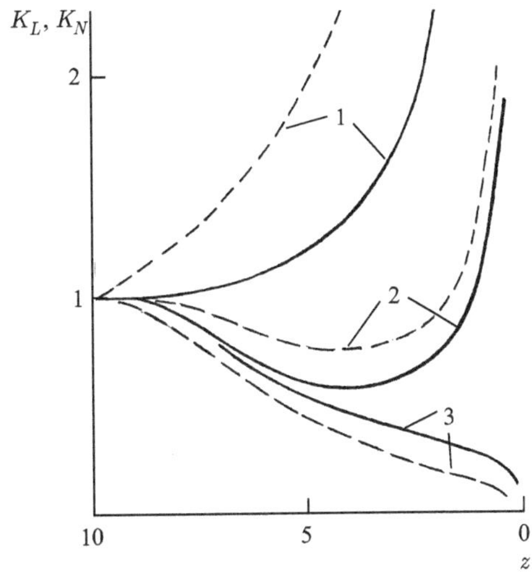

Fig. 9.11 Change in linear(1) and nonlinear (2) amplification coefficients and their relationship (3) during the wave propagation from the source ($z = 10$) to focus ($z = 0$): solid curves $\Gamma = 0.1$; dashed curves $\Gamma = 0$.

However, the nonlinearity can not only decrease, but also increase the amplification coefficient due to a stronger focusing of higher harmonics generated by the intense wave [70, 84].

Such an inverse effect is possible, when the nonlinear dumping does not result in appreciable energy losses along the entire path from the source of radiation to the focal region, i.e. even if a sawtooth wave is formed, this event takes place in the immediate proximity to the focus. The corresponding calculation is performed in [85] by the use of a step-by-step approach. It is assumed that at the first stage of propagation in the region $x_0 > x > x_*$ the wave undergoes only the nonlinear distortions like in a symmetric spherically converging wave [31]

$$\frac{p}{p_0'} = \frac{x_0}{x} \sin\left(\omega\tau + \frac{p}{p_0'}\frac{x}{x_{SH}} \ln\frac{x_0}{x}\right). \tag{9.36}$$

The boundary of the phase is selected from the compromise conditions: it must be small compared with the focal length ($x_* \ll x_0$) and large in comparison with the size of the focal region ($x_* \gg x_0^2/x_d$). At the second phase is assumed that the wave undergoes only diffraction distortion; here, nonlinear distortion is not accumulated due to the small size of the focal region, despite the high peak pressures and the steepness of the shock front.

By using (9.36) as a boundary condition (at $x = x_*$) for the solution of the diffraction problem (9.31)

$$p|_{x=0} = \frac{a_*^2}{2c_0 x_*}\left(\frac{\partial p}{\partial \tau}\right)_{x=x_*}, \quad a_* = a\frac{x_*}{x_0}, \quad \left(\frac{\partial p}{\partial \tau}\right)_{\max} = \omega p_0' \frac{x_0}{x_*}\left(1 - \frac{x_0}{x_{SH}} \ln\frac{x_0}{x_*}\right)^{-1},$$

it is possible to calculate the nonlinear amplification coefficient

$$\frac{K_N}{K_L} = \left(1 - \frac{x_0}{x_{SH}} \ln \frac{x_0}{x_*}\right)^{-1}. \tag{9.37}$$

It is seen that the stronger nonlinearity (the shorter the nonlinearity length x_{SH}) the more K_N is greater than K_L; the dependence on the undetermined boundary x_* of this stage is weak. An increase of the field at the focus in comparison with the linear case has been noted in experiments [86, 87].

For small angles of convergence of the wave front, it has been possible to obtain the solution [55] of the KZ equation describing the nonlinearly diffractive evolution of the profile. This solution is written in the parametric form (9.14), where now

$$f = \frac{Nz_0}{\sin\eta + Nz_0\cos\eta}, \qquad \eta = \pi\Theta(z - z_0) + \arctan\frac{Nz}{1 - z/z_0}. \tag{9.38}$$

The dimensionless distance $x = x/x_{SH}$ here changes from $z = 0$ (the source) towards growing values of z. The geometric focus is located at $z = z_0 = x_0/x_{SH}$.

The profile drawn according to the solution (9.14), (9.38) are shown in Fig. 9.12. In the process of propagation towards the focus, the amplitude increases and the leading front steepens. Apart from that, the zero points of the profile are shifted forward because of diffraction. In the geometric focus, due to the diffractive dephasing of harmonics, the profile becomes asymmetric; the region of positive pressure is amplified stronger. Immediately after the focus (the curve for $x/x_0 = 1.2$ in Fig. 9.12), the wave profile assumes the form similar to the derivative of the profile before the focus (the curve for $x/x_0 = 0.8$). The ratio of the coefficients of linear and nonlinear amplification at the focus, according to this solution for the positive peak pressure, is equal to

$$\frac{K_N}{K_L} = 1 + \frac{x_0}{2x_{SH}} Q\left(y = \frac{x_0}{x_d}\right), \quad Q = \frac{(\pi/2)y - \ln y}{1 + y^2}. \tag{9.39}$$

Equation (9.39) is somewhat different from the result of the step-by-step analysis (9.37), although it gives the same qualitative dependence on x_0/x_{SH}.

Let us now consider phenomena arising in the process of focusing nonlinear pulsed signals with shock fronts. Investigations of these problems in recent years have been stimulated by medical applications — above all the shock-wave extra-

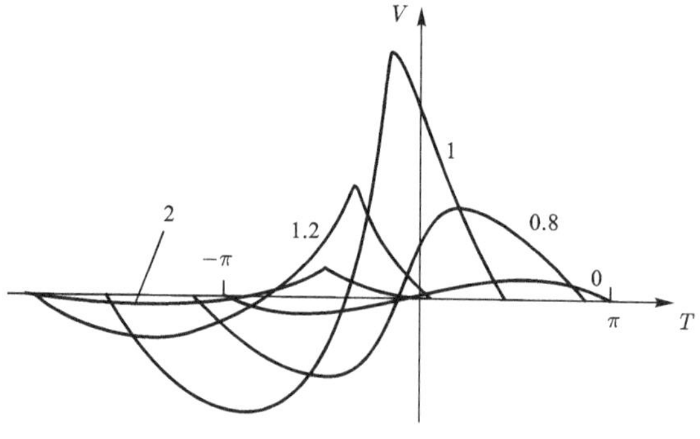

Fig. 9.12 Distortion of the profile of an initial harmonic signal on passing the focus. Numbers at the curves mark the dimensionless distance x/x_0 in units of the focal length x_0. Diffraction ($x_d = 10x_0$) and nonlinearity ($x_{SH} = 3.3x_0$) are substantial.

corporeal lithotripsy [18, 19]. Its goal is remote removal of kidney and gallbladder stones from a human body. Powerful acoustic pulses are generated outside a patient's body, are focused on a bio-concrement and break it into small fragments, which then exit in a natural way. Significant part of the works reported at recent conferences on nonlinear acoustics (see, e.g., [88–92]) are devoted to the physical aspects of generation of powerful pulses, their focusing, and also to the mechanisms of concrement destruction.

Usually, generators of the following three types are used: electrohydraulic, electromagnetic and piezoelectric [18, 91]. But for improving the characteristics of lithotripters and reducing undesirable side effects, alternative methods are developed, e.g. detonation of micro-portions of explosives [92].

Wide facilities to control the duration of a pulse, as well as its shape and directivity pattern of radiation are opened by the application of optoacoustic generators [93], in which a powerful pulse is excited under absorption of modulated laser radiation [94–97].

Fragmentation of concrements takes place due to several mechanisms. There is experimental evidence supporting the fact that the frontal surface of a target is destroyed mainly due to cavitation, i.e. by large pressures under the collapse of bubbles or by cumulative jets formed under their asymmetric collapse [90]. The rear surface may be destroyed by negative pressures ("spallation") formed under the reflection of the pulse front from the surface back inside the specimen [98].

In the process of developing commercial lithotripters and during measurements in the fields of powerful focused pulses excited by them, a number of interesting nonlinear phenomena have been observed: self-refraction, saturation of the peak pressure at the focus, growth of the focal region, its shift away from the source, etc. [99–101]. It has been necessary to clarify the nature of these phenomena and to provide them with a mathematical description. To this end, new experimental and theoretical studies have been needed.

Figure 9.13 illustrates the process of self-refraction of a shock front. For comparison, the dashed lines depict the spherical fronts corresponding to linear focusing; the finite size of the beam waist is here determined by diffraction, which is manifested in a different way for different components of the broadband spectrum of the signal.

Since the propagation speed of a weak shock wave $c = c_0\left[1 + \varepsilon A/\left(2c_0^2\rho_0\right)\right]$ depends on the value A of the pressure jump at the front, the displacements of the front points (marked by the arrows) near the beam axis are greater than at its periphery. As a result, near the source, the "straightening" of the front is observed. Simultaneously, the process of nonlinear attenuation takes place, and the distribution of A over the front becomes more homogeneous (see Sect. 9.3). This slows down self-refraction. As is shown in Fig. 9.13, the above described processes shift the nonlinear focus x_N with respect to the linear one x_0; the size of the nonlinear beam waist in this case is increased.

These phenomena have been observed in experiments [15], in which, in addition to that, the peak pulsed pressures at different distances from the source have been measured. For excitation, a pulsed neodymium-glass laser with electrooptical mod-

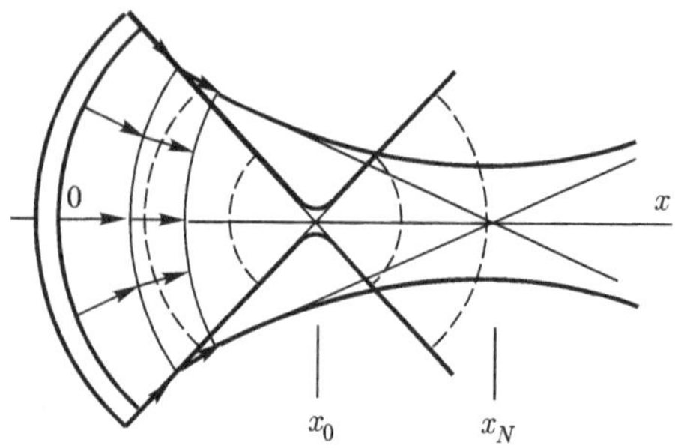

Fig. 9.13 Self-refraction of a shock front leading to a shift and broadening of the focal region.

ulation of the Q-factor has been used. It generated single light pulses of a duration of 30 ns at a wavelength of 1.06 mcm with an energy of 5–10 J. A special design [93] of an optoacoustic transducer allows one to obtain acoustic pulses of a duration of 0.1–1 mcs, with a peak pressure up to 1000 atm and to form converging beams of a diameter up to 50 mm and a focus length of 15–200 mm. A broadband hydrophone based on the piezo-film PVDF has been calibrated. It has a temporal resolution of the order of 10 ns, and a spatial one of 1 mm.

Fig. 9.14(a) shows the dependencies of the normalized pressure "amplitude" A/p_0 on the distance x along the beam axis at different values of the initial peak pressure p_0 equal to 9 atm (curve 1), 100 atm (2) and 500 atm (3). The initial radium of the beam is $a = 8$ mm. The dashed curves are drawn through the experimental points.

It is seen that an appreciable amplification is observed only at small p_0 (curve 1). Under the focusing of more powerful pulses, the amplification has been insignificant (curve 2) or absent altogether (curve 3). All experimental points in the focal region lie under the solid curve 1 calculated according to the linear theory, which signifies an appreciable effect of nonlinear phenomena. The theoretical dependencies 2 and 3 (solid curves) are calculated by taking into account absorption and self-refraction [14, 102] for describing the experimental (dashed) lines 2 and 3. In the theory, the ratio $x_0/x_d = 2x_0c_0T_0/a^2$ of the focal length to the diffractive length has been assumed to be equal to 0.3, and the ratio of x_0 to the length of shock formation $x_0/x_{SH} = \varepsilon x_0 p_0 / \left(c_0^3 \rho_0 T_0\right)$ for the curves 1, 2 and 3 has been equal to 0, 3.2 and 16, respectively.

Fig. 9.14(b) shows the axial dependencies of the peak pressure A for different convergence angles $\varphi = 2\arcsin\left(a/x_0\right)$ equal to 32°, 22° and 12° for the curves 1, 2 and 3. The initial amplitude $p_0' = 140$ atm has been fixed ($x_0/x_{SH} = 4.5$). The curves 1–3 correspond to the values of the parameters a and x_0/x_d equal to 14 mm and 0.1, 10 mm and 0.18, 5 mm and 0.75. In analogy with Fig. 9.14(a), near the focus, the growth of the peak pressure is observed, but not in all cases. For large angles φ, the effect is more pronounced: at the curves 1, 2, the magnitude of A considerably exceeds p_0'. At the dependence 3, the pressure drops with growing x due to nonlinear absorption and self-refraction, and a local maximum is weakly expressed only near the focus. Thus at low aperture angles of the wave front φ, it is not possible to achieve appreciable amplification.

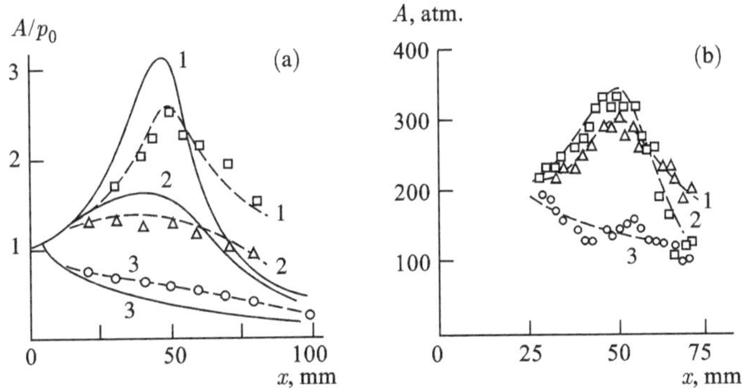

Fig. 9.14 (a) Axial dependences of the peak pressure under the focusing of pulsed beams with different initial values of the pressure, **(b)** and for different convergence angles.

In order to overcome the detrimental influence of nonlinear processes, it makes sense, firstly, to excite pulses with a very gently sloping leading front to delay the shock wave formation (the moment when nonlinear absorption starts to manifest itself); secondly, it is necessary to use strongly concave non-spherical sources of radiation to compensate for the straightening of the shock front due to refraction.

While discussing the focusing of powerful pulsed perturbations, we have not considered the transformation of the temporal profile of a signal during its passage through the focal region. These problems are very complex and their solution even within the framework of a simplified model — the KZ equation — are only possible through numerical methods [103, 104]. The problem is simplified, when strongly expressed self-refraction suppresses diffractive distortions in the focal region (see Fig. 9.13). These cases, important in practice, are analyzed by modified methods of the type of nonlinear geometric acoustics, in which for the description of smooth parts of the profile and shock fronts, different transport and eikonal equations are used [14, 102].

9.6 Nonlinear absorption and saturation

Nonlinear, i.e. depending on the magnitude of the perturbation (the amplitude, peak pressure, etc.) absorption is an important effect in the physics of sawtooth waves, whose fundamental role has many times been emphasized above. This phenomenon has intensively been investigated already in first works on nonlinear acoustics of condensed media (see the reviews [3–5]).

The peak values of the amplitude $A(x)/A_0$ in *plane* waves depicted in Fig. 9.1(a–c) decrease with distance according to the following laws:

$$\left(1+\frac{\varepsilon}{c_0^2}\omega A_0 x\right)^{-1}, \ \left(1+\frac{\varepsilon}{c_0^2 T_0}A_0 x\right)^{-1/2}, \ \left(1+c\gamma\omega A_0^2 x\right)^{-1/2}. \qquad (9.40)$$

The laws of decay (9.40) differ from the exponential law in linear dissipative media and depend on A_0 for quadratically nonlinear media (the first two formulas in (9.40)) or on A_0^2 for media with the cubic nonlinearity (the last formula in (9.40)).

Attenuation of sawtooth waves with an infinitely steep front does not depend on linear dissipative constants. This can be easily shown by means of the Burgers equation (7.32). Let us consider, for definitiveness, a periodic "saw" in a quadratically nonlinear medium. By multiplying the Burgers equation through by u and averaging over a period of the wave, we obtain

$$\frac{\partial \overline{u^2}}{\partial x} = -\frac{b}{c_0^3 \rho_0} \overline{\left(\frac{\partial u}{\partial \tau}\right)^2}. \tag{9.41}$$

It is seen that the decrease of the mean intensity $I = c_0\rho_0\overline{u^2}/2$ with distance proceeds faster when fronts with large values of the derivative $\partial u/\partial \tau$ are present. For linear absorption of a harmonic wave $u = A(x)\sin\omega\tau$, in which there are no steep parts of the profile, from (9.41) follows the standard law $A(x) = A_0\exp(-\alpha x)$, where the attenuation coefficient is equal to $\alpha = b\omega^2/\left(2c_0^3\rho_0\right)$. For a sawtooth wave with a finite front width, let us use the asymptotic (at $\Gamma \to 0$) solution (9.33), where $A(z)$ is given by the first of the formulas in (9.40). Thereby the squared derivative on the right-hand side of (9.41) $(\partial u/\partial \tau)^2 \sim b^{-2}$ is large for weakly absorbing media with small dissipation b. On averaging (9.41), the main contribution into the integral is given by the region of the shock front with the width $\sim b$. Thus, the dependence on b becomes weak, and (9.41) assumes the following form:

$$\frac{\partial \overline{u^2}}{\partial x} = -\frac{2\pi^2}{3}\frac{\varepsilon\omega}{c_0^2}A^3(x) + O(b \sim \Gamma). \tag{9.42}$$

At a vanishing dissipation ($b \to 0$), only the nonlinear term remains on the right-hand side of (9.42).

Dash-dotted lines in Fig. 9.15 show the distance dependences of the normalized mean intensity of the initial harmonic signal in a quadratically nonlinear medium. The numeric figures by the curves are the numbers $\Gamma = x_{SH}/x_a \sim b$. At $\Gamma = 0.01$, dissipation is weak and appreciable attenuation takes place only in the region $z = x/x_{SH} > 1$, after formation of steep fronts. With growing Γ, the fronts become less steep and the relative contribution of linear absorption increases.

Solid lines in Fig. 9.15 show the excess nonlinear attenuation

$$\frac{\alpha_N - \alpha}{\alpha} = -\frac{1}{2\Gamma}\frac{\partial}{\partial z}\ln\overline{u^2} - 1 \tag{9.43}$$

calculated according to the curves for the mean intensity. It is maximal at small Γ in the region of space, where there exist steep fronts.

In experiments, partial attenuation coefficients of different harmonics are often measured. In order to evaluate these coefficients, one needs to use spectral expansion of the Fay type [1] of the solutions (9.33) describing sawtooth waves.

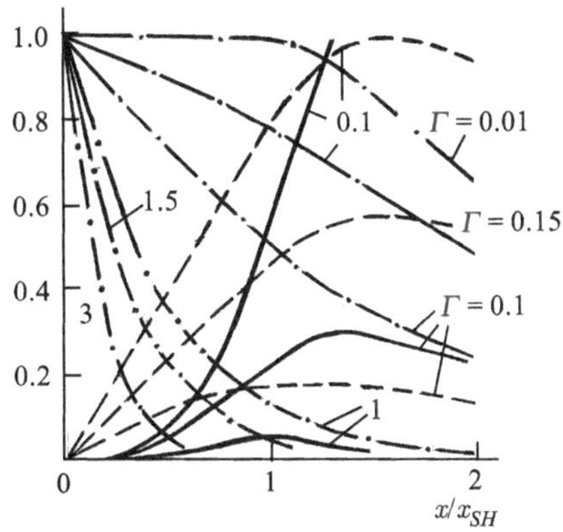

Fig. 9.15 Distance dependence of the normalized mean intensity (dash-dotted lines) and excess nonlinear attenuation (solid lines) at different numbers Γ. Dashed lines show the excess attenuation of the first harmonic.

In particular, for the first harmonic, the following expression is obtained [5]:

$$\frac{\alpha_N - \alpha}{\alpha} = \exp[-\Gamma(1+z)] \sinh^{-1}[-\Gamma(1+z)]. \tag{9.44}$$

This expression is valid in the region $x > 3x_{SH}$. At shorter distances ($0 < x < 2x_{SH}$), in order to draw the dashed curves in Fig. 9.15 ($\Gamma = 0.1$, 0.15 and 0.3), the results of numerical integration [31] have been used. The dashed curves in Fig. 9.15 also show that the most intense absorption takes place in a small neighborhood of the front of the "saw".

In order to take into account not only the losses, but also injection of energy into the wave, let us consider the inhomogeneous Burgers equation [105]

$$\frac{\partial u}{\partial x} - \frac{\varepsilon}{c_0^2} u \frac{\partial u}{\partial \tau} - \frac{b}{2c_0^3 \rho_0} \frac{\partial^2 u}{\partial \tau^2} = Q. \tag{9.45}$$

The field Q of external sources may be created due to, e.g., the heating of a surface by a moving "spot" of electromagnetic radiation [97] or because of the striction mechanism by counter-directional laser beams [106]. Let us assume, for definitiveness, that $Q = \partial(\beta T'/2)/\partial \tau$ is created by thermoelastic stresses $p' = c_0^2 \rho_0 \beta T'$, where β is the bulk expansion coefficient, T' is the temperature increment. When T' changes in time according to the harmonic law,

$$Q = \frac{p_0' \omega_0}{2c_0^2 \rho_0} \sin \omega \tau.$$

It convenient to write Eq. (9.45) in the following dimensionless form:

$$\frac{\partial U}{\partial z} - U \frac{\partial U}{\partial \theta} - \frac{\partial^2 U}{\partial \theta^2} = A \sin \theta, \tag{9.46}$$

where

$$U=\frac{2\varepsilon c_0\rho_0}{b\omega}u,\quad \theta=\omega\tau,\quad z=\frac{x}{x_a}=\frac{b\omega^2}{2c_0^3\rho_0}x,\quad A=\frac{\omega}{2c_0}\frac{x_a^2}{x_{SH}}. \tag{9.47}$$

At short distances z, travelled by the wave, its shape in time $U\approx zA\sin\theta$ duplicates the profile of the external sources. With growing amplitude, nonlinear distortions, which lead to the appearance of a shock front at each period of the wave, are amplified. At $z\to\infty$, the stationary profile [105]

$$U=2\frac{\partial}{\partial\theta}\ln ce_0\left(\frac{\theta}{2},A\right),\quad -\pi\leqslant\theta\leqslant\pi \tag{9.48}$$

is established, where ce_0 is the Mathiue function. At $A\gg 1$, the stationary wave assumes the shape of a "saw" with a finite front width

$$U=2\sqrt{A}\left[\cos\frac{\theta}{2}+\tanh\left(\sqrt{A}\theta\right)-1\right],\quad 0\leqslant\theta<\pi. \tag{9.49}$$

Hence the dynamics of the establishment are as follows. Energy is introduced by the sources into the entire domain $-\pi\leqslant\theta\leqslant\pi$ of the wave period under consideration. Due to nonlinear distortion of the profile, it tends to concentrate in the vicinity of $\theta=0$, where the shock front is formed. When the energy inflow from the source is compensated by the growing losses at the front, the stationary regime of propagation is established. The mean intensity is described by the following equation:

$$\frac{\partial\overline{U^2}}{\partial z}=-2\overline{\left(\frac{\partial U}{\partial\theta}\right)^2}+2A\overline{U\sin\theta}. \tag{9.50}$$

By using the solution (9.49), it is easy to show that both terms on the right-hand side of Eq. (9.50) are equal to $(8/3\pi)A^{3/2}$, but with the opposite signs, i.e. the balance of energy takes place. Thereby $\overline{U^2}=2A=const$.

Nonlinear absorption of sawtooth waves sometimes leads to a saturation effect. From the first formula in (9.40), it is seen that the peak perturbation of the vibration velocity of the periodic "saw" does not depend on its initial value A_0: $A_{\lim}=c_0^2/(\varepsilon\omega x)$ along a distance of a few nonlinearity lengths travelled by the wave on a quadratically nonlinear medium. This means that with growing A_0, nonlinear damping, which weakens the dependence $A(A_0)$ at a fixed x, intensifies. When $A_0\to\infty$, the perturbation ceases to depend on A_0 while reaching the limiting value $A_{\lim}$.

Similarly, a trapezoidal "saw" "saturates" is a cubically nonlinear medium (the third formula in (9.40)). On the contrary, a single pulse (the second formula in (9.40)) is not bounded; at $x>x_{SH}$, only a weaker (square-root) dependence $A(A_0)$: $A=\left(c_0^2T_0A_0/\varepsilon x\right)^{1/2}$ arises here. Therefore, by amplifying the initial pulsed signal A_0, it is possible to achieve an arbitrarily large amplification of the perturbation $A(x)$ in the medium.

The limiting values $A_{\lim}$, however, may be determined not only by nonlinear, but also by dissipative constants of the medium. If, at the input, a harmonic signal is given, whereas the reciprocal acoustic Reynolds number $\Gamma \ll 1$, at distances $x \approx 2x_{SH}$, a sawtooth wave is formed and within its domain there may be observed the saturation effect described above. At still greater distances ($x \approx 2x_a$), due to collective action of the nonlinear damping and dissipative smoothing of the profile, the wave again turns into a hamonic one with an amplitude, which does non depend on its initial value A_0 [1]. Thus the limiting fields within a single period of the wave ($-\pi \leqslant \theta \leqslant \pi$) can be described by the following equations:

$$u_{\lim} = \frac{c_0^2}{\varepsilon \omega x}\left[-\omega\tau + \pi \operatorname{sgn}(\omega\tau)\right], \quad 2x_{SH} < x < x_a;$$
$$u_{\lim} = \frac{2b\omega}{\varepsilon c_0 \rho_0} \exp\left(-\frac{x}{x_a}\right) \sin\omega\tau, \quad x > 2x_a. \tag{9.51}$$

By means of (9.51), it is easy to show that even in such a weakly dissipative medium as water, the intensity of ultrasound at a frequency of 4 MHz at a distance of 1 m cannot exceed 0.2 W/cm^2, and at a distance of 5 m it is less than 10^{-3} W/cm^2.

The impossibility of transporting high energy densities to a substantial depth of a weakly dispersive medium limits the application of the remote force and energetic impact of such waves.

In order to overcome this limitation of nonlinear acoustic waves, a method [107] has been proposed, which allows one to reduce nonlinear losses connected with shock-front formation. The ides is as follows. A steep front is evidently formed by higher harmonics, which are formed as a result of a cascade of nonlinear processes with the indispensable participation of the second harmonic. If the frequency 2ω is absent in the spectrum of a signal, the channel of energy outflow up the spectrum ($\omega \to 2\omega \to 3\omega \to \ldots$) is blocked. In order to remove the harmonic with the frequency 2ω from the coherent part of the wave field, it is possible to introduce selectively absorbing or scattering elements (monodisperse gas bubbles, narrowband filters, etc.) into the medium. It is, however, not clear *a priori* how this would influence the wave of the main frequency ω: whether it would have a weaker decay or the new channel of energy losses ($\omega \to 2\omega$ and further into heat or the scattered field) would simply replace the former flow of energy up the spectrum.

In order to calculate the wave profile in a nonlinear medium containing a selective absorber at the frequency 2ω, it is necessary to solve the integro-differential equation [107]

$$\frac{\partial V}{\partial z} - V\frac{\partial V}{\partial \theta} - \Gamma\frac{\partial^2 V}{\partial \theta^2} = -DB_2(z)\sin 2\theta, \; B_2(z) = \frac{2}{\pi}\int_0^{\pi} V(z,\theta)\sin 2\theta d\theta. \tag{9.52}$$

Here D is the coefficient of additional attenuation introduced by the selective elements, B_2 is the amplitude of the second harmonic. In writing (9.52), the dimentionless variables (9.9) have been used.

The distance dependences of the amplitudes of harmonics with the frequencies ω and 2ω [108] show that, with growing selective absorption D, the second harmonics is generated less effectively, and the decay of the amplitude of the first harmonic with growing z proceeds considerably slower than in the absence of absorption at the frequency 2ω ($D = 0$). Already at values of $D > 4$, the wave profile remains smooth within a few nonlinear lengths x_{SH}. Shock waves do not forms, nonlinear dumpling is suppressed.

This phenomenon has been investigated in the experiment [109]. A source of ultrasound at a frequency tunable near 1 MHz has been placed at one of the butt ends of an open acoustic resonator, and a mirror has been placed at the other end. It could be totally reflecting or partially transmitting a wave at the frequency 2ω (up to 40 % of amplitude). By means of the selectively transmitting mirror, losses at the second-harmonic frequency have been artificially introduced. It turns out that, in the nonlinear regime of oscillations of the resonator with losses, its Q-factor have grown more than twice. thus both calculation and experiments [107–109] revealed a surprising, at first glance, fact: introduction of dissipative elements into a medium leads to smaller losses.

Until now, only plane sawtooth waves formed as a result of distortion of signals, which have been harmonic at the input to the medium, have been discussed. In one-dimensional converging or diverging waves (spherical, cylindrical), saturation still takes place, only the rate of nonlinear processes is different [31].

A unipolar pulce propagating as a focused beam exhibits a fundamentally novel behavior. It has been mentioned above that the peak perturbation of the pulse — plane wave (the second formula in (9.40)) is not bounded. But in Sect. 9.5, it is shown that the effects of self-refraction and nonlinear damping decrease amplification on focusing and widen the focal region (see Figs. 9.13, 9.14). Precisely these effects limit the maximum pressures achievable at the focus of powerful pulsed concentrators. The limiting pressures are determined by the characteristic internal pressure of the medium $p_* = c_0^2\rho_0/2\varepsilon$ and by the convergence angle $\beta = a/x_0$ on focusing. In the case of Gaussian beams with an initial spherical front, a theoretical estimate has been obtained [14,98].

$$p_{\text{lim}} \approx 1{,}5\, p_* \beta^2. \tag{9.53}$$

For water, at the convergence angles $\beta = \pi/6$, the limiting pressures according to, (9.53) are approximately 1300 atm. This value is close to the experimental date [100] obtained during measurements of fields from commercial lithotripters. It is clear that the limiting pressures depend on the shape of the focusing surface and on the distribution of the initial field at this surface, which should influence the numerical coefficient in Eq. (9.53).

9.7 Kinetics of sawtooth waves

In many problems, it is expedient to use the similarity between an ensemble of weak shock waves (Fig. 9.16) and a gas of absolutely inelastic particles. Let us consider a single "step" with a finite front width, whose evolution in a dissipative quadratically nonlinear medium is described by the solution of the Burgers equation [1, 110]

$$u = \frac{u_{i+1}+u_i}{2} + \frac{u_{i+1}-u_i}{2}\tanh\left[\frac{\varepsilon c_0 \rho_0}{b}\frac{u_{i+1}-u_i}{2}\left(\tau + \frac{\varepsilon}{c_0^2}\frac{u_{i+1}+u_i}{2}x\right)\right]. \tag{9.54}$$

Here u_i and u_{i+1} are the values of the vibration velocity before and after the shock front. Let us link the height of the "step" $(u_{i+1}-u_i)$ with the mass m_i of the particle associated with the shock, and the change in the position in the co-moving coordinate system $(\tau = t - x/c_0)$ with the velocity v_i of this particle. In accordance with (9.54), the motion of the front proceeds according to the law

$$v_i = \frac{d\tau_i}{dx} = -\frac{\varepsilon}{2c_0^2}(u_{i+1}+u_i). \tag{9.55}$$

The velocity (9.55) grows with increasing number i. Therefore the subsequent, $(i+1)$st front catches up with the previous, ith one. They coalesce while conserving the mass and momentum:

$$m_i' = m_{i+1} + m_i, \quad m_i' v_i' = m_{i+1}v_{i+1} + m_i v_i. \tag{9.56}$$

The similarity with particles is even more direct, if, instead of the velocity perturbation (9.54), the acceleration wave is considered

$$\frac{\partial u}{\partial \tau} = D\cosh^{-2}\left[\left(\frac{\varepsilon c_0 \rho_0}{b}D\right)^{1/2}(\tau + x v_i)\right]. \tag{9.57}$$

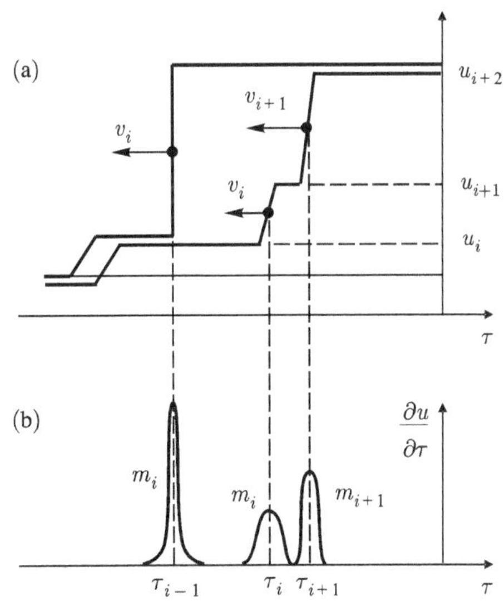

Fig. 9.16 Coalescence of two weak shock waves **(a)**, and the analogy with a nonelastic collision of particles **(b)**.

The expression (9.57) is similar to the soliton solution of the Korteweg-de Vries equation (Fig. 9.16(b)). As for a soliton, the duration of this pulsed perturbation with the growth of its "amplitude"

$$D = \frac{\varepsilon c_0 \rho_0}{4b} (u_{i+1} - u_i)^2$$

decreases as $D^{-1/2}$. The velocity v_i (9.55), however, does not depend on D; according to the solution (9.54), it is determined not by the magnitude of the jump $(u_{i+1} - u_i)$, but by the mean value of the perturbation at the front $(u_{i+1} + u_i)/2$. And, finally, the principal difference: whereas solitons collide as elastic particles (see, e.g., [46]), single pulses (9.57) do so as absolutely inelastic ones.

The sequence of several "steps", depicted in Fig. 9.16, may be realized, e.g., in experiments with shock tubes. But a more typical perturbation is represented by a sawtooth wave with irregularly spaced jumps of different magnitude. Such a wave is of interest for description of the properties of one-dimensional acoustic turbulence [111–113]. It is formed in the process of evolution of the profile of broadband noise waves travelling within a nonlinear weakly dissipative medium. As opposed to the "steps" (Fig. 9.16), the "teeth" in a sawtooth wave decrease (during time intervals between front collisions) due to nonlinear absorption of energy at discontinuities. This decrease may be interpreted as "evaporation" of the particles. Thus, a random sawtooth wave may be linked with a one-dimensional flow of evaporating particles moving relative to the flow (its velocity being c_0) with random velocities and pairwise colliding between each other according to the laws of absolutely inelastic collision.

Both types of ensembles — "steps" (Fig. 9.16) and "teeth" —- can be described by kinetic equations. Let us introduce a distribution function $G(x,t,m)$, which is the probability density of the event that the time interval between two neighboring discontinuities is equal to t, and the magnitude of the second of them is equal to m. Evolution of the distribution function G proceeds due to both free motion of the discontinuities according to (9.55) and as a result of their pairwise collisions.

The kinetic equation (of the type of the Boltzmann equation) for an ensemble of "steps" had the form of (7.91) [114]. The quadratically nonlinear right-hand side of (7.91) it responsible for pairwise inelastic collisions. A similar equation for en ensemble of "teeth" [115] takes into account the nonlinear attenuation of discontinuities ("evaporation" of particles) and also the change of slopes of slightly sloping parts of the profile. It it different from (7.91) in the presence of additional linear terms on the left-hand side of the kinetic equation describing a collisionless probability transfer.

The distribution function G, as it is seen from (7.91), happens to be normalized. When the function G is known, statistical averaging is performed in the following way:

$$\langle \Phi \rangle = \int dt \int_0^\infty \Phi(x,t,m) G(x,t,m) dm. \tag{9.58}$$

For the kinetic equation (7.91), a number of exact and approximate solutions have been obtained [114], integral of motion have been found. One of the exact solutions corresponds to a Poisson process; by introducing a new function and its Laplace transform according to Eqs. (7.92), we arrive at an equation of the Riemann wave type (7.93).

The solution of the latter, it given by an implicit function, whose form is determined by the initial (at $x = 0$) distribution function:

$$f = \Phi\left(s - \frac{\varepsilon x}{c_0^2 t_0} f\right), \quad \Phi(s) = \int_0^\infty f(x = 0, m) \exp(-sm)\, dm. \qquad (9.59)$$

In a similar way, the kinetic equation for an ensemble of "teeth" of a random sawtooth wave is solved [115].

Fig. 9.17 shows typical processes: the transformation of the exponential (a) and delta-like (b) initial mass distributions $G(x,m)$. Numbers at the curves mark the dimensionless distance $z = \varepsilon \langle m \rangle x / \left(c_0^2 t_0\right)$ travelled by the wave. As is seen from Fig. 9.17(b), collisions of the fronts in a sawtooth waves lead to formation of jumps of the double ($n = 2$), triple ($n = 3$), etc. height. They are depicted by the intervals of a corresponding length, whose vertices for n equal to 1, 2 and 3, at a given z are connected by dashed lines. Simultaneously, the magnitude of each of the jumps decreases as $(1+z)^{-1}$ due to nonlinear absorption.

Main tendencies of the transformation of the distribution functions (see Fig. 9.17) are the increase of the probability density for small and large values of $\mu = m/\langle m \rangle$ and its decrease in the middle region of the distribution. The growth of the probability of small values of μ is due to nonlinear damping of the discontinuities; the main contribution hear is from those intervals of the realization, at which the field decreases on average and collisions are rare. The increase of G at large μ is due to the coalescence of the discontinuities and to the formation of jumps of the combined

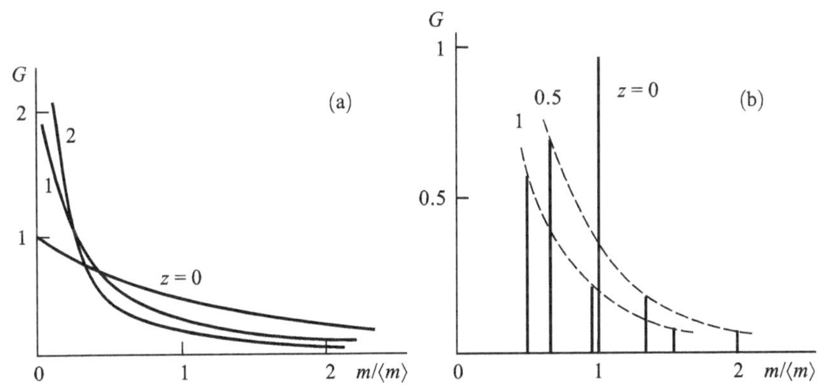

Fig. 9.17 Transformation of the probability distributions of the perturbation jumps at the discontinuities in a propagating sawtooth wave for the exponential **(a)**, and delta-like **(b)** initial mass distributions.

height. Competition of these two tendencies leads to the formation of a self-similar asymptotic, which, for Poisson processes, has the following form:

$$G \sim z^{-1/2}\mu^{-3/2}\exp\left(-\frac{\mu}{4z}\right). \tag{9.60}$$

The mean value $\langle\mu\rangle$ remains constant, and the dispersion $\langle\mu^2\rangle$ linearly grows with growing distance travelled by the wave.

Spectral characteristics of one-dimensional acoustic turbulence also may be calculated by means of the distribution function G and solutions of the type (9.54) taking into account the finiteness of the shock-front width. In particular, for the spectrum of the intensity of a Poisson process, the following equation in obtained [115]

$$\tilde{G}(\omega) = \frac{2\pi^3\Gamma^2}{1+z}\int_0^\infty \frac{G(z,\mu)\,d\mu}{\sinh^2(\pi\Gamma\omega t_0/\mu)}. \tag{9.61}$$

Here $\Gamma = \varepsilon c_0\rho_0\langle m\rangle t_0/b$. In order to illustrate the behavioral features of the spectrum, let us discuss the result obtained by averaging (9.61) with a self-similar distribution G. It turns out that in the spectrum there are two characteristic parts. For the frequencies $\omega t_0 \ll (\pi\Gamma)^{-1}$, there is the following universal dependence: $\tilde{G}(\omega) \sim \omega^{-2}$, which, as in the case of a regular wave, is due to the presence of shocks. In the region $\omega t_0 \gg (\pi\Gamma)^{-1}$, the asymptotic $\tilde{G}(\omega) \sim z^{-3/2}\omega^{-1/2}\exp(-\sqrt{\omega z})$ decays with the frequency slower than for a regular sawtooth wave (see also [116]), for which $\tilde{G}(\omega) \sim \exp(-2\Gamma\omega t_0 z)$ [1].

The behavior of the spectra of nonlinear nondispersive waves (non only sawtooth ones), which has earlier been studied without the kinetic approach described here, is discussed in detail in the literature [20, 117] on statistical nonlinear acoustics.

9.8 Interaction of waves containing shock fronts

Many studies have been devoted to the effects of wave interaction in nondispersive media, some of them are described in the monographs [1,3,6,31,50,70,117]. In different year, such interesting phenomena as the self-detection of modulated signals, scattering of sound by sound, excess attenuation of a signal due to its interaction with an external (in particular, noise) field and many others have been discovered and investigated. Special attention has been paid to the nonlinear generation of low (difference) frequencies in modulated high-frequency pumping fields. As is known, low frequencies can be radiated by that region of space, where the interaction takes place, and propagate as a directed weakly decaying beam at long distances; this property of theirs is used in parametric hydro-location systems [50].

But only few works contain information on the interaction of sawtooth waves. More and more often, computational methods are used to study these processes. So in order to solve various problems of interaction of weakly dispersive perturbations in early 1990s, researchers of the departments of computational mathematics and acoustics of Moscow State University created a universal package of applied programs NACSI (Nonlinear Acoustics — Computer Simulation) [118]. This software allows one to calculate profiles and spectra of strongly distorted waves and wave beams, whose propagation and generation are described by the evolution equations of the Burgers, Khokhlov-Zabolotskaya, Whitham types and by their modifications for media with various dispersive and dissipative properties. The problem of numerical solution of such equations consists in that in order to achieve high accuracy in both discontinuous regions (shock waves and contact discontinuities) and smooth parts of the profiles. To this end, it is necessary to eliminate the well-known defects of the classical schemes leading to spurious oscillations near the fronts (without introducing an appreciable viscosity), nonlinear instabilities and errors in calculating smooth parts generated by "numerical scattering", i.e. the influence of large field gradients. In order to eliminate the above listed difficulties, in recent years, novel shock-trapping, so-called "high-resolution" schemes are developed. Their main properties are: the order of accuracy for the smooth part is not lower than the second one; the possibility of discontinuity calculations without generating fictitious oscillations. Thereby, as opposed to the classics schemes of the second and higher orders of accuracy, they do not require the *a priori* knowledge of artificial viscosity.

By means of NACSI, the problems of interaction in plane, cylindrical and spherical (diverging and focused) waves, in diffracting and converging beams, and also in waveguides, tubes, horns and ray tubes under the geometric-acoustic approximation (see Sect. 9.4) are efficiently solved.

The initial profile may be represented by a single pulse of an arbitrary shape or by a sequence of several different pulses (if their interaction with each other is investigated). The profile may be given also as a sum of several (up to ten) harmonics with arbitrary amplitudes, frequencies, phases or approximated by a piecewise linear function. In order to obtain the results shown, e.g., in Figs. 9.4, 9.5 or 9.10, less than a minute's time is needed on a personal computer.

Numerical methods for studying interactions of sawtooth waves are currently perfected on the basis of well-known asymptotic formulas. The calculation time may be reduced for complex problems, if combined approaches are used, which mix direct integration of equations by means of difference schemes with fast calculations of available asymptotics. Another method for improving the schemes is a more complete regards for *a priori* information on the wave process. So calculation of discontinuous waves in the spectral representation requires solving a system of coupled equation for complex amplitudes of the harmonic components, whose number is equal to $10^2 - 10^3$. It is, however, *a priori* known that the high-frequency wing of the spectrum in the presence of shocks is formed by the phased harmonics, whose amplitudes decay as ω^{-1}. Therefore the calculation of the amplitudes and phases of the higher harmonics can be performed on the basis of simple algebraic relationships connecting these quantities with the calculated data for a few first (of the order of 10) components of the spectrum [119]. In this case, the calculation time may be reduced by 1–2 orders of magnitude.

Thus interactions of sawtooth waves are diverse, and the results are predominantly numerical. Therefore let us mention only some of the most fundamental or general properties of such phenomena.

First, let us consider how interaction of weak perturbations with smooth and discontinuous parts of sawtooth profiles takes place. Let the shape of a plane "saw" be given by the function V_0, and the perturbation is described by the function V_1. Then, from the homogeneous Burgers equation (see (9.52), $B = 0$), we obtain

$$\frac{\partial V}{\partial z} - \frac{\partial}{\partial \theta}(V_0 V_1) - \Gamma \frac{\partial^2 V}{\partial \theta^2} = 0. \tag{9.62}$$

For linear in time parts of the "saw" $V_0 = (\theta_0 - \theta)/(z_0 + z)$, the solution has the following form:

$$V_1 = \left[4\pi\Gamma z\left(1 + \frac{z}{z_0}\right)\right]^{-1/2} \int_{-\infty}^{\infty} \exp\left[-\frac{1 + z/z_0}{4\Gamma z}\left(\frac{\theta - \theta_0}{1 + z/z_0} - t\right)^2\right] V_0(t)\, dt. \tag{9.63}$$

Dashed lines in Fig. 9.18 show a half-period of the "saw" $V_0 = (\pi - \theta)/(1 + z)$. The peak perturbation at the shock situated at the point $\theta = 0$ decreases with growing travel distance z equal to 0, 0.3, 0.8, 1.5. The behavior of the harmonic initial perturbation $V_1(0, \theta) = m \sin 6\theta$, $m \ll 1$ is calculated according to Eq. (9.63) for the same distances z in the absence of dissipation ($\Gamma = 0$). It is seen that the amplitude and frequency of the perturbation decay as $(1 + z)^{-1}$. The inverse process of the amplification of the signal and the growth of its frequency at the steepening leading front is also possible [20, 120]. It appears during the formation of the "saw" (not shown in Fig. 9.18); the values of $z < 0$ in the solution (9.63) correspond to this process. Variation of the frequency of the signal under its interaction with linear in time parts of the "saw" have been observed in [121, 122]. These phenomena are illustrated in Fig. 7.1.

Thus the transformation of the profile of an intense sawtooth wave is the reason for the fact that a harmonic perturbation "overflows" the front on both ends (see Fig. 9.18) and vanishes at it due to nonlinear absorption (see Sect. 9.6).

In order to clarify the behavior of perturbations in the vicinity of a shock, let in (9.62) $V_0 = \tanh(\theta/2\Gamma)$ — this function describes the internal structure of a weak shock front. The solution of the equation is conveniently written for the normalized displacement S, with the velocity expressed via it as $V_1 = \partial S/\partial\theta$:

$$S_1 = \frac{\exp(-z/4\Gamma)}{(4\pi\Gamma z)^{1/2}\cosh(\theta/2\Gamma)} \int_{-\infty}^{\infty} \exp\left[-\frac{(\theta - t)^2}{4\Gamma z}\right] \cosh\left(\frac{t}{2\Gamma}\right) S_0(t)\, dt. \tag{9.64}$$

By using the result (9.64), it is easy to see how, with growing distance z, the initial perturbation (see Fig. 9.18) is concentrated near the front and absorbed at it.

The evolution picture of the interaction of perturbations with sawtooth profiles illustrated by Fig. 9.18 and the solution (9.64), is violated with growing wave intensity. The effect of self-reflection is observed [1], i.e. after the appearance of shocks,

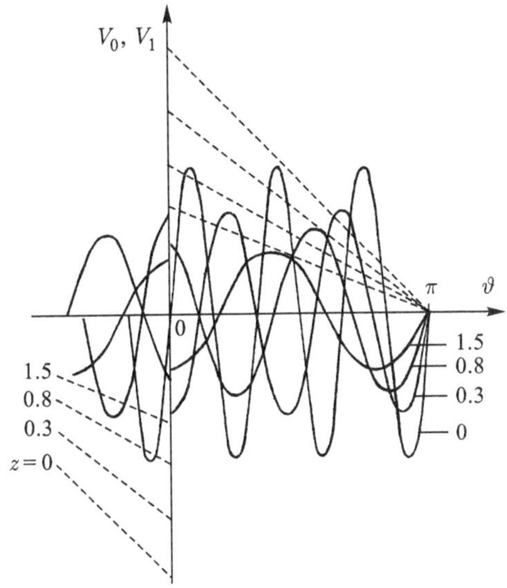

Fig. 9.18 Evolution of a harmonic perturbation of the linear parts of the profile of a sawtooth wave.

the wave ceases to propagate in a single direction. Due to a small jump in entropy at the shock [62], it plays the role of a weak inhomogeneity of the profile, and the "overflowing" of the perturbations onto the front leads to the appearance of reflected waves travelling in the opposite direction. In a periodic "saw", each of the shocks is a generator of reflected signals. Therefore the total effect of their superposition may be significant, leading, in particular, to the formation of acoustic wind [1].

Experimental observation of self-reflection [123, 124] have been performed in the radio range on a model of a nonlinear nondispersive medium, *viz.* a long line of the type of a low-frequency filter. A short pulse is emitted, in which, at a distance x_{SH}, shock waves are formed. From this moment on, the backward wave starts to be excited, which is registered at the input of the line with the time delay $2x_{SH}/c$ (c is the speed of signal propagation). Later, newer works have appeared [125, 126], which are devoted to the self-reflection of discontinuous waves.

Let us now turn to the interaction of waves intersecting at an angle with respect to each other. As is known [1], outside the intersection region of two beams of intense waves containing harmonics with the frequencies ω_1 and ω_2, there can be registered only a weak signal of the combination frequency $\omega_1 \pm \omega_2$. This is connected with the impossibility to organize a synchronous interaction of non-collinear waves in nondispersive media or, in other words, with the absence of the effect of the resonant scattering of sound by sound [127].

Solving this problem by the method of successive approximations shows that nonlinearity generates perturbations of two types, whose behavior in space is substantially different. Along the propagation direction of each of the beams, harmonics are generated, whose amplitude grows with increasing travel distance. On the contrary, harmonics observed in other directions oscillate in space, while remaining weak in comparison with the initial waves. By averaging the equations over rapid oscillations, it is possible to show [128] that for intense signals, which are periodic in time, the superposition principle approximately holds: nonlinear waves undergo self-action and their shape may be strongly distorted, but intersection of such waves does not lead to appearance of intense scattered signals (see Chapter 11).

Asynchronous perturbations are small in comparison with the amplitudes of resonantly excited waves at the intersection angles $\beta > (\varepsilon M)^{1/2}$, where ε is the nonlinearity of the medium, M is the acoustic Mach number. Under typical conditions, when, e.g., ultrasonic waves of intensities of $1\text{–}10^2\ \mathrm{W/cm^2}$ interact in water, the amplitudes of non-resonant perturbations are negligible at the intersection angles $\beta > 4^\circ$.

The idea of superposition of two strongly distorted counter-directional waves has been used in [128] for the construction of the field inside a resonator with rigid walls. It is shown that in the resonator, discontinuous oscillations appear after the counter-directional waves have acquired the sawtooth shape. The Q-factor in this case is strongly decreased due to nonlinear absorption. The field is no longer a standing wave; a front of the velocity perturbation appears, which moves between the walls. For higher modes, there may be several such fronts ("travelling nodes"). Ref. [128] also analyzes forced oscillations excited by a distributed force. They are represented as a sum of counter-directional sawtooth waves, which are described by the inhomogeneous Burgers equation (9.45). Oscillations of nonlinear resonators are described in detail in Chapter 11.

Let us now pass from resonators over to waveguide systems. It is well known [46] that normal (eigen) waves in a layer can be represented as a part of the interference pattern formed by two harmonic waves of equal frequencies propagating at the angles $\pm\beta$ to the x-axis (Fig. 9.19). In this case, in the node planes (e.g., $y = \pm a$) for the vertical component of the velocity, it is possible to place two rigid walls without distorting the pattern of motion. The width of such a waveguide $2a$ is connected with the wavelength by the relation $2a \sin\beta = n\lambda/2$. For intense perturbations, a similar representation of waveguide modes as a sum of two plane, nonlinear, periodic-in-time waves propagating at the angles $\pm\beta$ to the waveguide axis is possible [129].

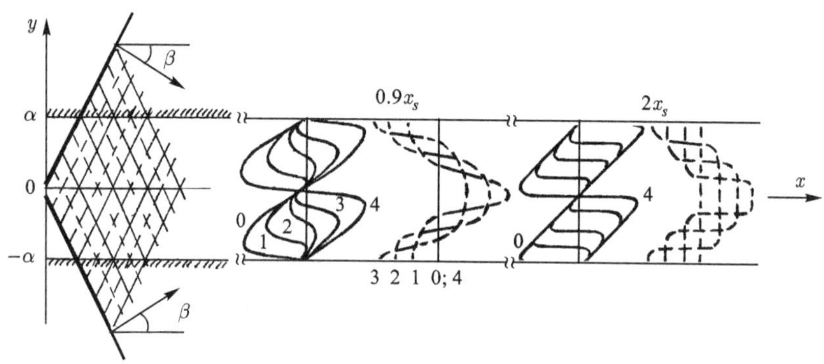

Fig. 9.19 Formation of a mode by the superposition of nonlinear waves propagating at equal angles with respect to the waveguide axis.

Fig. 9.19 shows the distributions of the longitudinal u_x (solid curves) and transverse u_y (dashed curves) components of the velocity in different cross-sections of the waveguide corresponding to the distances before ($x = 0,9x_{SH}$) and after ($x = 2x_{SH}$) the formation of the "saw". The curves are drawn for the second mode ($n = 2$); the numbers 0–4 correspond to equal time intervals $\Delta t = T/8$ within a half of the period T. It is seen that at the waveguide axis and at the walls, large gradients of the velocity u_x arise; the distribution at the cross-section has a sawtooth shape with two additional "travelling nodes". The pattern of stream lines, which undergo sharp bends [129], qualitatively changes; zones, where strong nonlinear losses take places, are formed.

Studies of intense acoustic and shock waves propagating in waveguides, tubes, jet flows, etc. are of practical interest [130]. The presence of boundaries reflecting the perturbations allows one to eliminate diffractive losses, which facilitate development of nonlinear effects; therefore tubes filled with gas or liquid are frequently used in experiments at large levels of sound pressure [131, 132]. The mode structure of the field in many experiments is of no importance, since waves, which are long in comparison with the cross-section, are used.

The propagation process of a high-frequency intense perturbation in a round tube with rigid wall has been investigated. A system of equations for the longitudinal and transverse components of the oscillatory velocity obtained under the same approximations as the KZ equation (9.10) has been solved [133]. The axes of the tube and beam coincide. It turns out that, contrary to the case of an unbounded medium, the intensity of the wave along the axis oscillates with a spatial period of the order of the diffractive length x_d. Such a behavior is connected with multiple reflections at the tube walls of the waves forming the beam. At lengths of 3–5x_d, as a results of diffusive "smearing" and the influence of the walls, the intensity is distributed practically uniformly across the cross-section and then the wave propagates as a plane one.

An interesting behavior is exhibited by the shape of the wave. Fig. 9.20 shows the dependencies of the longitudinal component of the velocity on time (within a single period) at three points of the cross-section of the tube; $r/a = 0$ (at the axis), 0.5 and 0.9 (at the wall). The number N (9.8) is assumed to be equal to unity. At the distance x equal to one half of the length of shock formation x_{SH}, nonlinear

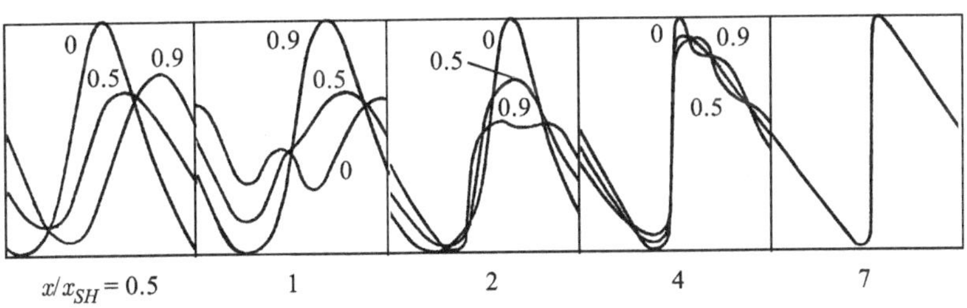

Fig. 9.20 Profile of one period of the wave at the point of the cross-section $r/a = 0$, 0.5 and 0.9, and at different cross-sections x of the tube.

effects are weakly expressed and the profiles are close to the harmonic ones. But the influence of diffraction leading to phase shifts and energy diffusion from the center of the beam to its edges is noticeable. At the distance $x = x_{SH}$, in the plane wave, a shock must have been formed. But the dephasing of the harmonics delays this process, especially far from the axis. Formation of a stable shock front $(x/x_{SH} = 7)$ takes place only after the effect of diffusion and reflection from the walls establishes a uniform across the cross-section distribution of all characteristics of the wave.

References

1. O.V. Rudenko, S.I. Soluyan, *Theoretical Foundations of Nonlinear Acoustics* (Plenum, New York, 1977)
2. V.A. Burov, V.A. Krasilnikov, Direct observation of the deformation of intense ultrasonic waves in liquids, Sov. Phys. Dokl. **3**, 173–176 (1958)
3. L.K. Zarembo, V.A. Krasil'nikov, *Introduction to Nonlinear Acoustics* (Nauka, Moscow, 1966). In Russian
4. L.K. Zarembo, V.A. Krasil'nikov, V.V. Shklovskaya-Kordi, On the absorption of ultrasonic waves of a finite amplitude in liquids, Sov. Phys. Dokl. **109**(4), 731–734 (1956)
5. K.A. Naugolnykh, in *High-Intensity Ultrasonic Fields*, ed. by L.D. Rosenberg (Plenum, New York, 1974)
6. R.T. Beyer, *Nonlinear Acoustics*, 2nd edn. (Acoustical Society of America, New York, 1997)
7. A.A. Karabutov, O.V. Rudenko, O.A. Sapozhnikov, Theory of thermal self-focusing with allowance for the generation of shock waves and acoustic streaming, Sov. Phys. Acoust. **34**, 371–374 (1988)
8. A.A. Karabutov, O.V. Rudenko, O.A. Sapozhnikov, Thermal self-focusing of weak sock waves, Sov. Phys. Acoust. **35**, 40–43 (1989)
9. O.V. Rudenko, M.M. Sagatov, O.A. Sapozhnikov, Thermal self-focusing of sawtooth waves, Sov. Phys. JETP **71**, 449–557 (1990)
10. O.V. Rudenko, O.A. Sapozhnikov, Inertialess self-focusing of nondispersive waves with a broadband spectrum, Quantum Electron. **23**, 896 (1993)
11. O.V. Rudenko, O.A. Sapozhnikov, Wave beams in cubically nonlinear nondispersive media., JETP **79**, 220–229 (1994)
12. O.V. Rudenko, O.A. Sapozhnikov, Theoretical description of thermal self-focusing of sawtooth sound waves, Moscow Univ. Phys. Bull. **43**(6), 106–107 (1989)
13. O.V. Rudenko, in *Advances in Nonlinear Acoustics*, ed. by H. Hobæk (World Scientific, Singapore, 1993), pp. 3–6
14. A.G. Musatov, O.V. Rudenko, O.A. Sapozhnikov, Accounting for nonlinear refraction and nonlinear absorption in focusing high-power pulses, Sov. Phys. Acoust. **38**, 274–279 (1992)
15. A.G. Musatov, O.A. Sapozhnikov, Nonlinear effects in process of focusing of acoustic pulses with shock front, Acoust. Phys. **39**, 266–269 (1993)
16. O.V. Rudenko, Nonlinear sawtooth-shaped waves, Phys. Usp. **38**, 965–989 (1995)
17. O.V. Rudenko, Nonlinear methods in acoustic diagnostics, Russ. J. Nondestructive Testing **29**(8), 583–588 (1993)
18. V.G. Andreev, V.Y. Veroman, G.A. Denisov, O.V. Rudenko, O.A. Sapozhnikov, Nonlinear acoustical aspects of extracorporeal lithotripsy, Sov. Phys. Acoust. **38**(4), 325–328 (1992)
19. O.V. Rudenko, O.A. Sapozhnikov, Intense acoustic beams: self-action of discontinuous waves, focusing of pulses and extracorporeal lithotripsy, Moscow Univ. Phys. Bull. **46**, 3–17 (1991)
20. O.V. Rudenko, Interactions of intense noise waves, Phys. Usp. **29**, 620–641 (1986)
21. O.V. Rudenko, A.K. Sukhorukova, A.P. Sukhorukov, Equations of high-frequency nonlinear acoustics of inhomogeneous media, Acoust. Phys. **40**, 264–268 (1994)

22. D.J. Maglieri, Overview of current knowledge and activity in sonic boom research, J. Acoust. Soc. Am. **92**, 2328–2337 (1992)
23. A.D. Pierce, in *Advances in Nonlinear Acoustics*, ed. by H. Hobæk (World Scientific, Singapore, 1993), pp. 7–20
24. S.A. Akhmanov, R.V. Khokhlov, *Problems of Nonlinear Optics* (VINITI, Moscow, 1964). In Russian
25. S.A. Akhmanov, B.A. Vysloukh, A.S. Chirkin, *Optics of Femtosecond Laser Pulses* (AIP, New York, 1992)
26. F.V. Bunkin, Y.A. Kravtsov, G.A. Lyakhov, Acoustic analogues of nonlinear-optics phenomena, Sov. Phys. Usp **29**(7), 607–619 (1986)
27. D.T. Blackstock, Connection between the fay and fubini solutions for plane sound waves of finite amplitude, J. Acoust. Soc. Am. **39**, 1019–1026 (1966)
28. G.A. Liakhov, O.V. Rudenko, The effect of parametric amplification of weak signals in nonlinear acoustics, Sov. Acoust. Phys. **20**(5), 738–744. (1974)
29. B.K. Novikov, O.V. Rudenko, Degenerate parametric amplification of sound, Sov. Phys. Acoust. **22**(3), 258–259 (1976)
30. R. Landauer, Parametric amplification along nonlinear transmission lines, J. Appl. Phys. **31**, 479–484 (1960)
31. O.A. Vasil'eva, A.A. Karabutov, E.A. Lapshin, O.V. Rudenko., *Interaction of One-Dimensional Waves in Nondispersive Media* (MGU, Moscow, 1983). In Russian
32. S.N. Gurbatov, A.N. Malakhov, On the possibility of using parametric interaction of waves to highlight the weak acoustic signals, Sov. Phys. Acoust. **25**(1), 53–59 (1979)
33. V.G. Andreev, A.A. Karabutov, O.V. Rudenko, Experimental study of the propagation of nonlinear sound beams in free space, Sov. Phys. Acoust. **31**, 252–255 (1985)
34. D.A. Webster, M.A. Theobald, D.T. Blackstock, in *Proc. 9th Int. Congress on Acoust.*, vol. 2(32) (Madrid, 1977), vol. 2(32), p. 740
35. D.A. Webster, D.T. Blackstock, Finite-amplitude saturation of plane sound waves in air, J. Acoust. Soc. Am. **62**, 518–523 (1977)
36. O.V. Rudenko, S.I. Soluyan, R.V. Khokhlov, Bounded quasiplane beams of periodic perturbations in a nonlinear medium,, Sov. Phys. Acoust. **19**, 871–876 (1973)
37. L.A. Ostrovskii, V.E. Fridman, Directivity of high-intensity acoustic radiation, Sov. Phys. Acoust. **18**, 478–482 (1973)
38. N.S. Bakhvalov, Y.M. Zhileikin, E.A. Zabolotskaya, *Nonlinear Theory of Sound Beams* (AIP, New York, 1987)
39. R.V. Khokhlov, Theory of shock radiowaves in nonlinear lines, Sov. Phys. - Radiotech. Electron. (new title: J. of Communications Technology and Electronics) **6**(6), 917–925 (1961)
40. E.A. Zabolotskaia, R.V. Khokhlov, Quasiplanar waves in nonlinear acoustics of bounded beams, Sov. Acoust. Phys. **15**(1), 40–46 (1969)
41. O.V. Rudenko, The 40th anniversary of the khokhlov-zabolotskaya equation, Acoust. Phys. **56**(4), 457–466 (2010)
42. V.P. Kuznetsov, Equations of nonlinear acoustics, Sov. Phys. Acoust. **16**, 467–470 (1970)
43. B.B. Kadomtsev, V.I. Petviashvili, On the stability of solitary waves in weakly dispersing media, Sov. Phys. Dokl. **15**(6), 539–542 (1970)
44. O.V. Rudenko, S.I. Soluyan, R.V. Khokhlov, Problems of the theory of nonlinear acoustics, Sov. Phys. Acoust. **20**(3), 356–359 (1974)
45. V.G. Andreev, O.V. Rudenko, O.A. Sapozhnikov, V.A. Khokhlova, Suppression of nonlinear damping of a sound wave in a medium which contains a resonant absorber with a finite line width, Moscow Univ. Physics Bulletin **40**(3), 3–17 (1985)
46. M.B. Vinogradova, O.V. Rudenko, A.P. Sukhorukov, *Theory of Waves*, 2nd edn. (Nauka, Moscow, 1990). In Russian
47. S.I. Aanonsen, T. Barkve, J.N. Tjotta, S. Tjotta, Distortion and harmonic generation in the near-field of a finite amplitude sound beam, J. Acoust. Soc. Am. **75**, 749–768 (1984)
48. M.F. Hamilton, J.N. Tjotta, S. Tjotta, Nonlinear effects in the far-field of a directive sound source, J. Acoust. Soc. Am. **78**, 202–216 (1985)

49. H. Hobaek. Parametric acoustic transmitting arrays — a survey of theories and experiment. Sci. Techn. Report 99 (1977)
50. B.K. Novikov, O.V. Rudenko, V.I. Timoshenko, *Nonlinear Underwater Acoustics* (AIP, New York, 1987)
51. O.V. Rudenko, S.I. Soluyan, R.V. Khokhlov, To the nonlinear theory of paraxial sound beams, Sov. Phys. Dokl. **225**(5) (1975)
52. S.A. Akhmanov, A.P. Sukhorukov, R.V. Khokhlov, Self-focusing and diffraction of light in a nonlinear medium, Sov. Phys. Usp. **10**, 609–636 (1968)
53. R. Courant, D. Hilbert, *Methods of Mathematical Physics* (Interscience, New York, 1953)
54. N.S. Bakhvalov, Y.M. Zhileikin, E.A. Zabolotskaia, R.V. Khokholov, Nonlinear propagation of a sound beam in a nondissipative medium, Sov. Acoust. Phys. **22**(4), 487–491 (1976)
55. M.F. Hamilton, V.A. Khokhlova, O.V. Rudenko, Analytical method for describing the paraxial region of finite amplitude sound beams, J. Acoust. Soc. Am. **96**, 3321–3332 (1994)
56. Y.R. Lapidus, O.V. Rudenko, New approximations and findings of theory of nonlinear acoustic beams, Sov. Phys. Acoust. **30**(6), 473–476 (1984)
57. Y.R. Lapidus, S.I. Soluyan, Evolution of nonlinear waves along the axis of a weakly diffracting and focused beams, Sov. Phys. Acoust **31**, 615–619 (1985)
58. J.H. Ginsberg, Nonlinear king integral for arbitrary axisymmetric sound beams at finite amplitude, J. Acoust. Soc. Am. **76**, 1201–1214 (1984)
59. F.Y. Coulouvrat, An analytical approximation of strong nonlinear effects in bounded sound beams, J. Acoust. Soc. Am. **90**, 1592–1600 (1991)
60. D.R. Bacon, A.C. Baker, Comparison of two theoretical models for predicting nonlinear propagation in medical ultrasonic fields, Phys. Med. Biol. **34**, 1633–1643 (1989)
61. A.C. Baker, K. Anastasiadis, V.F. Humphrey, The nonlinear pressure field of a planar circular piston: Theory and experiment, J. Acoust. Soc. Am. **84**, 1483–1487 (1988)
62. L.D. Landau, E.M. Lifshitz, *Fluid Mechanics*, 2nd edn. (Butterworth-Heinemann, Oxford, 1987)
63. C.C. Lin, E. Reissner, H.S. Tsien, On two-dimensional non steady motion of the slenderbody in a compressible fluid, J. Math. Phys. **27**, 3–15 (1948)
64. A.A. Karabutov, O.V. Rudenko, The modified Khokhlov method for investigation of nonsteady transonic flows of a compressed gas, Sov. Phys. Dokl. **24**, 835–838 (1979)
65. M.S. Cramer, A.R. Seebass, Focusing of weak shock waves at an arête, J. Fluid Mech. **88**, 209–222 (1978)
66. M.D. Spektor, Stability of weak shock waves with a finite-width front, JETP Lett. **35**, 221–223 (1982)
67. A.G. Munin, V.E. Kvitka, *Aviation Acoustics* (Mashinostroenie, Moscow, 1973). In Russian
68. A.D. Pierce, D.J. Maglieri, Effects of atmospheric irregularities on sonic boom propagation, J. Acoust. Soc. Am. **51**, 702–721 (1972)
69. V.E. Fridman. Ray theory of acoustic waves of finite amplitude. Dr. Sci. Thesis (1985). In Russian
70. K.A. Naugolnykh, L.A. Ostrovsky, *Nonlinear Wave Processes in Acoustics* (Cambridge University Press, 1998)
71. E.N. Pelinovskii, V.E. Fridman, Y.K. Engelbrecht, *Nonlinear Evolution Equations* (Valgus, Tallin, 1984). In Russian
72. G.. Whitham, *Linear and Nonlinear Waves* (Wiley Interscience, New York, 1999)
73. D.I. Blokhintsev, *Acoustics of Nonhomogeneous Moving Medium. Tech. Memo. 1399.* (National Advisory Committee for Aeronautics, Washington, 1956)
74. Y.A. Kravtsov, Y.I. Orlov, *Geometrical Optics of Inhomogeneous Media* (Springer, 1990)
75. V.E. Ostashev, *Sound Propagation in Moving Media* (Nauka, Moscow, 1992). In Russian
76. K.E. Gubkin, Propagation of discontinuities in the sound waves, J. Appl. Math. Mech. **22**(4), 561–564 (1958)
77. O.S. Ryzhov, Attenuation of shock waves in inhomogeneous media, J. Appl. Mech. Techn. Phys. **2**, 15–24 (1961)
78. Y.L. Zhilin, in *Trudy TsAGI* (1973), 1489, pp. 3–24. In Russian

79. E. Reiso, J.N. Tjotta, S. Tjotta, in *Frontiers of Nonlinear Acoustics*, ed. by M.F. Hamilton, D.T. Blackstock (Elsevier, London, 1990), pp. 177–182
80. L.K. Zarembo, I.P. Chunchuzov, Sound beam in an inhomogeneous medium with varying sound speed, Sov. Phys. Acoust. **23**, 78–79 (1977)
81. O.V. Rudenko, A.K. Sukhorukova, A.P. Sukhorukov, Two-dimensional nonlinear waves with discontinuities in stratified media, Acoust. Phys. **41**, 251–255 (1995)
82. A.G. Musatov, O.A. Sapozhnikov, Focusing of powerful acoustic pulses under different convergence angles of wave front, Acoust. Phys. **39**, 166–169 (1993)
83. K.A. Naugolnykh, S.I. Soluyan, R.V. Khokhlov, Spherical waves of finite amplitude in a viscous thermally conducting medium, Sov. Phys. Acoust. **9**, 42–48 (1963)
84. A.M. Sutin, in *Nonlinear Acoustics* (Appl. Phys. Inst., Gorky, 1980), pp. 45–67. In Russian
85. L.A. Ostrovskii, A.M. Sutin, Focusing of acoustic waves of a finite amplitude, [Sov, Phys. Dokl. **20**, 275–277 (1975)
86. Y.Y. Borisov, N.M. Gynkina, Investigation of elliptic sound concentrators, Sov. Phys. Acoust. **19**, 389–391 (1974)
87. C.W. Smith, R.T. Beyer, Ultrasonic radiation field of a focusing source at finite amplitudes, J. Acoust. Soc. Am. **46**, 806–813 (1969)
88. L. Agarval, V.R. Singh, S.P. Sud, in *Proc. 14th Int. Congress on Acoust.* (Beijing, 1992), pp. 1–10
89. D. Cathignol, J.Y. Chapelon, in *Advances in Nonlinear Acoustics*, ed. by H. Hobæk (World Scientific, Singapore, 1993), pp. 21–35
90. C.C. Church, L.A. Crum, in *Proc. 13th Int. Congress on Acoust.* (Belgrade, 1989), pp. 205–208
91. M. Delius, in *Frontiers of Nonlinear Acoustics*, ed. by M.F. Hamilton, D.T. Blackstock (Elsevier, London, 1990), pp. 31–46
92. K. Takayama, in *Proc. of 15th Int. Workshop Shock Wave Focusing* (Sendai, 1989), pp. 217–226
93. O.V. Rudenko, V.Y. Veromann, G.A. Denisov, *et al.* Optoacoustic radiator for contactless destruction of calculi in the body of a biological object. Certificate of authorship No. 1673085. In Russian
94. G.A. Askar'yan, L.D. Klebanov, The focusing and cumulation of photothermoacoustic shock pulses from a concave surface heated by a flash of laser light, Sov. J. Quantum Electron. **18**, 1359–1360 (1988)
95. S.A. Akhmanov, V.M. Gordienko, A.A. Karabutov, A.B. Reshilov, O.V. Rudenko, V.I. Shmalgauzen, in *Proc. 9th All-Union Acoustics Conference, 4 IV-6* (Acoustics Institute, Moscow, 1977), pp. 25–28. In Russian
96. A.I. Bozhkov, F.V. Bunkin, A.M. Galstyan, A.A. Kolomenskii, V.G. Mikhalevich, Laser excitation of sound in liquids, Bull. Acad Sci. USSR, Phys. Ser. **46**(8), 168–174 (1982)
97. V.E. Gusev, A.A. Karabutov, *Laser Optoacoustics* (AIP, New York, 1993)
98. A.G. Musatov, O.V. Rudenko, O.A. Sapozhnikov, in *Advances in Nonlinear Acoustics*, ed. by H. Hobæk (World Scientific, Singapore, 1993), pp. 321–326
99. A.J. Coleman, J.E. Saunders, R.C. Preston, D.R. Bacon, Pressure waveforms generated by dornier extracorporeal shock wave lithotripter, Ultrasound in Medicine and Biology **13**, 651–657 (1987)
100. A.J. Coleman, J. E.Saunders, A survey of the acoustic output of commercial extracorporeal shock wave lithotripters, Ultrasound in Medicine and Biology **15**, 213–227 (1989)
101. M. Muller, in *Proc. 13th Int. Congress on Acoust.*, vol. 1 (Belgrade, 1989), vol. 1, pp. 259–262
102. O.A. Sapozhnikov, Focusing of high-intensity acoustic pulses, Sov. Phys. Acoust. **37**, 395–404 (1991)
103. Y.M. Zhileikin, Y.I. Osipik, in *Modern Problems of Mathematical Modeling* (MGU, Moscow, 1984), pp. 363–366. In Russian
104. Y.M. Zhileikin, .V. Rudenko, Nonlinearly diffractive transformation of acoustic signals, Sov. Phys. Acoust. **27**(3), 200–203 (1981)

105. O.V. Rudenko, Feasibility of generation of high-power hypersound with the aid of laser radiation, JETP Lett. **20**, 203–206 (1974)
106. A.A. Karabutov, E.A. Lapshin, O.V. Rudenko, Interaction between light waves and sound under acoustic nonlinearity conditions, Sov. Phys. JETP **44**, 58–68 (1976)
107. O.V. Rudenko, Artificial nonlinear media with a resonant absorber, Sov. Phys. Acoust. **29**, 234–237 (1983)
108. V.G. Andreev, O.V. Rudenko, in *Proc. 10th All-Union Acoustics Conference, Sect. B* (Acoustics Institute, Moscow, 1983), p. 24. In Russian
109. V.G. Andreev, V.G. Gusev, A.A. Karabutov, O.V. Rudenko, O.A. Sapozhnikov, Enhancement of the q-factor of a nonlinear acoustic resonator by means of a selectively absorbing mirror, Sov. Phys. Acoust. **31**, 162–163 (1985)
110. O.V. Rudenko, S.N. Gurbatov, C.M. Hedberg, *Nonlinear Acoustics through Problems and Examples* (Trafford, 2010)
111. V.E. Zakharov, R.Z. Sagdeev, Spectrum of acoustic turbulence, Sov. Phys. Dokl. **15**, 439–442 (1970)
112. B.B. Kadomtsev, V.I. Petviashvili, Acoustic turbulence, Sov. Phys. Dokl. **18**, 115–117 (1973)
113. K.A. Naugolnykh, S.A. Rybak, Spectrum of sonic turbulence, Sov. Phys. JETP **41**, 39–43 (1975)
114. O.V. Rudenko, V.A. Khokhlova, Kinetic approach to the description of one-dimensional acoustic turbulence, Sov. Phys. Acoust. **34**, 289–293 (1988)
115. O.V. Rudenko, V.A. Khokhlova, Kinetics of one-dimensional sawtooth waves, Sov. Phys. Acoust. **37**, 90–93 (1991)
116. S.N. Gurbatov, A.I. Saichev, Degeneration of one-dimensional acoustic turbulence, Sov. Phys. JETP **53**, 347–350 (1981)
117. S.N. Gurbatov, A.N. Malakhov, A.I. Saichev, *Nonlinear Random Waves and Turbulence in Nondispersive Media: Waves, Rays and Particles.* (Manchester University Press, 1991)
118. E.A. Lapshin, O.A. Vasileva, *et al.* Application package NACSI (1-1.2: Plane, converging and diverging waves in dissipative and relaxing media; 2.1-2: diverging waves in dissipative and relaxing media; 2.1-4: High-intense acoustic beams in nonlinear media; etc.). Software package (1992)
119. V.A. Khokhlova, O.A. Sapozhnikov, Modification of the spectral method for describing nonlinear acoustic waves containing shocks, J. Acoust. Soc. Am. **96**, 3321–3326 (1994)
120. S.N. Gurbatov, A.I. Saichev, I. Yakushkin, Nonlinear waves and one-dimensional turbulence in nondispersive media, Sov. Phys. Usp. **26**, 857–864 (1983)
121. V.A. Burov, V.A. Krasilnikov, E.Y. Tagunov, Experimental investigation of collinear interaction of a weak ultrasonic signal with intense low-frequency perturbations in water, Moscow Univ. Phys. Bull. Ser. 3 Phys. Astron. **33**(4), 60–65 (1978)
122. M.B. Moffett, W.L. Konrad, L.F. Carlton, Experimental demonstration of the absorption of sound by sound in water, J. Acoust. Soc. Am. **63**, 1048–1051 (1978)
123. K.I. Volyak, *Nonlinear Waves in the Ocean. Selected Works* (Nauka, Moscow, 2002). In Russian
124. K.I. Volyak, A.S. Gorshkov, O.V. Rudenko, On the back-traveling wave appearance in homogeneous nonlinear media, Moscow Univ. Phys. Bull. **16**(1), 32–36 (1975)
125. S.N. Makarov, Self-reflection in nonlinear acoustics. theoretical ground and possible applications, Acustica **80**, 1–13 (1994)
126. C.L. Morfey, in *Advances in Nonlinear Acoustics*, ed. by H. Hobæk (World Scientific, Singapore, 1993), pp. 167–172
127. P.J. Westervelt, Nonscattering of sound by sound resulting from a head-on collision of two plane-wave pulses, J. Acoust. Soc. Am. **96**, 3320 (1994)
128. V.V. Kaner, O.V. Rudenko, R.V. Khokhlov, Theory of nonlinear oscillations in acoustic resonators, Sov. Phys. Acoust. **23**, 432–437 (1977)
129. V.V. Kaner, O.V. Rudenko, Propagation of waves of finite amplitude in acoustic waveguides, Mosc. Univ. Phys. Bulletin **33**, 63–70 (1978)
130. A.H. Nayfeh, J.E. Kaiser, D.P. Telionis, Acoustics of aircraft engine-duct systems, AIAA J. **13**, 130–146 (1975)

131. M.F. Hamilton, J.A. Ten Cate, Finite amplitude sound near cutoff in higher-order modes of a rectangular duct, J. Acoust. Soc. Am. **84**, 327–334 (1988)
132. D.A. Webster, D.T. Blackstock, Collinear interaction of noise with a finite-amplitude tone, J. Acoust. Soc. Am. **63**, 687–691 (1978)
133. Y.M. Zhileikin, T.M. Zhuravleva, O.V. Rudenko, Nonlinear phenomena under propagation of high-frequency sound waves in tubes, Sov. Phys. Acoust. **26**(1), 32–35 (1980)

Chapter 10
Self-action of Spatially Bounded Waves Containing Shock Fronts

10.1 Introduction

The term self-action is used in wave physics primarily to characterize nonlinear phenomena, where an intense wave, without changing its shape, acquires amplitude-dependent absorption coefficient or propagation velocity. In the first case, one speaks of nonlinear absorption (or amplification) of the wave, whereas in the second case, one speaks of nonlinear dispersion. Note that precisely this permanence or slow variation of its shape allows one to consider the wave as a single whole entity with its own propagation velocity. Discovery of self-focusing of light brought about the first appreciable interest towards self-action effects. Historical background is described in detail in Refs [1,2]. In nonlinear optics, quasi-harmonic waves are stable objects. Their stability appears due to strong dispersion, which prevents generation of waves at other frequencies, i.e. distortion of the profile of the original wave. Self-action of waves is connected with the response of a medium at the fundamental frequency; this response appears due to cubic and higher-order odd nonlinearities of the medium. Note, however, that while considering coupled waves at different frequencies, self-action may also occur in a quadratically nonlinear medium.

The theory of self-focusing of light contains a number of fundamental results important not only for the physics of strong laser radiation, but also for the general theory of nonlinear waves [3]. Ideas of the first theoretical papers in this field (see. [4–6]) had a marked impact on the formulation and development of similar studies in a number of other branches of physics, in particular, in nonlinear acoustics and the theory of nonlinear wave beams of other nature propagating in weakly dispersive media.

Note the wide dissemination in the literature of recent years of the term "self-focusing" having a completely different meaning. It is connected with the appearance of adaptive sources of sound and ultrasound using time-inversion of a signal for its focusing into an inhomogeneous medium. This new usage of the already "taken" term may lead to misunderstanding.

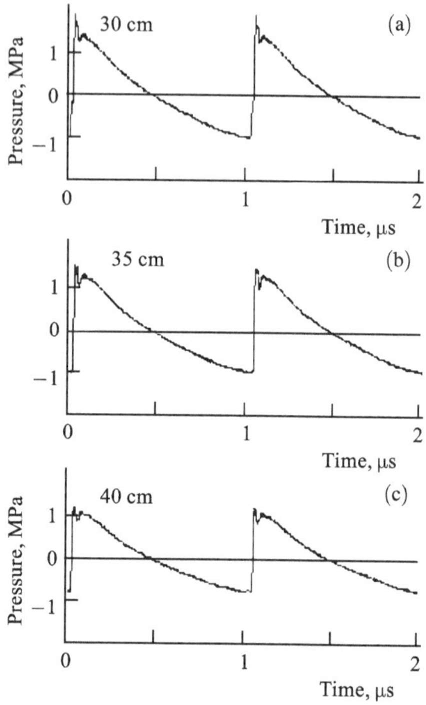

Fig. 10.1 Profile of an intense ultrasonic wave generated by a piezoelectric source with a frequency of 1 MHz, which is measured at the input of the near-field zone at various distances.

Harmonic waves are not the only example of stable patterns propagating in a nonlinear medium. Moreover, at an absent or small dispersion, initially harmonic finite-amplitude waves lose their stability, their profile gets distorted in the course of propagation, and their spectrum rather rapidly broadens due to the generation of higher harmonics of the original frequency. In media with certain types of nonlinearity and dispersion, e.g., solitons can become stable signals. If dispersion is weak, a new possibility for formation of stable broadband signals emerges. Dispersion is considered to be "weak" if the characteristic scale of dephasing of interacting waves with different frequencies (the coherence length) is much larger than the length of nonlinear interaction. Otherwise, one speaks of "strong dispersion".

It is well known that in the course of propagation of intense waves in a weakly dispersive medium, they get distorted, and their distortion accumulates with the distance travelled. It leads to disappearance of fine details and to formation of profiles of a universal shape [7]. So a single, isolated excitation, which is localized in time, as a result of joint action of a quadratic nonlinearity, absorption and diffraction, takes on the shape of an N-wave. Such waves are formed, e.g., during explosions [8], a sonic boom from supersonic airplanes also has such a form [9]. A periodic plane wave assumes the shape of a "saw" representing a sequence of rectilinear parts of the same slope connected by shock fronts. Figure 10.1 shows an example of an experimentally measured profile of such a sawtooth wave registered at the input of the near-field zone of a round piezoelectric source of ultrasound. The initial har-

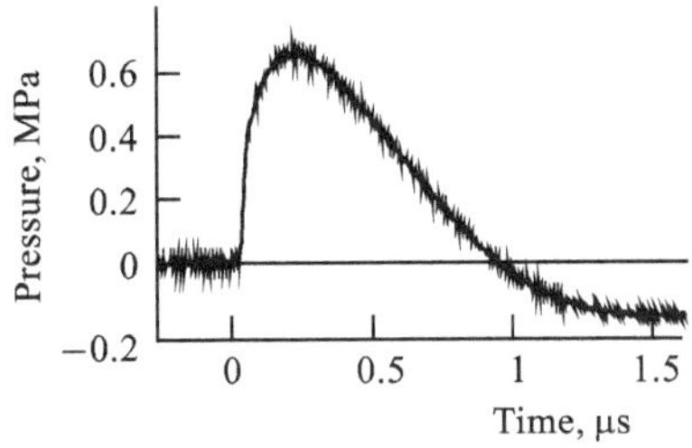

Fig. 10.2 Acoustic pulse with a shock front propagating in a relaxing liquid.

monic ultrasonic wave had been strongly distorted in the course of propagation until it became sawtooth-shaped. Measurements at consecutive distances show that the profile is practically distance-independent, only the amplitude of the wave changes. For the first time, sawtooth acoustic waves in a liquid had already been observed in the 1950s, and they were explained by the effect of a quadratic nonlinearity of the medium [10]. In media with more complex properties, asymptotically universal profile of other types may form. For instance, in a medium with relaxation, the shape of a wave behind a shock front is no longer rectilinear and it is determined by the parameters of the relaxation process. Fig. 10.2 shows the profile of an intense acoustic pulse travelled through a layer of a relaxing liquid (vinegar acid). Contrary to the wave profile in Fig. 10.1, here the shock part is followed by a gradually rising slope, with this structure of the front being determined by the parameters of the relaxation process. Due to the competition of nonlinear and dissipative processes, the profiles of these waves turn out to be quasi-stable. In the course of propagation of such structures, their shape is conserved. Only parameters vary, such as: the peak values of the excitations, and for pulses, also their duration (length).

As it has already been mentioned, a quasi-harmonic wave in a dispersive medium has a similar property of stability. This is precisely why, in order to describe its self-action, it is possible to transform from the field equations, containing the spatial derivatives and time, to simpler models of the type of the nonlinear Schrödinger equation for the parameter (complex amplitude), which depends only on spatial coordinates. Sometimes in this why (by eliminating time) it is possible to simplify also nonlinear equations describing behavior of wave-profile beams containing shock fronts.

This chapter is devoted to a survey of the problems of spatial self-action of waves with broad frequency spectra, whose time profiles contain discontinuities or steep shock fronts of a finite width, which is small compared with the period of the wave or with a characteristic length of a pulse signal.

10.2 Self-action of sawtooth ultrasonic wave beams due to the heating of a medium and acoustic wind formation

A possibility of thermal self-action of acoustic beams, similarly to laser beams, is mentioned in Ref. [11]. In media, where the sound speed c grows on heating (e.g., water at room temperature, with $\delta = (\partial c/\partial T)_p/c > 0$), defocusing takes place; while in media with a negative thermal coefficient $\delta < 0$ (most liquids), a beam self-focuses. A review of the first theoretical papers is given in the book [12]. Later, this effect had been observed [13, 14]. A bibliography of subsequent publications can be found in the review [15] and book [16]. It, however, cannot be considered exhaustive, since studies of self-action of harmonic waves in acoustics continue [17]. Thermal self-action of quasi-harmonic acoustic waves attracts attention of investigators by, above all, a possibility of transferring into acoustics many interesting results obtained in nonlinear optics [18].

Thermal self-action is determined by variation of the mean temperature of a medium because of wave-energy absorption, i.e. the corresponding nonlinear mechanism is non-local (the thermal inhomogeneity size is much greater than the wavelength) and slow (a thermal lens' development takes much longer than the wave period). Another mechanism of such inertial self-action is due to formation of hydrodynamic flows ("acoustic wind") in a medium under the influence of the radiation pressure of an intense ultrasonic wave [12]. This mechanism leads to defocusing, since, because of the drift by the flow, the wave velocity grows towards the beam axis (the wind is stronger in the region, where the intensity of ultrasound is greater).

Note that these phenomena of inertial self-action are quite simple and do not have any explicitly expressed nonlinear specifics. Since both the heating of a medium and formation of acoustic flows occur during times of the order of tens of seconds or even minutes, the self-actions described above are similar to the phenomena of modulation of acoustic properties of the medium by external sources of heat and given currents, which allow one to control the beams by means of thermal and convective lenses. It appears that these processes had been repeatedly observed in the 1950s, when piezo-transducers for excitation of intense ultrasound in liquids were created [19] (V. A. Burov and L. K. Zarembo, private communications), but they had not been interpreted as nonlinear effects. The structure of flows may be complicated by gravitational thermal convection appearing because of the heating of a medium by a wave. For instance, an original configuration in the form of a "wine glass," i.e. two axially-symmetric toroidal vortices rotating in opposite direction, had been observed in glycerin under a vertical orientation of a beam [20]. The inner vortex was due to an acoustic current, while the outer one was due to thermoconvection (see. Fig. 10.3). In the region, where the vortices nearly extinguish each other and the resultant velocity of the flow is small, an increase of the sound intensity by an order of magnitude and a 2- or 3-fold narrowing of the beam have been observed.

A simplified system of equations had been derived [21] to describe thermal self-actions under conditions corresponding to the experiment [20], i.e. accounting for both acoustic and thermoconvective flows. The equations for the axially-symmetric problem have the following form:

$$\frac{\partial}{\partial \tau}\left[\frac{\partial p}{\partial x} - \frac{1}{c}\left(\frac{U_x}{c} + \delta T\right)\frac{\partial p}{\partial \tau} - \frac{\varepsilon}{c^3 \rho} p \frac{\partial p}{\partial \tau} - \frac{b}{2c^3 \rho}\frac{\partial^2 p}{\partial \tau^2}\right] = \frac{c}{2}\Delta_\perp p, \tag{10.1}$$

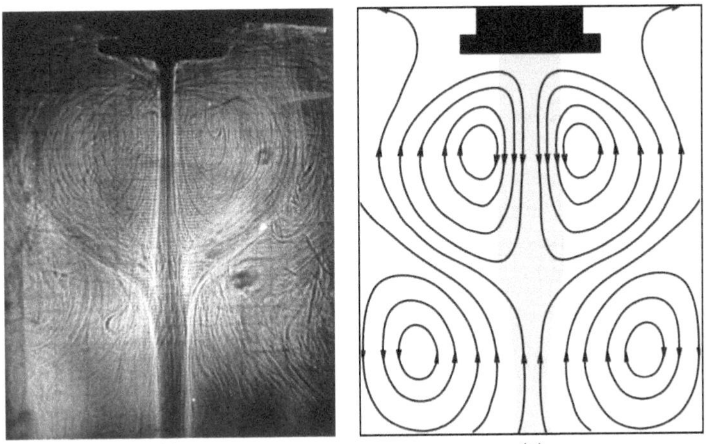

(a) (b)

Fig. 10.3 **(a)** Shadow picture of the inhomogeneities generated by a vertical ultrasonic beam with a frequency of 1 MHz in glycerine. Illumination is carried out by pulsed laser radiation The source of ultrasound is at the top. Dark areas correspond to heated regions. **(b)** Observed structure of thermodynamic flows corresponding to the shadow picture on the left-hand side. Black structure at the top is the source of radiation, the shaded area indicates the acoustic beam.

$$\frac{\partial U_x}{\partial t} + U_x \frac{\partial U_x}{\partial x} + U_r \frac{\partial U_x}{\partial r} = -\frac{1}{\rho}\frac{\partial P_0}{\partial x} + \frac{\eta}{\rho}\Delta_\perp U_x + F - \beta g T, \tag{10.2}$$

$$\frac{\partial}{\partial x}(rU_x) + \frac{\partial}{\partial r}(rU_r) = 0, \tag{10.3}$$

$$\frac{\partial T}{\partial t} + U_x \frac{\partial T}{\partial x} + U_r \frac{\partial T}{\partial r} = \frac{\kappa}{\rho c_p}\Delta_\perp T + \frac{c}{c_p}F. \tag{10.4}$$

Here x, r are cylindrical coordinates, the x-axis coincides with the beam axis, $\tau = t - x/c$ is the "retarded time" in the reference frame co-moving with the wave at the sound speed c, p is the acoustic pressure, $\mathbf{U} = (U_x, U_r)$ is the velocity of the hydrodynamic flow, T is the temperature of the medium, $\Delta_\perp$ is the Laplacian with respect to the radial coordinate, ε and b are the nonlinear and dissipative parameters, respectively, [22], η is the shear viscosity, β is the thermal coefficient of volume expansion, c_p and κ are the heat capacity and heat conductivity, respectively, of the medium and g is the acceleration of gravity. Equation (10.1) describes a beam by taking into account acoustic nonlinearity, dissipative effects and diffraction. In contrast to the well-known KZK equation [23], it also accounts for modulation of the velocity of wave propagation by variations of the temperature T and longitudinal component U_x of the velocity of the current. Absorption of the wave leads to generation of incompressible liquid flows described by Eqs. (10.2) and (10.3), and also to a change of the temperature field, whose dynamics are described by Eq. (10.4). The pressure P_0 in a quasi-Eckart current [22] depends on x, t and does not depend on r. The radiation force on the right-hand sides of (10.2) and (10.4) is given by the formula

$$F = \frac{b}{c^5\rho^3}\left\langle\left(\frac{\partial p}{\partial \tau}\right)^2\right\rangle, \tag{10.5}$$

where the angular brackets denote averaging over fast acoustic oscillations (with respect to time τ).

The system of coupled nonlinear equations (10.1)–(10.4) allows one to describe self-action of both harmonic and strongly distorted waves with a broad frequency spectrum. In those cases, when acoustic nonlinearity is unsubstantial (formally $\varepsilon = 0$), it is possible to eliminate the "fast time" in Eq. (10.1) by assigning

$$p = A(x,r)\exp(-i\omega\tau). \tag{10.6}$$

Thereby for the complex amplitude A, the following parabolic equation follows:

$$\frac{\partial A}{\partial x} + ik\left(\frac{U_x}{c} + \delta T\right)A + \frac{b\omega^2}{2c^3\rho}A = \frac{i}{2k}\Delta_\perp A. \tag{10.7}$$

The remaining Eqs. (10.2)–(10.4) are coupled with Eq. (10.7) by means of the "force" (10.5), which now has the following form:

$$F = \frac{b\omega^2}{c^5\rho^3}A^2. \tag{10.8}$$

In those cases, when it is necessary to take acoustic nonlinearity into account, the "fast time" can be eliminated only in the approximation of geometric acoustics. By assuming in Eq. (10.1)

$$p = p(x,r,\theta = \tau - \psi(x,r)/c), \tag{10.9}$$

in the short wave limit (short as compared with thermal and hydrodynamic inhomogeneities), we obtain

$$\frac{\partial p}{\partial x} - \frac{\varepsilon}{c^3\rho}p\frac{\partial p}{\partial \theta} - \frac{b}{2c^3\rho}\frac{\partial^2 p}{\partial \theta^2} + \frac{\partial p}{\partial r}\frac{\partial \psi}{\partial r} + \frac{p}{2}\Delta_\perp\psi = 0, \tag{10.10}$$

$$\frac{\partial \psi}{\partial x} + \frac{1}{2}\left(\frac{\partial \psi}{\partial r}\right)^2 + \frac{U_x}{c} + \delta T = 0. \tag{10.11}$$

The structure of the transport equation (10.10) reminds the Burgers equation used for plane nonlinear waves [22] and differs from it by the last two terms accounting for the cross-section variation of ray tubes. Equation (10.11) is the eikonal equation characterizing the bending of rays because of heterogeneity of the temperature and hydrodynamic fields.

Equation (10.10) describes formation and subsequent propagation of a sawtooth wave with a finite width of a shock front, each period of which is given by the following formula [22]

$$p(x,r,\theta) = A(x,r)\left[-\frac{\omega\theta}{\pi} + \tanh\left(\frac{\varepsilon}{b}A(x,r)\theta\right)\right], \quad -\frac{\pi}{\omega} \leqslant \theta < \frac{\pi}{\omega}. \tag{10.12}$$

The expression (10.12) may be considered as a generalization of Eq. (10.6) for an acoustically nonlinear problem. Here the unknown function A is the "peak" pressure in the "saw" — an analogue of the amplitude of a harmonic wave in Eq. (10.6).

By substituting (10.12) into Eqs. (10.10) and (10.5), we reduce them to the following form:

$$\frac{\partial A}{\partial x} + \frac{\varepsilon\omega}{\pi c^3\rho}A^2 + \frac{\partial A}{\partial r}\frac{\partial \psi}{\partial r} + \frac{A}{2}\Delta_\perp \psi = 0, \tag{10.13}$$

$$F = \frac{2}{3\pi}\frac{\varepsilon\omega}{c^5\rho^3}A^3. \tag{10.14}$$

The term $\sim \varepsilon A^2$ in Eq. (10.13) describes nonlinear absorption, which increases with growing A. The "force" (10.14), in contrast to (10.8), is determined not by the dissipative properties of the medium b, but only by the nonlinearity ε. Therefore self-actions of sawtooth waves should also occur in ideal media having no linear dissipation. Note also that according to Eq. (10.14), $F \sim A^3$, and not $F \sim A^2$, as in Eq. (10.8) for harmonic waves. This means that the radiation force, as well as the thermal flux, in a medium subject to an acoustic beam action, substantially grow in the transition from the regime of harmonic waves to the nonlinear regime with a sawtooth wave profile [24]. Both these effect have been observed [25].

Equation (10.13) can be solved for a parabolic shape of the wave front, assuming that

$$\psi(x,r,t) = \varphi(x,t) + \frac{r^2}{2}\frac{\partial}{\partial x}\ln f(x,t). \tag{10.15}$$

The exact solution of the nonlinear equation (10.13) accounting for (10.15) is

$$A = \frac{p_0}{f}\Phi\left(\frac{r}{af}\right)\left[1 + \frac{1}{x_{SH}}\Phi\left(\frac{r}{af}\right)\int_0^x \frac{dx'}{f(x',t)}\right]^{-1}. \tag{10.16}$$

Here p_0 is the initial amplitude at the beam axis, the function Φ describes the initial transverse distribution: $A(x=0,r) = p_0\Phi(r/a_0)$ and a_0 is the initial beam radius. The characteristic nonlinear length scale

$$x_{SH} = \frac{\pi c^3\rho}{\varepsilon\omega p_0} \tag{10.17}$$

is the distance of discontinuity formation in the harmonic wave profile, which determines the scale of nonlinear absorption of the wave [22]. When the acoustic nonlinearity is weak and the length x_{SH} is large, the integral term in the brackets of the solution (10.16) can be neglected; thereby the function f simultaneously describes variation of the beam width and peak pressure at the axis. When nonlinearity is substantial, the shape of the beam changes; nonlinear attenuation is more strongly expressed near the axis, where the peak pressure is larger, therefore a convex beam flattens, getting more homogeneous at the cross section.

The eikonal equation (10.11), given (10.15), assumes the following form:

$$\frac{\partial^2 f}{\partial x^2} = f\left(\frac{U_2}{c} + \delta T_2\right), \tag{10.18}$$

where $T_2(x,t)$ and $U_2(x,t)$ are the coefficients in the expansion of the temperature and velocity, respectively, into a series in powers of the transverse coordinate

$$T = T_0 - \frac{r^2}{2}T_2 + \ldots, \quad U = U_0 - \frac{r^2}{2}U_2 + \ldots$$

If the temperature and velocity fields are known, it is possible to determine the function f from Eq. (10.18) and, in so doing, to solve the problem, i.e. to calculate the spatial distribution of the peak pressure (10.16) of a sawtooth wave at any moment of time. In what follows, we assume that self-action occurs in a stationary medium. Phenomena connected with emergence of flows in the field of sawtooth waves and with taking hydrodynamic convective nonlinearity into account, are discussed in Ref. [26].

The first experiment observing thermal self-focusing due to nonlinear absorption of an ultrasonic wave is described in Ref. [27]. A beam of sawtooth waves of a power of 20 W, width of 33 mm, at a frequency of 2 MHz is transmitted through acetone — a weakly dissipative liquid with a negative thermal coefficient of the sound speed of $\delta = -4.6 \cdot 10^{-3} K^{-1}$. As a result, the wave intensity at the axis appreciably grows. After 20–30 s, a stationary level has been established, which exceeds the initial one by a factor of 1.5.

Significantly later, a series of papers appeared, which were devoted to experiments and computer modeling of self-action effects of sawtooth waves in biological tissues (see, e.g., [28, 29]). These studies are stimulated by specific problems of ultrasonic therapy (hyperthermia) and of surgery by means of focused high-intensity beams. It turns out, in particular, that thermal self-action leads to a shift of the focal region, which should be taken into account for a targeted impact of intense ultrasound on the treated area of the tissue.

In order to describe this phenomenon, let us consider the stationary regime assuming that the time derivative in the equation of thermal conductivity (10.4) is equal to zero. Thereby from (10.4) follows

$$T_2 = \frac{\rho c}{2\kappa}F = \frac{\varepsilon \omega p_0^3}{3\pi\kappa c^4 \rho^2}\frac{1}{f^3}\left[1 + \frac{1}{x_{SH}}\int_0^x \frac{dx'}{f(x')}\right]^{-3}. \tag{10.19}$$

By eliminating the variable T_2 from (10.19) and (10.18), we obtain the following equation for f [30]:

$$\left[1 + \Pi \int_0^z \frac{dz'}{f(z')}\right]^3 f^2 \frac{d^2 f}{dz^2} = \pm \Pi^3. \tag{10.20}$$

Here Π is the dimensionless amplitude of the wave at the input of the medium

$$\Pi = \frac{x_0}{x_{SH}} = \frac{\pi|\delta|c^2}{3\kappa\varepsilon\omega}p_0, \quad x_0 = \frac{\pi^2\delta c^5\rho}{3\kappa\varepsilon^2\omega^2},$$

$z = x/x_0$ is the dimensionless coordinate. The "plus" sign on the right-hand side of Eq. (10.20) corresponds to the positive values of the thermal coefficient δ, at which defocusing takes place; the "minus" sign corresponds to the properties of a focusing medium. In order to find the function $f(z)$, one needs to solve Eq. (10.20) with the boundary conditions

$$f(z=0)=1, \quad f'(z=0)=K,$$

where $K = x_0/R$ is the dimensionless curvature of the wave front at the input of the medium.

At the values of the parameters $\Pi = 1, K = -1$, the nonlinear integro-differential equation (10.20) has an exact solution $f = \exp(-z)$. In this special case, as it is seen from (10.16), $A(r=0,z) = p_0$, i.e. the initial focused beam retains a constant peak pressure at the axis as a result of self-focusing and nonlinear absorption. At other values of the parameters, Eq. (10.20) needs to be integrated numerically [30].

Figure 10.4 shows the distance dependencies of the normalized beam radius $a(z)/a_0$, where a_0 is the initial value of the beam radius. The beam radius $a(z)$ is defined as the transverse distance at which the peak pressure is $1/e$ times its value at the beam axis. The solid lines correspond to a defocusing medium ($\Pi = 10$), and the dashed straight lines correspond to a medium without self-action. Thermal defocusing leads to observed [28, 29] phenomena, *viz.* formation of a finite-sized beam waist and its separation from the linear focal point. For instance, the lower curve in Fig. 10.4 ($K = -100$) may correspond to the following values of the parameters: a frequency of 4 MHz, initial beam radius of 3 cm, radius of curvature of the front of 9.4 cm and peak pressure of 1.3 atm. In such an experiment (water, soft biological tissue) the beam waist would move relative the focus approximately by 1.4 cm, and it radius would be 3.6 mm, which is an order of magnitude smaller than the diffractive beam waist.

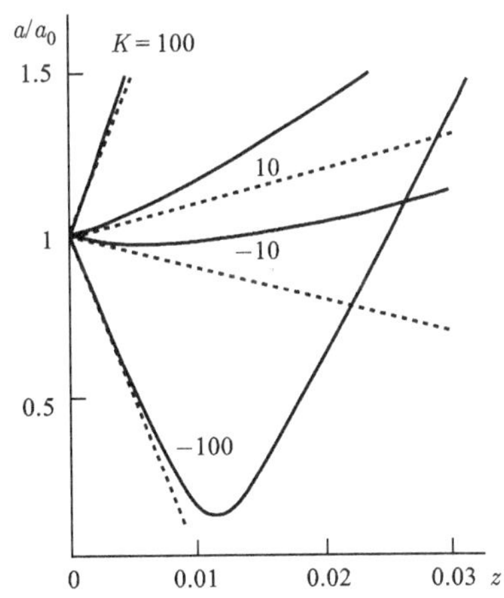

Fig. 10.4 Transverse radius of a beam of sawtooth waves as a function of the reduced coordinate z under the development of thermal defocusing. The numbers by the curves show the values of the dimensionless curvature of the wave front at the input of the medium (K). The dashed lines are plotted for the case of the absence of thermal self-action.

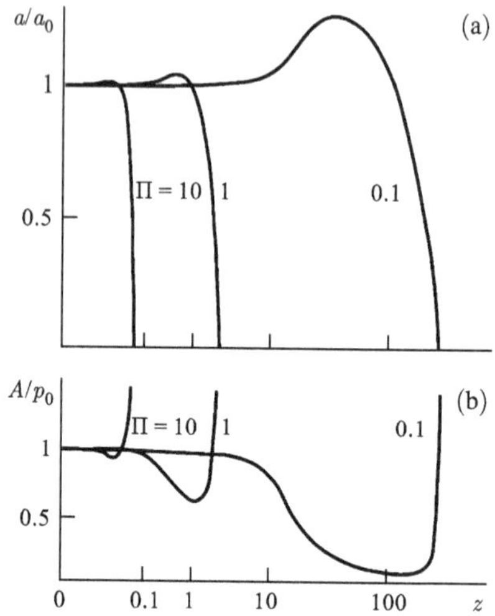

Fig. 10.5 **(a)** Transverse radius of a beam of sawtooth waves as a function of distance under self-focusing. The numbers by the curves indicate the dimensionless wave amplitude at the input of the medium (Π). **(b)** Dependence of the wave amplitude, corresponding to **(a)**, normalized by its initial value.

Figure 10.5 (a) shows similar dependencies of the beam radius $a(z)/a_0$ for the case of a self-focusing medium at different values of the dimensionless amplitude $\Pi = 0.1, 1, 10$. The initial wave front is planar. Figure 10.5 (b) shows the normalized amplitude $A(z)/p_0$ at the beam axis as a function of the distance. At a small value of $\Pi = 0.1$, in the course of wave propagation, the beam radius grows, i.e. the nonlinear broadening of the beam is clearly expressed. This effect is explained by the smoothening of the cross-sectional shape of the beam due to large absorption near the axis (isotropization of the directivity pattern [31,32]). At short distances, the amplitude decreases because of nonlinear attenuation, despite the self-focusing of the wave front. Near the nonlinear focus $z = z_f$, opposite dependences are observed: the beam width reduces to zero with unbounded growth of the amplitude. Thereby the description ceases to be correct, since it does not take diffractive divergence into account. The distance z_f, at which self-focusing takes place, rapidly decreases with growing amplitude Π.

Let us now consider the process of non-stationary self-action, when thermal conductivity is unsubstantial and the diffusive term in Eq. (10.4) may be neglected. Thus

$$\frac{\partial T}{\partial t} = \frac{c}{c_p} F = \frac{2\varepsilon\omega}{3\pi c^4 \rho^2 c_p} A^3. \qquad (10.21)$$

Let us determine T_2 from (10.21) by expanding it in powers of the transverse coordinate. By substituting the obtained expression into Eq. (10.18), we arrive at the following equation for the function $f(x,t)$ [30]:

$$f^5 \left[1 + \int_0^z \frac{dz'}{f(z',\theta)}\right]^4 \frac{\partial}{\partial \theta} \left(\frac{1}{f}\frac{\partial^2 f}{\partial z^2}\right) = \pm 1. \qquad (10.22)$$

Here we used the following new dimensionless variables:

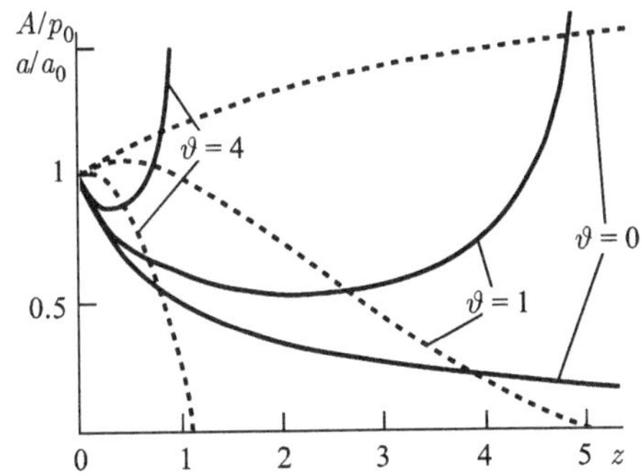

Fig. 10.6 Transverse beam radius a/a_0 (dashed lines) and wave amplitudes at the axis A/p_0 (solid lines) as functions of distance at non-stationary self-focusing. The curves correspond to the following three consecutive moments of time: $\theta = 0, 1, 4$.

$$z = \frac{x}{x_{SH}}, \quad \theta = \frac{t}{t_0}, \quad t_0 = \frac{\varepsilon\omega\rho c_p a_0^2}{4\pi|\delta| c^2 p_0}. \tag{10.23}$$

As before, (see. (10.20)), the "plus" sign on the right-hand side of Eq. (10.22) corresponds to the positive values of δ (defocusing), and the "minus" sign corresponds to self-focusing. The boundary and initial conditions for the formulation of the problem, should be chosen in the following way:

$$f(z=0) = f(\theta=0) = 1, \quad \frac{\partial f}{\partial z}(z=0) = \frac{K}{\Pi} = \frac{x_{SH}}{R}. \tag{10.24}$$

The problem (10.22), (10.24) has been solved numerically. Fig. 10.6 shows the calculated beam characteristics as functions of distance at several consecutive moments of time θ. Initially, the front was chosen to be planar, the medium was considered to be self-focusing. The dashed lines show the behavior of the transverse beam radius, the solid curves show the corresponding behavior of the wave amplitude at the axis. It is seen that at the initial moment of time, the width of the beam grows with z, and the peak pressure at the axis decreases due to nonlinear absorption. With time, the medium heats up. As a result of this, the thermal lens is amplificated. The beam focuses, and the focus moves towards the source of radiation. The velocity of this movement decreases with time. The wave amplitude, as in the stationary case, in the course of propagation, first decreases due to nonlinear absorption, and then, as it comes closer to the point of the nonlinear focus, it starts rapidly to grow.

10.3 Self-refraction of weak shock waves in a quardatically nonlinear medium

Already in the book [22], it has been shown that in a quadratically nonlinear medium without dispersion and under the conditions of low diffraction, the transverse intensity distribution, averaged over the wave period, does not change. Along with that, generation of harmonics takes place, whose spatial localization is different: the higher the number of a harmonic, the narrow the axial region, where it is concentrated. If a beam is sufficiently broad and diffraction is negligible for the wave of the fundamental frequency, it is even smaller for the higher harmonics. Hence quadratic nonlinearity cannot bend rays and lead to self-focusing. Self-action of a sawtooth wave under such conditions is reduced to amplitude-dependent absorption. As a result of this absorption, the beam is absorbed stronger in the near-axial region than at the sides, and there occurs a leveling (isotropization) of the transverse structure of the beam.

If diffraction appreciably manifests itself, a wave acquires a frequency-dependent phase shift. In a nonlinear wave, this leads to appearance of corresponding phase shifts between harmonics. As a result of superposition of the misphased harmonics, instead of a usual "saw" , a profile of a more complex shape is formed [33]: within each period, the region of compression becomes "high and sharp," and the region of rarefaction gets smoothened. A positive pressure peak may even exceed the initial magnitude. Figure 10.7 shows signals observed in experiments with powerful beams. Two periods of an initially harmonic wave at a certain distance from an ultrasonic source are shown [34]. Figure 10.7, (a) shows an oscillogram of the signal (without focusing) in the far field zone. Figure 10.7, (b) shows the profile of the focused wave in the focal region. Predictions of the theory concerning the features of the distorted profile are confirmed. Such an asymmetric wave profile is typical for powerful beams radiated by piezoelectric transducers in the MHz range, which are widely used in medical diagnostics and therapy [34, 35].

Excess of the positive peak pressure over the negative one leads to some acceleration of the shock front's motion. For example, during the focusing of a beam, a concave shock front, as it approaches the focus, gets rectified because of the supersonic propagation near the axis. Thus, defocusing occurs and the peak pressure in the focal region becomes bounded. Nonlinear absorption caused by dissipation of the wave energy at shocks also plays an important role in lowering the focal intensity, especially within the intervals before the focus, where the effects of diffraction are not very substantial (see also a discussion of self-refraction of pulses below).

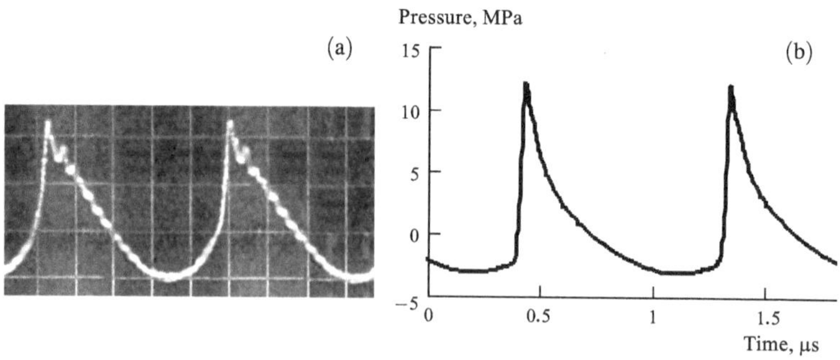

Fig. 10.7 Asymmetric distortion of an initially harmonic wave due to simultaneous action of nonlinearity and diffraction. **(a)** Wave profile in the far field zone (no focusing). **(b)** Wave profile in the focal region of a powerful focusing source of radiation. In both cases the frequency is equal to 1 MHz.

But nonlinear absorption, in itself, cannot forbid creation of caustics and build-up of infinitely large intensities during the focusing of a sawtooth wave.

Ref. [36] describes a possibility of self-localized propagation of sound beams (similarly to the optic effect [5]), for which diffractive divergence is compensated by nonlinear non-inertial refraction. Such localization, perhaps, may be realized within a certain bounded interval of wave propagation with a suitable choice of wave profiles of a special shape.

The effect of self-refraction for periodic sawtooth waves has been discussed above. This effect is much stronger expressed in the case of single pulses. Self-actions of single pulsed signals containing shock fronts [32] is of interest to a number of applications of nonlinear acoustics and mechanics. Nonlinear pulses are excited by explosive sources [8], electric discharges [37], laser radiation [38,39]. In recent years, studies of powerful pulses have been stimulated by medical applications: for shock-wave extracorporeal lithotripsy (non-contact non-invasive destruction of kidney stones) [38,40] and remote ultrasonic elastometry of shear elastic moduli of soft biological tissues [41].

When constructing lithotripters, measurements of parameters of generated by them focused pulses have been taken. A typical shape of an acoustic pulse in the focus of an electrohydraulic lithotripter is shown in Fig. 10.8. Note that the peak pressure in typical cases is about several tens of MPa, and the characteristic pulse duration is about several microseconds. While investigating acoustic fields of lithotripters, there have been discovered such nonlinear phenomena as self-refraction, saturation of the peak pressure at the focus, growth of the focal region, its shifting away from the generator and a few others [38–40]. For understanding the nature of these phenomena, and for their mathematical description, additional studies have been required.

The phenomenon of self-refraction [32] occurs due to nonlinear variation of the velocity Δc of shock-front propagation. This fact is illustrated in Fig. 10.9, where oscillograms of a signal from a broadband hydrophone are shown at several distances from an optoacoustic source radiating a short intense acoustic pulse into water. The signal has a steadily triangular shape with a shock front. With growing distance from the source, the peak pressure increases. The origin of the time scale in the consecutive oscillograms is chosen so as to take into account the delay calculated on the

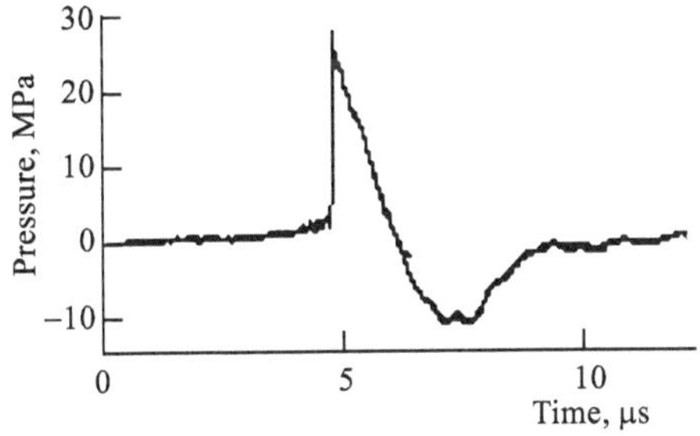

Fig. 10.8 Acoustic wave profile measured by a PVDF membrane hydrophone at the focus of an electrohydraulic lithotripter. The positive pressure peak usually precedes the more stretched negative pressure tail. In order completely to destroy a kidney stone, it usually takes about 2000 pulses sent with a repetition rate of 1–2 Hz.

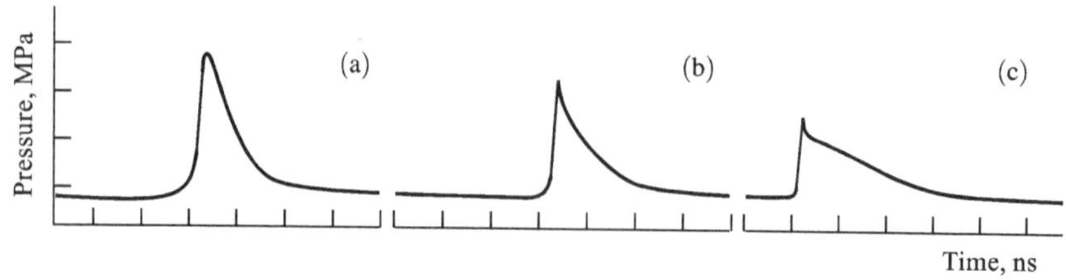

Fig. 10.9 Powerful acoustic pulse, propagating in water, at different distances from an optoacoustic source of radiation: $x = 0$ **(a)**, 4 **(b)** and 8 cm **(c)**. The vertical scale is 4 MPa/div. and the horizontal scale is 200 ns/div.

basis of the known velocity of small acoustic perturbations in the medium (sound speed). With such a choice of the initial delay, signals of a small amplitude at different distances show up in precisely the same part of the oscillogram. It is seen that, contrary to weak signals, the shock front in the oscillogram shifts to the left, i.e. it propagates faster than waves of an infinitesimal amplitude.

For pulse propagating in an unperturbed medium, the nonlinear increment to the velocity of the shock front Δc grows with the magnitude A of the pressure jump as $\Delta c = \varepsilon A/2c\rho$. Since the magnitude A is greater near the axis than at the periphery of the beam, the front of the focused wave gets straightened. Self-refraction is often accompanied by formation of breaks in the shock front (so-called "shock-shocks" [3]), thereby the structure of the shock front resembles the structure of the front at a "Mach" reflection of a shock wave from a solid surface. Simultaneously with self-refraction, the process of nonlinear attenuation takes place and the distribution of A over the front becomes more uniform. This slows down self-refraction and leads to the fact that, in the near-axis region close to the focus, the wave has an almost planar wave front. It is not difficult to see that the described processes must shift the nonlinear focus relative to the geometric focus and increase the size of the beam waist. These phenomena have been observed in experiments described in the review [7].

Nonlinear behavior of a single focused pulse is described in Ref. [42] on the basis of the standard Khokhlov-Zabolotskaya equation ($U_x = T = b = 0$ in Eq. (10.1)). By using the substitution (10.9) and transforming to the approximation of nonlinear geometric acoustics, we obtain the following pair of equations:

$$\frac{\partial p}{\partial x} - \frac{\varepsilon}{c^3\rho}\left(p - \frac{A}{2}\right)\frac{\partial p}{\partial \theta} + \frac{\partial p}{\partial r}\frac{\partial \psi}{\partial r} + \frac{p}{2}\Delta_\perp \psi = 0, \tag{10.25}$$

$$\frac{\partial \psi}{\partial x} + \frac{1}{2}\left(\frac{\partial \psi}{\partial r}\right)^2 = -\frac{\varepsilon}{2c^2\rho}A \tag{10.26}$$

in that region, where the wave contains a shock front with the peak pressure A. A similar system, in which $A = 0$, describes the pulse at the stage preceding shock-front formation.

Assuming the front is parabolic (10.15) and using the change of variables

$$P = f(x)p, \quad B = f(x)A, \quad \zeta = r/af, \quad \xi = \int_0^x \frac{dx'}{f(x')}, \tag{10.27}$$

let us reduce the transport equation to an equation of the type of the simple wave equation

$$\frac{\partial P}{\partial \xi} - \frac{\varepsilon}{c^3\rho}\left(P - \frac{B}{2}\right)\frac{\partial P}{\partial \theta} = 0, \tag{10.28}$$

which is easy to solve. The result for the peak pressure in a single pulse, having the initial time profile in the form of an isosceles triangle with a duration of $2T_0$, is

$$A(x,r) = \frac{p_0}{f}\Phi\left(\frac{r}{af}\right)\left[1 + \frac{1}{2x_{SH}}\Phi\left(\frac{r}{af}\right)\int_{x_1}^{x} \frac{dx'}{f(x',t)}\right]^{-1/2}. \tag{10.29}$$

Here $x_1 = R[1 - \exp(-x_{SH}/R)]$ is the distance, at which a shock forms in the focused wave, $x_{SH} = c^3\rho T_0/\varepsilon p_0$ is the shock-formation distance in the corresponding plane wave. By substituting the result (10.29) into the eikonal equation (10.26), we reduce it to the following form [43]:

$$f^2\frac{d^2 f}{dx^2} = \frac{1}{2x_{SH}x_d}\left[1 + \frac{1}{4x_{SH}}\int_{x_1}^{x} \frac{dx'}{f(x',t)}\right] \cdot \left[1 + \frac{1}{2x_{SH}}\int_{x_1}^{x} \frac{dx'}{f(x',t)}\right]^{-3/2}. \tag{10.30}$$

Here $x_d = a^2/2cT_0$ is the characteristic length scale of diffraction. The boundary conditions at $x = x_1$ are the following relations:

$$f = 1 - \frac{x_1}{R}, \quad \frac{df}{dx} = -\frac{1}{R}. \tag{10.31}$$

The solution of the problem (10.30), (10.31) depends on two dimensionless parameters, which can be chosen as $\Pi = R/x_s$ (the dimensionless peak pressure) and $D = R/x_d$ (dimensionless radius of the different beam waist).

In Ref. [42], Eq. (10.30) with the conditions (10.31) has been solved numerically. A typical nonlinear dependence of the pressure on distance contains four characteristic intervals (Fig. 10.10). In the beginning, the peak pressure grows because of the convergence of the wave towards the focus (the interval *ab*). Then, after shock formation, nonlinear attenuation sets in and, despite focusing, the peak pressure may even decrease (the interval *bc*). In course of approaching the focus (the interval *cf*), the pressure grows and, at some point $x > R$ reaches its maximum. Finally, in the fourth interval, behind the focus, the pulse weakens because of both geometric divergence and nonlinear absorption.

An important feature is the decrease of the maximum peak pressure $A_{\max}$ with growing p_0. At small values of Π, the maximum of the peak pressure is reached at the focus $x = R$ and is equal to a large quantity of p_0/D. At sufficiently large initial values (e.g., at $\Pi \geqslant 100$ for $D = 0.01$ — see Fig. 10.10), there is no amplification at all. It should be noted that the nonlinear decrease of the pulse amplitude also occurs in the absence of self-refraction, since the wave undergoes nonlinear absorption due

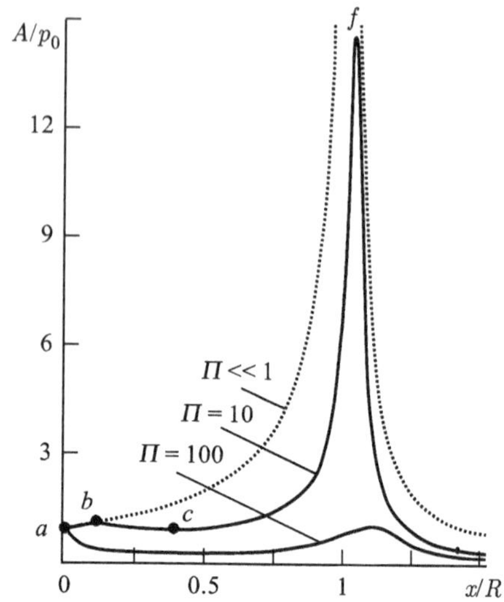

Fig. 10.10 The peak pressure of an acoustic pulse at the beam axis A, normalized by its initial value p_0, as a function of the dimensionless distance x/R at $D = 0.01$. Solid lines show the dependencies for the dimensionless amplitude of the pulse $\Pi = 10$ and 100, and the dashed line corresponds to the linear theory ($\Pi \ll 1$).

to dissipation of energy at the shock front. But this mechanism in the case of pulses (as opposed to periodic sawtooth signals) cannot limit the level of the peak pressure at a certain distance from the source. For instance, at one-dimensional propagation, the peak pressure in an acoustic pulse at a given distance grows as the square root of the initial peak pressure: $A_{\max} \sim \sqrt{p_0}$ [22]. Self-refraction (self-defocusing) additionally decreases the maximum attainable peak pressure. In order to identify the role of this effect, a detailed numerical study of the problem (10.29)–(10.31) has been performed. The magnitude of the nonlinear "amplification coefficient" $A_{\max}/p_0$ with a high accuracy happened to be inversely proportional to the product ΠD in a wide range of variation of the parameters Π and D. This fact allows one to make an important conclusion that the maximum attainable peak pressure $A_{\max}$ is independent of the initial amplitude of the wave p_0.

Thus refraction leads to a new phenomenon of "nonlinear saturation," i.e. to a bounded peak pressure in focused pulsed signals. According to calculations [42],

$$A_{\max} \sim 1.5 \cdot p_* \cdot \alpha^2, \tag{10.32}$$

where $p_* = \rho c^2/2\varepsilon$ is a characteristic internal pressure of a liquid, $\alpha = a_0/R$ is the tangent of the convergence half-angle of the initial focused beam. As it is seen from the empirical formula (10.32), the level of the maximum attainable pressure in the focus is approximately equal to the product of the characteristic internal pressure in the medium and the squared convergence half-angle of the initial beam. For water ($p_* = 320$ MPa) at a convergence of $30°$, the estimate (10.32) gives $A_{\max} = 130$ MPa, which corresponds to experimental data [40].

Thus nonlinearity strongly affects the focusing processes of pulsed signals. Apart from absorption at a shock front, self-focusing occurs, which is due to the dependence of the shock velocity on the peak pressure. Because of this, the size of the focal spot may be considerably larger that its linear value, and it grows with the initial "amplitude". The longitudinal size of the focal spot also increases, i.e. the nonlinear effects, on the whole, are smearing this focal volume. Moreover, the transverse distribution of the "amplitude" becomes more uniform; the nonlinear focus forms at longer distances than the linear one. The "amplitude" of the pulse in the focus, at larger values of p_0, is practically independent of p_0 — nonlinear saturation sets in.

10.4 Non-inertial self-action in a cubically nonlinear medium

In general, a nonlinear response of a medium occurs with some delay. An example is the thermal self-action described above, when the nonlinear response is due to the inertial process of the heating of the medium. There is also the opposite situation, when a nonlinear response is nearly instantaneous, i.e. the delay is much shorter than the wave period or the pulse duration. In nonlinear optics problems, all fundamental effects of non-inertial self-action are connected with a cubic nonlinearity of a medium, developing in the background of strong dispersion. Therefore, the interest towards the role of the cubic nonlinearity is natural also when dispersion is small. It is possible to show that propagation of nondispersive wave beams in media with the cubic nonlinearity is described by the following equation:

$$\frac{\partial}{\partial \tau}\left[\frac{\partial p}{\partial x} + \gamma p^2 \frac{\partial p}{\partial \tau} - \beta \frac{\partial^2 p}{\partial \tau^2}\right] = \frac{c}{2}\Delta_\perp p, \tag{10.33}$$

where the coefficients β and γ characterize, respectively, the dissipative and nonlinear properties of the medium, as in Eq. (10.1); the function $p(x, y, z, \tau = t - x/c)$ describes the wave profile; x is the coordinate along the propagation direction of the beam; y and z are the transverse coordinates in the cross-section of the beam [44].

For instance in acoustics, the cubic nonlinearity is the main nonlinearity type for shear waves in a defect-free solid. In this case, in Eq. (10.33), the role of p is played by the shear stress or vibrational velocity of the particles in the medium. Along with classical solids, shear waves can exist in gel-like materials, in particular in resins and soft biological tissues. In such media, the shear modulus is small compared with the bulk modulus and, as a consequence, large shear deformations are easily achievable, i.e. there are favorable conditions for appearance of a notable nonlinearity in the elastic response. Despite the fact that attenuation of shear waves in a biological tissue is usually high, nonlinear effects might be noticeable before a wave is fully absorbed. Shear waves in a biological tissue are of great interest in connection with the possibility of their use for diagnostics of tumors. In diseased tissues, the shear modulus, as a rule, is markedly increased (this has been known for a long time and is the basis of the traditional diagnostic by palpation). An effective method for excitation of shear waves in the bulk of a biological tissue is the use of the radiation force, appearing when beams of longitudinal ultrasonic waves are absorbed in the medium [41]. Efficiency of such a source of shear stress may be increased by using focused ultrasound with a sawtooth profile, whose radiation pressure on the medium is amplified due to the effect of nonlinear absorption [45]. Another method for bulk generation of shear waves with a large amplitude is connected with the use of a source moving at a "trans-sonic" speed, i.e. at the speed of shear waves excited by it. The theory of this method for excitation of nonlinear waves has been considered in Refs. [46,47]. While moving at a "supersonic" speed, efficient excitation occurs along the corresponding Mach cone. The velocity of shear waves in biological tissues in relatively small, about several meters per second. Therefore a trans-sonic or supersonic source may be created by scanning an exciting ultrasonic beam in space.

Non-inertial self-action based on the model (10.1) has been studied in Refs. [44, 48–51]. The transformation (10.6) from the field description (10.33) to the Schrödinger-type equation for the complex amplitude

$$\frac{\partial A}{\partial x}+\beta\omega^2 A=\frac{i}{2k}\Delta_\perp A+i\gamma\omega|A|^2 A \qquad (10.34)$$

($k=\omega/c$), which is common for dispersive media, is not valid here for the following reasons.

On the one hand, as it has been shown in Ref. [4], Eq. (10.34) at $\beta=0$ describes instability of the planar front of a wave in those cases, when its intensity exceeds the critical value:

$$A^2>A_{cr}^2=\frac{c}{\gamma\omega^2}\frac{a_1^2+a_2^2}{a_1^2a_2^2}. \qquad (10.35)$$

Thereby the amplitude of any spatial harmonic of the excitation $A'(x)\cos(y/a_1)$ $\cos(z/a_2)$ (here y, z are the transverse coordinates in the cross-section of the beam) grows exponentially as a function of distance. Thus, in a self-focusing medium, a plane wave under the condition (10.35) is unstable — it is broken into separate self-focusing beams, carrying the power, which is of the order of the critical value.

On the other hand, Equation (10.34) is written under the assumption that the wave profile is harmonic. But the initial plane harmonic wave, described by Eq. (10.33), gets distorted in the course of propagation because of the absence of dispersion and transforms into a signal with a sawtooth profile [44, 52]. Unlike the quadratically nonlinear media [22], the "saw teeth" in a cubic medium have a trapezoidal shape (Fig. 10.11). As a result of nonlinear absorption at shock fronts, the "amplitude" of an excitation decreases according to the law $A(x)=A_0\left(1+\alpha\gamma\omega A_0^2x\right)^{-1/2}$, where $\alpha=(3-2\ln 2)/4\pi\approx 0.1284$.

Thus the nonlinear term $\gamma p^2\partial p/\partial\tau$ in Eq. (10.33) is responsible for the following two opposite processes: the amplitude growth due to self-focusing and nonlinear attenuation because of shock-front formation. It is clear that is not possible to use Eq. (10.34) for nondispersive wave, since, in this case, nonlinear attenuation is a strong competitor of nonlinear dispersion. The importance of nonlinear attenuation can be illustrated by considering the behavior of a plane sawtooth wave. In this case, nonlinear dispersion is manifested in the amplitude-dependent growth of the propagation velocity of the sawtooth wave. It is possible to show that, in the course of propagation, the corresponding time shift of the wave profile $\Delta\tau$ grows logarithmi-

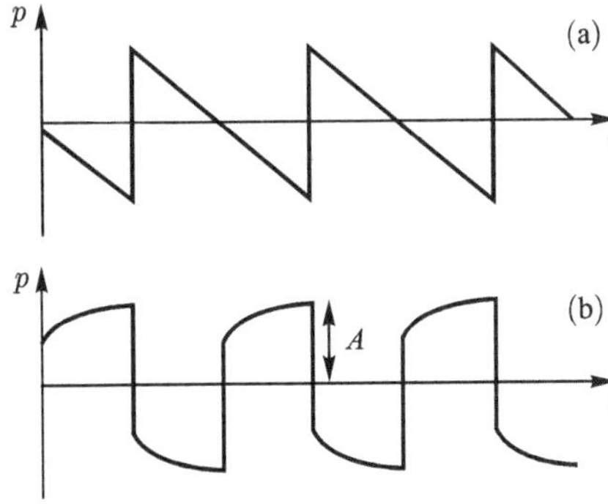

Fig. 10.11 Profile of a sawtooth wave in a medium with the cubic nonlinearity **(b)** differs from the shape of the wave in the case of the quadratic nonlinearity **(a)**.

cally with distance: $\omega \cdot \Delta\tau = (4\alpha)^{-1}\ln\left(1+\alpha\gamma\omega A_0^2 x\right)$ [44]. As it is seen, at long distances, nonlinear dispersion manifests itself weaker and weaker. The reason for that is the simultaneous decrease of the wave amplitude because of nonlinear absorption. Since the law of decay of the amplitude is known (see above), the wave amplitude can be related to the nonlinear phase shift: $A(x) = A_0 \exp(-2\alpha\omega \cdot \Delta\tau)$. At the distance, where the nonlinear increment to the phase is equal to 2π (one-wave phase shift), the amplitude notably decreases $A \approx 0.2A_0$, and with the three-wave phase shift, the sawtooth excitation is already practically damped: $A \approx 0.008A_0$. And although diffraction may change the character of self-action in a wave beam, these estimates of nonlinear attenuation say that while describing self-focusing, one needs to develop adequate approaches, which take the specifics of the sawtooth-wave behavior into account — their appreciable damping, in particular.

By using (10.9) and transforming to the approximation of nonlinear geometric acoustics, instead of (10.33) we obtain the following two equations of: transport

$$\frac{\partial p}{\partial x} + \gamma(p^2 - \langle p^2 \rangle)\frac{\partial p}{\partial \theta} - \beta\frac{\partial^2 p}{\partial \theta^2} + \nabla_\perp \psi \nabla_\perp p + \frac{p}{2}\Delta_\perp \psi = 0 \qquad (10.36)$$

and eikonal

$$\frac{\partial \psi}{\partial x} + \frac{1}{2}(\nabla_\perp \psi)^2 = \gamma c \langle p^2 \rangle . \qquad (10.37)$$

Let us now multiply (10.36) by p and average it over the period. As a result, we obtain the equation for mean intensity

$$\frac{\partial I}{\partial x} + \nabla_\perp \psi \cdot \nabla_\perp I + I \cdot \Delta_\perp \psi = -2\beta \left\langle \left(\frac{\partial p}{\partial \theta}\right)^2 \right\rangle, \quad I = \langle p^2 \rangle . \qquad (10.38)$$

The right-hand side of Eq. (10.38) is connected with nonlinear energy dissipation at shock fronts. It is calculated on the basis of expressions describing the structure of the fronts. In a periodic trapezoidal "saw," the shock wave of compression has the form of a jump between the values $-A$ and $A/2$, while the wave of rarefaction drops between A and $-A/2$ [52]. The interval of compression in the nth period is described by the following implicit expression:

$$\ln\left|\frac{1+2p/A}{1-p/A}\right|+\frac{3}{1-p/A}=\frac{9\gamma}{2\beta}A^2(\theta-\theta_n). \tag{10.39}$$

A similar formula is valid for the negative half-periods of the sawtooth wave (intervals of rarefaction). By calculating the right-hand side of (10.38) on the basis of (10.39), in the limit of vanishing linear dissipation, we arrive at the following system of equations [44]:

$$\frac{\partial I}{\partial x}+\frac{\partial}{\partial r}(I\cdot V)+\frac{m}{r}I\cdot V=-\alpha\omega\gamma I^2, \tag{10.40}$$

$$\frac{\partial V}{\partial x}+V\frac{\partial V}{\partial r}=\gamma c\frac{\partial I}{\partial r}. \tag{10.41}$$

Here $m=0$ for a planar (slit) beam, $m=1$ for an axially symmetric round beam, and $V=\partial\psi/\partial r$ is the tilt angle between the corresponding acoustic ray and the beam axis. The above mentioned coefficient $\alpha\approx 0.13$ is determined by the structure of the trapezoidal "saw" profile. The system (10.40), (10.41) is similar to the equations describing the flow of a barotropic compressible liquid, which have been used before for the analysis of the aberrational self-focusing of light [1]. The principal difference is in that nonlinearity $\sim\gamma$ is present in both equations. Thereby the left-hand side of Eq. (10.40) is responsible for nonlinear absorption, and the right-hand side of (10.41) accounts for the bending of rays. In the optical problem, nonlinear absorption is absent, and the system (10.40), (10.41) at $m=0$ is exactly solvable.

In our case, the system (10.40), (10.41) also has interesting solutions For a parabolic shape of the front (10.15), the exact solution of Eq. (10.40) is the expression ($m=1$)

$$I=\frac{1}{f^2(x)}I_0\left(\frac{r}{af}\right)\left[1+\alpha\omega\gamma I_0\left(\frac{r}{af}\right)\int_0^x\frac{dx'}{f^2(x')}\right]^{-1}, \tag{10.42}$$

where the functions $I_0=I_0(r/a)=\left\langle p^2\right\rangle\big|_{x=0}$ gives the transverse distribution of the wave intensity at the input of the medium, a is the characteristic transverse size (radius) of the initial beam, $f(x)$ is the function, which describes variation of the wave amplitude and beam width. Given (10.42), Eq. (10.41) is reduced to the following nonlinear integro-differential equation for the function f:

$$f^3\frac{d^2f}{dx^2}=-\frac{1}{2x_d x_{SH}}\left[1+\frac{\alpha}{x_{SH}}\int_0^x\frac{dx'}{f^2(x')}\right]^{-2}, \tag{10.43}$$

where the characteristic distances of shock formation x_{SH} and diffraction x_d are expressed as the following combinations of constants: $x_{SH}=1/\left(\omega\gamma p_0^2\right)$, $x_d=\omega a^2/2c$; while p_0 and ω are the characteristic initial amplitude and frequency of the wave. Eq. (10.43) should be solved subject to the following boundary conditions:

$$f|_{x=0}=1,\quad \left.\frac{df}{dx}\right|_{x=0}=\frac{1}{R}. \tag{10.44}$$

Here R is the curvature radius of the wave front at the input of the medium. The Cauchy problem (10.43), (10.44) has the following exact solution [44]:

$$f(x)=\left(1+\frac{x}{R}+\delta_1\frac{x}{x_s}\right)^{\frac{\delta_2}{\delta_1+\delta_2}}\cdot\left(1+\frac{x}{R}-\delta_2\frac{x}{x_s}\right)^{\frac{\delta_1}{\delta_1+\delta_2}}, \tag{10.45}$$

where $\delta_{1,2}=\left(\sqrt{\alpha^2+2x_{SH}/x_d}\pm\alpha\right)/2$. From here it is seen that, neglecting diffraction, the beam at the distance $x_{sf}=(\delta_2/x_{SH}-1/R)^{-1}$ converges into a point. It is clear that at this stage, it is no longer possible to neglect diffraction. In order to remove the singularity at the focus, it is possible to add a diffractive correction on the right-hand side of Eq. (10.43) [44, 51]:

$$f^3\frac{d^2f}{dx^2}=-\frac{1}{2x_dx_{SH}}\left[1+\frac{\alpha}{x_{SH}}\int_0^x\frac{dx'}{f^2(x')}\right]^{-2}+\frac{1}{x_d^2}. \tag{10.46}$$

Surprisingly, but even in this case, there exists an exact analytic solution. It can be found due to the fact that Eq. (10.46) is linearized by means of the following change of variable:

$$\xi=\frac{x_{SH}}{\alpha x_d}+\frac{1}{x_d}\int_o^x\frac{dx'}{f^2(x')}. \tag{10.47}$$

Given (10.47), Eq. (10.46) assumes the following form:

$$\frac{d^2}{d\xi^2}\left(\frac{1}{f}\right)+\left(1-\frac{x_{SH}}{\alpha^2x_d}\frac{1}{\xi^2}\right)\cdot\left(\frac{1}{f}\right)=0. \tag{10.48}$$

The general solution of (10.48) is expressed through the Bessel functions:

$$f(\xi)=\frac{\xi^{-1/2}}{C_1J_\nu(\xi)+C_2Y_\nu(\xi)},\quad \nu=\frac{1}{2}\sqrt{1+\frac{2x_{SH}}{\alpha^2x_d}}. \tag{10.49}$$

The constants C_1, C_2 in the solution (10.49) are determined from the boundary conditions (10.44) at $x=0$, i.e. at $\xi=x_{SH}/\alpha x_d$: $f=1$, $df/d\xi=x_d/R$. A detailed analysis of this exact solution (determination of the minimum width of the beam, angular divergence in the far field, dependences of the beam width and wave amplitude at the axis on the distance) is carried out in Ref. [51].

Fig. 10.12 shows dependences of the beam width on the distance normalized by the value characterizing the position of the nonlinear focus in the absence of diffraction $x_{sf}=x_s/\delta_2$. At the input, the front has been planar. Curves 1–4, in ascending order, correspond to decreasing values of the wave amplitude. It is seen that at weakly expressed diffraction, the beam appreciably narrows (lines 1 and 2), while at strong diffraction, self-focusing is not observed (curves 3 and 4).

In Fig. 10.13, dashed lines 1 show the behavior of the function f determining the beam width in the absence of diffraction; the curves are plotted according to Eq. (10.45). Solid lines 2 (for f) and 3 (for the "amplitude of the saw" A) are plotted with diffractive corrections taken into account, i.e. on the basis of the solution to

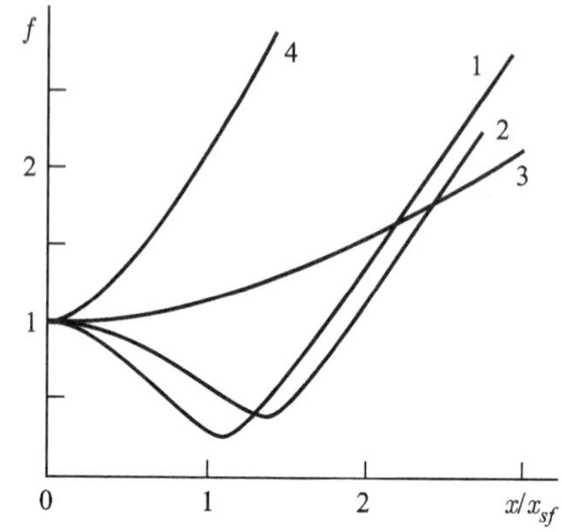

Fig. 10.12 Function f, describing the transverse radius of a beam, *vs.* the distance along the axis x/x_{sf}. Lines 1–4 are calculated at different ratios of the diffractive and nonlinear length scales $x_{SH}/x_d = 0.01; 0.1, 0.5$ and 2, respectively.

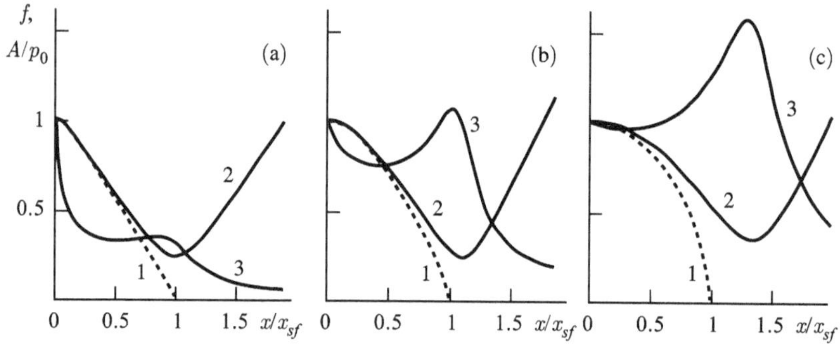

Fig. 10.13 Beam parameters during the self-focusing of a sawtooth wave in a cubically nonlinear medium as functions of distance. Panels **(a), (b), (c)** correspond to different values of the nonlinear to diffractive length-scale ratio $x_{SH}/x_d = 10^{-3}, 10^{-2}$ and 10^{-1}, respectively. Dashed lines 1 show the dimensionless transverse radius in the absence of diffraction. Curves 2 show the behavior of the transverse radius while accounting for diffraction. Curves 3 represent the behavior of the wave amplitude A normalized by its initial value p_0.

Eq. (10.46). As it is seen, at small distances, the amplitude decreases because of nonlinear energy dissipation at the fronts of the sawtooth wave. Then nonlinear focusing slows down this process and it can even slightly amplify the wave in the focal region. Beyond the focus, the beam diverges — as a result of divergence and nonlinear absorption, the wave amplitude decreases Figs. 10.13 (a–c) are plotted in the order of decreasing initial wave amplitude, for the values of the parameter x_{SH}/x_d equal to 10^{-3}, 10^{-2} and 10^{-1}, respectively.

As it follows from Fig. 10.13, in the absence of diffraction, self-focusing at the cubic nonlinearity does not lead to a substantial amplitude growth. Although the beam appreciably narrows and has a nonlinear beam waist, the amplification factor is small because of the fundamentally unavoidable absorption at the shock fronts of the "saw". The largest amplification at the focus $\sim$1.65 is reached at $x_{SH}/x_d \approx 0.06$ [44]. Thus, for sawtooth waves, appearance of strong growth of the wave intensity due to self-focusing turns out to be fundamentally impossible, i.e.

the nondispersive character of the medium "turns on" one of the striking nonlinear effects characteristic of optic beams.

10.5 Symmetries and conservation laws for an evolution equation describing beam propagation in a nonlinear medium

From the foregoing, it is seen that nonlinear evolution equations of the kind of (10.1) and (10.33), obtained for media with different nonlinearity types, describe various properties of nonlinear wave beams. It is interesting to study such general properties of this kind of equations as symmetries and conservation laws. Let us consider the following generalized nonlinear equation:

$$\frac{\partial}{\partial\tau}\left[\frac{\partial u}{\partial x}+P(u)\frac{\partial u}{\partial\tau}\right]=\frac{\partial^2 u}{\partial y^2}+\frac{\partial^2 u}{\partial z^2}, \tag{10.50}$$

where u is the function describing the wave profile, τ is the "running" time, x is the longitudinal (along the beam axis) coordinate, y and z are the transverse coordinates. In the absence of diffraction, Eq. (10.50) turns into the equation of Riemann waves $\partial u/\partial x+P\partial u/\partial\tau=0$, i.e. $P(u)$ characterizes the nonlinear correction to the linear velocity of the wave. Eq. (10.50) is a generalization of the Khokhlov-Zabolotskaya (KZ) equation for media with an arbitrary nonlinearity. It is possible to show that (10.50) is the quasi-optic approximation of the nonlinear wave equation

$$\Delta u-\frac{1}{c^2}\frac{\partial^2 u}{\partial t^2}=\frac{\partial^2 N(u)}{\partial t^2},$$

the right-hand side of which may also be either the mixed derivative with respect to space and time or the second derivative with respect to space of the nonlinear function $N(u)$. The function P entering Eq. (10.50) is proportional to the derivative of the function N with respect to the argument. This connection of the generalized KZ equation with the nonlinear wave equation means that Eq. (10.50) describes wave beams of various nature. For sound beams in liquids and gases, u is the vibration velocity of acoustic pressure, and the nonlinearity is quadratic: $P(u)=u$. In the case of the cubic nonlinearity considered above, $P(u)=u^2$.

Equation (10.50) describes two main effects determining the behavior of wave beams: nonlinearity and diffraction. It does not, however, take into account wave-energy dissipation, which plays a significant role in viscous media, and also in low-viscosity media after formation of shocks in the wave profile. Until shock formation, the description of a nonlinear beam on the basis of Eq. (10.50) is correct. In order take dissipation into account, an additional term proportional to $\partial^2u/\partial\tau^2$ should be added in the square brackets on the left-hand side of Eq. (10.50) (see Eq. (10.58) below, and also Eqs. (10.1) and (10.33)).

By virtue of nonlinearity of Eq. (10.1), its solution in the general case can be obtained only numerically. Such calculations, however, requite a large amount of computer time and are not always possible. This is why alternative approached to the analysis of the KZ equation are also important. Along with various approximate methods of simplification (precisely such an approach has been used above), finding symmteries of this equation may be of interest. Such symmetries allow one both to reveal certain general properties of its solutions and to find some classes of exact solutions and conservation laws. As an example of such an approach, we can refer to the well-known theory of similarity and dimensions using the invariance of an equation with respect to a consistent stretching of the coordinates and the function u itself. The symmetry class of differential equations is often wider that it follows from a dimensional analysis (similarity relationships). For finding these symmetries, there is a well-known technique connected with the group analysis of differential equations [53–56]. First, the symmetries of the two-dimensional KZ equation have been studied for the quadratic character of nonlinearity ($\partial/\partial y = 0$, $P(u) = u$). An approach is known, which connects in the corresponding limit the two-dimensional KZ equation with the Kadomtsev-Petviashvili equation. The results of the group analysis of the two- and three-dimensional KZ equations in the case of quadratic nonlinearity $P(u) = u$ can be found in the handbook [57–59]. In papers by Kudryavtsev and Sapozhnokov (see [25]), the groups of all point (classical) symmetries of the three-dimensional KZ equation (10.50) are calculated for an arbitrary smooth function $P(u)$.

This equation may also be represented in a somewhat different form, if, along with the function u, we use the related to it quantity

$$w = \int u\,d\tau'. \tag{10.51}$$

If u is the vibration velocity, then w has the meaning of displacement of the particles in a medium. By introducing the notation $w_\mu \equiv \partial w/\partial x_\mu$, $w_{\mu\nu} = \partial^2 w/\partial x_\mu \partial x_\nu$, let us write Eq. (10.50) as

$$w_{01} + P(w_1)\,w_{11} - w_{22} - w_{33} = 0 \tag{10.52}$$

A point symmetry of a differential equation is a set of invertible variable transformations depending on a continuous parameter λ of the following form:

$$\tilde{x}_\mu = X_\mu\,(x_0,x_1,x_2,x_3,w;\lambda), \quad \tilde{w} = W\,(x_0,x_1,x_2,x_3,w;\lambda), \tag{10.53}$$

which map a solution of the equation into a solution of the same equation, i.e. the new function $\tilde{w}$, considered as a function of the new variables $\tilde{x}_\mu$, also is a solution [56]. The parameter λ is usually chosen so that at $\lambda = 0$, the transformation would be identical. Then, in the first order with respect to λ, the so-called infinitesimal transformations are obtained

$$\tilde{x}_\mu = x_\mu + \lambda \cdot \varphi_\mu\,(x_0,x_1,x_2,x_3,w), \quad \tilde{w} = w + \lambda \cdot \psi(x_0,x_1,x_2,x_3,w), \tag{10.54}$$

where the functions φ_μ and ψ give the components of the tangent vector field of the point-symmetry group. From the known φ_μ and ψ, the corresponding finite transformations (10.53) can be reconstructed by solving the Lie equations

$$\frac{d\tilde{x}_\mu}{d\lambda} = \varphi_\mu(\tilde{x}_0,\tilde{x}_1,\tilde{x}_2,\tilde{x}_3,\tilde{w}), \quad \frac{d\tilde{w}}{d\lambda} = \psi(\tilde{x}_0,\tilde{x}_1,\tilde{x}_2,\tilde{x}_3,\tilde{w}), \tag{10.55}$$

with the initial ($\lambda = 0$) conditions $\tilde{x}_\mu = x_\mu$, $\tilde{w} = w$. For Eq. (10.50), everything is done in a similar way. For instance, the infinitesimal transformations of the point-symmetry group have the following form: $\tilde{x}_\mu = x_\mu + \lambda\cdot\vartheta_\mu(x_0,x_1,x_2,x_3,u)$, $\tilde{u} = u + \lambda\cdot\eta(x_0,x_1,x_2,x_3,u)$. The technique of group analysis [54–56] allows one to calculate components of the tangent vector field and reconstruct the finite invariant transformations (10.53). The total number of symmetries here is over 20. A number of symmetries, corresponding to the invariance of the equation with respect to translations and rotations, has turned out to be independent of the form of the nonlinear term. Symmetries specific for particular types of nonlinearity have also been discovered. For instance, in the case of the cubic nonlinearity, there is the following symmetry of Eqs. (10.50) and (10.52):

$$\tilde{u} = u\cdot(1+\lambda x_0), \quad \tilde{w} = w\cdot(1+\lambda x_0), \quad \tilde{x}_0 = x_0/(1+\lambda x_0), \tag{10.56}$$

$$\tilde{x}_1 = x_1 - \frac{\lambda}{4}\cdot\frac{x_2^2+x_3^2}{1+\lambda x_0}, \quad \tilde{x}_2 = x_2/(1+\lambda x_0), \quad \tilde{x}_3 = x_3/(1+\lambda x_0).$$

As it is seen from the structure of this invariant transformation, this symmetry may be called a “lens” transformation, similarly to an analogous transformation found in Ref. [60] for Eq. (10.34), describing self-action of monochromatic waves in a dispersive medium. The transformation parameter λ has the meaning of the inverse focal length of the lens, i.e. it is equal to its “power”. Note that this lens transformation also exists in the linear case. It is manifested, e.g., by the well-known in the theory of beam diffraction result of the identity of the cross-sectional distribution of the wave amplitude in the focal plane of a focused source and the directivity pattern of a similar defocused source in the far field zone. An unusual fact is that this property is valid also in a cubically nonlinear medium, regardless of the shape of the wave. An analysis of the group properties of two-dimensional (slit) beams has shown that the lens transformation is invariant for the fifth-order (fifth power) nonlinearity, but not for the cubic one.

In the case of the quadratic nonlinearity, which is also important in practice, there is a symmetry that resembles the lens transformation:

$$\tilde{u} = u\cdot(1+\lambda x_0)^{8/5} - \frac{2}{5}\lambda x_1(1+\lambda x_0)^{3/5} + \frac{3}{50}\frac{\lambda^2(x_2^2+x_3^2)}{(1+\lambda x_0)^{2/5}},$$

$$\begin{aligned}\tilde{w} &= w\cdot(1+\lambda x_0)^{6/5} - \frac{1}{5}\lambda x_1^2(1+\lambda x_0)^{1/5} \\ &+ \frac{3}{50}\frac{\lambda^2 x_1(x_2^2+x_3^2)}{(1+\lambda x_0)^{4/5}} - \frac{3}{500}\frac{\lambda^3(x_2^2+x_3^2)^2}{(1+\lambda x_0)^{9/5}},\end{aligned} \tag{10.57}$$

$$\tilde{x}_0 = \frac{x_0}{1+\lambda x_0}, \quad \tilde{x}_1 = \frac{x_1}{(1+\lambda x_0)^{2/5}} - \frac{3}{10}\lambda \frac{x_2^2+x_3^2}{(1+\lambda x_0)^{7/5}},$$

$$\tilde{x}_2 = \frac{x_2}{(1+\lambda x_0)^{6/5}}, \quad \tilde{x}_3 = \frac{x_3}{(1+\lambda x_0)^{6/5}}.$$

For the quadratic and cubic nonlinearities ($P = u$ and $P = u^2$), Sapozhnikov and Kudryavtsev carried out a group analysis of the equation, which is different from Eq. (10.50) in the presence of the dissipative term:

$$\frac{\partial}{\partial \tau}\left[\frac{\partial u}{\partial x} + P(u)\frac{\partial u}{\partial \tau} + A\frac{\partial^2 u}{\partial \tau^2}\right] = \frac{\partial^2 u}{\partial y^2} + \frac{\partial^2 u}{\partial z^2}. \tag{10.58}$$

It turns out that this term forbids many symmetries, which exist in the absence of dissipation, in particular the symmetries (10.56) and (10.57). No new symmetries in comparison with Eq. (10.50) appear. The total number of symmetries for this equation is 8, thereby one symmetry is connected with the scale transformation, and all the rest have purely geometric meaning of translations and rotations.

Apart from the possibility to construct new solutions on the basis of the already-known solutions, the equation symmetries may be used for finding exact solutions and conservation laws of the generalized KZ equation. Note that Eq. (10.52) is a Lagrangian equation. Indeed, if we introduce the specific Lagrangian function

$$\Lambda = \frac{w_0 w_1}{2} - \frac{w_2^2+w_3^2}{2} + \int_0^{w_1} F(u)\,du, \tag{10.59}$$

where $F(u)$ is the twice integrated function $P(u)$ (i.e. $d^2F/du^2 = P$), then Eq. (10.52) assumes the form of the Lagrange equation:

$$\frac{\partial}{\partial x_\mu}\left(\frac{\partial \Lambda}{\partial w_\mu}\right) - \frac{\partial \Lambda}{\partial w} = 0. \tag{10.60}$$

The possibility to write an equation in the Lagrangian form, as it is known [61], means that it is equivalent to the principle of least action. Similarly to the above-described search for point symmetries of Eq. (10.52), one may be interested in such transformations of the type (10.53), which do not change the Lagrangian function (10.59). It has been shown that all point symmetries of Eq. (10.52), apart from a single scaling transformation, are variational. According to the Noether theorem, each variational symmetry is associated with a conservation law of the form $D_\mu j_\mu = 0$, where D_μ is the operator of total differentiation with respect to the coordinate x_μ, and j_μ are the components of the "current". From here it follows that for each variational symmetry, the quantity $I = \iiint j_0 dx_1 dx_2 dx_3$ is an integral of motion, i.e. $dI/dx_0 = 0$. Knowing such conserved quantities may be useful both for controlling numerical calculations and for revealing certain general properties of solutions to the generalized KZ equation. In papers by Kudryavtsev and Sapozhnikov (see [25]), a list of all corresponding integrals of motion is given. The physical meaning of some of them is quite clear. For instance, one of them is proportional to the Hamiltonian, and another is proportional to the total energy of the wave. It is not so easy to interpret the other integrals but it is possible to obtain certain simple relations from them, if moments of the acoustic field are introduced. The moments are introduced as averages, defined by means of the distribution function $u^2 = w_1^2$:

$$\langle F \rangle \equiv \iiint F w_1^2 dx_1 dx_2 dx_3 \Big/ \iiint w_1^2 dx_1 dx_2 dx_3,$$

where F is a variable, for which the moment is defined. For example, the quantity $\langle x_1 \rangle$ characterizes the center of the wave averaged over time, $\langle x_{2,3} \rangle$ are the transverse coordinates of the center of the beam's cross-section, $\langle r_\perp^2 \rangle = \langle x_2^2 + x_3^2 \rangle$ is the mean square radius of the beam's cross-section. Combined consideration of several integrals in the case of the quadratic nonlinearity leads, e.g., to the relation

$$\frac{d\langle r_\perp^2 \rangle}{dx_0} - 4\langle x_1 \rangle/3 = C_1 + C_2 x_0,$$

i.e. the mean square transverse radius of the beam $\sqrt{\langle r_\perp^2 \rangle}$ and the position of the temporal center of the acoustic field $\langle x_1 \rangle$ happen to be unambiguously related. In the case of the cubic nonlinearity, the behavior of the mean square radius of the beam is even simpler. By using together several variational integrals of motion, one of which follows from the lens transformation (10.56), it is possible to obtain the following important relation:

$$\frac{d^2}{dx_0^2}\langle r_\perp^2 \rangle = const = 8\frac{\iiint (w_2^2 + w_3^2 - w_1^4/6) dx_1 dx_2 dx_3}{\iiint w_1^2 dx_1 dx_2 dx_3}, \tag{10.61}$$

i.e. $\langle r_\perp^2 \rangle$ depends on the distance travelled by the wave according to a parabolic law. The integral in the numerator of the right-hand side of (10.61) has the meaning of a Hamiltonian. If it is negative, then at a certain finite distance, the quantity $\langle r_\perp^2 \rangle$ turns into zero, i.e. the beam collapses into a point. Thus the negativity of the right-hand side of (10.61) gives a sufficient criterion of self-focusing. This criterion very much resembles the Vlasov-Petrishchev-Talanov criterion of a wave collapse, found in 1971 in the framework of the nonlinear Schrödinger equation (10.34) (where $\beta = 0$), which has played a significant part in the description of the self-focusing of light beams [2]. Similar criteria have later been obtained for a wide class of wave models, such as the nonlinear Schrödinger equation, nonlinear Klein-Gordon equation, non-stationary Ginsburg-Landau equation, Boussinesq equation and generalized Kadomtsev-Petviashvili equation [62]. However, while calculating the Hamiltonian, in all these examples, integration is carried out only over the transverse coordinates; but in the case described here, integration is carried out also with respect to time $\tau = x_1$.

In Ref. [44], the moment $\langle r_\perp^2 \rangle$ is calculated in the case, when Gaussian beam of harmonic waves is given at the input of a medium. It turns out that self-focusing can arise in that case, if the characteristic nonlinearity length is almost an order of magnitude longer than the diffractive length. Thereby the distance to the nonlinear focus could well be equal to many nonlinear lengths. And although the criterion of self-focusing (10.61) is only a sufficient one, this estimate indicates that self-focusing is hardly possible without distortion of the wave profile and formation of shocks. Calculations described in the previous section confirm this feature of self-action in the absence of dispersion.

We emphasize once again that the possibility of formulating the relation (10.61) appeared due to the existence of the lens transformation (10.56), which, in the case of three-dimensional beams, exists only in the case on the cubic nonlinearity. For slit beams, the relation of the type (10.61) may be written in a medium with the fifth-order nonlinearity, again due to the fact that, in this case, the lens invariant transformation exists. In these two cases — for a three-dimensional beam in a cubically nonlinear medium and a two-dimensional beam in a medium with the fifth-order nonlinearity — it is possible to conclude that stable soliton-like (self-canalized, or self-trapped) solutions cannot exist. Indeed, under self-canalization, the quantity $\left\langle r_{\perp}^{2}\right\rangle$ must be conserved, i.e. the right-hand side of the relation (10.61) must be equal to zero. But fluctuations of the initial field may modify the right-hand side of (10.61). The mean square radius of the beam will in this case start to vary according to (10.61) and the beam eventually either diverges or collapses. A question arises as to whether it is possible for stable soliton-like solutions to exist in the framework of Eq. (10.50) with other types of nonlinearity, similarly to the situation with wave beams under strong dispersion? A possibility of such solutions seems improbable, since the two effects — nonlinearity and diffraction — must not only provide stable self-canalization, but also prevent nonlinear distortions of the wave profile and formation of shock waves.

10.6 Conclusions

The contents of this chapter expand on, and add to the review articles [24,63]. As in those references, here we collected the fundamental results relevant either to already observed phenomena of self-action or to effects, which, in our opinion, can realistically be observed in the near future. There are, however, many interesting creative publications devoted to such self-actions of strongly distorted waves, whose feasibility of observation is not evident. These results have not been discussed in Chap. 10.

One of the fundamental effects of self-action of shock waves is the thermal self-action appearing due to increased heat production in the vicinity of shock fronts. This effect is inevitable in any nonlinear medium, even if its viscosity is very small. Such a regime of thermal self-defocusing and focusing is typical for applications of intense acoustic waves in medicine (therapy), where ultrasonic beams are used to up to an intensity of several thousand Watt per 1 cm^2. In this case, shock waves are formed at distances of the order of a centimeter.

The fact that shock waves of compression propagating in an unperturbed medium are supersonic causes another important effect of self-action, *viz.* non-inertial self-refraction of beams of shock-wave pulses. Such self-action is one of the main reasons for limitation of the maximum reachable intensities in focusing powerful pulsed signals.

The effects of self-action of shock waves in media with the cubic nonlinearity and weak dispersion are still comparatively little studied. The properties of such waves are in many respects different from the properties of well-studied nonlinear quasi-harmonic waves in strongly dispersive media. The complexity of the corresponding equations requires development of adequate analytical and numerical methods. Much remains to be done in this direction.

References

1. S.A. Akhmanov, A.P. Sukhorukov, R.V. Khokhlov, Self-focusing and diffraction of light in a nonlinear medium, Sov. Phys. Usp. **10**, 609–636 (1968)
2. S.N. Vlasov, V.I. Talanov, *Self-focusing of Waves* (Appl. Phys. Inst., Nizhny Novgorod, 1997). In Russian
3. G.B. Whitham, *Linear and Nonlinear Waves* (Wiley, New York, 1974)
4. V.I. Bespalov, V.I. Talanov, Filamentary structure of light beams in nonlinear liquids, JETP Lett. **3**, 307–312 (1966)
5. V.I. Talanov, On self-focusing of electromagnetic waves in nonlinear media, Radiophys. **7**, 254–255 (1964)
6. V.I. Talanov, On self-focusing of waves beams in nonlinear media, JETP Lett. **2**, 138–141 (1965)
7. O.V. Rudenko, Nonlinear sawtooth-shaped waves, Phys. Usp. **38**, 965–989 (1995)
8. E.V. Lavrent'ev, O.I. Kuzyan, *Explosions in the Sea* (Sudostroenie, Leningrad, 1977). In Russian
9. L.J. Runyan, E.J. Kane. Sonic boom literature survey. Fed. Av. Admin. Rep. FAA-RD-73-129-II, AD771-274 (1973)
10. L.K. Zarembo, V.A. Krasilnikov, *Introduction to Nonlinear Acoustics; Sonic and Ultrasonic High-Intensity Waves* (Nauka, Moscow, 1966). In Russian
11. G.A. Askar'yan, Self-focusing and focusing of ultra- and hypersound, JETP Lett. **4**, 78–81 (1966)
12. N.S. Bakhvalov, Y.M. Zhileikin, E.A. Zabolotskaya, *Nonlinear Theory of Sound Beams* (AIP, New York, 1987)
13. V.G. Andreev, A.A. Karabutov, O.V. Rudenko, O.A. Sapozhnikov, Observation of the self-focusing of sound, JETP Lett. **41**, 466–469 (1985)
14. V.A. Assman, F.V. Bunkin, A.V. Vernik, G.A. Lyakhov, K.F. Shipilov, Observation of thermal self-action of a sound beam in a liquid, JETP Lett. **41**, 182–184 (1985)
15. F.V. Bunkin, G.A. Lyakhov, K.F. Shipilov, Thermal self-action of acoustic wave packets in a liquid, Phys. Usp. **38**, 1099–1118 (1995)
16. K.A. Naugolnykh, L.A. Ostrovsky, *Nonlinear Wave Processes in Acoustics* (Cambridge University Press, 1998)
17. E.A. Vinogradov, K.F. Shipilov, Evaluation of the thermal nonlinear self-action of the intensive acoustic beam in air. Thermal self-focusing, Phys. Vibrations **10**, 72–77 (2002)
18. F.V. Bunkin, Y.A. Kravtsov, G.A. Lyakhov, Acoustic analogues of nonlinear-optics phenomena, Sov. Phys. Usp. **29**, 607–619 (1986)
19. A.K. Burov, Attainment of large intensities of ultrasound in a liquid, Sov. Phys. Acoust. **4**, 315–320 (1958)
20. V.Y. Armeev, A.A. Karabutov, A.A. Sapozhnikov, Peculiarities of thermal self-focusing of ultrasound in a liquid, Sov. Phys. Acoust. **33**, 109–112 (1987)

21. A.A. Karabutov, O.V. Rudenko, O.A. Sapozhnikov, System of equations for description of thermal self-focusing of sound in a liquid, Moscow Univ. Phys. Bull. **29**(4), 68–71 (1988)
22. O.V. Rudenko, S.I. Soluyan, *Theoretical Foundations of Nonlinear Acoustics* (Plenum, New York, 1977)
23. B.K. Novikov, O.V. Rudenko, V.I. Timoshenko, *Nonlinear Underwater Acoustics* (AIP, New York, 1987)
24. O.V. Rudenko, Self-action of wave beams containing shock fronts, Radiophys. Quantum Electron. **46**, 338–351 (2003)
25. O.V. Rudenko, O.A. Sapozhnikov, Self-action effects for wave beams containing shock fronts, Phys. Usp. **47**, 907–922 (2004)
26. A.A. Karabutov, O.V. Rudenko, O.A. Sapozhnikov, Thermal self-focusing theory with allowance for the formation of shock waves and acoustic flows, Sov. Phys. Acoust. **34**, 371–375 (1988)
27. A.A. Karabutov, O.V. Rudenko, O.A. Sapozhnikov, Thermal self-focusing of weak sock waves, Sov. Phys. Acoust. **35**, 40–43 (1989)
28. I.M. Hallaj, R.O. Cleveland, K. Hynynen, Simulations of the thermo-acoustic lens effect during focused ultrasound surgery, J. Acoust. Soc. Am. **109**, 2245–2253 (2001)
29. C. Le Floch, M. Tanter, M. Fink, Self-defocusing in ultrasonic hyperthermia: experiment and simulation, Appl. Phys. Lett. **74**, 3062–3064 (1999)
30. O.V. Rudenko, M.M. Sagatov, O.A. Sapozhnikov, Thermal self-focusing of sawtooth waves, Sov. Phys. JETP **71**, 449–557 (1990)
31. V.E. Fridman, *Ray Theory of Finite-Amplitude Acoustic Waves: Dr. Sci. Thesis* (General Phys. Inst., Moscow, 1985). In Russian
32. V.E. Fridman, Self-refraction of weak shock waves, Sov. Phys. Acoust. **28**, 551–559 (1982)
33. O.V. Rudenko, S.I. Soluyan, R.V. Khokhlov, To the nonlinear theory of paraxial sound beams, Sov. Phys. Doklady **225**, 1053–1055 (1975)
34. V.G. Andreev, A.A. Karabutov, O.V. Rudenko, Experimental investigation of sound beams of a finite amplitude, Moscow Univ. Phys. Bull. Ser. 3 Phys. Astron. **25**(3), 35–38 (1984)
35. R.C. Preston (ed.), *Output Measurements for Medical Ultrasound* (Springer, New York, 1991)
36. Y.N. Makov, Waveguide propagation of sound beams in a nonlinear medium, Acoust. Phys. **46**, 596–600 (2000)
37. K.A. Naugolnykh, N.A. Roi, *Electric Discharges in Water* (Nauka, Moscow, 1971). In Russian
38. V.G. Andreev, V.Y. Veroman, G.A. Denisov, O.V. Rudenko, O.A. Sapozhnikov, Nonlinear-acoustical aspects of extracorporeal lithotripsy, Sov. Phys. Acoust. **38**, 325–330 (1992)
39. G.A. Askar'yan, M.G. Korolev, A.V. Yurkin, Generation of intense ultrasonic pulses by planar or concave focusing surface exploded by a current or by a laser beam, JETP Lett. **51**, 667–671 (1990)
40. A.J. Coleman, J.E. Saunders, R.C. Preston, D.R. Bacon, Pressure waveforms generated by Dornier extracorporeal shock wave lithotripter, Ultrasound Med. Biol. **13**, 651–657 (1987)
41. A.P. Sarvazyan, O.V. Rudenko, S.D. Swanson, J.B. Fowlkes, S.Y. Emelianov, Shear wave elasticity imaging - a new ultrasonic technology of medical diagnostic, Ultrasound Med. Biol. **24**, 1419–1436 (1998)
42. A.G. Musatov, O.V. Rudenko, O.A. Sapozhnikov, Accounting for nonlinear refraction and nonlinear absorption in focusing high-power pulses, Sov. Phys. Acoust. **38**, 274–279 (1992)
43. O.A. Sapozhnikov, Focusing of high-power pulse, Acoust. Phys. **37**, 760–769 (1991)
44. O.V. Rudenko, O.A. Sapozhnikov, Wave beams in cubically nonlinear nondispersive media., JETP **79**, 220–229 (1994)
45. O.V. Rudenko, A.P. Sarvazyan, S.Y. Emelianov, Acoustic radiation force and streaming induced by focused nonlinear ultrasound in a dissipative medium, J. Acoust. Soc. Am. **99**, 2791–2798 (1996)
46. A.A. Karabutov, O.V. Rudenko, The modified Khokhlov method for investigation of nonsteady transonic flows of a compressed gas, Sov. Phys. Dokl. **24**, 835–838 (1979)
47. A.A. Karabutov, O.V. Rudenko, Nonlinear plane waves excited by volume sources in a medium moving with transonic velocity, Sov. Phys. Acoust. **25**, 306–309 (1979)

48. O.V. Rudenko, in *Advances in Nonlinear Acoustics*, ed. by H. Hobæk (World Scientific, Singapore, 1993), pp. 3–6
49. O.V. Rudenko, O.A. Sapozhnikov, Inertialess self-focusing of nondispersive waves with a broadband spectrum, Quantum Electron. **23**, 896 (1993)
50. O.V. Rudenko, A.A. Sukhorukov, Diffracting beams in cubically nonlinear media without dispersion, Acoust. Phys. **41**(5), 725–730 (1995)
51. O.V. Rudenko, A.A. Sukhorukov, Self-action of light beams in media with two-photon absorption, Bull. Russian Acad. Sci. Physics **60**(12), 6–25 (1996)
52. I.P. Lee-Bapty, D.G. Crighton, Nonlinear wave motion governed by modified Burgers equation, Philos. Trans. R. Soc. London Ser. A **323**, 173–209 (1987)
53. A.M. Vinogradov, I.S. Krasil'shchik, V.V. Lychagin, *Introduction to the Geometry of Linear Differential Equations* (Nauka, Moscow, 1986). In Russian
54. N.H. Ibragimov, *Transformation Groups Applied to Mathematical Physics* (D. Reidel, Dordrecht, 1985)
55. L.V. Ovsyannikov, *Group Analysis of Differential Equations* (Academic Press, New York, 1982)
56. P.J. Olver, *Applications of Lie Groups to Differential Equations* (Springer, New York, 1986)
57. N.H. Ibragimov (ed.), *Symmetries, Exact Solutions and Conservation Laws, CRC Handbook of Lie Group Analysis of Differential Equations*, vol. 1 (CRC Press, Boca Raton, 1994)
58. N.H. Ibragimov (ed.), *Applications in Engineering and Physical Sciences, CRC Handbook ofLie Group Analysis of Differential Equations*, vol. 2 (CRC Press, Boca Raton, 1995)
59. N.H. Ibragimov (ed.), *New Trends in Theoretical Developments and Computational Methods, CRC Handbook Of Lie Group Analysis of Differential Equations*, vol. 3 (CRC Press, Boca Raton, 1996)
60. V.I. Talanov, Focusing of light in cubic media, JETP Lett. **11**, 199–201 (1970)
61. L.D. Landau, E.M. Lifshitz, *The Classical Field Theory* (Pergamon Press, Oxford, 1975)
62. E.A. Kuznetsov, Integral criteria of wave collapses, Radiophys. Quantum Electron. **46**, 307–322 (2003)
63. O.V. Rudenko, O.A. Sapozhnikov, Intense acoustic beams: self-action of discontinuous waves, focusing of pulses and extracorporeal lithotripsy, Moscow Univ. Phys. Bull. **46**, 3–17 (1991)

Chapter 11
Nonlinear Standing Waves, Resonance Phenomena and Frequency Characteristics of Distributed Systems

11.1 Introduction

Resonance is one of the most interesting and fundamental phenomena in the physics of oscillations and waves. Resonance manifests itself clearly when the dependence of the amplitude of induced oscillations on frequency (frequency response of the system) has a sharp maximum. In these cases, the ratio of the central frequency ω_0 of the spectral line, representing a response, to the characteristic width of this line is a large value. This ratio, called the quality- or Q-factor, is used as a "quality" measure of the resonance system. At large values of Q, the system may contain a high energy density, since the ratio of the amplitude of induced oscillations to the amplitude of oscillations of the external source providing an influx of energy to the system is also equal to Q. In high-Q systems, approaching a state of equilibrium is slow process with a characteristic relaxation time on the order of Q/ω_0. The build-up time of oscillations (or their attenuation after the source is switched off) occurs over the course of many periods, the number of which is $\sim Q$. Excitation of strong oscillations during resonance may lead to the appearance of nonlinear effects, the most well-known of which is destruction of the system. On the other hand, high-Q systems are used for taking high-precision physical measurements.

The problem of increasing the quality of acoustic resonator is topical for many areas of physics and engineering. In distributed high-Q systems, it is possible to accumulate significant energy and to create conditions for observing strongly expressed nonlinear effects even with weak pumping [1]. High-precision measurement systems used, in particular, for detecting hits of gravitational radiation [2] contain mechanical resonators made of sapphire and silicon, the quality of which has attained record values of 10^9 for sound frequency ranges at liquid helium temperatures. The minimization of all possible losses (by means of growing perfect crystals, thorough polishing of faces, etc.) has made it possible even at room temperature to achieve values of $Q \sim 10^8$ (the corresponding time of relaxation is on the order of three years [3]). In such high-Q systems, when linear (amplitude-independent) losses are almost completely excluded, nonlinear absorption can play the role of a limiting factor.

Nonlinearity is the main reason that Q-factor is limited in less perfect resonators, but in the presence of intensive pumping. In such situations, foremost is the problem of suppressing nonlinear distortions of the wave profile, leading to the emergence of steep shock fronts, since it is mainly at the fronts where absorption occurs, independently of the dissipating characteristics of the medium [1]. There are at least three known methods for suppressing the emergence of a shock front.

In [4], a method was proposed for artificially introducing detunings between harmonics in the resonator, one of the walls of which possesses frequency-dependent impedance. Detunings between rigidly phased harmonics, which make up the shock front, "extend" (widen) it and decrease nonlinear losses.

In [5–7], the idea has been implemented of controlling a wave profile and phase shifts between harmonics at the expense of using resonators of complex form-conical, bulb-shaped, etc. With this method, it was possible to obtain, in gas-filled volumes, positive excess pressure in certain atmospheres and to achieve suppression of shock fronts under strong nonlinearity (for relatively large acoustic Mach numbers).

The third method is based on introducing selective absorbers into the medium. Generally speaking, the idea in [8] of suppressing "key" harmonics, the presence of which leads to uncontrolled difference of the wave energy across the spectrum, makes it possible to control energy flows and, in particular, to concentrate energy in the necessary harmonic components. A number of possibilities for controlling wave interactions, described in [9], can be used to increase the quality of a nonlinear acoustic resonator. In experiment [10], for instance, there was an increase in quality linked to the fact that one of the boundaries partially let the second harmonic outside, reflecting the wave of the fundamental frequency inward. Thus, to increase Q-factor, losses on the wavelength of the second harmonic were artificially introduced.

Therefore, methods exist for suppressing both linear and nonlinear losses in a resonator, which lead to an increase in quality.

11.2 Methods of evaluation of the characteristics of nonlinear resonators

It is obvious that a standing wave in a one-dimensional linear resonator can be represented in the form of two waves traveling toward each other. This idea was generalized for nonlinear waves localized between two parallel rigid walls [11]; oscillation are described by the sum of counter-propagating Riemann and Burgers waves. Each of these waves can be strongly distorted due to nonlinear self-action, which transforms the initial harmonic profile into a profile of sawtooth form; however, "cross" action appears to be negligibly weak. In other words, each of the two opposing waves is distorted, in and of itself, in the process of propagation, but there is almost no energy exchange between them. A similar approach has been used [12] to describe a nonlinear field in a flat waveguide, where nonlinear Brillouin modes form as two noninteracting between themselves strongly distorted waves traveling under the same angles toward the axis of the waveguide. This idea is not quite obvious, but can be easily explained.

The explanation given below is correct for any nonlinear equation describing nondispersive waves in a quadratic nonlinear medium. For certainty, we examine a very simple model equation [13]:

$$\frac{\partial^2 p}{\partial x^2}-\frac{1}{c^2}\frac{\partial^2 p}{\partial t^2}=-\frac{\varepsilon}{c^4\rho}\frac{\partial^2 p^2}{\partial t^2}. \tag{11.1}$$

Here p is acoustic pressure, c and ρ are the speed of sound and the density of the medium, and ε is the nonlinearity parameter. Eq. (11.1) can describe both Riemann waves traveling in opposite direction, and the interaction between them. We seek a weak nonlinear solution by the method of successive approximations:

$$p=p^{(1)}+p^{(2)}+\cdots \tag{11.2}$$

Let in the first approximation the solution describe two counter-propagating harmonic waves:

$$p^{(1)}=B_1\cos(\omega_1 t-k_1x+\varphi_1)+B_2\cos(\omega_2 t+k_2x+\varphi_2),\ k_{1,2}=\omega_{1,2}/c. \tag{11.3}$$

The second approximation is found from the linear inhomogeneous equation

$$\frac{\partial^2 p^{(2)}}{\partial x^2}-\frac{1}{c^2}\frac{\partial^2 p^{(2)}}{\partial t^2}=F(2\omega_1)+F(2\omega_2)+F(\omega_1+\omega_2)+F(\omega_1-\omega_2), \tag{11.4}$$

the right-hand side of which is calculated on the basis of the first approximation (11.3):

$$F(2\omega_{1,2})=\frac{2\varepsilon}{c^4\rho}\omega_{1,2}^2B_{1,2}^2\cos\left[2\left(\omega_{1,2}t\mp k_{1,2}x+\varphi_{1,2}\right)\right], \tag{11.5}$$

$$F(\omega_1\pm\omega_2)=\frac{\varepsilon}{c^4\rho}(\omega_1\pm\omega_2)^2B_1B_2\cos[(\omega_1\pm\omega_2)t-(k_1\mp k_2)x+(\varphi_1\pm\varphi_2)].$$

By using method (11.2), we can examine the four terms on the right-hand side of Eq. (11.4) as "external forces" exciting "induced waves" of the second approximation at frequencies of the second harmonic of $2\omega_1$, $2\omega_2$ as well as the sum $(\omega_1+\omega_2)$ and difference $(\omega_1-\omega_2)$ frequencies.

It is important that excitation of secondary waves can have a resonant or nonresonant character. The first two "forces" $F(2\omega_1)$ and $F(2\omega_2)$ of Eq. (11.5) lead to resonance excitation. The corresponding induced waves

$$p_{1,2}^{(2)}=-\frac{\varepsilon}{2c^2\rho}B_{1,2}^2\left(\omega_{1,2}t\right)\sin\left[2\left(\omega_{1,2}t\mp k_{1,2}x+\varphi_{1,2}\right)\right] \tag{11.6}$$

accumulate with time. Their amplitudes grow linearly with an increase in t similar to the amplitude of induced oscillations of a pendulum when the eigenfrequency and the frequency of the inducing force coincide.

Unlike concentrated systems, resonance in distributed systems occurs when the phase velocities of motion of the inducing force and the eigen wave coincide [13].

Differently from waves (11.6), the amplitudes of which grow with an increase in t, partial solutions of Eq. (11.4), which correspond to two different inducing forces $F(\omega_1 \pm \omega_2)$ in Eq. (11.5):

$$p_{3,4}^{(2)} = \frac{\varepsilon}{c^4\rho} \frac{(\omega_1 \pm \omega_2)^2}{4k_1k_2} B_1 B_2 \cos\left[(\omega_1 \pm \omega_2)t - (k_1 \mp k_2)x + (\varphi_1 \pm \varphi_2)\right], \quad (11.7)$$

have amplitudes independent of time t.

Comparison of resonant (11.6) and nonresonant (11.7) solutions shows that after several periods of oscillations $\omega_{1,2}t \gg 1$, waves (11.7) seem much weaker in comparison to resonant waves (11.5) and therefore they cannot effectively participate in nonlinear energy exchange. Therefore, each of the two opposing waves generates its own high harmonics (11.6), but it is possible to neglect processes of cross interaction (11.7) if the waves oscillate with time. This conclusion is also correct for periodic waves that intersect at quite large angles (the values of the latter are determined by the acoustic Mach numbers [12]).

We switch now to the deduction of simplified equations, first taking into account only the quadratic nonlinearity of the medium. Let the left boundary $x = 0$ of the layer oscillate according to the law

$$u(x=0,t) = Af(\omega t), \quad (11.8)$$

where A is the characteristic amplitude, u is the velocity and f is the periodic function with period of 2π. The right boundary $x = L$ is immobile:

$$u(x=L,t) = 0. \quad (11.9)$$

Using the method of a slowly changing profile [1, 13] and correlation $p = \pm\rho c u$, linking the linear waves of pressure and vibration velocity, we reduce the second order (11.1) nonlinear equation to a pair of first order equations for traveling Riemann waves:

$$\frac{\partial u}{\partial x} \pm \frac{1}{c}\frac{\partial u}{\partial t} - \frac{\varepsilon}{c^2} u \frac{\partial u}{\partial t} = 0. \quad (11.10)$$

Here the "+" corresponds to a wave traveling to the right along the x-axis, and the "−", to a wave traveling in the opposite direction. The solution of (11.10) has the form of an implicit function. The sum of the two solutions is written as

$$\begin{aligned} u = F&\left[\omega t - \frac{\omega}{c}(x-L) + \frac{\varepsilon}{c^2}\omega(x-L)F\right] \\ -F&\left[\omega t + \frac{\omega}{c}(x-L) - \frac{\varepsilon}{c^2}\omega(x-L)F\right], \end{aligned} \quad (11.11)$$

where F is an arbitrary function describing the profiles of nonlinear traveling waves. It is clear that solution (11.11) satisfies boundary condition (11.9). The second condition (11.8) transforms Eq. (11.11) into a functional equation with respect to unknown F:

$$F\left[\omega t + kL - \frac{\varepsilon}{c}kLF\right] - F\left[\omega t - kL + \frac{\varepsilon}{c}kLF\right] = Af(\omega t). \tag{11.12}$$

Equations of type (11.12) are complex and cannot be solved analytically. In order to understand in general terms what information is contained in (11.12), let us consider first a very simple case, assuming nonlinearity equal to zero, $\varepsilon = 0$, and boundary oscillations being harmonic $f = \sin(\omega t)$:

$$F(\omega t + kL) - F(\omega t - kL) = A\sin(\omega t). \tag{11.13}$$

The solution of Eq. (11.13),

$$F = -\frac{A\cos(\omega t)}{2\sin(kL)} + \sum_{n=0}^{\infty}[A_n\cos(n\omega_0 t) + B_n\sin(n\omega_0 t)], \tag{11.14}$$

is the sum of the partial solution of inhomogeneous equation (11.13) and of the general solution to the corresponding homogeneous equation. Here,

$$\omega_0 = \pi c/L, \quad L = \lambda_0/2 \tag{11.15}$$

is the frequency of the main resonance. If the oscillation frequency of the boundary approaches one of the eigenfrequencies, $\omega \to n\omega_0$, non-steady-state resonance growth begins. In order to demonstrate this, we let in the solution (11.14)

$$A_m = \frac{A}{2\sin(kL)}, \quad B_n = 0, \quad A_n = 0 \quad (n \neq m). \tag{11.16}$$

Solution (11.14), taking into account (11.16), contains an uncertainty of the type (0/0). By expanding this solution, we obtain

$$F = \frac{A}{2}\lim_{\omega \to n\omega_0}\frac{\cos(n\omega_0 t) - \cos(\omega t)}{\sin(\omega L/c)} = \frac{A}{2\pi}(-1)^n(\omega_0 t)\sin(n\omega_0 t). \tag{11.17}$$

Expression (11.17) describes a resonant oscillation with increasing amplitude. This simple example illustrates the unobvious, at first glance, fact that functional equations of type (11.12), (11.13) describe not only steady-state oscillations, but also various transition processes.

We proceed now to nonlinear functional equation (11.12). It can be reduced to a simplified evolutionary equation in satisfying a number of conditions. First, the length of the resonator should be small in comparison to the characteristic nonlinear length. Second, the boundary oscillation frequency of the resonator should not greatly differ from the eigenfrequencies (for instance, the frequencies of the main mode):

$$L \ll \frac{c^2}{\varepsilon\omega F_{\max}}, \quad kL = \pi + \Delta, \quad \Delta = \pi\frac{\omega - \omega_0}{\omega_0} \ll 1. \tag{11.18}$$

Here, $F_{\max}$ is the maximum value of function F, and Δ is dimensionless frequency detuning. By taking into account (11.18), the right-hand side of Eq. (11.12) can be expanded in series:

$$F[\omega t+\pi+\Delta-\pi\frac{\varepsilon}{c}F]-F[\omega t-\pi-\Delta+\pi\frac{\varepsilon}{c}F]$$
$$\approx[F(\omega t+\pi)-F(\omega t-\pi)]+(\Delta-\pi\frac{\varepsilon}{c}F)[F'(\omega t+\pi)+F'(\omega t-\pi)]. \quad (11.19)$$

It is obvious that F is an almost periodic function with parameters that slowly change with time. Therefore,

$$F(\omega t+\pi)-F(\omega t-\pi)\approx 2\pi\mu\frac{\partial F}{\partial(\mu\omega t)}, \quad (11.20)$$

where $\mu \ll 1$ is a small parameter whose the physical meaning is explained below. Eq. (11.12) now takes the form

$$\mu\frac{\partial F}{\partial(\mu\omega t/\pi)}+\left(\Delta-\pi\frac{\varepsilon}{c}F\right)\frac{\partial F(\omega t+\pi)}{\partial(\omega t)}=\frac{A}{2}f(\omega t). \quad (11.21)$$

By introducing new dimensionless variables and constants,

$$\xi=\omega t+\pi, \quad U=F/c, \quad M=A/c, \quad T=\omega t/\pi, \quad (11.22)$$

we rewrite Eq. (11.21) as follows:

$$\frac{\partial U}{\partial T}+\Delta\frac{\partial U}{\partial\xi}-\pi\varepsilon U\frac{\partial U}{\partial\xi}=\frac{M}{2}f(\xi-\pi). \quad (11.23)$$

It is now clear that small parameter μ has a value of the order of the small numbers: Δ, M and $U\sim M$.

In [14], an equation was obtained that generalizes (11.23). Namely, the effects of linear dissipation and the finiteness of displacement of a moving boundary were taken into account. The equation is derived in the similar way and has the form

$$\frac{\partial U}{\partial T}-M\Phi(\xi)\frac{\partial U}{\partial\xi}+\Delta\frac{\partial U}{\partial\xi}-\pi\varepsilon U\frac{\partial U}{\partial\xi}-D\frac{\partial^2 U}{\partial\xi^2}=\frac{M}{2}\Phi'(\xi), \quad (11.24)$$

where $\Phi(\xi)$ is a periodic function and

$$D=\frac{b\omega^2}{2c^3\rho}L\ll 1 \quad (11.25)$$

is dimensionless dissipative parameter that determines weak absorption of wave traveled one resonator length L, and b is the effective viscosity of the medium [1,13].

11.3 Standing waves and the Q-factor of a resonator filled with a dissipating medium

In considering quadratic nonlinearity and dissipation conditioned by the effects of viscosity and thermal conductivity of the medium, each of the two counter-propagating nonlinear waves is described by an equation that follows from (11.23), (11.24):

$$\frac{\partial U}{\partial T}+\Delta\frac{\partial U}{\partial \xi}-\pi\varepsilon U\frac{\partial U}{\partial \xi}-D\frac{\partial^2 U}{\partial \xi^2}=\frac{M}{2}f\left(\xi-\pi\right). \tag{11.26}$$

Eq. (11.26) is known as the "inhomogeneous Burgers equation with detuning" [15]. Its main properties have been studied in [15–17]. The non-steady-state solution of Eq. (11.26) can be found in the most interesting resonance case ($\Delta=0$) for certain special forms of boundary oscillations. These exact solutions can help in understanding the general properties of induced nonlinear oscillations of resonators.

Let the boundary performs periodic sawtooth movements. In one period, the form of oscillations is given by the expression:

$$f\left(\omega t\right)=\left(1-\frac{\omega t}{\pi}\right)\mathrm{sgn}\left(\omega t\right),\quad -\pi\leqslant\omega t\leqslant\pi. \tag{11.27}$$

We seek the solution of Eqs. (11.26), (11.27) in the form

$$U=-a(T)\,\xi/\pi,\quad f=-\xi/\pi,\quad -\pi\leqslant\xi\leqslant\pi. \tag{11.28}$$

For the "amplitude" of "saw" we obtain an ordinary differential equation and corresponding solution

$$\frac{da}{dT}+\varepsilon a^2=\frac{M}{2},\quad a=\sqrt{\frac{M}{2\varepsilon}}\tanh\left(\sqrt{\frac{\varepsilon M}{2}}T\right). \tag{11.29}$$

It is seen, that the "amplitude" increases with time, tending, at $T\to\infty$, toward the maximum value $(M/2\varepsilon)^{1/2}$.

The form of standing waves is described by solution (11.11), in which we can neglect the nonlinearity if oscillations are concidered within one period. As well, (11.11) takes the simple form

$$u/c=U\left(\omega t-kx\right)-U\left(\omega t+kx\right). \tag{11.30}$$

The time profiles of a standing wave described by formulas (11.28)–(11.30) are constructed in Fig. 11.1 for various sections of the resonator situated at $x=L/8$, $L/4$, $L/2$, $3L/4$, $7L/8$. It is seen, that the form of the velocity of induced nonlinear oscillations changes in the transition from one cross section to another. In the middle of the layer, each period consists of alternating areas of positive and negative polarity of the same rectangular shape. Upon approaching the end of $x=L$, the area of positive polarity converges, but its "height" grows, right up to a value twice that

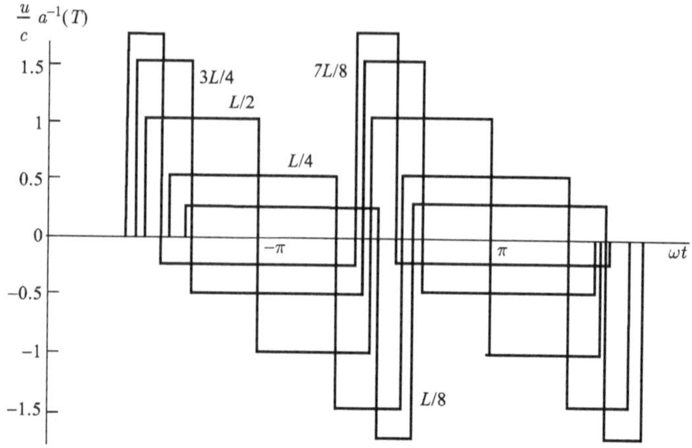

Fig. 11.1 Profiles of the standing wave described by Eqs. (11.28)– (11.30), constructed in various sections of the resonator $x = L/8,\, L/4,\, L/2,\, 3L/4,\, 7L/8$.

of the middle section $x = L/2$. The section of negative polarity decreases in value, but stretches along the time axis. The total area bound by the graph (the integral of u over the period) is equal to zero.

Upon approaching the other boundary, $x = 0$, convergence with time and growth in amplitude of the area of negative polarity occur. At both boundaries $x = 0$ and $x = L$, movement disappears and $u = 0$, in accordance with boundary conditions (11.8), (11.9).

For a moving boundary, satisfying the condition (11.8) should not be understood literally; it is necessary to bear in mind that the amplitude of wall oscillations is very small compared to the characteristic oscillation amplitude of the velocity field u in the cavity of the resonator.

The mean volume density of energy for the period,

$$\rho\overline{u^2} = \frac{\rho}{2\pi}\int_0^{2\pi} u^2 d(\omega\tau) = \rho c^2 \cdot 8kx\left(1 - \frac{kx}{\pi}\right) a^2(T), \qquad (11.31)$$

has a maximum at the center of the layer $kx = \pi/2$, and is equal to zero at both boundaries. The total energy in volume V of the resonator, calculated by integration of Eq. (11.31) with respect over coordinate, is

$$E = \frac{1}{3}\rho c^2 V \cdot \frac{M}{\varepsilon}\tanh^2\left(\sqrt{\frac{\varepsilon M}{2}}\frac{\omega t}{\pi}\right). \qquad (11.32)$$

The ratio of the “amplitude” of standing wave and boundary oscillations increases with an increase in time,

$$Q = \frac{a(T)}{M} = \frac{1}{\sqrt{2\varepsilon M}}\tanh\left(\sqrt{2\varepsilon M}\frac{\omega t}{2\pi}\right), \qquad (11.33)$$

reaching the maximum value having the meaning of a stationary nonlinear Q-factor:

$$Q_{NL} = \sqrt{c/2\varepsilon A}. \tag{11.34}$$

It is seen, that the Q-factor decreases with growing amplitude A of boundary oscillations. If the nonlinearity is very small, the Q-factor does not depend on amplitude A and is determined by regular linear absorption (see, e.g. [14]) :

$$Q_{LIN} = \frac{1}{2D} = \frac{c^3\rho}{b\omega^2 L} = \frac{c^2\rho}{\pi b\omega}. \tag{11.35}$$

In contrast to nonlinear Q-factor (11.34), linear Q-factor (11.35) is fully determined by the resonator geometry and the properties of the medium it is filled with. For an amplitude of the boundary-vibration velocity of $A = 10$ cm/s, the nonlinear Q-factor of an air resonator is $Q_{NL} \approx 40$. On the other hand, for typical frequency values on the order of 4 kHZ, the linear Q-factor is much higher, on the order of $10^3 - 10^4$. However, when there is a high linear Q-factor, the amplitude of standing wave grows with time; the conditions of manifestation of nonlinear effects become even more favorable, and nonlinear absorption can lead to a significant drop in Q-factor.

For the harmonic law of wall oscillations, the right-hand side of the Eq. (11.26) has the form: $-(M/2)\sin\xi$. In this and certain other cases, the inhomogeneous Burgers equation is solved with the help of linearization. Using the transformation

$$U = \frac{2D}{\pi\varepsilon}\frac{\partial}{\partial\xi}\ln W, \tag{11.36}$$

it is possible to reduce Eq. (11.26) to the following linear equation:

$$\frac{\partial W}{\partial T} + \Delta\frac{\partial W}{\partial\xi} - D\frac{\partial^2 W}{\partial\xi^2} = \frac{1}{2}qD\cos\xi\cdot W, \quad q = \frac{\pi\varepsilon M}{2D^2}. \tag{11.37}$$

Yet another substitution:

$$W = \exp(-\lambda DT/4)\cdot y(z = \xi/2), \tag{11.38}$$

where λ is constant, reduces (11.37) to the ordinary differential equation for function $y(z)$:

$$\frac{d^2y}{dz^2} - 2\frac{\Delta}{D}\frac{dy}{dz} + (\lambda + 2q\cos 2z)y = 0. \tag{11.39}$$

At zero detuning, $\Delta = 0$, Equation (11.39) represents the canonical form of differential equation for the Mathieu function [18]. Namely, the resonance ($\Delta = 0$) case allows for complete analytical study.

For the zero initial condition $U(T = 0, \xi) = 0$, the solution of Eq. (11.37) is written in the form of a series of even Mathieu functions:

$$W = \sum_{n=0}^{\infty} a_{2n} \exp\left[-\frac{1}{4}\lambda_{2n}(q)DT\right] ce_{2n}\left(\frac{\xi}{2}, q\right), \tag{11.40}$$

where the coefficients are determined by the formulas

$$a_{2n} = \left[\int_0^{2\pi} ce_0\left(\frac{\xi}{2}, q\right) d\xi\right] \Big/ \left[\int_0^{2\pi} ce_{2n}^2\left(\frac{\xi}{2}, q\right) d\xi\right]. \tag{11.41}$$

The notation used here corresponds to the book by Strutt [18].

A simple formula is obtained for the steady-state at ($T \to \infty$) profile of a wave [17]:

$$U = \frac{2D}{\pi\varepsilon}\frac{d}{d\xi} \ln ce_0\left(\frac{\xi}{2}, q = \frac{\pi\varepsilon M}{2D^2}\right). \tag{11.42}$$

For large values of the parameter $q \gg 1$, the solution (11.42) takes form [16]

$$U = \sqrt{\frac{2M}{\pi\varepsilon}}\left[\cos\frac{\xi}{2} - \frac{3\exp\left(-2\sqrt{q}\xi\right)}{1+2\exp\left(-2\sqrt{q}\xi\right)}\right], \quad 0 \leqslant \xi \leqslant \pi, \tag{11.43}$$

and at $q \to \infty$ it does not depend on linear absorption (i.e., on q) at all:

$$U = \sqrt{\frac{2M}{\pi\varepsilon}} \cos\frac{\xi}{2} \cdot \operatorname{sgn}\xi, \quad -\pi \leqslant \xi \leqslant \pi. \tag{11.44}$$

Figures 11.2 (a, b) show the process of the profiles of a standing wave being established under harmonic boundary oscillations in the middle section of the resonator ($x = L/2$, Fig. 11.2(a)) and close to the right end face ($x = 7L/8$, Fig. 11.2 (b)). The profiles have been constructed [16] according to formulas (11.40), (11.30) taking into account transformation (11.36) for the values of "slow time" $DT = 0.15, 0.3, 0.5, 0.9$. The parameter was set equal to $q = 20$.

In contrast to the curves in Fig. 11.1, the curves in Fig. 11.2 are smoothed because formation of the shock front for the considered moments of time in traveling waves U have still not terminated. Even at $DT \to \infty$ the shock front for the parameter $q = 20$ possesses significant width. A discontinuity occurs at $q \to \infty$.

The steady-state profiles of standing waves are shown in Fig. 11.3 for very strong boundary oscillations, corresponding to $q \to \infty$ [19]. The standing wave in Fig. 11.3 has a shape similar to the wave during sawtooth boundary oscillations (see Fig. 11.1). However, the upper areas of impulses of positive and negative polarity are not flat; they have the shape of arcs described by trigonometric functions. For the wave in Fig. 11.1, the peak value u/c tends (at $T \to \infty$) to a value $\sqrt{2M/\varepsilon}$, whereas for the wave in Fig. 11.3, the corresponding value is $2\sqrt{2M/\pi\varepsilon}$.

Let us turn to the calculations of energy characteristics of the resonator with harmonic excitation. Note that the steady-state solution (11.42) satisfies the ordinary differential equation

$$D\frac{d^2U}{d\xi^2} + \pi\varepsilon U\frac{dU}{d\xi} = \frac{M}{2}\sin\xi, \tag{11.45}$$

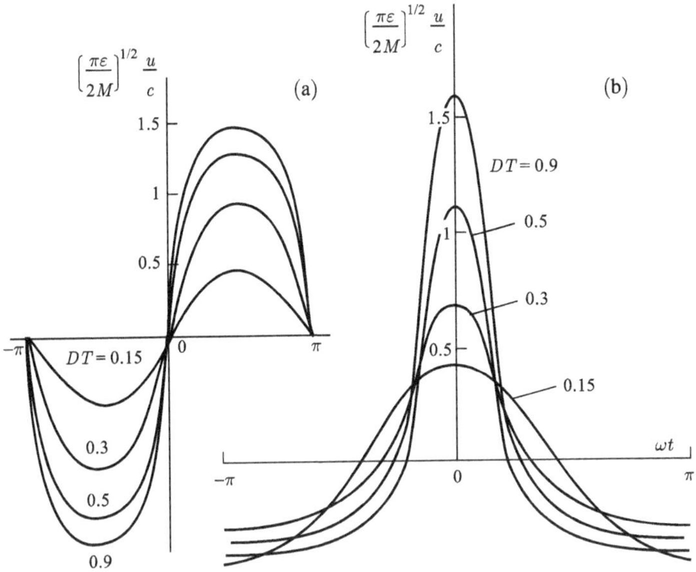

Fig. 11.2 The process of the shaping of a standing wave during harmonic boundary oscillations in the midsection of the resonator $x = L/2$ **(a)**, and near the right end face $x = 7L/8$ **(b)**. The value of "slow time" $DT = 0.15, 0.3, 0.5, 0.9$. Parameter $q = 20$.

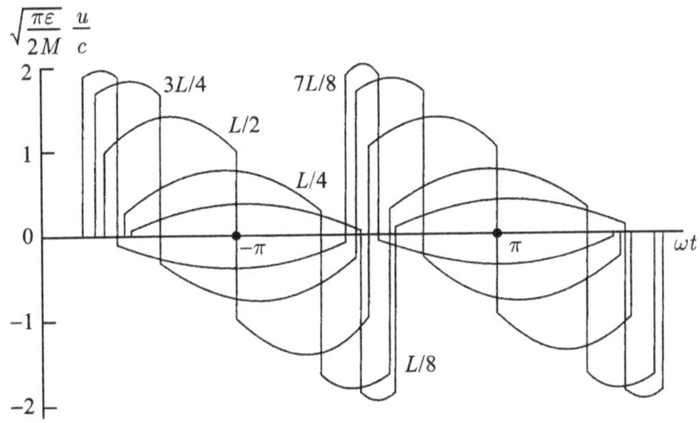

Fig. 11.3 Established profile of standing waves at $q \to \infty$, constructed in various sections of the resonator: $x = L/8, L/4, L/2, 3L/4, 7L/8$.

which follows from (11.26) at $T \to \infty$, $\Delta = 0$ and $f(\xi) = -\sin\xi$. By integrating (11.45), we obtain

$$D\frac{dU}{d\xi} + \frac{\pi\varepsilon}{2}\left(U^2 - C^2\right) = -\frac{M}{2}\cos\xi. \qquad (11.46)$$

Since the average over a period should equal zero, $\overline{U} = 0$, from Eq. (11.46) it follows that the constant is

$$C^2 = \overline{U^2} = \frac{1}{2\pi}\int_0^{2\pi} U^2(\xi)\,d\xi. \tag{11.47}$$

Thus, constant (11.47) is proportional to the acoustic energy density. Using the transformation (11.36), we reduce nonlinear equation (11.46) to the linear one for Mathieu functions:

$$\frac{d^2W}{dz^2} + \left[-\left(\frac{\pi\varepsilon}{D}\right)^2 C^2 + \frac{\pi\varepsilon M}{D^2}\cos 2z\right] = 0, \tag{11.48}$$

where $z = \xi/2$. Comparing Eqs. (11.48) and (11.39), we arrive at the conclusion that the energy is proportional to the eigenvalue λ_0 of the function ce_0 [17]:

$$\overline{U^2} = -\left(\frac{D}{\pi\varepsilon}\right)^2 \cdot \lambda_0\left(q = \frac{\pi\varepsilon M}{2D^2}\right). \tag{11.49}$$

The full energy stored in the resonator is $E = \rho c^2 V \cdot 2\overline{U^2}$.

When there is a weak excitation, and $\lambda_0 \approx -q^2/2$ [18], we obtain the known result of linear theory:

$$E \approx (M/2D)^2 \cdot \rho c^2 V. \tag{11.50}$$

For strong boundary oscillations, using a different asymptotic λ_0 at $q \gg 1$ [18], we obtain

$$E = \left[\frac{2M}{\pi\varepsilon} - \frac{2D}{(\pi\varepsilon)^2}\sqrt{2\pi\varepsilon M} + \frac{1}{2}\frac{D^2}{(\pi\varepsilon)^2} + \cdots\right]\rho c^2 V. \tag{11.51}$$

At $q \to \infty$, coefficient $2/\pi$ in the first (the main) term in parentheses in formula (11.51) differs from the result of Eq. (11.32), where for $T \to \infty$ the corresponding coefficient is 1/3.

Thus, comparison of the results of [19] for sawtooth and harmonic laws of boundary oscillations of a resonator demonstrates their quality correspondence.

11.4 Frequency responses of a quadratically nonlinear resonator

The results of the previous Sect. 11.3 have been obtained for zero detuning. We examine the case of exact correspondence of frequency oscillations of a fundamental mode of the resonator. Taking into account the dependence of the intensity of oscillations on detuning makes it possible to describe the frequency response [20] and thereby to explore the phenomenon of resonance features in a nonlinear regime.

The establishment of steady-state oscillations in a resonator occurs as a result of competition between the energy flow from the oscillating wall and losses to linear and nonlinear absorption. The steady state achieved at $T \to \infty$ is described by the ordinary differential equation obtained by integration of Eq. (11.26). If the boundary performs periodic sawtooth movements of type (11.27) and right-hand side of Eq. (11.26) is described by the expression $-(M/2)\xi/\pi$, the corresponding steady-state equation has the form

$$D\frac{dU}{d\xi}+\frac{\pi\varepsilon}{2}\left(U^2-C^2\right)-\Delta U=\frac{\pi M}{4}\left(\frac{\xi^2}{\pi^2}-\frac{1}{3}\right). \tag{11.52}$$

Constant C in (11.52) has an important physical meaning. As follows from Eq. (11.52), it is described by formula (11.47) and is equal to the normalized average intensity of the two opposing waves. At the same time, it is assumed that the average over period of the function U is equal to zero, $\overline{U}=0$.

For a very weak manifestation of linear dissipation, $D\to 0$, the solution of Eq. (11.52) has the form

$$U=\frac{\Delta}{\pi\varepsilon}\pm\sqrt{\left(\frac{\Delta}{\pi\varepsilon}\right)^2+C^2+\frac{M}{2\varepsilon}\left(\frac{\xi^2}{\pi^2}-\frac{1}{3}\right)}. \tag{11.53}$$

In the case of small Mach numbers, $M\ll 3\Delta^2/\pi^2\varepsilon$, a linear solution is obtained from one of the branches of Eq. (11.53), namely, from the branch with "$-$" for positive detunings $\Delta>0$ and "$+$" for negative detunings $\Delta<0$:

$$U=-\frac{\pi M}{4|\Delta|}\operatorname{sgn}\Delta\cdot\left(\frac{\xi^2}{\pi^2}-\frac{1}{3}\right),\quad C^2=\overline{U^2}=\frac{\pi^2M^2}{180\Delta^2}\ll\frac{M}{3\varepsilon}. \tag{11.54}$$

The inequality in the latter formula (11.54) is based on neglect of the term C^2 in deducing the first of formulas (11.54) from the solution (11.53).

With an increase in the Mach number right up to the limit value M_*, which will be determined later, the wave undergoes progressive nonlinear distortion (Fig. 11.4, a), but it is described as earlier by one of the branches of the solution (11.53). Solid lines in Fig. 11.4, *a* built for positive detuning of $\Delta=0.1\pi\varepsilon$ and dashed lines — for the same in magnitude negative detuning. The lines are numbered in the order of growing amplitude of the boundary oscillations: $10^2(M/2\varepsilon)=1{,}2.25,4$. In constructing the profiles, constant C^2 was determined with the solution to an algebraic problem on the eigenvalues:

$$\frac{2\Delta}{\pi\varepsilon}=\sqrt{\left(\frac{\Delta}{\pi\varepsilon}\right)^2+C^2+\frac{M}{3\varepsilon}}+\frac{(\Delta/\pi\varepsilon)^2+C^2-M/6\varepsilon}{\sqrt{M/2\varepsilon}}\operatorname{arsinh}\frac{\sqrt{M/2\varepsilon}}{(\Delta/\pi\varepsilon)^2+C^2-M/6\varepsilon}. \tag{11.55}$$

The maximum value $M=M_*$, where Eq. (11.55) has a real solution $C=\Delta/\left(\pi\varepsilon\sqrt{3}\right)$, is determined by the condition

$$\sqrt{\frac{M}{2\varepsilon}}=\frac{2|\Delta|}{\pi\varepsilon},\quad M=\frac{8\Delta^2}{\pi^2\varepsilon}\equiv M_*. \tag{11.56}$$

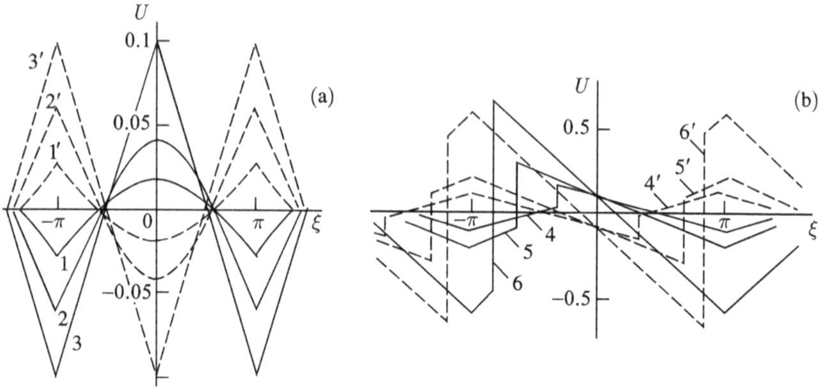

Fig. 11.4 Time profiles for one of the opposing waves forming the field in the resonator. Wall oscillations are sawtooth in shape. Profiles **(a)** do not contain discontinuities; for curves 1–3, the value of parameter $10^2\,(M/2\varepsilon) = 1, 2.25, 4$. Profiles 4–6 contain discontinuities **(b)**; they are constructed for values $10^2\,(M/2\varepsilon) = 4, 9, 49$.

At $M = M_*$ bifurcation occurs and the steady-state form of the wave becomes discontinuous. The shock front appears during every period of the wave, combing the two branches of the solution (11.53).

Let solution U at the moment of"fast" time ξ_0 be described by the "−" branch of the solution (11.53). With an increase in time $\xi > \xi_0$, the solution should perform a "jump" onto "+" branch; otherwise the condition $\overline{U} = 0$ cannot be fulfilled. The moment of the "jump" $\xi = \xi_{SH}$ corresponds to the situation of compression of the shock front in the wave profile. However, rarefaction jumps cannot exist in quadratic-nonlinear media in which the propagation velocity increases with an increase in the magnitude of perturbation. Therefore, both branches of the solution (11.53) should have one common point in each period. If and only if a common point exists, a transition can occur in it the opposite direction, from the "+" branch to the "−" branch, but without the forbidden jump.

A common point exists if the radicand in the solution (11.53) goes to zero, or

$$C^2 = \frac{M}{6\varepsilon} - \left(\frac{\Delta}{\pi\varepsilon}\right)^2. \tag{11.57}$$

For the eigenvalue (11.57) which is now known, solution (11.53) has been simplified:

$$U = \frac{\Delta}{\pi\varepsilon} \pm \sqrt{\frac{M}{2\varepsilon}}\left|\frac{\xi}{\pi}\right|. \tag{11.58}$$

To discover the state of the front in the wave profile, we apply condition $\overline{U} = 0$ to the solution (11.58). This gives

$$\xi_{SH} = -\pi\sqrt{1 - \frac{2\Delta}{\pi}\sqrt{\frac{2}{\varepsilon M}}}. \tag{11.59}$$

Expression (11.59) is valid at $M \geqslant M_*$ (see (11.56)).

The shape of the discontinuous wave described by the solution of (11.58), (11.59), is shown in Fig. 11.4 (b), which is a continuation of Fig. 11.4 (a) for the case of Mach numbers $M \geqslant M_*$. With increasing M, discontinuity, that has appeared at point $\xi = 0$ in the profile, moves toward the state $\xi = -\pi$ (for positive detunings), but it reaches this state only at $M \to \infty$ (see (11.59)). Solid curves 4, 5, 6 in Fig. 11.4 (b) are constructed for values $10^2(M/2\varepsilon) = 4, 9, 49$. Dashed curves show a similar behavior of a wave profile for an equivalent negative detuning of $\Delta = -0.1\pi\varepsilon$. In this case, the discontinuity at $M = M_*$, appears at point $\xi = 0$, but moves toward the state $\xi = +\pi$ at $M \to \infty$.

In Fig. 11.5 , the nonlinear frequency characteristic is shown. Curves 1–3, constructed for various Mach numbers $(M/2\varepsilon) = 0.25, 1, 2.25$, give the dependence $C = \sqrt{\overline{U^2}}$ on detuning (11.18). Straight lines $\sqrt{\overline{U^2}} = \Delta/(\pi\varepsilon\sqrt{3})$ are separatrices. Below these lines, the curves in Fig. 11.5 have been constructed with the help of the solutions (11.53), (11.55) for wave profiles not containing discontinuities. Precisely on the lines, the Mach number $M = M_*$. Above the straight lines, the response has been constructed on the basis of the discontinuity solution (11.58), (11.59).

The dependence of the mean-square velocity $C = \sqrt{\overline{U^2}}$ on detuning, shown in Fig. 11.5, is not the only possible determination of the frequency response of a nonlinear resonator. Sometimes it is important to know the dependence $U_+(\Delta)$, where U_+ is the positive peak value of vibration velocity U. The response determined in this way is shown in Fig. 11.6 by the solid curves for three values of $(M/2\varepsilon) = 0.25$, 1, 2.25. An analytical representation of sectors *AB*, *BC*, *CD*, and *DE* is given, respectively, by the formulas

$$\frac{\Delta}{\pi\varepsilon} - \sqrt{\left(\frac{\Delta}{\pi\varepsilon}\right)^2 + C^2 - \frac{M}{6\varepsilon}}, \quad \frac{\Delta}{\pi\varepsilon} + \sqrt{\frac{M}{2\varepsilon} - 2\frac{\Delta}{\pi\varepsilon}\sqrt{\frac{M}{2\varepsilon}}},$$

$$-\frac{|\Delta|}{\pi\varepsilon} + \sqrt{\frac{M}{2\varepsilon}}, \quad -\frac{|\Delta|}{\pi\varepsilon} + \sqrt{\left(\frac{\Delta}{\pi\varepsilon}\right)^2 + C^2 + \frac{M}{3\varepsilon}}.$$

Here, the eigenvalue C^2 is determined by Eq. (11.55).

Another important case corresponds to the harmonic law of motion of the boundary. In this case, the ordinary differential equation (11.52) has the following form

$$D\frac{dU}{d\xi} + \frac{\pi\varepsilon}{2}\left(U^2 - C^2\right) - \Delta U = \frac{M}{2}\cos\xi. \tag{11.60}$$

If the linear dissipation is weak, $D \to 0$, the solution is given by the formula

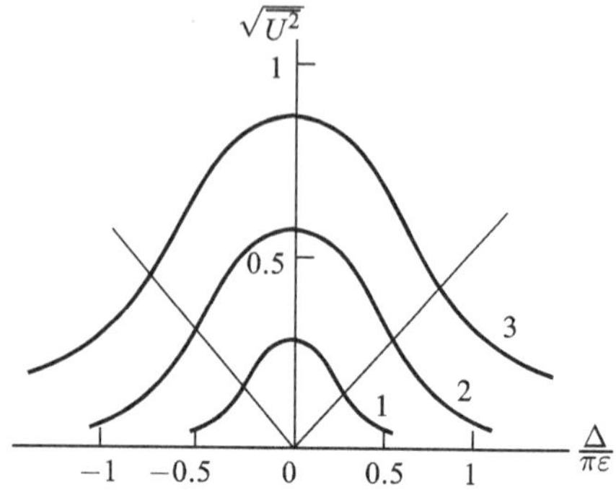

Fig. 11.5 Nonlinear frequency response determined as the dependence of the mean-square velocity as a function of frequency. Curves 1–3 are constructed for values of $(M/2\varepsilon) = 0.25,\ 1,\ 2.25$. The periodic boundary oscillations are sawtooth in shape.

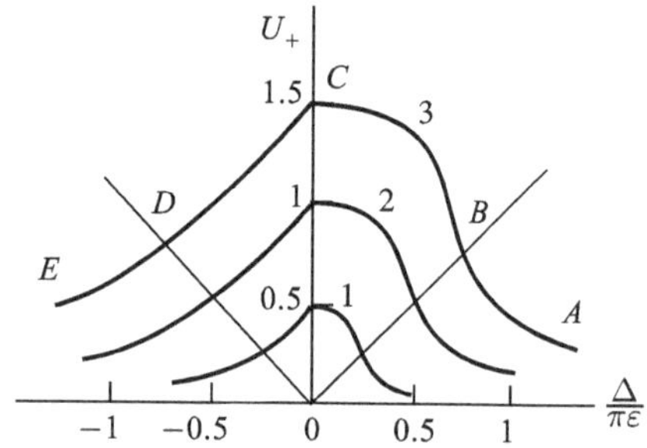

Fig. 11.6 Nonlinear frequency response determined as the dependence of the positive peak value as a function of frequency. Curves 1–3 are constructed for values of $(M/2\varepsilon) = 0.25,\ 1,\ 2.25$. The periodic boundary oscillations are saw-tooth in shape.

$$U = \frac{\Delta}{\pi\varepsilon} \pm \sqrt{\left(\frac{\Delta}{\pi\varepsilon}\right)^2 + C^2 + \frac{M}{\pi\varepsilon}\cos\xi}, \tag{11.61}$$

which is analogous to solution (11.53) for a sawtooth shape of boundary oscillation. For a small Mach numbers, $M \ll \Delta^2/\pi\varepsilon$, we obtain the linear solution

$$U = -\frac{M}{2\,|\Delta|}\,\mathrm{sgn}\,\Delta \cdot \cos\xi, \quad C^2 = \overline{U^2} = \frac{M^2}{8\Delta^2} \ll \frac{M}{\pi\varepsilon}. \tag{11.62}$$

With increasing M the shape of the wave is distorted (Fig. 11.7 (a)), but it can still be described by one branch of the solution of (11.61). Solid curves 1, 2, 3 in Fig. 11.7 (a) constructed for positive detuning of $\Delta = 0.1\pi\varepsilon$, and the dashed curves, for the same values but for a negative detuning. The lines are numbered in the order of growing amplitude of the boundary oscillations: $10^3\,(M/2\varepsilon) = 5.6,\ 9.1,\ 12.3$. In constructing curves, constant C^2 was found from the solution to an algebraic problem for the eigenvalues (cf. (11.55)):

$$\frac{\Delta}{\pi\varepsilon} = \frac{2}{\pi}\sqrt{\left(\frac{\Delta}{\pi\varepsilon}\right)^2 + C^2 + \frac{M}{\pi\varepsilon}} \cdot E\left\{\left(\frac{2M}{\pi\varepsilon}\right)\left[\left(\frac{\Delta}{\pi\varepsilon}\right)^2 + C^2 + \frac{M}{\pi\varepsilon}\right]^{-1/2}\right\}. \tag{11.63}$$

Here, E is a complete elliptic integral of second kind [21].

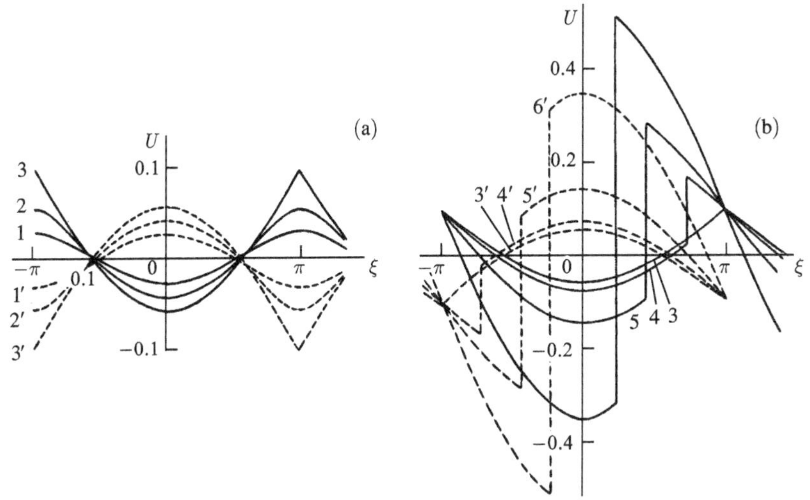

Fig. 11.7 **(a)** Time profile of one of two opposing waves that do not contain discontinuities for a value of parameter $10^3\,(M/2\varepsilon) = 5.6, 9.1, 12.3$ (curves 1–3). **(b)** Discontinuous profiles for values of $10^2\,(M/2\varepsilon) = 1.5, 3, 10$ (curves 4–6).

It is convenient to seek the solution, having written (11.63) in parametric form (m is the parameter):

$$C^2 = \frac{M}{\pi\varepsilon}\left[\frac{2}{m} - 1 - \frac{8}{\pi^2}\frac{E^2(m)}{m}\right], \quad \frac{\Delta}{\pi\varepsilon} = \pm\frac{2\sqrt{2}}{\pi}\sqrt{\frac{M}{\pi\varepsilon}}\frac{E(m)}{\sqrt{m}}. \tag{11.64}$$

The argument of function $E(m)$ is determined in the domain $0 \leqslant m \leqslant 1$ [21]. From (11.63), it follows that the corresponding domain of the detuning variations is given by the inequalities

$$\frac{2\sqrt{2}}{\pi}\sqrt{\frac{M}{\pi\varepsilon}} \ll \frac{|\Delta|}{\pi\varepsilon} < \infty \quad \Rightarrow \quad M \ll \frac{8}{\pi\varepsilon}\Delta^2 \equiv M_*. \tag{11.65}$$

At $M = M_*$, a bifurcation takes place and standing wave becomes discontinuous. A jump appears in each period of the profile, combining the two branches of the solution (11.61).For a discontinuous wave,

$$C^2 = \frac{M}{\pi\varepsilon} - \left(\frac{\Delta}{\pi\varepsilon}\right)^2. \tag{11.66}$$

For eigenvalue (11.66), the solution (11.61) takes the form

$$U = \frac{\Delta}{\pi\varepsilon} \pm \sqrt{\frac{2M}{\pi\varepsilon}}\left|\cos\frac{\xi}{2}\right|. \tag{11.67}$$

The location of the front is found from the condition $\overline{U}=0$ and is determined by the equation

$$\sin\frac{\xi_{SH}}{2}=\frac{\Delta}{2}\sqrt{\frac{\pi}{2\varepsilon M}}. \tag{11.68}$$

From the latter expression (11.68), it follows that condition $|\sin(\xi_{SH}/2)|\leqslant 1$ is equivalent to the condition $M\geqslant M_*$ (11.65).

The solution of (11.67), (11.68) is shown in Fig. 11.7 (b), which is a continuation of Fig. 11.7 (a) for the case of large Mach numbers. Curve 3 in Fig. 11.7 (b), corresponding to $M=M_*$, coincides with curve 3 in Fig. 11.7 (a). With growing Mach number, in the domain $M\geqslant M_*$, the discontinuity that appeared first at point $\xi=\pi$ of the profile (for $\Delta>0$), tends toward the state $\xi=0$, which is achieved at $M\to\infty$ (cf. (11.68)). Solid curves 4, 5, 6 in Fig. 11.7 (b) have been constructed for values of $10^2(M/2\varepsilon)=1.5$, 3, 10. Dashed curves in Fig. 11.7 (b) demonstrate an analogous behavior for the profile with equivalent values for the negative detuning $\Delta=-0.1\pi\varepsilon$. In this case, a discontinuity arises at $M=M_*$ at point $\xi=-\pi$ and it shifts with increasing Mach number to the state $\xi=0$.

Figure 11.8 shows the nonlinear frequency characteristic for the case of harmonic wall oscillations of the resonator. Curves 1–5 have been constructed for various Mach numbers $10^2(M/2\varepsilon)=1$, 4, 9, 16, 25. They demonstrate the dependence of the mean-square velocity $C=\sqrt{\overline{U^2}}$ on detuning. The straight lines

$$\sqrt{\overline{U^2}}=\pm\frac{\Delta}{\pi\varepsilon}\sqrt{\frac{\pi^2}{8}-1} \tag{11.69}$$

are separatrices. Beneath these lines, the curves of Fig. 11.8 have been constructed with the help of the solution (11.62) for profiles containing no discontinuities. $M=M_*$ if points fall on the straight lines described by (11.69). Above the lines of (11.69), another solution (11.67), (11.68) is used to find the nonlinear frequency response of the system.

Here and earlier, the Q-factor can be determined in two ways: as the ratio of the amplitude of field oscillations in the resonator to the amplitude of wall oscillations (at $\Delta=0$) and as the ratio of the resonance frequency to the characteristic width of the frequency response. The first definition leads to the formula (cf. (11.34))

$$Q_{NL}=\frac{c}{A}\sqrt{\overline{U^2}}\Big|_{\Delta=0}=\frac{c}{A}\sqrt{\frac{M}{\pi\varepsilon}}=\frac{1}{\sqrt{\pi\varepsilon M}}. \tag{11.70}$$

The second definition gives an expression that differs only in the numerical coefficient:

$$Q_{NL}=\frac{1}{\Delta}=\frac{\pi}{2\sqrt{2}}\frac{1}{\sqrt{\pi\varepsilon M}}. \tag{11.71}$$

Dependence $U_+(\Delta)$, where U_+ is the peak positive value of vibration velocity U, is shown by the solid curves in Fig. 11.9 for two values of $(M/2\varepsilon)=0.09$, 0.25. The analytical description of sectors AB, BC, CD, DE given by the formulas

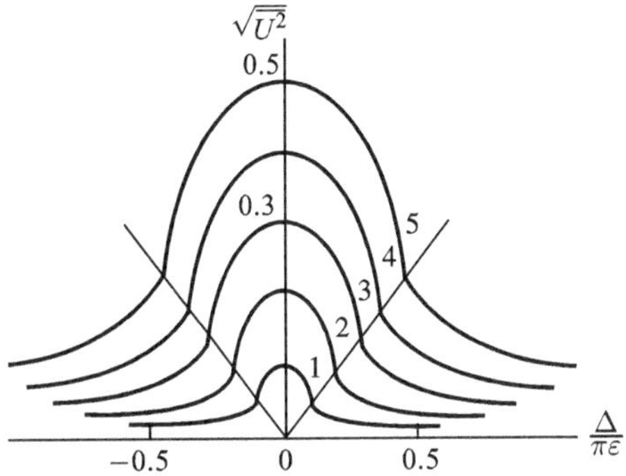

Fig. 11.8 Nonlinear frequency response determined as the dependence of the mean-square vibration velocity in the resonator as a function of frequency for the harmonic law of boundary movement. Curves 1–5 correspond to various values of parameter $10^2\,(M/2\varepsilon) = 1, 4, 9, 16, 25$.

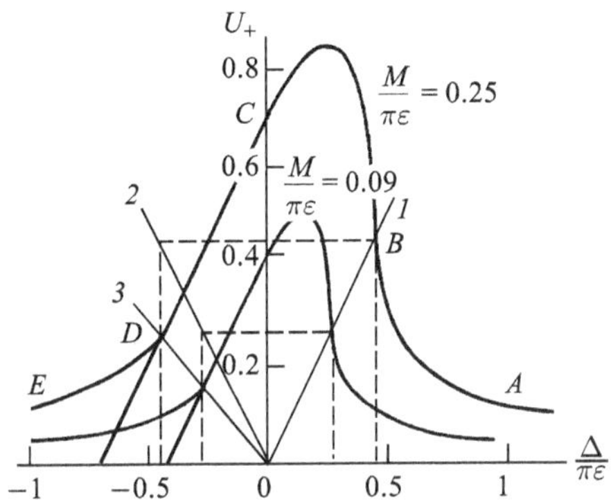

Fig. 11.9 Nonlinear frequency response determined as the dependence of the positive "peak" of the vibration velocity in the resonator as a function of frequency for the harmonic law of boundary movement. The amplitude of boundary oscillations is supposed equal to $(M/2\varepsilon) = 0.09, 0.25$.

$$\frac{\Delta}{\pi\varepsilon} - \sqrt{\left(\frac{\Delta}{\pi\varepsilon}\right)^2 + C^2 - \frac{M}{\pi\varepsilon}}, \quad \frac{\Delta}{\pi\varepsilon} + \sqrt{2}\sqrt{\frac{M}{\pi\varepsilon} - \frac{\pi^2}{8}\left(\frac{\Delta}{\pi\varepsilon}\right)^2},$$

$$-\frac{|\Delta|}{\pi\varepsilon} + \sqrt{2}\sqrt{\frac{M}{\pi\varepsilon}}, \quad -\frac{|\Delta|}{\pi\varepsilon} + \sqrt{\left(\frac{\Delta}{\pi\varepsilon}\right)^2 + C^2 + \frac{M}{\pi\varepsilon}}.$$

Here the eigenvalue C^2 is determined by Eq. (11.64). Straight lines 1, 2 here are the same separatrices in Fig. 11.8. Line 3, which divides sectors CD and DE, is given by the formula

$$U_+ = \left(\frac{\pi}{2} - 1\right)\frac{\Delta}{\pi\varepsilon}. \tag{11.72}$$

Note that the peak positive value U_+ reaches the peak of the shock front the only for sector BC. For the other three sectors of the frequency characteristic, U_+ lies in the smooth sector of the wave profile. In contrast to the curves in Fig. 11.8, the maximum value of U_+ in Fig. 11.9 corresponds not to $\Delta = 0$, but to a certain positive detuning:

$$(U_+)_{\max} = \sqrt{2}\left(1 + \frac{4}{\pi^2}\right)\sqrt{\frac{M}{\pi\varepsilon}}, \quad \left(\frac{\Delta}{\pi\varepsilon}\right)_{\max} = \frac{2\sqrt{2}}{\pi\sqrt{1+\pi^2/4}}\sqrt{\frac{M}{\pi\varepsilon}}. \tag{11.73}$$

In conclusion, we have the approximate formulas for the mean intensity of the field in a resonator in the case of weak and strong manifestation of nonlinearity taking into account linear dissipation:

$$\overline{U^2} = \frac{M^2}{8D^2} - \frac{7}{2048}\frac{(\pi\varepsilon)^2 M^4}{D^6}$$
$$\overline{U^2} = \frac{M}{\pi\varepsilon} - \sqrt{2}\frac{D}{\pi\varepsilon}\sqrt{\frac{M}{\pi\varepsilon} + \frac{1}{4}\left(\frac{D}{\pi\varepsilon}\right)^2 + \frac{1}{16}\left(\frac{D}{\pi\varepsilon}\right)^4 \frac{\pi\varepsilon}{M}}. \tag{11.74}$$

It is possible to simultaneously take into account detuning and dissipation in the case when nonlinear effects are weakly manifested:

$$\overline{U^2} = \frac{M^2}{8(\Delta^2+D^2)} - \frac{(\pi\varepsilon)^2 M^4}{512}\frac{7D^2-5\Delta^2}{(\Delta^2+D^2)^3(\Delta^2+4D^2)}. \tag{11.75}$$

To derive the formula (11.75), it is necessary to solve Eq. (11.60) by the perturbation method and to calculate the first four approximations. Formula (11.75) becomes the first of the formulas (11.74) at zero detuning.

When nonlinearity is strongly manifested, it is possible simultaneously to take into account dissipation and detuning by calculating the wave profile by the method of matched asymptotic expansions [20, 22]. The result of averaging is as follows:

$$\overline{U^2} = \left[\frac{M}{\pi\varepsilon} - \left(\frac{\Delta}{\pi\varepsilon}\right)^2\right] - \sqrt{2}\frac{D}{\pi\varepsilon}\sqrt{\frac{M}{\pi\varepsilon} - \frac{\pi^2}{8}\left(\frac{\Delta}{\pi\varepsilon}\right)^2}. \tag{11.76}$$

When there is exact resonance, from (11.76) we obtain the first two terms of the second formula (11.74), which follows from the theory of Mathieu functions.

Note that the wave profiles for the case of periodic oscillations of boundaries are constructed in [23], but the frequency response (see the curves in Figs. 11.8, 11.9) is calculated latter in [20].

11.5 Q-factor increase under introduction of losses

There exists a paradoxical, at first glance, phenomenon: an outflow of energy from the cavity of the resonator, performed in the appropriate manner, leads not a weakening of nonlinear oscillations, but, on the contrary, to a noticeable strengthening. The effect of an increase in the Q-factor and the energy accumulating in it is well expressed in those cases when the frequencies of higher harmonics generated in a nonlinear medium are close to the eigenfrequencies of the resonator. An important example of system with the desired properties, is an acoustic resonator with selective losses.

The spectrum of eigenfrequencies of a resonator with rigid walls is equidistant (see (11.15)), $\omega_n = n\omega_0 = n\pi c/L$. Therefore, a generated harmonic with number

n is the n-th mode, and in the resonator, a cascade of nonlinear processes takes place that lead to an efficient energy transfer upward across the spectrum. In the high-frequency area, the energy of oscillations is intensively absorbed as a result of dissipative processes usually connected to the viscosity and thermal conductivity of the medium.

The general ideas on controlling wave interactions at the expense of introducing selective losses have been set down in [8, 9]. In the given case, it is necessary to introduce an absorber at frequency $2\omega_0$; quenching of the second harmonic disrupts the cascade process of transfer of energy upward across the spectrum or, in the other words, it "quenches" the formation of shock fronts. Technically, losses at frequency $2\omega_0$ can be brought about either by the introduction of resonance scatterers in the bulk of the medium (e.g., gas bubbles in a liquid) or by using selective boundaries (e.g., borders that are transparent to a wave $2\omega_0$ and that reflect all other frequencies inward [10])

Let us represent the field oscillating between the walls of resonator $x = 0$ and $x = L$ as the superposition of two opposing nonlinear waves (see Sect. 11.2). The auxiliary function u describing the "right" wave of the vibration velocity obeys the equation

$$\frac{1}{c}\frac{\partial u}{\partial t} - \frac{\varepsilon}{c^2}u\frac{\partial u}{\partial \tau} - \frac{b}{2c^3\rho}\frac{\partial^2 u}{\partial \tau^2} = \frac{A}{2L}\sin\omega t - \frac{\alpha}{c}b_2(t)\sin 2\omega t. \tag{11.77}$$

Here t is "slow time", describing the establishment processes in the resonator; τ is "fast time", describing oscillations; α is the coefficient of selective absorption; $b_2(t)$ is the amplitude of the second harmonic:

$$b_2(t) = \frac{2}{\pi}\int_0^{\pi} u(t,\tau)\sin 2\omega\tau d(\omega\tau), \tag{11.78}$$

which is a priori unknown. Thus, model (11.77), (11.78) by itself represents integro-differential equation. In cases when the right-hand side of (11.77) is known, model (11.77) becomes inhomogeneous equation of the Burgers type [17].

It is convenient to use the following dimensionless variables

$$V = \frac{u}{u_0}, \quad \theta = \omega\tau, \quad T = \frac{t}{t_{SH}}; \quad t_{SH} = \frac{c}{\varepsilon\omega u_0}, \quad u_0 = \sqrt{\frac{Ac}{2\pi\varepsilon}}. \tag{11.79}$$

Here, t_{SH} is the characteristic "nonlinear" time in which a discontinuity is able to form in the wave and u_0 is the characteristic amplitude. Eqs. (11.77), (11.78), taking into account (11.79), take the form

$$\frac{\partial V}{\partial T} - V\frac{\partial V}{\partial \theta} - \Gamma\frac{\partial^2 V}{\partial \theta^2} = \sin\theta - D\sin 2\theta \cdot \frac{2}{\pi}\int_0^{\pi} V(T,\theta')\sin 2\theta' d\theta'. \tag{11.80}$$

Here the dimensionless numbers

$$\Gamma = \frac{b\omega}{2\varepsilon\rho c u_0} = \frac{t_{SH}}{t_{DIS}}, \quad D = \frac{\alpha c}{\varepsilon\omega u_0} = \alpha t_{SH} \tag{11.81}$$

are determined by the ratio of nonlinear time t_{SH} to the time of regular dissipative (viscous) absorption (number Γ), or to the characteristic time α^{-1} of selective absorption (number D).

To calculate the process of excitation of induced oscillations in the resonator, it is necessary to solve (11.80) with the zero initial condition $V(T=0,\theta)=0$. At large values of "slow" time, $T \to \infty$, balance is achieved between the supply of the energy from the source (an oscillating wall) and the losses of three types: viscous , nonlinear and selective. Analysis of the steady-state oscillations can be performed analytically; at the same time, in the steady state, nonlinearity is expressed most strongly, therefore this regime is the most interesting. The solution has the form [24]

$$\frac{V_{ST}(\theta)}{\sqrt{2}} = \pm\left[(1+\cos\theta)+D(1-\cos^2\theta)\frac{2}{\pi}\int_0^\pi V_{ST}(\theta')\sin 2\theta' d\theta'\right]^{1/2}. \tag{11.82}$$

A "+"-sign is used for the half-period $0<\theta\leqslant\pi$; a "−"-sign for $-\pi\leqslant\theta<0$. In the neighborhood of $\theta=0$, a shock front forms. Having no interest in its structure, we have placed the parameter $\Gamma=0$ into the solution (11.82). Allowance for the finiteness of Γ can be done by the method of matched asymptotic expansions (see, e.g. [22]) and it can give only small corrections (in the regime of strongly expressed nonlinearity) to the energy characteristics of the field.

The profiles of one period of oscillations (11.82) are shown in Fig. 11.10 for various values of selective absorption $D=0$, 1, 4, 10, 20. The profile in the presence of only nonlinear absorption ($D=0$) corresponds to the known solution of the inhomogeneous Burgers equation [16]

$$V_{ST}(\theta) = 2\cos(\theta/2)\cdot\operatorname{sgn}\theta. \tag{11.83}$$

With an increase in selective absorption D, the dimensionless amplitude of discontinuity in Fig. 11.10 does not increase, however, an increase in perturbations V_{ST} is observed in the smooth sectors of the profile. At $D \gg 1$, oscillation occurs nearly according to the harmonic law $V_{ST}\approx V_0\sin\theta$ and only at point $\theta=0$ remains a jump at the small relative value $2\ll V_0$.

Thus, with an increase in D, a significant drop in amplitude B_2 of second harmonic 2ω is observed. The beginning of this process is shown in Fig. 11.11. Quenching of wave 2ω slows the energy transfer to higher harmonics 3ω, 4ω, ..., therefore, energy accumulates in the wave of main frequency ω, which practically does not attenuate at all. The increase in the amplitude of the first harmonic $B_1(D)$ is also shown in Fig. 11.11. Here are as well, the dependence $DB_2(D)$ is given. The maximum perturbation value (11.82) $V_{ST}=2$ is achieved at $\theta=0$ for $DB_2\leqslant 0.5$, but for $DB_2>0.5$, the maximum (see Fig. 11.10) shifts to the point θ_{max}, where

$$V_{max}(\theta_{max}) = \frac{1+2DB_2}{\sqrt{2DB_2}}, \quad \theta_{max} = \arccos\frac{1}{2DB_2}. \tag{11.84}$$

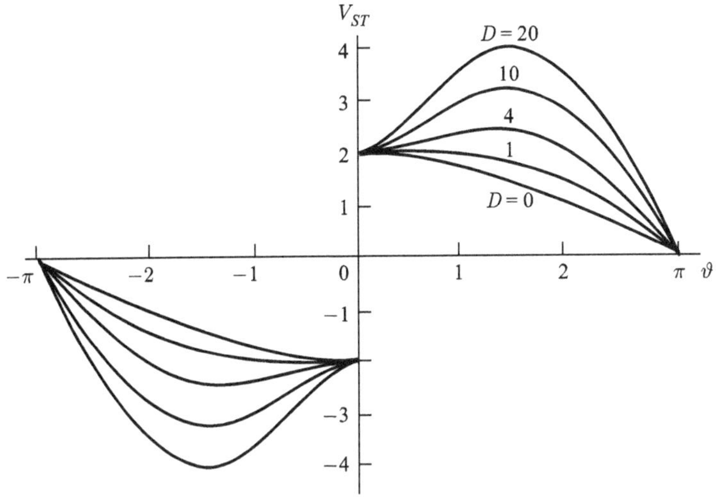

Fig. 11.10 Profiles of one period of one of the two traveling waves forming the nonlinear field in the resonator with selective losses at a frequency of the second harmonic of $D = 0, 1, 4, 10, 20$.

Fig. 11.11 Dependences of the amplitudes of the first and second harmonics, as well as of the product of DB_2, for various values of selective absorption D (solid lines) and "strengthening coefficient" of oscillation energy K accumulated in the cavity of the resonator (dashed line).

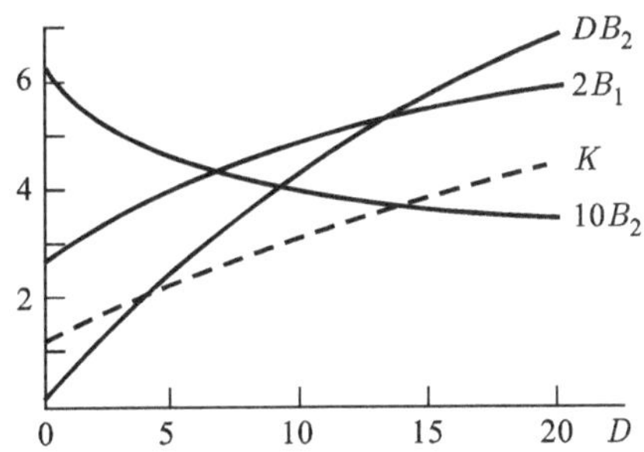

The mean intensity

$$I = \overline{V_{ST}^2} = 2 + DB_2(D) \tag{11.85}$$

also increased with strengthening of selective absorption.

The Q-factor of the resonator in the regime of nonlinear oscillations, which have a complex spectrum, can be determined as the ratio of the maximum velocity in a spectral standing wave $2u_{\max}$ to the amplitude of the velocity A of boundary oscillations:

$$Q = \frac{2u_{\max}}{A} = \sqrt{\frac{2c}{\pi\varepsilon A}}\Phi(2DB_2); \tag{11.86}$$

$$\Phi\,(x \equiv 2DB_2) = \frac{1+x}{\sqrt{x}},\ x > 1; \quad \Phi = 2,\ x \leqslant 1.$$

It is also possible to determine the square of the Q-factor by means of the ratio of these oscillations:

$$Q^2 = \frac{2\overline{u^2}}{A^2/2} = \frac{2c}{\pi\varepsilon A}(2+DB_2)\,. \tag{11.87}$$

Both formulas (11.86), (11.87) describe the increase in Q-factor with an increase in selective absorption D.

Estimates according to these formulas show that, if the right wall $x=L$ of the resonator selectively lets out 98% of the power of decreasing radiation at the frequency of the second harmonic, the Q-factor of the resonator increases by approximately a factor of 3.5, and the energy of oscillations increase by an order of magnitude [24].

11.6 Geometric nonlinearity due to boundary motion

As mentioned in Sect. 11.1, there are methods for suppressing linear and nonlinear losses in a resonator. When it is possible to reduce these losses to a minimum, a process having a geometrical nature can become the defining one. This is caused by nonlinear character of the relationship between the law of motion of a radiating surface and the shape of the running away wave. In problems on radiation of waves, manifestation of such nonlinearity do not accumulate; they are therefore noticeably expressed only at speeds comparable to the speed of sound. Studies [25,26] describe the processes of distortion of noise spectra generated by intensive chaotic oscillations of a piston in a medium with low speed of sound (e.g., in bubbly fluids), as well as interaction of a regular signal and noise (signal attenuation in the presence of the noise component, an avalanche-type broadening of the noise spectrum due to generation of the signal harmonics and others).

At the same time, effects of such geometric (boundary) nonlinearity can be strongly expressed in a resonator where the process of the accumulation of such effects with time is possible. As a result, as shown below, in the steady-state regime, nonlinear effects are determined by the ratio of two small parameters $M=A/c$ and Δ (where A is the amplitude of velocity oscillations for a radiating surface, c is the speed of sound, Δ is the detuning from an exact resonance, the minimum values of which are $\Delta \sim Q^{-1}$). The ratio M/Δ can be a relatively large value in high-Q resonators or during intensive pumping.

Let us examine a layer of linear medium between $x=0$ and $x=L$. The left boundary of the layer completes oscillations and shifts according to the law $x=X(t)$ relative to the mean position $x=0$. The right boundary $x=L$ is immovable.

Let us write the solution of one-dimensional equations of linear acoustics for waves with velocity u and pressure p in the form

$$\begin{aligned} u &= F\left(t-\frac{x-L}{c}\right) - F\left(t+\frac{x-L}{c}\right), \\ \frac{p}{\rho c} &= F\left(t-\frac{x-L}{c}\right) + F\left(t+\frac{x-L}{c}\right). \end{aligned} \tag{11.88}$$

Here c and ρ are the speed of sound and the density of the medium, $F(t)$ is the shape of the traveling wave. This way of writing Eqs. (11.88) ensures fulfillment of the boundary condition $u(t,x=L)=0$. The form of the function $F(t)$ for the steady-state process is determined by the second boundary condition: on the shifted left wall of the resonator, the vibration velocity of the medium should coincide with velocity of the moving wall, e.g.:

$$u(t,x=X(T))=dX/dt. \tag{11.89}$$

Hence,

$$\frac{dX}{dt}=F\left[t+\frac{L}{c}-\frac{1}{c}X(t)\right]-F\left[t-\frac{L}{c}+\frac{1}{c}X(t)\right]. \tag{11.90}$$

With the known low of motion $X(t)$ expression (11.90) is a functional-difference equation for determining the waveform $F(t)$. The inverse problem is of interest when it is necessary to determine the law $X(t)$ of boundary motion, resulting in a wave with the given profile $F(t)$ in the resonator. Note that the inverse problem has an independent significance; since its solution reduces to simper mathematical procedures, we begin our analysis precisely with the inverse problem.

Let us examine the important case of harmonic oscillations of a medium, supposing

$$F(t)=-\frac{A}{2}\frac{\cos\omega t}{\sin kL},\quad k=\frac{\omega}{c}. \tag{11.91}$$

The solution of Eq. (11.88) in this case is

$$u=A\frac{\sin k(L-x)}{\sin kL}\sin\omega t. \tag{11.92}$$

It describes the linear induced oscillations of the layer. If we neglect the movement of the left wall from the mean position $x=0$, the law of its motion, as is seen from (11.92), should also be harmonic:

$$X'(t)=u(t,x=0)=A\sin\omega t. \tag{11.93}$$

At $kL=\pi n$, $n=1,2\ldots$, resonance occurs and the amplitude of oscillations (11.92) increases without limit nearly everywhere, with the exception of point $x=0$ and nodes of the standing wave (11.92). When the established amplitude values are limited by dissipative processes, to find the increase in the level of the limit, it is necessary to increase the amplitude of wall oscillations. Such increase makes it necessary to take into account movement of the boundary, and the law of its movement (11.93) changes significantly.

Thus, we pose the following question: how should the left boundary of the resonator oscillate so that inside the layer, movement of the medium in the form of (11.92) is preserved? By defining $X(t)$, we thus can demonstrate the way how to approach the resonances at high excitation levels. Expression (11.90) for the known function $F(t)$ (11.91) takes the form of an ordinary differential equation:

$$\frac{dX}{dt} = \frac{A}{\sin kL} \sin\left[kL - kX(t)\right] \sin \omega t. \tag{11.94}$$

Solving (11.94), we obtain

$$\cos\left[kX(t) - kL\right] = \frac{\cos kL - \tanh \beta}{1 - \cos kL \cdot \tanh \beta}, \quad \beta = \frac{A}{c}\frac{\cos \omega t}{\sin kL} + D, \tag{11.95}$$

where D is the integration constant.

For definiteness, let us consider at the neighborhood of the main resonance, setting $kL = \pi + \Delta$. Here, detuning $\Delta = \pi\left(\omega - \omega_0\right)/\omega_0$ is taken to be small, which corresponds to the smallness of the relative width of the resonance curve $\omega_0 = \pi c/L$. We also assume a small displacement of the wall in comparison to the wavelength, $k|X| \ll 1$. In other words, the acoustic Mach number $M = A/c$ — defined as the ratio of amplitude of the vibration velocity A for particles in the medium to the speed of sound c — is presumed small. In solving this, the solution (11.95) is simplified and leads to the following form:

$$kX(t) = \Delta\left[1 - I_0^{-1}\left(\frac{M}{\Delta}\right)\exp\left(\frac{M}{\Delta}\cos \omega t\right)\right]. \tag{11.96}$$

Here, I_0 is the modified Bessel function. In going from (11.95) to (11.96), constant D is chosen such that the mean, averaged over period, movement of the wall is equal to zero. The vibration velocity of the boundary is equal to

$$X'(t) = AI_0^{-1}\left(\frac{M}{\Delta}\right)\sin \omega t \cdot \exp\left(\frac{M}{\Delta}\cos \omega t\right). \tag{11.97}$$

Expansion of function (11.97) into Fourier series over sine,

$$X'(t) = 2A\left[I_0\left(\frac{M}{\Delta}\right)\frac{M}{\Delta}\right]^{-1}\sum_{n=1}^{\infty} nI_n\left(\frac{M}{\Delta}\right)\sin n\omega t, \tag{11.98}$$

determines the spectral component of wall oscillations; the term of series (11.98) with number n gives the expression for amplitude of the nth harmonic. Finally, we give here the formula for the mean intensity of boundary oscillations,

$$\overline{X'^2} = \frac{A^2}{2} I_1\left(2\frac{M}{\Delta}\right)\left[\frac{M}{\Delta} I_0^2\left(\frac{M}{\Delta}\right)\right]^{-1}. \tag{11.99}$$

By setting $M \to 0$ in expressions (11.96)–(11.99), we arrive at the obvious result for the linearized problem:

$$X = -\frac{A}{\omega}\cos \omega t, \quad X' = A \sin \omega t, \quad \overline{X'^2} = \frac{A^2}{2}. \tag{11.100}$$

A fundamentally important fact is that small parameters M and Δ are presented in formulas (11.96)–(11.99) in the form of ratio. This means that, in the vicinity of resonance, nonlinear distortions can be noticeably expressed even at small Mach numbers M. This is the essential difference between problems on induced oscillations of a resonator with movable boundaries and waves radiating from an oscillating piston into an unbounded medium. In the latter case, the effects of geometric nonlinearity in passing from $X'(t)$ to $F(t)$ become noticeable only for rates of movement of the piston comparable to the speed of sound [25, 26].

In the opposite case, in a high-Q resonator, small nonlinear distortion caused by the finiteness of wall displacement from the median state $x = 0$ can accumulate with time and lead to strongly expressed nonlinear effects.

Figure 11.12 shows the solution (11.97) to inverse problem [27] for the velocity of the left boundary of the resonator. Precisely this movement of the wall leads to establishment of "linear", in the form of (11.92) oscillations of the medium. The dashed curve in Fig. 11.12 corresponds to small oscillations of wall movement or large detunings from resonance: $M/\Delta \ll 1$. Curves 1–4 correspond to positive detunings and ratios of M/Δ of 1, 2, 4, and 10, respectively. Clearly, with increasing M/Δ , the shapes of the curves are distorted; the spectrum is enriched in harmonics (11.98). At large values of M/Δ, to maintain harmonic oscillations of the medium (11.92), it is necessary to excite the resonator with short bipolar "jerkings" of the wall (curve 5 in Fig. 11.12) one after another with a period of $2\pi/\omega$. The form of these "jerkings" and the maximum value (at $M/\Delta \to \infty$) of their amplitude are described by the following expressions:

$$X'(t) = \sqrt{4\pi}A\left(\frac{M}{2\Delta}\omega^2 t^2\right)^{1/2}\exp\left(-\frac{M}{2\Delta}\omega^2 t^2\right),\ X'_{\max} = A\sqrt{\frac{2\pi}{e}} \approx 1.52A. \quad (11.101)$$

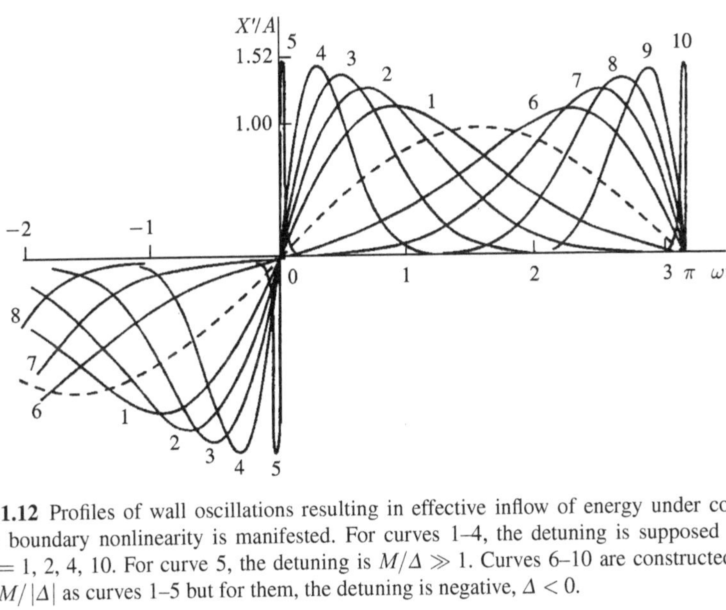

Fig. 11.12 Profiles of wall oscillations resulting in effective inflow of energy under conditions where boundary nonlinearity is manifested. For curves 1–4, the detuning is supposed equal to $M/\Delta = 1, 2, 4, 10$. For curve 5, the detuning is $M/\Delta \gg 1$. Curves 6–10 are constructed for the same $M/|\Delta|$ as curves 1–5 but for them, the detuning is negative, $\Delta < 0$.

The intensity (11.99) of boundary oscillations with an increase in M/Δ decreases, and at large values of this parameter, it behaves as

$$\overline{X'^2} = \frac{A^2}{2}\sqrt{\pi\frac{\Delta}{M}} = \frac{\sqrt{\pi}}{2}c^2M^{3/2}\Delta^{1/2}. \quad (11.102)$$

Curves 6–10 in Fig. 11.12 have been constructed for the same $M/|\Delta|$ as curves 1–5, but for these, the value of detuning is negative, $\Delta < 0$.

Note that the energy stored in the resonator of a medium oscillating according to law (11.92),

$$E = \int_0^L \overline{u^2}dx \approx \frac{A^2L}{4\Delta^2} = \frac{Lc^2}{4}M^2\Delta^{-2}, \quad (11.103)$$

on the contrary, increases with an increase in $M/|\Delta|$. Thus, the ratio of the intensity of oscillations of source $\overline{X'^2}$ (11.102) to the stored energy E (11.103) — a constant in the linear case — with allowance for mobility of the boundary decreases as $A^{-1/2}$.

Lets now turn to solving direct problem [27], assuming that movement of the left boundary of the resonator occurs according to the harmonic law

$$X' = A\sin\omega t, \quad X = -(A/\omega)\cos\omega t. \quad (11.104)$$

Substituting (11.104) into boundary condition (11.90), we arrive at the following form:

$$\sin\omega t = V(\omega t + kL + M\cos\omega t) - V(\omega t - kL - M\cos\omega t). \quad (11.105)$$

Here, it is designated $V = F/A$, $M = A/c$. It is clear that the unknown function $V(\omega t)$ should be periodic (with a period 2π) and the even function of its argument.

In the vicinity of the primary resonance $kL = \pi + \Delta$, formula (11.105) is written as follows:

$$V(y + M\cos y - \Delta) - V(y - M\cos y + \Delta) = \sin y, \quad (11.106)$$

where $y = \omega t$. Using the properties of parity and periodicity $V(y)$, let us look for the solution of the functional equation (11.106) in the form of series,

$$V(y) = \sum_{n=1}^{\infty} B_n\cos ny, \quad (11.107)$$

with the unknown coefficients B_n. We obtain

$$\sum_{n=1}^{\infty} B_n\cdot\sin ny\cdot\sin n(\Delta - M\cos y) = 0.5\sin y. \quad (11.108)$$

Now we multiply both sides (11.108) of $\sin my$ $(m = 1,2,3,\ldots)$ and average the obtained correlation over a period. As a result, we arrive at a system of equations for determing B_n, which has the form

$$\sum_{n=1}^{\infty} B_n J_n(nM)\cos\left(n\Delta - n\frac{\pi}{2}\right) = \frac{M}{4}, \tag{11.109}$$

$$\sum_{n=1}^{\infty} B_n \Big\{ J_{|n-m|}(nM)\sin(n\Delta - |n-m|\frac{\pi}{2}) \\ - J_{n+m}(nM)\sin(n\Delta - (n+m)\frac{\pi}{2}) \Big\} = 0. \tag{11.110}$$

In Eq. (11.110), it is necessary to suppose that $m = 2, 3, \ldots$, but Eq. (11.109) corresponds to a value of $m = 1$.

At $M \to 0$, system (11.109), (11.110) contains an evident transition to the solution of the linear problem: $B_2 = B_3 = \ldots = 0$,

$$B_1 \approx \frac{1}{2\sin\Delta}, \quad V(y) \approx \frac{\cos y}{2\sin\Delta}. \tag{11.111}$$

In general case this system can be solved only by numerical methods. An analytical solution can be obtained only for small values of M and $|\Delta|$. Nevertheless, it is more convenient to start with the functional equation (11.106), which is approximately reduced to the following differential equation:

$$\frac{dV}{dy} = \frac{1}{2}\frac{\sin y}{M\cos y - \Delta}. \tag{11.112}$$

Its solution at $M < |\Delta|$ has the form

$$V = \frac{1}{2M}\ln\frac{1+\sqrt{1-(M^2/\Delta^2)}}{2\left[1-(M/\Delta)\cos y\right]}. \tag{11.113}$$

The integration constant here is chosen such that the average over period $\overline{V} = 0$.

The form of oscillations V as a function of time $y = \omega t$ is shown in Fig. 11.13. The numbers of curves 1–4 correspond to various values of the ratio of small parameters M/Δ of 0.5, 0.7, 0.9 and 0.95. it is clear that at $M/\Delta < 0.5$, the form of oscillations is close to harmonic. As M/Δ approaches unity, nonlinear distortions are manifested even more strongly, leading to the formation of sharp and high positive "peaks".

It is important to note, that curves in Fig. 11.13 exactly describe the pressure pulsations at the closed end of the resonator, since, according to the second of formulas (11.88)

$$p(x = L, t)/\rho c^2 = 2MV(\omega t = y). \tag{11.114}$$

Once the function V (11.113) is found, it is not difficult to calculate the field of the vibration velocity (11.88) in the resonator:

$$u = \frac{c}{2}\ln\frac{1-\frac{M}{\Delta}\cos\left[\omega t + k(x-L)\right]}{1-\frac{M}{\Delta}\cos\left[\omega t - k(x-L)\right]}. \tag{11.115}$$

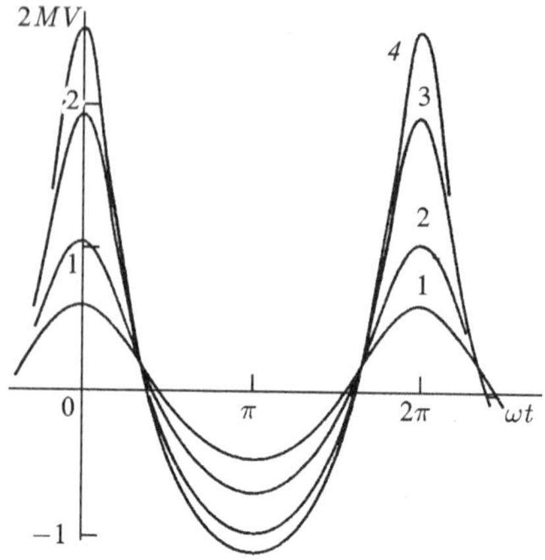

Fig. 11.13 Form of oscillations over time. The numbers of curves 1–4 correspond to the ratio values of $M/\Delta = 0.5$, 0.7, 0.9 and 0.95. At $M/\Delta < 0.5$, the form is close to harmonic. At $M/\Delta \to 1$, nonlinear distortions result in sharp, high positive "peaks". The curves describe pulsations in pressure on the closed end wall of the resonator.

The boundary conditions

$$u(x=L,t)=0,\quad u\left(x=-(A/\omega)\cos\omega t,t\right)=0 \tag{11.116}$$

in the solution (11.115) are fulfilled, but the second of them is approximate, taking into account the smallness of M and Δ, in the neighborhood of the main resonance $kL=\pi$.

The corresponding (11.115) field of acoustic pressure is described by the expression

$$p=\rho c^2\ln\frac{1}{2}\left(1+\sqrt{\frac{M^2}{\Delta^2}}\right)-$$
$$-\frac{\rho c^2}{2}\ln\left\{\left[1-\frac{M}{\Delta}\cos(\omega t+k(x-L))\right]\left[1-\frac{M}{\Delta}\cos(\omega t-k(x-L))\right]\right\}. \tag{11.117}$$

The shapes of pressure oscillations in various sections of the resonator are shown in Fig. 11.14. Curves 1–6 correspond to sections x/L equal 1/6, 1/3, 1/2, 2/3, 5/6 and 1. In order that the curves do not overlap with each other, the first (independent of t) term in formula (11.117) is not taking into account in plotting the graphs. However, it should be remembered that oscillations have a zero constant component and each of curves 1–6 should shift downward along the ordinate axis. As comparison of the curves shows, the temporal forms and spectra of oscillations in various sections of the resonator strongly differ from one another.

The solutions (11.115) and (11.117) can be represented in the form of an expansion into series over the harmonics:

$$\begin{pmatrix}u\\p\end{pmatrix}=\frac{1}{2}\begin{pmatrix}c\\\rho c^2\end{pmatrix}\sum_{n=1}^{\infty}B_n\begin{pmatrix}\sin(n\omega t)\sin(nk(x-L))\\\cos(n\omega t)\cos(nk(x-L))\end{pmatrix}, \tag{11.118}$$

where the coefficients of expansion are

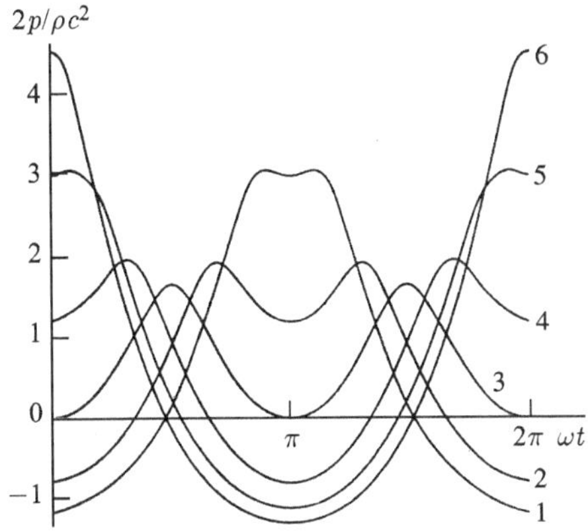

Fig. 11.14 Profiles of pressure oscillations in various sections of the resonator. Curves 1–6 correspond to sections x/L, of 1/6, 1/3, 1/2, 2/3, 5/6 and 1.

$$B_n = \frac{1}{n}\left(\frac{\Delta}{M}\right)^n\left(1-\sqrt{1-\frac{M^2}{\Delta^2}}\right)^n. \tag{11.119}$$

The energy of oscillations (11.103) in the vicinity of the main resonance is

$$E = c^2L\cdot\mathrm{Li}_2\left[\left(\frac{\Delta}{M}\right)^2\left(1-\sqrt{1-\frac{M^2}{\Delta^2}}\right)^2\right], \tag{11.120}$$

here, Li_2 is the second order polylogarithm. The ratio of the energy of nonlinear (11.120) and linear (11.103) oscillations at small M/Δ increases with increasing the Mach number as

$$\frac{E}{E_{lin}} \approx 1+\frac{1}{8}\left(\frac{M}{\Delta}\right)^2. \tag{11.121}$$

At $M/\Delta \to 1$, this ratio tends to $2\pi^2/3$.

In conclusion, we estimate the observability of the described effects of boundary nonlinearity. The condition $M/\Delta \sim 1$ is equivalent to

$$\left(2I/c^3\rho\right)^{1/2}Q \sim 1, \tag{11.122}$$

where I is the intensity of the source exciting the resonator. Clearly, that condition (11.122) is fulfilled for a resonator with a quality-factor of $Q \sim 10^4$ if the intensity $I \sim 2\ \mathrm{W/cm}^2$ (here ρ and c are assumed the same as in water).

The estimate shows that the boundary nonlinearity probably manifested itself in experiments conducted earlier. However, we do not know if these phenomena have been observed in "pure" form, whereas in high-Q resonators it was possible to exclude the background of volume effects and focus the attention on boundary nonlinearity.

The problem on approaching resonance, in the proximity of which the ratio $M > |\Delta|$ remains open. In the steady-state solution, particular features arise; therefore it is necessary to analyze the establishment of oscillations. It is interesting to take into account in a competing factor — weak loss owing to linear dissipation. Let us to discuss these issues.

Proceeding from Eq. (11.24), in which we consider the movement of wall harmonic $\Phi(\xi) = \cos\xi$, by ignoring volume nonlinearity and supposing $\varepsilon = 0$, we have:

$$\frac{\partial U}{\partial T} - M\cos\xi\frac{\partial U}{\partial \xi} + \Delta\frac{\partial U}{\partial \xi} - D\frac{\partial^2 U}{\partial \xi^2} = -\frac{M}{2}\sin\xi. \tag{11.123}$$

If we neglect the mobility of the boundary, that is the second term in the left-hand side of Eq. (11.123), it is not difficult to obtain formulas that describe the transient process of linear oscillations corresponding to the zero initial conditions $U(T = 0,\xi) = 0$:

$$U = B(T)\cos\left[\xi + \varphi(T)\right],$$

$$B = \frac{M}{2}\left[\frac{1 - 2\exp(-DT)\cos\Delta T + \exp(-2DT)}{\Delta^2 + D^2}\right]^{1/2}, \tag{11.124}$$

$$\varphi(T) = \arctan\frac{D}{\Delta} + \arctan\left[\frac{\exp(-DT)\sin\Delta T}{1 - \exp(-DT)\cos\Delta T}\right].$$

At small T, solution (11.124) describes the beginning of the process of establishment and linear increase in amplitude: $U \approx -(MT/2)\sin\xi$. At $T \to \infty$, the solution (11.124) tends to the steady-state form:

$$U \approx \frac{M}{2\sqrt{\Delta^2 + D^2}}\cos\left(\xi + \arctan\frac{D}{\Delta}\right). \tag{11.125}$$

Now proceeding from Eq. (11.123), we solve the direct and inverse problems. The simpler inverse problem consists in finding the law of boundary motion resulting in the establishment of the given waveform in the resonator. One of its solutions,

$$M\Phi(\xi) = kX(\xi - \pi) = \Delta\left[1 - \frac{\exp\left(-\frac{M}{\Delta}\exp(-DT)\cos\xi\right)}{I_0\left(\frac{M}{\Delta}\exp(-DT)\right)}\right],$$
$$U = \frac{M}{2\Delta}\exp(-DT)\cos\xi, \tag{11.126}$$

in the presence of attenuation ($D = 0$) coincides with the accuracy of notation with formula (11.96). In contrast to the formula (11.96), the solution (11.126) is non-stationary. It describes the transition from the "strongly nonlinear" (for values $M/\Delta \gg 1$) regime of wall oscillations to purely harmonic linear oscillations (at $T \to \infty$) occurring as the result of dissipation. Despite the complex from of wall oscillations, oscillations in the layer remain harmonic at any moment of time; at $T \to \infty$ they also attenuate.

Let us now find the law of periodic movement of a wall leading to the formation of "linear" (nonattenuating at $T \to \infty$) oscillations (11.124). Using the fact that (11.124) satisfies the equation

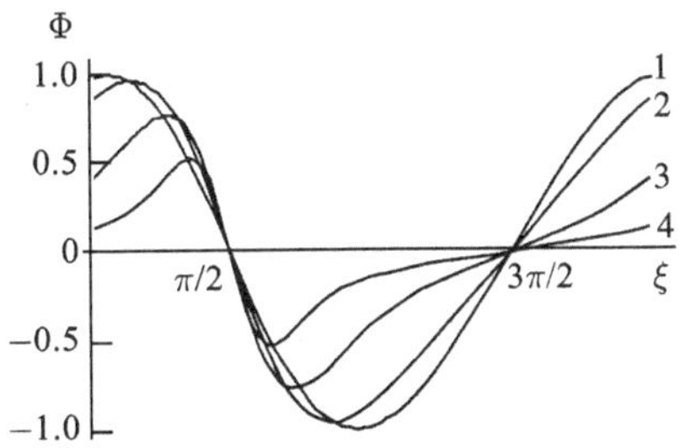

Fig. 11.15 Law of motion of the wall forming "linear" oscillations in the resonator. Values of detuning, dissipation parameter, and "slow" time, are chosen, respectively, as $\Delta = 0, D = 0.01, T = 10^{-1}$, 1, 10, 10^2. At small T, motion is almost harmonic; at large T, the boundary moves in a complex way.

$$\frac{\partial U}{\partial T} + \Delta \frac{\partial U}{\partial \xi} + DU = -\frac{M}{2}\sin\xi, \tag{11.127}$$

and subtracting (11.127) from (11.123), we obtain the equation for function $\Phi(\xi)$:

$$d\Phi/d\xi = 2\Phi\sin(\xi+\varphi) - \sin\xi. \tag{11.128}$$

The solution of Eq.(11.128), which corresponds to a zero average value for the period, is shown in Fig. 11.15. The following parameters have been chosen $\Delta = 0$, $D = 0.01$, $T = 10^{-1}$, 1, 10, 10^2. It is clear from the figure that at small values of time T, movement of the wall is almost harmonic; at large T, the boundary should perform fairly complex movement.

Let us now turn to the solution of the direct problem for determining the waveform according to the given law of motion of the wall of a resonator. If we do not take into account dissipation, it is necessary to solve the equation

$$\frac{\partial U}{\partial T} + (\Delta - M\cos\xi)\frac{\partial U}{\partial \xi} = -\frac{M}{2}\sin\xi. \tag{11.129}$$

The solution (11.129), which periodic in ξ and satisfies the zero initial conditions $U(T=0,\xi) = 0$, takes the following form

$$\begin{gathered}
U = -\frac{1}{2}\ln\left[A(T)\cos\xi + B(T)\sin\xi + C(T)\right], \\
A = \frac{M\Delta}{M^2-\Delta^2}\left[1-\cosh\left(T\sqrt{M^2-\Delta^2}\right)\right], \\
B = \frac{M}{\sqrt{M^2-\Delta^2}}\sinh\left(T\sqrt{M^2-\Delta^2}\right), \\
C = \frac{M^2\cosh\left(T\sqrt{M^2-\Delta^2}\right)-\Delta^2}{M^2-\Delta^2}
\end{gathered} \tag{11.130}$$

for small detunings, when $\Delta^2 < M^2$, and the same form, but with different functions

$$A = \frac{M\Delta}{\Delta^2 - M^2}\left[\cos\left(T\sqrt{\Delta^2 - M^2}\right) - 1\right],$$

$$B = \frac{M}{\sqrt{\Delta^2 - M^2}}\sin\left(T\sqrt{\Delta^2 - M^2}\right), \tag{11.131}$$

$$C = \frac{\Delta^2 - M^2\cosh\left(T\sqrt{\Delta^2 - M^2}\right)}{\Delta^2 - M^2}$$

for large detunings, when $\Delta^2 > M^2$.

Let us discuss formulas obtained in [14]. For small detunings $|\Delta| < M$, the expression under logarithm (11.130) is positively determined and a solution at finite T has no singularities. At $T \to \infty$, it takes the form

$$U = -\frac{1}{2}\ln\left(\frac{\exp(M\sin\xi_* T)}{\sin^2\xi_*}\sin^2\frac{\xi + \xi^*}{2}\right), \quad \sin\xi_* \equiv \sqrt{1 - \frac{\Delta^2}{M^2}}. \tag{11.132}$$

The form of established wave (11.132) has a logarithmic singularity at $\xi = -\xi_*$. Let us introduce the notation

$$U_e(\xi) = \lim_{T\to\infty}\left[U(T,\xi) + \frac{1}{2}MT\sin\xi_*\right] = \ln\sin\xi_* - \ln\sin\frac{\xi + \xi_*}{2}. \tag{11.133}$$

Figure 11.16 shows the graphs of function (11.133) at the moments of time $T =$ 10, 20, 30, 40; for the values of the parameters of $\Delta = 0$, $M = 0.1$. It is seen that at point $\xi = -\xi_*$ in the wave profile, a sharp peak forms, the value of which increases with time. Clearly, growth of the peak is limited by dissipation and at $T \to \infty$, it is necessary to take into account the term $D\partial^2 U/\partial\xi^2$, discarded in transition from (11.123) to (11.129). The solution to the problem with small dissipation by means of matched asymptotic expansions has given the following results. The peak value of perturbation in the established wave profile takes a finite value.

$$U_{\max} = \eta + \ln\left(2\sqrt{\frac{M}{D}}\sin^{3/2}\xi_*\right),$$

$$\eta = \lim_{y\to\infty}\left[\sqrt{2}\ln\int_0^y F\left(\frac{x}{\sqrt{2}}\right)dx - \ln y\right] \approx 0.635. \tag{11.134}$$

The time it takes for steady-state oscillations to form in the resonator is estimated by the formula

$$T_{ST} \sim \frac{1}{M\sin\xi_*}\ln\left(\sqrt{\frac{M}{D}}\sin^{3/2}\xi_*\right). \tag{11.135}$$

Let us draw attention to the fact that in an ordinary resonator (without absorption and nonlinearity), unlimited growth of the amplitude in time is observed when excitation frequencies and eigenfrequencies coincide ($\Delta = 0$). When we take into account the finiteness of displacement of the boundary, such "resonance" behavior

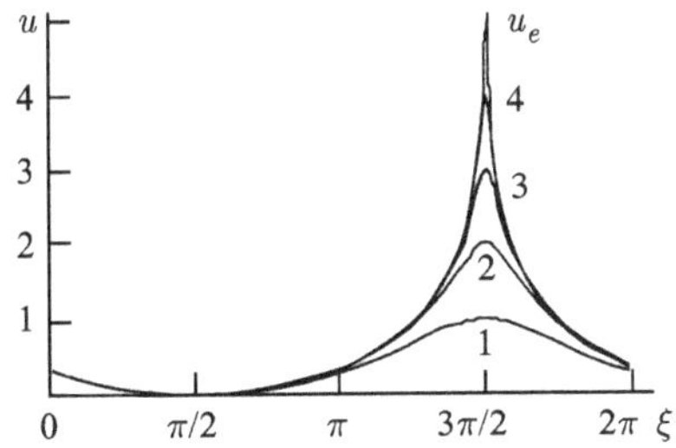

Fig. 11.16 Process of establishing the wave profile $U(T,\xi)$ for small detunings. Moments of time $T = 10$, 20, 30, 40 for values of parameters $\Delta = 0$, $M = 0.1$ are examined.

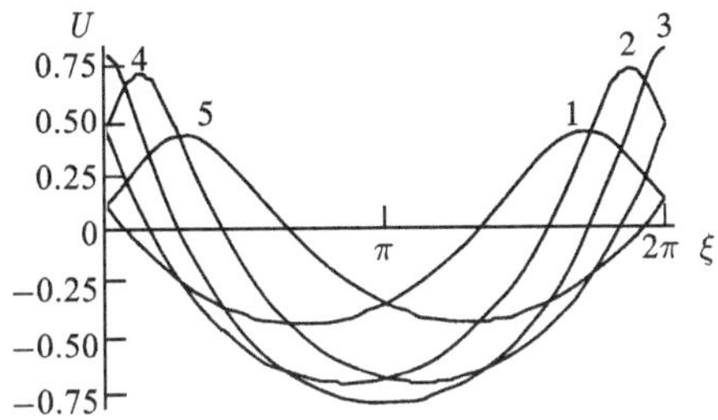

Fig. 11.17 Process of establishing the wave profile $U(T,\xi)$ for large detuning $|\Delta| > M$. Moments of time $T = 2\pi n/6\sqrt{\Delta^2 - M^2}$, $n = 1$, 2, 3, 4, 5, for values of parameters $\Delta = 0.15$, $M = 0.1$ are examined.

occurs not only at $\Delta = 0$, but also in the range of detunings $|\Delta| < M$. In addition, the wave form is essentially non-harmonic. Fig. 11.16 shows that many high harmonics appear in the spectrum.

In the second case, for large detunings $|\Delta| > M$, there are no singularities and the solution takes the form of (11.131). The wave profiles $U(T,\xi)$ for values of the parameters of $\Delta = 0.15$, $M = 0.1$ are shown in Fig. 11.17. Moments of time $T = 2\pi n/6\sqrt{\Delta^2 - M^2}$, $n = 1$, 2, 3, 4, 5 have been chosen. Clearly, "beats" are observed the frequency of which depends on the normalized amplitude M of wall oscillations. The frequency decreases at $M \to |\Delta|$.

11.7 Resonator filled with a cubically nonlinear medium

Cubic nonlinear systems have been studied to a far lesser extent. Their study is interesting for two reasons. First, it is a novel object, the evolution of which significantly differs from the evolution of quadratic nonlinear wave.This problem has been studied in relation to the general theory of nonlinear waves in nondispersive media for plane waves by Lee-Bapty and Crighton [28], and for multidimensional beams by Rudenko and Sapozhnikov [29]. Second, cubic-nonlinear medium attracted great interest in connection with new applied problems. One group of such problems associated with the excitation of strong shear waves for medical applications [30, 31]; another with various geophysical applications [32]. New data have appeared on measuring the cubic nonlinearity of such media as rubber and phantom biological tissue [30].

As shown in Sect. 11.2, the success in the study of standing waves in ordinary quadratic nonlinear resonators has been achieved with the help of an approximation based on the assumption of superposition of two nonlinear waves traveling toward each other. A similar approach can be applied to a cubic resonator, but now the idea of complete independence of counter-propagating waves is unjustified.

In order to show how it is possible to modify these ideas, let us consider a wave equation that models shear waves in any homogeneous solid body (cf. (11.1)):

$$\frac{\partial^2 u}{\partial x^2}-\frac{1}{c^2}\frac{\partial^2 u}{\partial t^2}=-\frac{2\varepsilon}{3c^4}\frac{\partial^2 u^3}{\partial t^2}. \qquad (11.136)$$

Using the method of a slowly changing profile [13], we can deduce from (11.136) a simplified evolutionary equation of the first order,

$$\frac{\partial u}{\partial x}-\frac{\varepsilon}{c^3}u^2\frac{\partial u}{\partial \tau}=0, \qquad (11.137)$$

for simple (Riemann) waves traveling in cubic nonlinear media. Here $\tau=t-x/c$; x is the "slow" coordinate [13].

The properties of cubic nonlinear Riemann waves have been studied in [28] (see also [33]). It is shown that progressive distortion of the initial harmonic wave leads to the formation of an asymmetrical time profile. During further propagation in the profile, discontinuities appear. Unlike to the quadratic nonlinear wave, which contains only compression shocks, each period of the wave in a cubic medium contains both a compression shock front and a rarefaction shock front. Cubic nonlinearity changes velocity of propagation; for acoustic beams, a change in the velocity in a cross section leads to the appearance of self-focusing phenomena [29, 34, 35].

We seek the solution of the Eq. (11.136) in the following form:

$$u=u_+\left(x_1=\mu x,\tau_+=t-\frac{x}{c}\right)+u_-\left(x_1=\mu x,\tau_-=t+\frac{x}{c}\right). \qquad (11.138)$$

Here, $\mu \ll 1$ is a small parameter of the problem; for a cubic nonlinear wave, it is of the order of the acoustic Mach number squared ($\sim \varepsilon u_{\max}^2/c^2$). After substituting (11.138) in (11.136) and neglecting terms on the order of μ^2, μ^3, it is possible to obtain

$$\left(-\frac{2\varepsilon}{3c^4}\right)^{-1}\left(-\frac{2}{c}\frac{\partial^2 u_+}{\partial x\partial\tau_+}+\frac{2}{c}\frac{\partial^2 u_-}{\partial x\partial\tau_-}\right)=\frac{\partial^2 u_+^3}{\partial\tau_+^2}+3\frac{\partial^2 u_+^2}{\partial\tau_+^2}u_-+3u_+^2\frac{\partial^2 u_-}{\partial\tau_-^2}$$
$$+6\frac{\partial u_+^2}{\partial\tau_+}\frac{\partial u_-}{\partial\tau_-}+3\frac{\partial^2 u_+}{\partial\tau_+^2}u_-^2+3u_+\frac{\partial^2 u_-^2}{\partial\tau_-^2}+6\frac{\partial u_+}{\partial\tau_+}\frac{\partial u_-^2}{\partial\tau_-}+\frac{\partial^2 u_-^3}{\partial\tau_-^2}.$$

Let u_+ is a rapidly oscillating function of variable τ_+ and, analogously, u_- be a rapidly oscillating function of variable τ_-. Let the average period values be equal to zero: $\langle u_+\rangle_{\tau_+}=\langle u_-\rangle_{\tau_-}=0$. Averaging the latter expression subsequently over the variables τ_- and τ_+, we obtain the following system [36]:

$$\frac{\partial u_+}{\partial x} - \frac{\varepsilon}{c^3}\left(\langle u_-^2\rangle + u_+^2\right)\frac{\partial u_+}{\partial \tau_+} = 0, \tag{11.139}$$

$$\frac{\partial u_-}{\partial x} + \frac{\varepsilon}{c^3}\left(\langle u_+^2\rangle + u_-^2\right)\frac{\partial u_-}{\partial \tau_-} = 0. \tag{11.140}$$

Equations (11.139) and (11.140), in contrast to analogous equations for a quadratic nonlinear medium, are not independent. They are connected through the mean squares (mean intensities) $I_+ = \langle u_+^2\rangle \neq 0$, $I_- = \langle u_-^2\rangle \neq 0$ of variables u_+, u_-. For standing waves, clearly it is necessary to suppose $I_+ = I_- = I$.

With the method, described in Sect. 11.2, it is not difficult to check that all discarded terms are nonresonant and cannot significantly affect the energy exchange between the harmonics of two waves traveling toward each other.

Nonlinear field in a resonator can be represented as the sum of two exact solutions of Eqs. (11.139) and (11.140) by analogy with the representation for the problem with quadratic nonlinearity. Let us write these two solutions in a convenient for us form:

$$\begin{aligned} u_+ &= F_+\left[\omega t - k(x-L) + \frac{\varepsilon}{c^2}k(x-L)\left(I + u_+^2\right)\right], \\ u_- &= F_-\left[\omega t + k(x-L) - \frac{\varepsilon}{c^2}k(x-L)\left(I + u_-^2\right)\right]. \end{aligned} \tag{11.141}$$

Here $k = \omega/c$ is wavenumber and $x = L$ is the coordinate of the right boundary of the nonlinear medium occupying the region $0 < x < L$. Functions F_+, F_- are determined from boundary conditions.

As is known, during excitation of a field by a harmonic source at frequency ω in cubic medium, only odd harmonic with frequencies of $(2n+1)\omega$ are excited. If ω is close to the frequency of the main mode ω_1, then purely standing wave can be formed only in the case when the frequencies of the higher harmonics are close to the frequencies of the corresponding higher modes. Such a regime is the most interesting, since it allows to accumulate significant amount of energy in the cavity of the resonator even when there is a weak external source. A resonator, whose one wall (e.g., $x = 0$) is rigid, with $u(x = 0, t) = 0$, and at the other wall the vibration velocity has a maximum, i.e.

$$\left.\frac{\partial u}{\partial x}\right|_{x=L} = \left(\frac{\partial u_+}{\partial x} + \frac{\partial u_-}{\partial x}\right)_{x=L} = 0, \tag{11.142}$$

has the required spectrum

$$\omega_{2n+1} = (2n+1)\omega_1, \quad \omega_1 = \frac{\pi c}{2L}, \quad n = 0, 1, 2\ldots \tag{11.143}$$

From boundary condition (11.142), we find that arbitrary functions F_+, F_- in the solutions (11.141) should be the same, $F_+ = F_- = F$. At that, the field in resonator can be written as

$$u = F\left[\omega t - \frac{\omega}{c}(x-L) + \frac{\varepsilon\omega}{c^3}(I+F^2)(x-L)\right] + F\left[\omega t + \frac{\omega}{c}(x-L) - \frac{\varepsilon\omega}{c^3}(I+F^2)(x-L)\right]. \tag{11.144}$$

Let the border $x = 0$ oscillate according to the harmonic law

$$u(x=0,t) = A\sin(\omega t). \tag{11.145}$$

Using (11.145), we reduce (11.144) to the nonlinear functional equation

$$F\left[\omega t + kL - \frac{\varepsilon}{c^2}kL(I+F^2)\right] + F\left[\omega t - kL + \frac{\varepsilon}{c^2}kL(I+F^2)\right] = A\sin(\omega t). \tag{11.146}$$

In order to linearize Eq. (11.146) and formally setting $\varepsilon = 0$, we can find its general solution:

$$F = \frac{A\sin(\omega t)}{2\cos(kL)} + \sum_{n=0}^{\infty}\left[A_{2n+1}\cos(2n+1)\,\omega_1 t + B_{2n+1}\sin(2n+1)\,\omega_1 t\right]. \tag{11.147}$$

When exact resonance takes place, for instance, in the main mode $\omega = \omega_1$, solution (11.147) describes oscillations infinitely increasing in time according to the linear law

$$F = -\frac{A}{\pi}(\omega_1 t)\cos(\omega_1 t). \tag{11.148}$$

This growth, as is known, is limited by absorption, nonlinearity, or the frequency detuning from exact resonance:

$$kL = \frac{\pi}{2} + \Delta, \quad \Delta = (\omega - \omega_1)\frac{L}{c} = \frac{\pi}{2}\frac{(\omega - \omega_1)}{\omega_1} \ll 1. \tag{11.149}$$

Here and further, dimensionless detuning Δ is considered as a small quantity. When taking into account $\Delta \neq 0$, oscillations appear to be modulated; they described by a function limited in time:

$$F = -A\sin^{-1}\left(\frac{\pi}{2}\frac{\omega - \omega_1}{\omega_1}\right)\sin\left(\frac{\omega - \omega_1}{2}t\right)\cos\left(\frac{\omega + \omega_1}{2}t\right). \tag{11.150}$$

Using the method described in [19], we reduce the functional equation (11.142) to the differential equation

$$\frac{\partial U}{\partial T} + \left(\Delta - \frac{\pi\varepsilon}{2}J - \frac{\pi\varepsilon}{2}U^2\right)\frac{\partial U}{\partial \xi} - D\frac{\partial^2 U}{\partial \xi^2} = -\frac{M}{2}\cos\xi. \tag{11.151}$$

For simplicity in writing and comparing the results, here we use the same dimensionless notation as in [19]:

$$U = \frac{F}{c}, \; M = \frac{A}{c}, \; J = \frac{I}{c^2}, \; \xi = \omega t + \frac{\pi}{2}, \; T = \frac{\omega t}{\pi}, \; D = \frac{b\omega^2}{2c^3\rho}L. \tag{11.152}$$

The dissipative term with the second derivative is introduced into Eq. (11.151) in accordance with the procedure described earlier in [19]. Parameter D is also a small quantity; it is proportional to the effective viscosity b and equal to the product of the coefficient of absorption of the wave by the length of the resonator L. In Eq. (11.151), we use two variables: "fast" time ξ and "slow" time T. "Slowness" T is provided by the smallness of the three coefficients in Eq. (11.151), namely: Δ, D and $M \sim U$ (see also [19]).

It is reasonable to begin analysis of standing waves by examining the very simple case of free oscillations. Let the left boundary of the resonator be immobile; therefore, the vibration velocity on it is equal to zero $u(x,t) = 0$, at $x = 0$. On the right boundary, $x = L$, the derivative is equal to zero $\partial u/\partial x = 0$. At the initial moment of time $t = 0$, large-amplitude oscillations arise between the fixed walls. Further evolution of the acoustic field takes place without inflow of additional energy from outside.

This problem is solved on the basis of the approach described above in Sect. 11.2. At that, instead of inhomogeneous equation (11.151) for auxiliary function U, it is necessary to solve a homogeneous equation ($M = 0$). The results of analysis of homogeneous equation corresponding to (11.103) are known and described in detail in [28, 29] for propagating perturbations. However, as shown above, it is possible to construct a standing wave as the sum of two waves traveling toward each other. This procedure is clarified in Fig. 11.18.

It is evident that each of the two initially harmonic waves over the course of a sufficiently long time takes a sawtooth shape. However, in contrast to a quadratic nonlinear medium, every "tooth" (half-period) now has not a triangular, but a trapezoidal shape. The peak of the positive vibration velocity at the front compression jump exceeds two times the module of the negative value of velocity at this jump. On the other hand, the absolute value of the negative value on the expansion jump is twice as large as the positive value.

Using the idea of linear superposition of two waves strongly distorted by cubic nonlinearity, it is possible to construct the profiles of standing waves by a formula that follows from (11.144):

$$\frac{u}{c} = U\left[\omega t - k(x-L)\right] + U\left[\omega t + k(x-L)\right]. \tag{11.153}$$

Here, U describes the distorted profile of a wave propagating in a positive or negative direction along the x-axis. The arguments of both functions U in formula (11.153) do not contain nonlinear terms, because the profiles are constructed within the limits of one period of oscillations. Here it necessary to recall that nonlinear effects are capable of accumulating and significantly distorting the profile over the course of many periods; and their number is proportional to $(\varepsilon M^2)^{-1} \gg 1$ (see, e.g., [1]).

The time profiles measured in various sections of resonator, equal to $L/4$, $L/2$, L, are shown in Fig. 11.19. It is seen as two narrow "impulses" in velocity (positive and negative) form as the section approaches the left end of the resonator. Upon

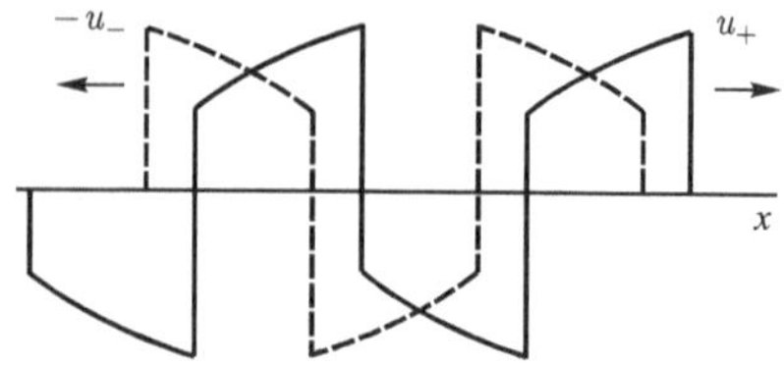

Fig. 11.18 Profiles of waves propagating toward each other in a cubic nonlinear medium.

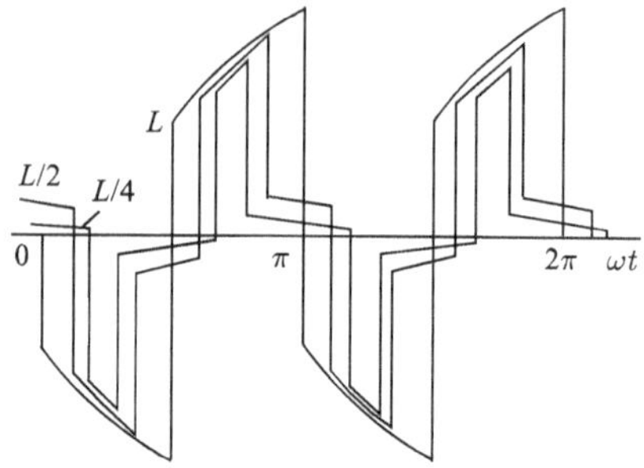

Fig. 11.19 Profiles of a standing wave with time, measured in various sections of the resonator at distances of $L/4$, $L/2$, L from the left end wall.

reaching the wall $x = 0$, these peaks disappear and the velocity here is identically zero.

Let us now consider induced standing waves. Unlike to the homogeneous equation, the complete version of inhomogeneous equation (11.151) has not been investigated and there are no reference results for traveling waves which could possibly be adapted to describe standing waves.

The first attempt at analysis here deals with a very simple method of "harmonic balance", which is well known in the theory of oscillations. According to this method, a weakly nonlinear solution of Eq. (11.151) should be sought in the form

$$U = A(T)\cos\xi + B(T)\sin\xi. \tag{11.154}$$

By separating the factors in front of the functions $\sin\xi$, $\cos\xi$, we obtain a system of two coupled ordinary differential equations:

$$\begin{aligned} \frac{dB}{dT} - \left[\Delta - \frac{3\pi\varepsilon}{8}\left(A^2+B^2\right)\right]A + DB = 0, \\ \frac{dA}{dT} + \left[\Delta - \frac{3\pi\varepsilon}{8}\left(A^2+B^2\right)\right]B + DA = -\frac{M}{2}. \end{aligned} \tag{11.155}$$

It is not difficult to analyze this system by numerical methods.

However, an analytical solution exists that corresponds to the steady-state regime of oscillations being established . This solution is achieved at $T \to \infty$, when the time derivatives in (11.155) vanish: $dA/dT = dB/dT = 0$. The steady-state solution of Eqs. (11.155) looks as follows:

$$\left[\Delta - \frac{3\pi\varepsilon}{8}\left(A^2+B^2\right)\right]^2 + D^2 = \frac{M^2}{4}\left(A^2+B^2\right)^{-1}. \tag{11.156}$$

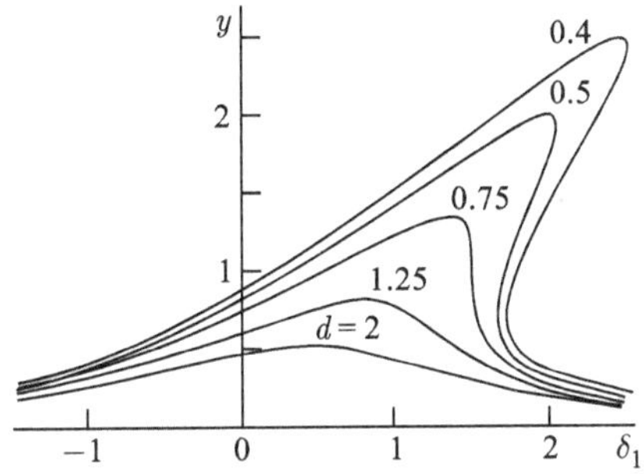

Fig. 11.20 Resonance profiles for the average intensity of oscillations in a cubic-nonlinear resonator for various values of dissipation parameter d.

This solution can be written in a very simple form

$$\delta_1 = y \pm \sqrt{y^{-1} - d^2}, \tag{11.157}$$

by using the following notation:

$$\delta_1 = \frac{\Delta}{C},\ d = \frac{D}{C},\ y = \frac{3}{4}\pi\varepsilon\frac{J}{C},\ C = \left(\frac{3\pi\varepsilon M^2}{32}\right)^{1/3},\ J = \frac{1}{2}(A^2 + B^2). \tag{11.158}$$

The resonance profiles for the average intensity $y(\delta_1)$ are shown in Fig. 11.20 for various values of dissipation parameter $d = 2, 1.25, 0.75, 0.5, 0.4$. With strengthening absorption, , the profile of the frequency response is distorted in shape. When there is a weak absorption, $d < \sqrt{3}/2$, this profile describes an ambiguous function in a certain region of positive values of detuning δ_1.

Let us now consider induced standing waves with discontinuities. Solution (11.156) has been obtained by the method of "harmonic balance" (11.154). Its accuracy is low for strongly distorted waves, especially in the most interesting case when the wave profile contains shock fronts. Therefore, let us consider induced waves described by Eq. (11.151) using a different approach. The steady-state regime, achieved in the limiting case $T \to \infty$, is described by the ordinary differential equation which follows from (11.151):

$$\left(\Delta - \frac{\pi\varepsilon}{2}J - \frac{\pi\varepsilon}{2}U^2\right)\frac{dU}{d\xi} - D\frac{d^2U}{d\xi^2} = -\frac{M}{2}\cos\xi. \tag{11.159}$$

After integration (11.159) taking into account condition $\langle U \rangle = 0$ we obtain the equation of the first order

$$D\frac{dU}{d\xi} + \frac{\pi\varepsilon}{6}U^3 + \left(\frac{\pi\varepsilon}{2}J - \Delta\right)U = \frac{M}{2}\sin\xi. \tag{11.160}$$

To simplify the subsequent formulas, we introduce the new notation

$$V = U\left(\frac{3M}{\pi\varepsilon}\right)^{-1/3}, \quad j = J\left(\frac{3M}{\pi\varepsilon}\right)^{-2/3},$$
$$\Gamma = D\left(\frac{\pi\varepsilon}{24}M^2\right)^{-1/3}, \quad \delta = \frac{\Delta}{3}\left(\frac{\pi\varepsilon}{24}M^2\right)^{-1/3}, \tag{11.161}$$

which differ somewhat from those previously used notation of (11.158). Thus, the average intensities j and y differ only by a numerical factor on the order of unity, as well as other pairs: the dimensionless dissipation coefficients Γ and d, and normalized detunings δ and δ_1. These differences are a result of considerations of simplicity. The notation in (11.158) allows us to write solutions (11.155), (11.156) in its simplest form (11.157), while the notation (11.161) makes it possible to reduce the equation (11.160) to the following form:

$$\Gamma\frac{dV}{d\xi} + V^3 + 3(j-\delta)V = \sin\xi. \tag{11.162}$$

Clearly, weakly absorbing media are the most interesting, since nonlinear phenomena in such media can be strongly expressed. In order to describe the wave profile in a perfect medium without dissipation, we set $\Gamma = 0$ in Eq. (11.162). As is shown below, the approximation $\Gamma \to 0$ is everywhere correct, with the exception of a small neighborhood of shock fronts. This approximation corresponds to neglecting the derivative, which turns differential equation (11.162) into an algebraic equation. However, this new equation

$$f(V) = V^3 + 3(j-\delta)V = \sin\xi, \tag{11.163}$$

is not a usual cubic equation, because its solution should satisfy the additional integral conditions

$$\langle V\rangle = \frac{1}{2\pi}\int_0^{2\pi} V d\xi = 0, \quad \langle V^2\rangle = \frac{1}{2\pi}\int_0^{2\pi} V^2 d\xi = j. \tag{11.164}$$

Therefore, constant j in (11.163) is not known a priori; it should be determined only after a solution is found (11.163) with an arbitrary value of j.

Here various situations are possible, and we will examine them individually.

1. Let the mean intensity be larger that the detuning, i.e., $j - \delta \equiv a^2 > 0$. Equation (11.163) for this case takes the form

$$f(V) = V^3 + 3a^2V = \sin\xi. \tag{11.165}$$

The qualitative behavior of the solution is shown in Fig. 11.21. The form of the solution in time (the wave profile) is found simply by constructing a graph. First, in accordance with the equation $f(V) = \sin\xi$, an illustrative point is found that slides along the profile $f(V)$ with increasing time ξ in the cycle $A \to B \to C \to A$. Second, we construct "horizontal" projection of the motion of this point, which gives the wave profile $V(\xi) = f^{-1}[V(\xi)]$, where f^{-1} is the inverse function with respect to function f.

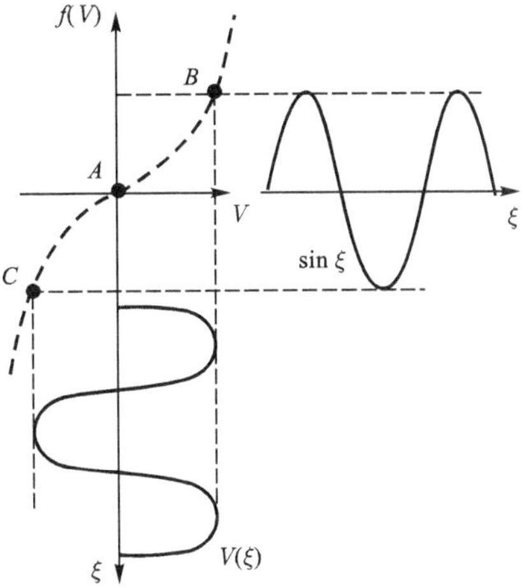

Fig. 11.21 Analysis of the wave profile in graph form. Profile $f(V)$ is shown by the dashed line, along which moves the "vertical" projection of function $\sin\xi$. Movement begins at moment $\xi = 0$ at point A; then oscillations occur between points B and C.

Clearly, profile $V(\xi)$ for this case has no singularity, since the function $f(V)$ is monotonous. The period and polarity of $V(\xi)$ are the same as in right-hand side of Eq. (11.165), formed by the function $\sin\xi$. Of course, wave $V(\xi)$ is distorted; its spectrum contains higher harmonics, because the graph of function $f(V) = V^3 + 3a^2V$ is not a straight line. The difference between $V(\xi)$ and $\sin\xi$, which manifests itself in nonlinear distortion of the wave, strengthens with increasing amplitude of oscillations.

2. Let the mean intensity be equal to the detuning, i.e., $j - \delta = 0$. Equation (11.163) for this case

$$f(V) = V^3 = \sin\xi, \tag{11.166}$$

has an exact solution:

$$V = \sin^{1/3}(\xi) = \sum_{n=1}^{\infty} B_{2n-1}\sin[(2n-1)\xi],\; j = \frac{1}{\sqrt{\pi}}\Gamma\left(\frac{5}{6}\right) \approx 0.64. \tag{11.167}$$

Expansion into Fourier series contains only odd harmonics with amplitudes of

$$B_{2n-1} = \frac{3}{2^{4/3}}\frac{\Gamma(7/3)}{\Gamma(2/3+n)\Gamma(5/3-n)},\; B_{2n} = 0,\; n = 1, 2, 3, \ldots \tag{11.168}$$

Obviously, there are no even harmonics in this expansion, since the nonlinearity of the medium is not quadratic, but cubic.

Numerical estimate (11.167) points to an upper limit for the case $j - \delta > 0$. Apparently, the increase in the detuning in the limits of the interval $-\infty < \delta < 0.64$ leads to an increase in intensity from zero to 0.64.

3. Let the positive detuning be larger than the mean intensity, i.e., $j - \delta \equiv -a^2 < 0$, **and, in addition,** $2a^3 > 1$. Equation (11.163) for this case is

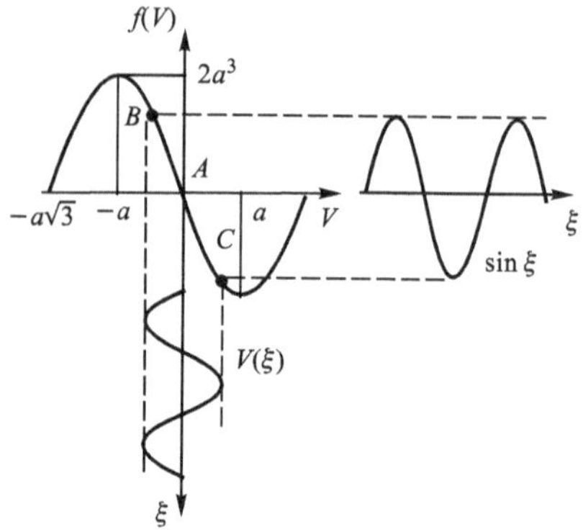

Fig. 11.22 Analysis of the wave profile in graph form (by analogy to Fig. 11.21) for large detunings $\delta = j + a^2$ in the case $2a^3 > 1$.

$$f(V) = V^3 - 3a^2 V = \sin\xi. \tag{11.169}$$

The behavior of the solution of (11.169) is analyzed in Fig. 11.22. It is seen that oscillations of the right-hand side of Eq. (11.169) lead to the movement of the illustrative point in the cycle $A \to B \to C \to A$ along the profile $V(\xi)$. Analogously to case 1, the wave profile $V(\xi)$ is distorted by nonlinearity, but does not contain discontinuities. The polarity of oscillations in function $V(\xi)$ is inverse to $\sin\xi$, in contrast to the profile shown in Fig. 11.21.

4. Let a positive detuning be greater than the mean intensity, i.e., $j - \delta \equiv -a^2 < 0$, **but** $2a^3 < 1$. This case is most difficult for analysis because in some sectors of the wave profile discontinuities occur.

Let us examine Eq. (11.169), supposing that $0 < 2a^3 < 1$. As well, algebraic equation (11.169) has one real root for $|\sin\xi| > 2a^3$ and three real roots for $|\sin\xi| < 2a^3$. Supposing $2a^3 < \sin\xi < 1$, we find the single root V_1:

$$V_1 = \sqrt[3]{0.5\sin\xi + 0.5\sqrt{\sin^2\xi - 4a^6}} + \sqrt[3]{0.5\sin\xi - 0.5\sqrt{\sin^2\xi - 4a^6}}. \tag{11.170}$$

For values $0 < \sin\xi < 2a^3$ we find the three real roots

$$V_1 = 2a\cos f(\xi), \quad f(\xi) \equiv \frac{1}{3}\arccos\frac{\sin\xi}{2a^3}, \tag{11.171}$$

$$V_2 = -a\cos f(\xi) - \sqrt{3}a\sin f(\xi), \tag{11.172}$$

$$V_3 = -a\cos f(\xi) + \sqrt{3}a\sin f(\xi). \tag{11.173}$$

From Eq. (11.169) it follows that the solution should change sign if function $\sin\xi$ becomes negative.

In order qualitatively to construct the shape of the wave profile, we turn to Fig. 11.23. Let movement begin at point A from a value of $V = 0$ at $\xi = 0$. From expressions (11.171)–(11.173) we find that at $\xi = 0$ there are three roots: $V_1 = a\sqrt{3}$, $V_2 = -a\sqrt{3}$, $V_3 = 0$. It is clear that as the argument increases in the in-

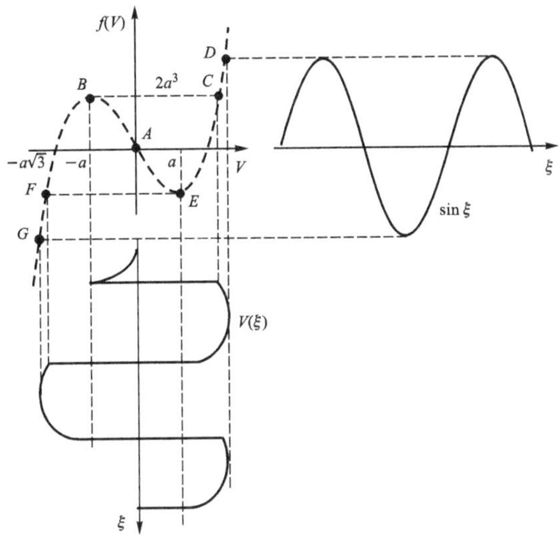

Fig. 11.23 Analysis of the wave profile in graph form (by analogy to Fig. 11.22) for large positive detunings $\delta = j + a^2$ in the case $2a^3 < 1$.

terval $0 \leqslant \xi < \xi_S$, which is denoted $\sin \xi_S = 2a^3$, it is necessary to choose the third root $V = V_3$.

When the argument achieves a value of $\xi = \xi_S$, the solution changes abruptly from the value of $V = V_3(\xi_S) = -a$ to $V = V_1(\xi_S) = 2a$, which corresponds to a jump from state B to state C. On interval CD there is a unique real solution $V = V_1$ (11.170), which reaches a maximum at point D with $\xi = \pi/2$:

$$V(\pi/2) = V_1(\pi/2) = \sqrt[3]{0.5 + 0.5\sqrt{1-4a^6}} + \sqrt[3]{0.5 - 0.5\sqrt{1-4a^6}}. \quad (11.174)$$

With further growth of variable ξ it passes through $\xi = \pi - \xi_S$ and solution V_1 changes its analytical representation from (11.170) to (11.171).

With the value of the argument of $\xi = \pi$, function $\sin\xi$ changes its sign and root V_1, as follows from Eq. (11.169), should change from $a\sqrt{3}$ to $-a\sqrt{3}$. However, solution V should not be discontinuous at a value of $\xi = \pi$, so its representation should be changed, using instead of V_1 the roots V_2 or V_3. In this case, from formulas (11.172) and (11.173), we choose root V_2, which changes from $-a\sqrt{3}$ to $a\sqrt{3}$ at $\xi = \pi$, while $V_3 = 0$ at $\xi = \pi$. Thus, if $\xi = \pi$ the solution $V = V_1(\xi)$ changes to $V = V_2(\xi)$, remaining thereby continuous.

This latter representation is correct up to a value of $\xi = \pi + \xi_S$. With an argument of $\xi = \pi + \xi_S$ solution completes a new jump from value of $V = V_2(\pi + \xi_S) = a$ to $V = V_1(\pi + \xi_S) = -2a$, corresponding to a jump from point E to point F.

With further increase in the argument to a value of $\xi = 3\pi/2$, solution $V = V_1(\xi)$ achieves a minimum corresponding to point G in Fig. 11.23:

$$V(3\pi/2) = V_1(3\pi/2) = -\sqrt[3]{0.5 + 0.5\sqrt{1-4a^6}} - \sqrt[3]{0.5 - 0.5\sqrt{1-4a^6}}. \quad (11.175)$$

Expression (11.175) differs from (11.174) only in sign.

In the transition from increasing argument ξ by means of a value $\xi = 2\pi$, function $\sin\xi$ again changes its sign and root V_1 changes from $-a\sqrt{3}$ to $a\sqrt{3}$. Since the solution should be continuous at $\xi = 2\pi$, it is necessary to describe it not by root $V_1(\xi)$, but one of the other roots $V_2(\xi)$ or $V_3(\xi)$. From expressions (11.172) and (11.173) we find that with the argument ξ, which increases from a value of $\xi = 2\pi$, the roots are $V_2(2\pi) = -a\sqrt{3}$, $V_3(2\pi) = 0$.

Thus, when passing through the value of the argument $\xi = 2\pi$ to maintain continuity of the solution, it is necessary to replace its representation from $V_1(2\pi - 0) = -a\sqrt{3}$ on to $V_2(2\pi + 0) = -a\sqrt{3}$. Note here that use of the root $V_3 = 0$ in the beginning of movement $\xi = 0$ was an exception related to choosing an initial condition that does not agree with the established oscillation regime. To describe steady-state periodic movement, it is necessary to use a different root and to set $V(2\pi) = V_2(2\pi) = -a\sqrt{3}$.

The next jump occurs at $\xi = 2\pi + \xi_S$, where V changes from $V = V_2(2\pi + \xi_S) = -a$ to $V = V_1(2\pi + \xi_S) = 2a$. This jump has already been described at $\xi = \xi_S$ and, thus, the first period of oscillations $V(\xi)$ has been studied in its entirety.

In analyzing the behavior of the solution in the latter case, $j - \delta \equiv -a^2 < 0$, $0 < 2a^3 < 1$, we supposed that the function describing the wave profile contains discontinuities. The above-discussed compression jumps (from $V = -a$ to $V = 2a$) and expansion jumps (from $V = a$ to $V = -2a$) can occur only in the case when states B and E of the illustrative point are unstable and, in the opposite case, if states C and F of the point are stable.

To analyze the stability, we examine Eq. (11.162) taking into account the term contained in the derivative, as well as the small parameter Γ:

$$\Gamma dV/d\xi + V^3 - 3a^2V = \sin\xi. \tag{11.176}$$

Here there are two time scales: "slow" time ξ and "fast" time ξ/Γ. For movement along segment BC, the "slow" time should be "frozen", $\xi = \xi_S$, and $\sin\xi_S = 2a^3$. Consequently, Eq. (11.176) takes the form

$$\Gamma dV/d\xi = -(V+a)^2(V-2a). \tag{11.177}$$

To study the stability of point B, it is necessary to set $V = -a + V'$ in (11.177) and linearize this equation in relation to the small deviation V':

$$\Gamma dV'/d\xi = 3aV'^2. \tag{11.178}$$

The solution of this equation,

$$V' = \frac{V'(0)}{1 - 3aV'(0)\xi/\Gamma}, \tag{11.179}$$

shows that any positive initial perturbation $V'(0) > 0$ is an increasing function of "fast" time and point B is unstable. Leaving point B, the perturbation increases and the system moves in the direction of point C. Eq. (11.177) demonstrates that C is an immobile point, because in it $V = 2a$ and $dV/d\xi = 0$. To study the stability of state C, in Eq. (11.177), we set $V = 2a + V'$. The corresponding linearized equation has the form

$$\Gamma \frac{dV'}{d\xi} = -9a^2 V', \quad V' = V'(0) \exp\left(-9a^2 \frac{\xi}{\Gamma}\right), \tag{11.180}$$

demonstrating stability: any initial perturbation $V'(0)$ fades with an increase in "fast" time. The instability of point E and stability of point F, validating the second jump of EF, is proved by an analogous method.

We now construct a resonance curve for induced discontinuous oscillations. An analysis of the frequency characteristic can be performed now by numerical methods with the solutions to Eqs. (11.169). Clearly, the resonance curve for discontinuous waves should differ significantly from quasi linear characteristics calculated by the method of harmonic balance, which are illustrated in Fig. 11.20.

Here, in order to clarify the fundamental features, we confine ourselves only to a qualitative analysis of the simplified model problem by taking into account the complex nonlinear behavior of the system, discussed with the help of Figs. 11.21–11.23.

To obtain the analytical formulas, we pass from statement of the problem based on cubic equation (11.163) with the additional conditions (11.164),

$$f(V) = V^3 + 3(j-\delta)V = \sin\xi, \quad \langle V \rangle = 0, \quad \langle V^2 \rangle = j, \tag{11.181}$$

to the "model" statement of the problem:

$$f(V) = V|V| + 2(j-\delta)V = \varphi(\xi), \quad \langle V \rangle = 0, \quad \langle V^2 \rangle = j. \tag{11.182}$$

Here, the cubic parabola is approximated by the two arcs of a quadratic parabola, and the sine in the righthand side of (11.181) is replaced by the function

$$\varphi(\xi) = 1 - \xi^2, \ -1 < \xi < 1; \quad \varphi(\xi) = -1 + (\xi - 2)^2, \ 1 < \xi < 3, \tag{11.183}$$

which periodically continues with period four. Model (11.182), (11.183) admits a full analytical solution. An analysis is carried out below according to the scheme described above for induced shocked waves; paragraphs (1 – 4) both there and here fully consistent with each other.

1. Let the mean intensity be greater than the detuning, i.e., $j - \delta \equiv a^2 > 0$. Eq. (11.182) for this case in the half-period $-1 < \xi < 1$ takes the form

$$f(V) = V^2 + 2a^2 V = 1 - \xi^2. \tag{11.184}$$

Averaging the solution to quadratic equation (11.184), we find

$$\langle V^2 \rangle = j = \delta(a^2) + a^2, \tag{11.185}$$

where

$$\delta(a^2) = a^4 - a^2 + \frac{2}{3} - a^2\left(1+a^4\right)\arcsin\left(1+a^4\right)^{-1/2}. \tag{11.186}$$

2. Let the mean intensity be equal to the detuning, i.e., $j - \delta = 0$. Eq. (11.182) for this case at $-1 < \xi < 1$ takes the form

$$f(V) = V^2 = 1 - \xi^2. \tag{11.187}$$

Averaging the solution, we find $\delta = j = 2/3$.

3. Let a positive detuning be greater than the mean intensity, i.e., $j - \delta \equiv -a^2 < 0$, **and, in addition,** $a^2 > 1$. Eq. (11.182) for this case in interval $-1 < \xi < 1$ has the form

$$f(V) = V^2 - 2a^2V = 1 - \xi^2. \tag{11.188}$$

Calculation gives the formula

$$\delta(a^2) = a^4 + a^2 - \frac{2}{3} - a^2\left(a^4 - 1\right)\ln\sqrt{\frac{a^2+1}{a^2-1}}. \tag{11.189}$$

4. Let a positive detuning be greater than the mean intensity, i.e., $j - \delta \equiv -a^2 < 0$,**but** $a^2 < 1$. Averaging of the solution to Eq. (11.188) taking into account the jumps described in Fig. 11.23, leads in this case to the expression

$$\begin{aligned}\delta(a^2) = {} & 3a^4 + a^2 + \sqrt{1-a^4}\left[\frac{2}{3} + \left(\frac{1}{3} + \frac{\sqrt{2}}{2}\right)a^4\right] \\ & + \frac{1}{2}a^2\left(1-a^4\right)\ln\sqrt{\frac{1-a^2}{1+a^2}} \\ & + \frac{1}{2}a^2\left(1+a^4\right)\left[\arcsin\sqrt{\frac{1-a^4}{1+a^4}} + \arcsin\frac{1}{\sqrt{1+a^4}}\right].\end{aligned} \tag{11.190}$$

The three branches of the resonance curve (11.186), (11.189) and (11.190) are continuously sewn together, as is shown in Fig. 11.24. Comparing the curves in Figs. 11.24 and 11.20, we can draw the conclusion that the frequency characteristic in Fig. 11.24 is the limit curve for the characteristics of Fig. 11.20 in the case when viscosity tend to zero or the amplitude of boundary oscillations tends to infinity. As well, nonlinear absorption in the shock fronts exceeds the regular linear absorption. As seen in Fig. 11.24, the intensity of the field in the resonator cannot exceed a certain maximal value; that is, nonlinear saturation takes place.

The ambiguity in the dependence of field intensity on detuning in Fig. 11.24 is apparently eliminated when a maximum is achieved by smooth increase or decrease in the frequency of wall oscillations, by analogy to induced oscillations in the Duffing equation model. The latter problem is laid out in many textbooks on the theory

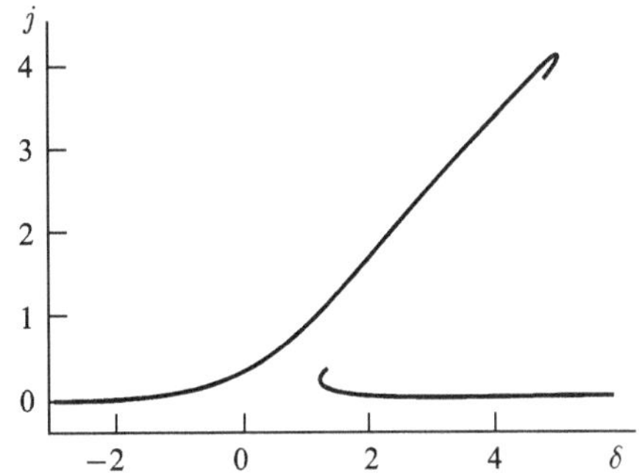

Fig. 11.24 Resonance profile for discontinuous oscillations in a cubic nonlinear acoustic resonator.

of oscillations and is very detailed in [37]. If this analogy is true, for the maximum field intensity to be achieved, the frequency of wall oscillations should increase; after the maximum has been achieved, the intensity decreases jumpwise to some small value. If we now decrease the frequency, then the inverse jump from the lower to the higher branch takes place at another, lower, value of detuning δ.

Thus, the gradual change in the frequency of wall oscillations at high amplitudes leads to a hysteresis. In the codomain of the detuning values, where there is a hysteresis, bistability is possible in connection with the described jumps, as well as a transfer from regular to chaotic oscillations of the field in the resonator. This analogy, however, can seem incorrect, because a resonator is a more complex system that is not described by ordinary differential equations. To check the validity of the analogy and ascertain the behavioral features of the resonator as those of a nonlinear distributed system, further investigations are necessary.

References

1. O.V. Rudenko, S.I. Soluyan, *Theoretical Foundations of Nonlinear Acoustics* (Plenum, New York, 1977)
2. V.B. Braginsky, V.P. Mitrofanov, V.I. Panov, *Systems with Small Dissipation* (University of Chicago Press, Chicago, 1986)
3. V.B. Braginsky, V.P. Mitrofanov, K.V. Tokmakov, Energy dissipation in the pendulum mode of the test mass suspension of the gravitational wave antenna, Phys. Lett. A **218**, 164–166 (1996)
4. L.K. Zarembo, O.Y. Serdobolskaya, I.P. Chernobai, Effect of phase shifts accompanying the boundary reflection on the nonlinear interaction of longitudinal waves in solids, Sov. Phys. Acoust. **18**, 333–338 (1972)
5. Y.A. Ilinskii, B. Lipkens, T.S. Lucas, T.W.V. Doren, E.A. Zabolotskaya, A theoretical model of nonlinear standing waves in an oscillating closed cavity, J. Acoust. Soc. Am. **104**, 623–636 (1998)
6. R. Landbury, Ultrahigh-energy sound wave promise new technologies, Physics Today **51**, 23–24 (1998)
7. C.C. Lawrenson, B. Lipkens, T.S. Lucas, D.K. Perkins, T.W.V. Doren, Measurements of macrosonic standing waves in oscillating closed cavities, J. Acoust. Soc. Am. **104**, 623–636 (1998)
8. O.V. Rudenko, Artificial nonlinear media with a resonant absorber, Sov. Phys. Acoust. **29**, 234–237 (1983)

9. O.V. Rudenko, Nonlinear acoustics - achievements, prospects, problems, Priroda (Nature) (7), 16–26 (1986). In Russian
10. V.G. Andreev, V.E. Gusev, , A.A. Karabutov, O.V.Rudenko, O.A. Sapozhnikov, Enhancement of the q-factor of a nonlinear acoustic resonator by means of a selectively absorbing mirror, Sov. Phys. Acoust. **31**, 162–163 (1985)
11. V.V. Kaner, O.V. Rudenko, R.V. Khokhlov, Theory of nonlinear oscillations in acoustic resonators, Sov. Phys. Acoust. **23**, 432–437 (1977)
12. V.V. Kaner, O.V. Rudenko, Propagation of waves of finite amplitude in acoustic waveguides, Mosc. Univ. Phys. Bulletin **33**, 63–70 (1978)
13. M.B. Vinogradova, O.V. Rudenko, A.P. Sukhorukov, *Theory of Waves*, 2nd edn. (Nauka, Moscow, 1990). In Russian
14. O.V. Rudenko, A.V. Shanin, Nonlinear phenomena accompanying the development of oscillations excited in a layer of a linear dissipative medium by finite displacements of its boundary, Acoust. Phys. **46**, 334–341 (2000)
15. A.A. Karabutov, O.V. Rudenko, Nonlinear plane waves excited by volume sources in a medium moving with transonic velocity, Sov. Phys. Acoust. **25**, 306–309 (1979)
16. A.A. Karabutov, E.A. Lapshin, O.V. Rudenko, Interaction between light waves and sound under acoustic nonlinearity conditions, Sov. Phys. JETP **44**, 58–68 (1976)
17. O.V. Rudenko, Feasibility of generation of high-power hypersound with the aid of laser radiation, JETP Lett. **20**, 203–206 (1974)
18. M.J.O. Strutt, *Lame, Mathieu and Related Functions in Physics and Technology* (Edwards Brothers, New York, 1944)
19. O.V. Rudenko, C.M. Hedberg, B.O. Enflo, Nonlinear standing waves in a layer excited by the periodic motion of its boundary, Acoust. Phys. **47**, 452–460 (2001)
20. B.O. Enflo, C.M. Hedberg, O.V. Rudenko, Resonant properties of a nonlinear dissipative layer excited by a vibrating boundary: Q-factor and frequency response, J. Acoust. Soc. Am. **117**, 601–612 (2005)
21. M. Abramovitz, I.A. Stegun, *Handbook of Mathematical Functions* (Dover, N.Y., 1970)
22. M.V. Dyke, *Perturbation Methods in Fluid Mechanics* (Parabolic, Stanford, 1975)
23. W. Chester, J. Resonant oscillations in closed tubes, Fluid Mech. **18**, 44–66 (1964)
24. O.V. Rudenko, A.L. Sobisevich, L.E. Sobisevich, C.M. Hedberg, Enhancement of energy and q-factor of a nonlinear resonator with an increase in its losses, Dokl. Phys. **47**, 188–191 (2002)
25. O.V. Rudenko, Nonlinear distortion of waves excited in a linear medium by finite chaotic piston vibrations, Dokl. Phys. **43**, 346–348 (1998)
26. O.V. Rudenko, Nonlinear interactions of regular and noise spectra in intense radiation from a piston in a linear medium, Acoust. Phys. **44**, 717–721 (1998)
27. O.V. Rudenko, Nonlinear oscillations of linearly deformed medium in a closed resonator excited by finite displacements of its boundary, Acoust. Phys. **45**, 351–356 (1999)
28. I.P. Lee-Bapty, D.G. Crighton, Nonlinear wave motion governed by the modified burgers equation, Philos. Trans. Roy.Soc. London **323**, 173–209 (1987)
29. O.V. Rudenko, O.A. Sapozhnikov, Wave beams in cubically nonlinear nondispersive media, JETP **79**, 220–229 (1994)
30. V.G. Andreev, T.A. Burlakova, Measurement of shear elasticity and viscosity of rubberlike materials, Acoust. Phys. **53**, 44–47 (2007)
31. A.P. Sarvazyan, O.V. Rudenko, S.D. Swanson, J.B. Folwkes, S.Y. Emelianov, Shear wave elasticity imaging - a new ultrasonic technology of medical diagnostics, Ultrasound in Medicine and Biology **24**, 1419–1436 (1998)
32. L.A. Ostrovsky, P.A. Johnson, Dynamic nonlinear elasticity in geomaterials, La Rivista del Nuovo Cimento **24**, 1–47 (2001)
33. O.V. Rudenko, S.N. Gurbatov, C.M. Hedberg, *Nonlinear Acoustics through Problems and Examples* (Trafford, 2010)
34. O.V. Rudenko, Nonlinear sawtooth-shaped waves, Phys. Usp. **38**, 965–989 (1995)
35. O.V. Rudenko, O.A. Sapozhnikov, Self-action effects for wave beams containing shock fronts, Phys. Usp. **47**, 907–922 (2004)

36. O.V. Rudenko, C.M. Hedberg, B.O. Enflo, Finite-amplitude standing acoustic waves in a cubically nonlinear medium, Acoust. Phys. **53**, 455–464 (2007)
37. A.P. Kuznetsov, S.P. Kuznetsov, N.M. Ryskin, *Nonlinear Oscillations* (Fizmatlit, Moscow, 2002). In Russian

Appendix
Fundamental Properties of Generalized Functions

A.1 Definition of generalized functions

First of all, let us give some material from mathematics, which is necessary for defining the concept of a *generalized function*. Let us consider the following *linear functional*:

$$T[\varphi(x)] = \int f(x)\varphi(x)dx. \tag{A.1}$$

Here $\varphi(x)$ is the argument of the functional, and $f(x)$ is its *kernel*, which determines the properties of the functional. Almost everywhere below, we consider these functions being real, mapping points x of the number line **R** onto **R**. Thereby, the linear functional $T[\varphi(x)]$ maps the "points" $\varphi(x)$ of a certain *functional space* $\mathscr{D}$ ($\varphi(x) \in \mathscr{D}$) onto points of the real line **R**. Let us call the above mentioned "functional points" $\varphi(x)$ *test functions*, and $\mathscr{D}$ — a *space of test functions*. Let us also note that indefinite integrals, in our notation, symbolize definite integrals over the entire x-axis, i.e. having the integration limits $\pm\infty$.

As soon as the space $\mathscr{D}$ of test functions is chosen, the *conjugate to it* set $\mathscr{D}'$ of *linear continuous functionals* $T[\varphi]$, underlying the following definition of generalized functions, becomes automatically defined.

The space $\mathscr{D}$ of test functions is subject to several natural requirements: it needs to be sufficiently large, in order to identify any continuous kernel $f(x)$ through values of the integral (A.1). In other words, as soon as values of the functional $T[\varphi]$ are known for a certain set of test functions $\varphi \in \mathscr{D}$, values of the kernel $f(x)$ may be defined for all x. On the other hand, the space $\mathscr{D}$ of test functions is subjected to quite strict limitations, in order to obtain as rich a set $\mathscr{D}'$ of linear continuous functions $T[\varphi]$ as possible.

It so happens that the *family of infinitely differentiable compact functions* is a suitable candidate for the space $\mathscr{D}$. Below, we reserve the notation $\mathscr{D}$ precisely for this functional space. Recall that a function $\varphi(x)$ is called *compact*, if it has a bounded *support*. In its turn, the support supp φ of a function $\varphi(x)$ is the closure of the set of the points on the x-axis, where $\varphi(x) \neq 0$. Now we are fully prepared to formulate the definition of a generalized function.

By definition: *any linear functional $T[\varphi]$, which is continuous on the set $\mathscr{D}$ of infinitely differentiable compact functions is called a generalized function.*

Let us give a few comments on the above-formulated definition of a generalized function:

1. Recall that a functional $T[\varphi]$ is called *linear*, if, for all test functions $\varphi(x) \in \mathscr{D}$ and $\psi(x) \in \mathscr{D}$, the following equality holds:

$$T[\alpha\varphi + \beta\psi] = \alpha T[\varphi] + \beta T[\varphi] ,$$

where α and β are arbitrary constants.

2. A functional T on $\mathscr{D}$ is called *continuous*, if for any functional sequence $\{\varphi_k(x)\}$, whose elements belong to the space $\mathscr{D}$ and converge at $k \to \infty$ to a certain test function $\varphi(x) \in \mathscr{D}$, the corresponding numerical sequence $\{T[\varphi_k]\}$ converges to the number $T[\varphi]$.

Thereby convergence of the sequence $\{\varphi_k(x)\}$ is understood in the following sense:

a) The supports of all elements of the sequence $\{\varphi_k\}$ belong to some bounded set of the x-axis.

b) At $k \to \infty$, the functions $\varphi_k(x)$ and all their derivatives $\varphi_k^{(n)}(x)$ uniformly converge to the function $\varphi(x)$ and its derivatives, respectively.

If it is possible to express a linear continuous functional $T[\varphi(x)]$ in the form of the integral (A.1), whose kernel $f(x)$ is an everywhere continuous, bounded function, then such a functional is called a *regular generalized function* and it is identified with the kernel $f(x)$. In this sense, all ordinary continuous functions are regular generalized functions.

There are, however, linear continuous functionals $T[\varphi]$, which cannot be identified with a certain continuous kernel $f(x)$. In this case, such a linear continuous functional $T[\varphi(x)]$ is called a *singular generalized function.*

Perhaps the most important example of a singular generalized function is the functional

$$\delta[\varphi(x)] = \varphi(0), \tag{A.2}$$

mapping the test function $\varphi(x) \in \mathscr{D}$ onto its value at $x = 0$. This, obviously linear and continuous, functional is called a *delta function.* Although this functional cannot be expressed by means of the usual integral (A.1), it is often written in the following symbolic integral form:

$$\delta[\varphi(x)] = \int \delta(x)\varphi(x)dx = \varphi(0), \tag{A.3}$$

where $\delta(x)$ is the symbol for the delta function, which is defined by its *sifting property*, according to which the value $\varphi(0)$ corresponds to the "integral" in (A.3).

The advantage of such a symbolic notation consists in its clarity during actual computations using delta functions. Let us illustrate the "transparency" of the symbolic integral notation of generalized functions, related to the delta function, by expressing the functional $\delta_a[\varphi(x)] = \varphi(a)$ by means of the equality

$$\int \delta(x-a)\varphi(x)dx = \varphi(a) \tag{A.4}$$

via a delta function $\delta(x-a)$ with a shifted argument. In the following, we will predominantly use the mathematically not quite correct, but convenient while solving applied problems, symbolic integral notation of the form (A.3), (A.4).

While discussing properties of generalized functions, an important role is played by the concept of the *support* of a generalized function. Namely, a linear continuous functional T is considered to be equal to zero in an open domain B of the x-axis, if $T[\varphi(x)] = 0$ for all test functions $\varphi(x)$, whose supports belong to the set B. The closure of the largest open domain, where a generalized function T is not equal to zero is called the *support of the generalized function* T, and it is denoted by supp T. From the definition, it immediately follows that the support of the delta function consists of the only point $x = 0$, i.e.

$$\operatorname{supp} \delta(x) = \{0\}. \tag{A.5}$$

Note that if a generalized function T is compact, i.e. it has a bounded support, then it is possible to relax the conditions, imposed on the set of test functions $\varphi(x)$, by requiring only their infinite differentiability ($\varphi \in C^\infty$). For instance, it is possible to assign in (A.6) $\varphi(x) \equiv 1$, which leads to the *normalization condition* of the delta function

$$\int \delta(x)dx = 1. \tag{A.6}$$

In conclusion, let us discuss an important for physical applications, but ignored by mathematicians, property of the delta function. It belongs to a comparatively narrow class of *scale-invariant* functions, whose argument may be dimensional; e.g., it may be a spatial coordinate x or time t; and which has a non-zero dimension depending on the dimension of the argument. Namely, the delta function, which has the spatial coordinate x as its argument, has the dimension of the reciprocal of x:

$$[\delta(x)] = L^{-1},$$

as it is seen from the normalization condition (A.6). Thus $\delta(x)$ has the same dimension as the power function $1/x$.

A.2 Fundamental sequences

Although the delta function is, in principle, non-representable in the integral form (A.3), it can, nevertheless, be obtained as the limit of a sequence of ordinary integrals

$$T_k[\varphi(x)] = \int f_k(x)\varphi(x)dx, \tag{A.7}$$

corresponding to the sequence of locally integrable functions $\{f_k(x)\}$. This limit is understood in the sense that, for some sequence $\{f_k(x)\}$, $k = 1,2,\ldots$, and for any test function $\varphi(x) \in \mathscr{D}$, the following limiting equality holds:

$$T_k[\varphi(x)] \to \varphi(0) \quad (k \to \infty).$$

It this is indeed so, it is said that the sequence $\{f_k(x)\}$ *weakly converges* to the delta function.

The choice of a weakly converging to the delta function $\delta(x)$ sequence of regular linear functionals $\{T_k\}$, defined by their kernels $\{f_k(x)\}$, is not unique. Therefore it is useful to discuss several such sequences, which give an opportunity better to understand the "internal structure" of delta functions.

Example 1. Let us consider a family of Gaussian functions (see Fig. A.1)

$$\gamma_\varepsilon(x) = \frac{1}{\sqrt{2\pi\varepsilon}} \exp\left(-\frac{x^2}{2\varepsilon}\right), \tag{A.8}$$

depending on the parameter $\varepsilon > 0$, and take the sequence of functions $f_k(x) = \gamma_{1/k}(x)$, $k = 1,2,\ldots$ as a weakly convergent sequence. Note that the factor in front of the exponential function on the right-hand side of Eq. (A.8) is chosen so that the normalization condition holds:

$$\int \gamma_\varepsilon(x)dx = 1.$$

At $k \to \infty$, the value of the parameter ε tends to zero, and the Gaussian function, "approximating the delta function," becomes progressively higher and narrower, "concentrating" at the origin, while conserving the total area under the Gaussian curve so that, for all elements of the Gaussian-function sequence, the above-mentioned normalization condition is satisfied. ∎

Example 2. Another, important for theory and applications, weakly convergent to the delta function sequence is generated by the *Cauchy distribution*

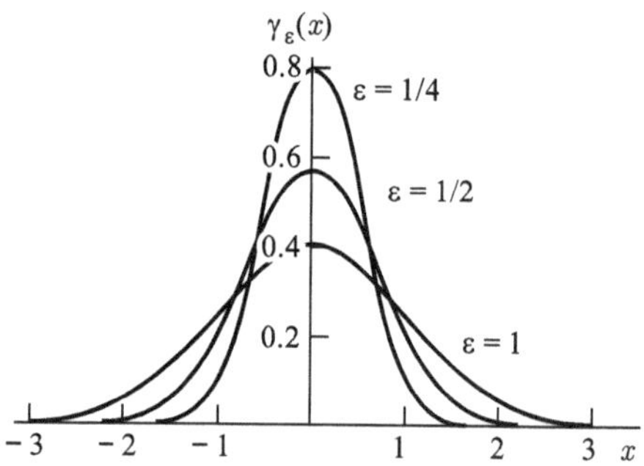

Fig. A.1 Three elements of the sequence of Gaussian functions (A.8), weakly convergent to the delta function, for $k = 1;2;4$ ($\varepsilon = 1;1/2;1/4$).

$$c_\varepsilon(x) = \frac{1}{\pi} \frac{\varepsilon}{x^2 + \varepsilon^2}. \tag{A.9}$$

Although, at first sight, the profiles of the Cauchy distribution seem similar to the Gaussian curves discussed above, there are significant distinctions between them. The main one is the fact that the Cauchy distribution tends to zero at $x \to \pm\infty$ rather slowly, according to the power law

$$c_\varepsilon(x) \sim \frac{\varepsilon}{\pi x^2}.$$

Nevertheless, it can be rigorously proved that for any continuous function $\varphi(x)$ with a bounded support, the following limiting relation holds:

$$\lim_{\varepsilon \to 0} \int c_\varepsilon(x)\varphi(x)dx = \varphi(0),$$

which means that the sequence $\{c_{1/k}(x)\}$ is weakly convergent to the delta function. ∎

Example 3. Let us consider the following complex-valued function

$$f_\varepsilon(x) = \sqrt{\frac{i}{2\pi\varepsilon}} \exp\left(-\frac{ix^2}{2\varepsilon}\right), \tag{A.10}$$

depending on the parameter $\varepsilon > 0$. Note that the absolute value of this function does not depend on x:

$$|f_\varepsilon(x)| = \frac{1}{\sqrt{2\pi\varepsilon}}$$

and tends to ∞ at $\varepsilon \to 0$. When $\varepsilon \to 0$, the functions (A.10) weakly converge to the delta function. Physicists explain this, at first sight, surprising phenomenon by the fact that, with decreasing ε, the function (A.10) oscillates faster and faster, coming to a standstill only in a small neighborhood of the point $x = 0$. As a result, the integral of the product of the function (A.10) and any test function $\varphi(x) \in \mathscr{D}$, converges to $\varphi(0)$ at $\varepsilon \to 0$. The real part of the function $f_{\varepsilon=1}(x)$ (A.10), demonstrating its oscillatory nature, is plotted in Fig. A.2. ∎

Example 4. Note that in all examples shown above, the elements of the weakly converging to the delta function fundamental sequences $\{f_\varepsilon(x)\}$ have been constructed by using one *mother function* $f(x)$, scaled according to the following general rule:

$$f_\varepsilon(x) = \frac{1}{\varepsilon} f\left(\frac{x}{\varepsilon}\right). \tag{A.11}$$

Thereby the properties of the limiting delta function do not depend on the specific shape of the original function $f(x)$. Indeed, any function satisfying the normalization condition

$$\int f(x)dx = 1, \tag{A.12}$$

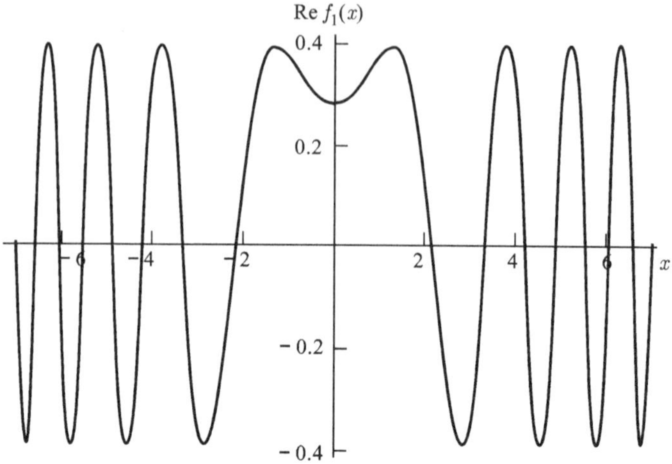

Fig. A.2 Real part of the first element of the sequence $\{f_{1/k}(x)\}$ (A.10) weakly converging to the delta function.

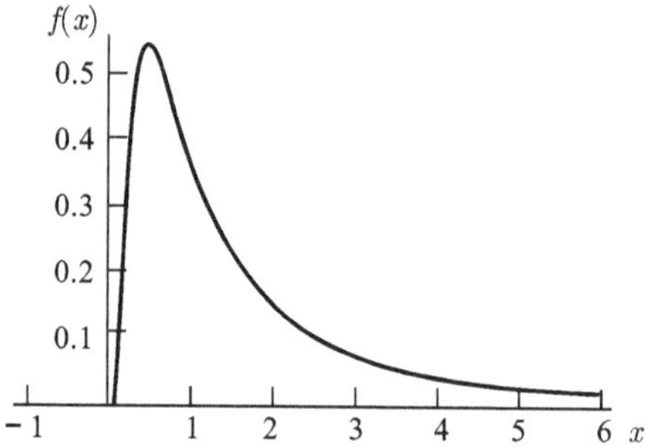

Fig. A.3 Function $f(x)$ (A.13) generating the family of scaled functions (A.11), which are weakly converging to the delta function at $\varepsilon \to 0$.

generates its own fundamental sequence, which weakly converges to the delta function. In particular, the function $f(x)$ does not have to be symmetrical (even), For instance, the fundamental sequence (A.11), generated by scaling the function

$$f(x) = \begin{cases} x^{-2} e^{-1/x}, & x > 0; \\ 0, & x \leqslant 0, \end{cases} \tag{A.13}$$

which is plotted in Fig. A.3, also approximates the delta function. ∎

In the following, we will write such *right-sided*, similar to (A.13), functions, which are identically equal to zero at all $x < 0$, in a more compact form

$$f(x) = x^{-2} e^{-1/x} \Theta(x),$$

which uses the so-called *Heaviside function* (it is also called *unit step function*)

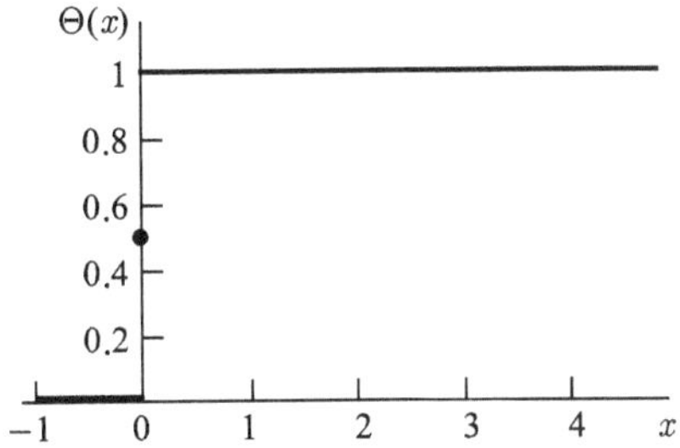

Fig. A.4 Heaviside function $\Theta(x)$ (A.14).

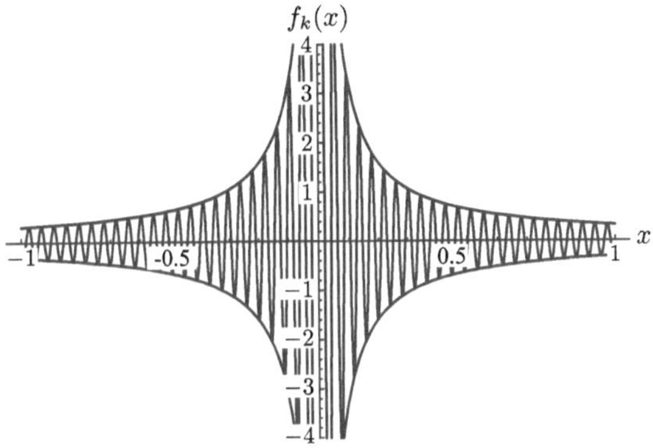

Fig. A.5 Function $f_k(x)$ (A.15) at $k = 150$ and its envelope $\pm 1/\pi|x|$.

$$\Theta(x) = \begin{cases} 1, & x > 0, \\ \frac{1}{2}, & x = 0, \\ 0, & x < 0. \end{cases} \tag{A.14}$$

The Heaviside function, which plays an important role in the subsequent analysis, is depicted in A.4.

Example 5. Let us consider a fundamental sequence, which, at first sight, contradicts common sense,

$$f_k(x) = \frac{1}{\pi} \frac{\sin(kx)}{x}, \tag{A.15}$$

weakly converging to the delta function at $k \to \infty$. Contrary to the sequences of Gaussian functions and Cauchy distributions, it does not converge at $k \to \infty$ to zero for all $x \neq 0$. Instead, it "cross-hatches" the area between the branches of the hyperbola $\pm 1/\pi|x|$ (see Fig. A.5). Nevertheless, even here, it is possible to prove that the sequence $\{f_k(x)\}$ (A.15) weakly converges to the delta function at $k \to \infty$.

Example 6. Another instructive example of a fundamental sequence, weakly convergent to the delta function, is given by the related symmetric

$$s_\varepsilon(x) = \frac{\varepsilon}{2} |x|^{\varepsilon - 1} \tag{A.16}$$

and right-sided

$$a_\varepsilon(x) = \varepsilon x^{\varepsilon-1}\Theta(x) \tag{A.17}$$

functions. Let us rigorously prove that the latter indeed converges to the delta function at $\varepsilon \to 0$. To this end, we take the integral

$$T_\varepsilon[\varphi(x)] = \int a_\varepsilon(x)\varphi(x)dx$$

and find its limit at $\varepsilon \to 0$ for an arbitrary test function $\varphi(x) \in \mathscr{D}$. According to (A.17), we have

$$T_\varepsilon[\varphi(x)] = \varepsilon \int_0^M x^{\varepsilon-1}\varphi(x)dx.$$

The lower, zero limit of integration takes the presence of the Heaviside function on the right-hand side of Eq. (A.17) into account. The bounded upper limit $M < \infty$ is due to the compactness of the function $\varphi(x)$. In other words, the upper limit takes into account the fact that for any test function $\varphi(x)$, there is such $M < \infty$ that $\varphi(x) \equiv 0$ as soon as $x > M$.

Recall that for any continuously differentiable function, there is such $\theta_x \in (0,x)$, that the following equality holds:

$$\varphi(x) = \varphi(0) + x\varphi'(\theta_x).$$

Here the prime denotes the derivative of the function $\varphi(x)$ with respect to its argument x. Hence

$$T_\varepsilon[\varphi(x)] = \varphi(0)\varepsilon \int_0^M x^{\varepsilon-1}dx + \varepsilon \int_0^M x^\varepsilon \varphi'(\theta_x)dx. \tag{A.18}$$

Note also that since

$$\varepsilon \int_0^M x^{\varepsilon-1}dx = M^\varepsilon \to 1 \qquad \varepsilon \to 0,$$

the first term on the right-hand side of Eq. (A.18) converges to $\varphi(0)$ at $\varepsilon \to 0$, while the second term in (A.18) converges to zero. Indeed, $\varphi'(x)$ — as any differentiable function — is everywhere bounded, i.e. it satisfies the inequality $|\varphi'(x)| < N, N < \infty$. Apart from that, the remaining integral

$$\varepsilon \int_0^M x^\varepsilon dx = \frac{\varepsilon}{1+\varepsilon} M^{\varepsilon+1}$$

converges to zero at $\varepsilon \to 0$. In other words, the last term in (A.18) tends to zero at $\varepsilon \to 0$. Hence, summarizing the above said, we have

$$\lim_{\varepsilon \to 0} T_\varepsilon[\varphi(x)] = \varphi(0).$$

The latter equality precisely means that the function $a_\varepsilon(x)$ (A.17) weakly converges to the delta function $\delta(x)$ at $\varepsilon \to 0$. ∎

Note that some of the above listed fundamental sequences, which are weakly convergent to the delta function, look, at first sight, rather peculiar. Nevertheless, we will encounter all of them while analyzing various specific problems of the theory of generalized functions.

A.3 Derivatives of generalized functions

Infinite differentiability of the chosen set $\mathscr{D}$ of test functions $\varphi(x)$ allows us to define for any generalized function T derivatives of any order. Existence of generalized derivatives of any, even singular, generalized functions is one of important advantages of the generalized function theory in comparison with the ordinary differential calculus. Before giving the definition of the derivative of a generalized function, we recall the well-known formula of integration by parts, applied to a continuously differentiable function $f(x)$ and an arbitrary test function $\varphi(x)$.

$$\int f'(x)\varphi(x)dx = -\int f(x)\varphi'(x)dx. \qquad \text{(A.19)}$$

The non-integral term is absent here, since a compact test function is identically equal to zero outside a certain domain o the x-axis, hence

$$f(x)\varphi(x)|_{-\infty}^{\infty} = 0.$$

By interpreting a continuous function $f(x)$ as a regular generalized function T (as the kernel of a regular linear continuous functional), let us rewrite Eq. (A.19) in terms of generalized functions

$$T'[\varphi(x)] = -T[\varphi'(x)]. \qquad \text{(A.20)}$$

Note also that if $\varphi(x) \in \mathscr{D}$, then, by virtue of infinite differentiability of any test function, its derivative also belongs to the chosen set of test functions: $\varphi'(x) \in \mathscr{D}$. In other words, both sides of Eq. (A.20) are generalized functions on the set of test functions $\mathscr{D}$. Therefore Eq. (A.20) is used in order to define the derivative of a generalized function:

If T is a generalized function, its derivative T' is defined as a generalized function appearing on the right-hand side of Eq. (A.20).

Similarly, the nth derivative of a generalized function T is defined as the right-hand side of the equality

$$T^{(n)}[\varphi(x)] = (-1)^n T[\varphi^{(n)}(x)]. \qquad \text{(A.21)}$$

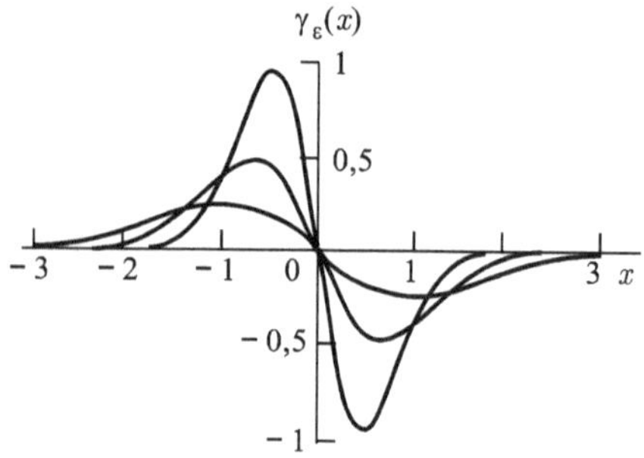

Fig. A.6 Profiles of the function $\gamma'_\varepsilon(x)$ (A.22) weakly convergent at $\varepsilon \to 0$ to the derivative of the delta function $\delta'(x)$. The curves are shown for the following values of $\varepsilon = 1; 1/2; 1/4$.

Example 1. Let us consider a translated delta function $\delta(x-a)$, defined by the sifting property (A.4). As follows from (A.21), its nth derivative $\delta^{(n)}(x-a)$ is defined by the equality

$$\int \delta^{(n)}(x-a)\varphi(x)dx = (-1)^n \varphi^{(n)}(a).$$

In particular,

$$\int \delta'(x-a)\varphi(x)dx = -\varphi'(a).$$

Note also that it is easy to find a fundamental sequence weakly converging to $\delta'(x)$ by differentiating, with respect to x, the elements of a fundamental sequence weakly converging to the delta function $\delta(x)$. For instance, the derivative of the Gaussian function (A.8)

$$\gamma'_\varepsilon(x) = -\frac{x}{\varepsilon\sqrt{2\pi\varepsilon}} \exp\left(-\frac{x^2}{2\varepsilon}\right) \tag{A.22}$$

weakly converges at $\varepsilon \to 0$ to the derivative $\delta'(x)$. The function $\gamma'_\varepsilon(x)$ is plotted in Fig A.6 for several values of ε. ∎

A.4 The Leibniz formula

Another linear operation, generating a new generalized function on the basis of an arbitrary generalized function T and an infinitely differentiable[1] function $g(x) \in C^\infty$, is the operation of multiplication of the generalized function T by $g(x)$. The corresponding, natural from the point of view of ordinary calculus, definition is:

The *product* gT *of a function* $g(x) \in C^\infty$ *and a generalized function* T *is the generalized function, defined by the equality*

$$(gT)[\varphi(x)] = T[g(x)\varphi(x)]. \tag{A.23}$$

[1] In the following, for brevity, we will call infinitely differentiable functions *smooth functions*.

Indeed, this definition copies, in terms of functionals, the obvious integral identity

$$\int [g(x)f(x)]\varphi(x)dx \equiv \int f(x)[g(x)\varphi(x)]dx.$$

The right-hand side of Eq. (A.23) remains within the framework of the definition of a generalized function as a linear continuous functional on the set of test functions $\mathscr{D}$, since the product $g(x)\varphi(x)$ of an arbitrary smooth function $g(x)$ and a test function $\varphi(x)$ from the set $\mathscr{D}$ also belongs to the set $\mathscr{D}$.

Example 1. Let us apply the just formulated definition to the product of a smooth function $g(x)$ and the delta function $\delta(x)$. By using the symbolic integral notation, let us write

$$\int g(x)\delta(x-a)\varphi(x)dx = g(a)\varphi(a).$$

It is possible to interpret the factor $\varphi(a)$ on the right-hand side as a consequence of the sifting property of the delta function $\delta(x)$. Accordingly, let us rewrite the last equality in the symbolic form

$$g(x)\delta(x-a) = g(a)\delta(x-a). \tag{A.24}$$

Figuratively speaking, the delta function "kills" its prefactor $g(x)$, by turning the function $g(x)$ into the constant $g(a)$. In the following, we will uncover a deeper meaning in the noted *sifting property of a factor of the delta function.*

The operations of differentiation of generalized functions and multiplication of them by a smooth function obey the familiar from ordinary calculus *Leibniz formula* for the derivative of the product of two functions. In particular, it is easy to prove that

if $g(x)$ is a smooth function, and T is a generalized function, then

$$(g(x)T)' = g'(x)T + g(x)T'. \tag{A.25}$$

It is also possible to prove the validity of the *general Leibniz formula*

$$(g(x)T)^{(n)} = \sum_{m=0}^{n} \binom{n}{m} g^{(m)}(x)T^{(n-m)}. \tag{A.26}$$

Sometimes, it is more convenient to use not the "classical" formulas of generalized differentiation (A.25) or (A.26), but other relations, which take into account the specifics of singular generalized functions. Let us verify this by using the following example.

Example 2. According to the definition of generalized derivative, we have

$$\int \left(g(x)\delta(x-a)\right)^{(n)} \varphi(x)dx = (-1)^n \int \delta(x-a)g(x)\varphi^{(n)}(x)dx = g(a)\varphi^{(n)}(a)\,.$$

By writing this relation in the form similar to (A.24), we obtain

$$(g(x)\delta(x-a))^{(n)} = g(a)\delta^{(n)}(x-a). \tag{A.27}$$

This equation considerably expands possibilities of the sifting property of a factor of the delta function (A.24):

A smooth factor of the delta function may be replaced with a constant, which can be taken outside the symbol of the functional.

Thus, e.g., the following identities hold:

$$\cos(x)\delta(x) \equiv \delta(x), \quad \sin(x)\delta(x) \equiv 0.$$

We emphasize that only the delta function possesses the sifting property of its factor. Let us verify this by using the product of $g(x)$ and $\delta'(x)$ as an example. It is easy to show, by applying the rules of differentiation and multiplication of a generalized function by a smooth fanction, that

$$g(x)\delta'(x-a) = g(a)\delta'(x-a) - g'(a)\delta(x-a). \tag{A.28}$$

From here, it is seen that the product of $g(x)$ and $\delta'(x)$ depends not only on $g(a)$, but also on the value $g'(a)$ of the derivative of the factor at the point a.

In the particular case $g(x) = x$ and $a = 0$, Eq. (A.28) is reduced to

$$x\delta'(x) = -\delta(x). \tag{A.29}$$

It is also not difficult to derive more general, useful relations, e.g.,

$$x^n\delta^{(n)}(x) = (-1)^n\, n!\, \delta(x), \quad n = 0, 1, 2, \ldots$$

or

$$x^m\delta^{(n)}(x) = (-1)^m \frac{n!}{(n-m)!}\,\delta^{(n-m)}(x) \quad (0 \leqslant m \leqslant n).$$

Example 3. Equation (A.29) may be interpreted in the sense that $\delta(x)$ serves as a generalized solution of the differential equation

$$xy'(x) + y(x) = 0.$$

In other words, the generalized solution of this ordinary differential equation of the first order has the following form:

$$y(x) = \frac{A}{x} + B\delta(x),$$

and contains two arbitrary constants A and B. Such generalized solutions of differential equations may play an important role during an analysis of various scientific and applied problems.

We also note that the sifting property of a factor of the delta function discovered above and other properties of singular generalized functions allow us to find

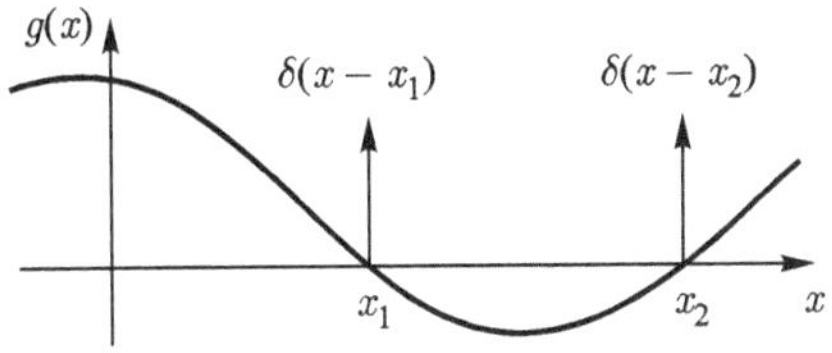

Fig. A.7 Schematic illustration of the solution of the algebraic equation (A.30). Here x_1 and x_2 are roots of the equation $g(x) = 0$. The bold arrows symbolize delta functions, satisfying Eq. (A.30).

generalized solutions of the "algebraic" equations

$$f(x)g(x) = 0. \tag{A.30}$$

Here $g(x)$ is some known smooth function. Indeed, according to the sifting property of a factor of the delta function, if $g(x)$ is equal to zero at some point x_0, then the generalized function

$$f(x) = C\delta(x - x_0)$$

satisfies the equation (A.30). Here C is an arbitrary constant. Equation (A.30) and its singular solutions are schematically illustrated in Fig. A.7.

Example 4. As an exercise, it makes sense to verify that the equation

$$f(x)x^n = 0 \tag{A.31}$$

has a generalized solution

$$f(x) = C_0\delta(x) + \cdots + C_{n-1}\delta^{(n-1)}(x), \tag{A.32}$$

where $C_0, C_1, \ldots, C_{n-1}$ are arbitrary constants, and the generalized solution of the "quadratic equation"

$$(x^3 + 2x^2 + x)y(x) = 0$$

is equal to

$$y(x) = A\delta(x-1) + B\delta'(x-1) + C\delta(x),$$

where A, B and C are arbitrary constants. ∎

A.5 Derivatives of discontinuous functions

Apparently, the Heaviside function $\Theta(x)$ (A.14) does not have the ordinary derivative at the point of discontinuity $x = 0$. But there exists the generalized derivative of the Heaviside function. Indeed, the corresponding continuous linear functional has the following form:

$$\Theta(x)[\varphi(x)] = \int \Theta(x)\varphi(x)dx = \int_0^\infty \varphi(x)dx.$$

From here and from the definition of the generalized derivative (A.20), we obtain

$$\Theta'(x)[\varphi(x)] = -\int_0^\infty \varphi'(x)dx = -\varphi(x)\Big|_0^\infty = \varphi(0).$$

The latter means that

$$\Theta'(x) = \delta(x). \tag{A.33}$$

Example 1. Let us find the nth derivative of the function

$$y = e^{\lambda x}\Theta(x).$$

Let us first work out its first derivative. From the Leibniz rule of the derivative of the product of functions, it follows that

$$y' = (e^{\lambda x})'\Theta(x) + e^{\lambda x}\Theta'(x).$$

By using Eq. (A.33) and the sifting property of a factor of the delta function, we obtain

$$y' = \lambda e^{\lambda x} + \delta(x).$$

By differentiating the last equality $n-1$ times more and using similar reasoning, we arrive at the final expression

$$y^{(n)} = \lambda^n e^{\lambda x}\Theta(x) + \sum_{k=1}^{n} \lambda^{k-1}\delta^{(n-k)}(x).$$ ∎

Having worked out the derivative of the Heaviside function, it is not difficult to find the generalized derivative of any piecewise-smooth function $f(x)$, which has discontinuities at points x_k, $k = 1,2,\ldots,n$. It is convenient to represent such a function in the form of the sum of everywhere continuous $f_c(x)$ and piecewise-constant discontinuous components

$$f(x) = f_c(x) + \sum_{k=1}^{n} \lfloor f_k \rceil \Theta(x - x_k). \tag{A.34}$$

Here

$$\lfloor f_k \rceil = f(x_k + 0) - f(x_k - 0)$$

denotes the magnitude of a discontinuity. Decomposition (A.34) of a discontinuous function into the sum of continuous and piecewise-constant components it illustrated in Fig. A.8.

Since differentiation is a linear operation, we have

$$f'(x) = \{f_c'\}(x) + \sum_{k=1}^{n} \lfloor f_k \rceil \delta(x - x_k). \tag{A.35}$$

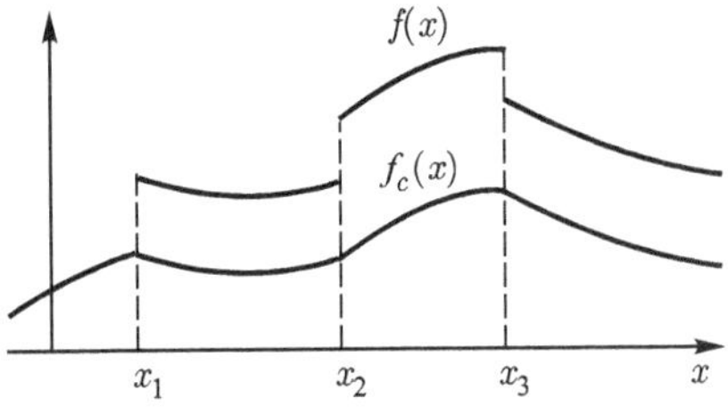

Fig. A.8 Discontinuous function $f(x)$ and the corresponding continuous function $f_c(x)$ obtained from $f(x)$ by elimination of discontinuities.

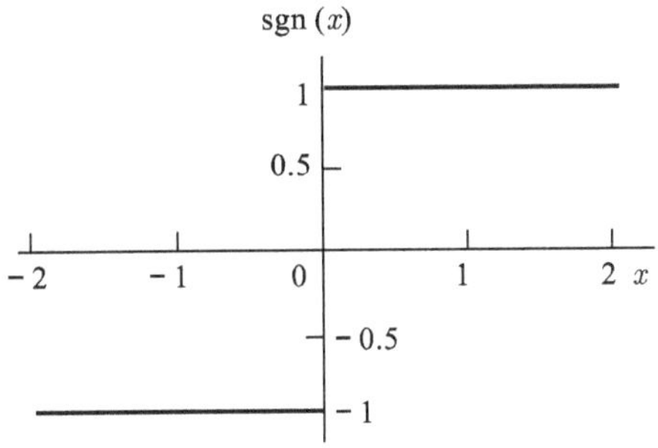

Fig. A.9 One of the most known discontinuous functions — the sign function $\mathrm{sgn}(x)$.

Here $\{f'\}(x)$ denoted a function, which is equal to the derivative $f'(x)$ everywhere, where this derivative exists in the ordinary sense, and supplemented by arbitrary bounded values, where the ordinary derivative does not exist.

It may happen that a certain function has the first $n-2$ derivatives in the ordinary sense, and the $n-1$th derivative has discontinuities, so that the nth derivative exists only in the generalized sense. Before giving a corresponding example, we define another discontinuous function $\mathrm{sgn}(x)$, which will be encountered in the following. By definition

$$\mathrm{sgn}(x) = \begin{cases} +1, & x > 0, \\ 0, & x = 0, \\ -1, & x < 0\,. \end{cases} \tag{A.36}$$

This function, which is sometimes called the *sign function*, is depicted in Fig. A.9. A derivation, similar to the one described above, shows that $\mathrm{sgn}'(x) = 2\delta(x)$.

Example 2. Let us consider the function $f(x) = x^2\,\mathrm{sgn}(x)$. It is differentiable in the classical sense, and its derivative

$$f'(x) = 2|x|$$

exists at all x. This derivative is, however, non-differentiable in the ordinary sense at the point $x = 0$, but it has the generalized derivative. Indeed, it is easy to verify that

$$f''(x) = 2\ \mathrm{sgn}(x), \qquad f^{(3)}(x) = 4\delta(x)\,.$$ ■

A.6 Generalized functions of a composite argument

The reader have already noticed that, while having at our disposal only one singular generalized function, *viz.* the delta function $\delta(x)$, we have constructed many other singular functions, by using the operations of multiplication of a generalized function by a smooth function and differentiation of generalized functions. In this section, we will augment the arsenal of singular generalized functions by means of another operation with generalized functions. As before, we will be guided by the known formulas of calculus, which we express in terms of linear continuous functionals (generalized functions).

Note that (in the case of a continuous kernel $f(x)$) the following integral equality holds:

$$\int f(\alpha(x))\varphi(x)dx = \int f(y)\varphi(\beta(y))|\beta'(y)|dy,$$

where $y = \alpha(x)$ is a given continuous function, and $x = \beta(y)$ is the inverse to $\alpha(x)$ function, i.e. such that $\beta(\alpha(x)) \equiv x$. For this integral equality to be satisfied, it is necessary for the function $\alpha(x)$ to be strictly monotonous, mapping all points of the x-axis onto the y-axis.

Let us use the last equality to define a generalized function of a composite argument. To this end, we require the function $\varphi(\beta(y))|\beta'(y)|$ on the right-hand side of the last equality to belong to the set $\mathscr{D}$. For that, it is necessary for the function $\beta(y)$ to be infinitely differentiable and to map $\mathbf{R}$ onto $\mathbf{R}$. Assuming that these conditions are satisfied, we arrive at the following definition: *the equality*

$$T(\alpha(x))[\varphi(x)] = T[\varphi(\beta(y))|\beta'(y)|] \tag{A.37}$$

defines a generalized function T of a composite argument $\alpha(x)$.

Let us consider a delta function of a composite argument $\delta(\alpha(x) - a)$, where $\alpha(x)$ is such that the inverse function $\beta(y)$ is strictly monotonous, infinitely differentiable and maps $\mathbf{R}$ onto $\mathbf{R}$. Apart from that, a is some constant. Then, as it follows from (A.37), we have

$$\int \delta(\alpha(x) - a)\varphi(x)dx = \int \delta(y - a)\varphi(\beta(y))|\beta'(y)|dy = \varphi(\beta(a))|\beta'(a)|. \tag{A.38}$$

By noting also that $\beta'(a) = 1/\alpha'(\beta(a))$, we rewrite the last equality in the following form:

$$\delta(\alpha(x) - a) = \frac{\delta(x - b)}{|\alpha'(b)|}. \tag{A.39}$$

Here $b = \beta(a)$ is the root of the equation

$$\alpha(x) = a. \tag{A.40}$$

By applying the "inverse" sifting property of a factor of the delta function, i.e. by "reviving" the factor $1/\alpha'(b)$, to the right-hand side of the equality (A.39) we rewrite (A.40) in the following form:

$$\delta(\alpha(x)-a)=\frac{\delta(x-b)}{|\alpha'(x)|} \tag{A.41}$$

or in another, equivalent, form

$$|\alpha'(x)|\delta(\alpha(x)-a)=\delta(x-\beta(a)). \tag{A.42}$$

Example 1. Let $\alpha(x)=cx$, where c is a constant factor. Then the relation (A.41) is transformed as

$$\delta(cx)=\frac{1}{|c|}\,\delta(x). \tag{A.43}$$

This, at first sight, trivial relationship deserves a thorough discussion. First of all, recall the normalization condition (A.6). It can be given an illustrative geometric interpretation. According to it, the area under the (extremely narrow) delta function $\delta(x)$ is equal to unity. Accordingly, the substitution of cx for the argument of the delta function $\delta(x)$, from the geometric point of view, means compression (when $c>1$) of the delta function along the x-axis. As a result, the area under $\delta(cx)$ becomes $1/|c|$ times less than that under $\delta(x)$, in full agreement with Eq. (A.43). Note also that the right-hand side of Eq. (A.43) does not depend on the sign of the multiplier c of the argument of the delta function. Some interpret this in the sense that $\delta(x)$ is an even function. ∎

The general relation (A.39) also has a similar geometric interpretation. In order to arrive at it, we use a geometrically illustrative technique of the "smearing" of the delta-function. It consists in substitution of some element of a fundamental sequence converging to the delta function for the delta function itself. As applied to our case, this technique is reduced to replacement of the functional on the left-hand side of Eq. (A.38) by the following ordinary integral

$$\int \gamma_\varepsilon(\alpha(x)-a)\varphi(x)dx,$$

where the delta function is replaced by the Gaussian function (A.2) with a small value of the parameter ε. Figure A.10 shows a "smeared" delta function of a composite argument $\gamma_\varepsilon(\alpha(x)-a)$, the composite argument itself $\alpha(x)$ and a certain test function $\varphi(x)$. It is seen that, at a small ε, it is possible to replace the composite argument $\alpha(x)-a$ by the linear term of its Taylor series expansion

$$\alpha(x)-a\simeq\alpha'(b)(x-b)$$

in a neighborhood of the root $x=b$ of Eq. (A.40). As a result we arrive at the equality

$$\lim_{\varepsilon\to 0}\int \gamma_\varepsilon(\alpha(x)-a)\varphi(x)dx=\lim_{\varepsilon\to 0}\int \gamma_\varepsilon(\alpha'(b)(x-b))\varphi(x)dx=\frac{\varphi(b)}{|\alpha'(b)|},$$

which is equivalent to the relation (A.39).

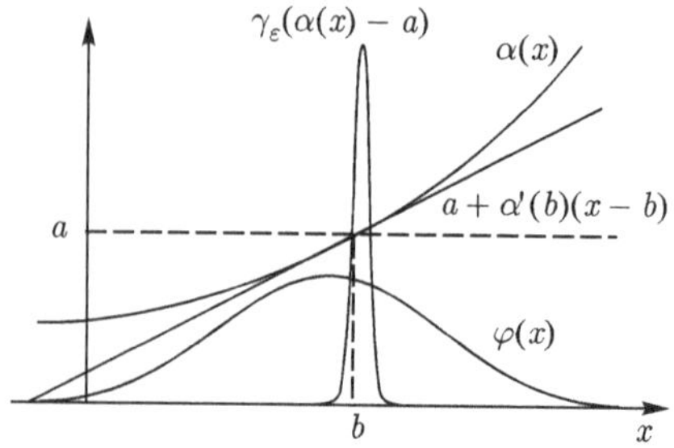

Fig. A.10 Geometric illustration of the relation (A.39).

A.7 Multidimensional generalized functions

Similarly to generalized functions defined as functionals on the real line **R**, generalized functions in the space $\mathbf{R}^n$ are defined as linear continuous functionals on the space $\mathscr{D}(\mathbf{R}^n)$ of infinitely differentiable, compact in the space $\mathbf{R}^n$ function $\varphi(\mathbf{x})$. Analogously, if a function $f(\mathbf{x})$ of a n-dimensional argument $\mathbf{x}=(x_1,x_2,\dots,x_n)$ is locally integrable, it defines a regular generalized function in the space $\mathbf{R}^n$ by means of the multiple integral

$$T[\varphi(\mathbf{x})]=\int\dots\int f(\mathbf{x})\varphi(\mathbf{x})d^n x.$$

Below, in order to avoid unwieldy formulas, we will denote multiply integrals by a single symbol of integration $\int$. Thereby, the dimensionality of a generalized function or the multiplicity of a multiple integral will be clear from the form of the integrand.

Many concepts introduced for one-dimensional generalized functions are, in a natural way, transferred on to the case of multidimensional generalized functions. So, it is not difficult to define the multidimensional delta function $\delta(\mathbf{x}-\mathbf{a})$ by means of its sifting property

$$\delta(\mathbf{x}-\mathbf{a})[\varphi(\mathbf{x})]=\varphi(\mathbf{a}). \tag{A.44}$$

Below, we confine ourselves to a discussion of the properties of the delta function, and multidimensional generalized functions related to it, by using generalized functions in three- and two-dimensional spaces as examples. As in the one-dimensional case, the three-dimensional delta function may be obtained as a weak limit of fundamental sequences of ordinary functions $f_k(\mathbf{x})$ of a three-dimensional vector argument. These elements of a fundamental sequence are sometimes represented as products

$$f_k(\mathbf{x})=g_k(x_1)g_k(x_2)g_k(x_3),$$

where $g_k(x)$ are the elements of a fundamental sequence weakly converging to the one-dimensional delta function $\delta_1(x)$[2]. In this sense, the three-dimensional delta

---

[2] In the following, we will express the three- and two-dimensional delta functions through the more familiar one-dimensional ones. Therefore, in order to avoid misunderstanding, we denote one-dimensional delta functions in multidimensional formulas as $\delta_1(x)$, where the subscript explicitly indicates the one-dimensional character of the corresponding delta function.

function may be interpreted as the product of one-dimensional delta functions

$$\delta(\mathbf{x}) = \delta_1(x_1)\delta_1(x_2)\delta_1(x_3). \tag{A.45}$$

Such a construction of the three-dimensional delta function, however, disguises the important property of *isotropy* of the three-dimensional delta function, which means that it is invariant with respect to rotations in the three-dimensional space. This isotropy becomes more visual, if we take, as the elements of the fundamental sequence weakly converging to the one-dimensional delta function, the Gaussian functions $g_\varepsilon(x) = \gamma_\varepsilon(x)$ (A.8) with $\varepsilon = 1/k$. Their product

$$f_\varepsilon(\mathbf{x}) = \left(\frac{1}{\sqrt{2\pi}\varepsilon}\right)^3 \exp\left(-\frac{r^2}{2\varepsilon^2}\right), \tag{A.46}$$

weakly convergent to the three-dimensional delta function at $\varepsilon \to 0$, depends only on the absolute value $r = |\mathbf{x}| = \sqrt{x_1^2 + x_2^2 + x_3^2}$ of the radius vector $\mathbf{x}$ and does not depend on its orientation. Fig. A.11 shows the two-dimensional version of the function $f_\varepsilon(\mathbf{x})$ (A.46) illustrating its isotropy.

As the next step, we discuss the three-dimensional delta function of a composite argument $\delta(\alpha(\mathbf{x}) - \mathbf{a})$, where $\mathbf{a}$ is a constant vector, and $\alpha(\mathbf{x})$ is a vector function of a vector argument $\mathbf{x}$ defined by its three components

$$y_k = \alpha_k(\mathbf{x}), \quad k = 1, 2, 3\,.$$

If the function $\mathbf{y} = \alpha(\mathbf{x})$ bijectively maps the three-dimensional space $\mathbf{R}^3$ onto $\mathbf{R}^3$ and satisfies the necessary conditions of differentiability, then the following equality holds:

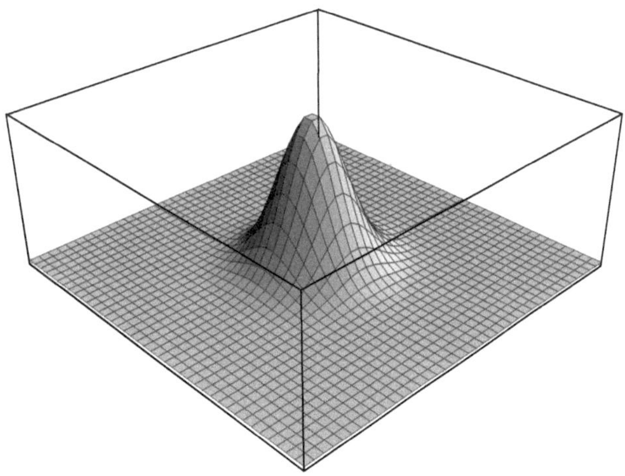

Fig. A.11 Two-dimensional illustration of the isotropy of a multidimensional delta function.

$$\delta(\alpha(\mathbf{x})-\mathbf{a})=\frac{\delta(\mathbf{x}-\beta(\mathbf{a}))}{|J(\mathbf{x})|}, \tag{A.47}$$

where $\mathbf{x}=\beta(\mathbf{y})$ performs the mapping inverse to $\alpha(\mathbf{x})$, and J is the corresponding Jacobian

$$J(\mathbf{x})=\left|\frac{\partial\alpha_k(\mathbf{x})}{\partial x_m}\right|. \tag{A.48}$$

In order to prove the relation (A.47), let us consider the classical formula of change of variables in the three-dimensional integral

$$\int f(\alpha(\mathbf{x})-\mathbf{a})\varphi(\mathbf{x})d^3x=\int f(\mathbf{y}-\mathbf{a})\varphi(\beta(\mathbf{y}))I(\mathbf{y})d^3y, \tag{A.49}$$

which is valid if the Jacobian

$$I(\mathbf{y})=\left|\frac{\partial\beta_k(\mathbf{y})}{\partial y_m}\right| \tag{A.50}$$

is everywhere bounded and not equal to zero. By replacing $f(\mathbf{x})$ in (A.49) by the delta function $\delta(\mathbf{x})$ and using the sifting property (A.44) of the three-dimensional delta function we have

$$\int\delta(\alpha(\mathbf{x})-\mathbf{a})\varphi(\mathbf{x})d^3x=\varphi(\beta(\mathbf{a}))I(\mathbf{a}) \tag{A.51}$$

or, in the symbolic notation,

$$\delta(\alpha(\mathbf{x})-\mathbf{a})=|I(\mathbf{a})|\,\delta(\mathbf{x}-\beta(\mathbf{a})). \tag{A.52}$$

Having further recalled the following identity, well-known from ordinary calculus:

$$I(\mathbf{a})J(\beta(\mathbf{a}))\equiv 1,$$

and the sifting property of a factor of the delta function, which is also valid for multidimensional delta functions, we transform (A.52) into Eq. (A.47).

Example 1. Sometimes it is useful to write Eqs. (A.47), (A.52) in the coordinate representation similar to Eq. (A.45). For instance, the two-dimensional variant of Eq. (A.52) may be written as

$$\delta(\alpha_1-a_1)\delta(\alpha_2-a_2)=I(a_1,a_2)\delta(x_1-\beta_1(a_1,a_2))\delta(x_2-\beta_2(a_1.a_2)). \tag{A.53}$$

Let the function β perform the transformation from the polar to Cartesian coordinates

$$\beta:\quad x_1=\rho\cos\theta,\quad x_2=\rho\sin\theta,$$

and the coordinates of the point $\mathbf{a}$ in the polar coordinate system are equal to (ρ_0,θ_0). In this case

$$I(\mathbf{a}) = \begin{vmatrix} \dfrac{\partial x_1}{\partial \rho} & \dfrac{\partial x_2}{\partial \rho} \\ \dfrac{\partial x_1}{\partial \theta} & \dfrac{\partial x_2}{\partial \theta} \end{vmatrix} = \rho_0,$$

and Eq. (A.53) is transformed into

$$\delta(\rho - \rho_0)\delta(\theta - \theta_0) = \rho_0 \delta(x_1 - \rho_0 \cos\theta_0)\delta(x_2 - \rho_0 \sin\theta_0).$$

By using the sifting property of a factor of the delta function, it is possible to rewrite this expression in the following form:

$$\delta(x_1 - a_1)\delta(x_2 - a_2) = \frac{1}{\rho}\delta(\rho - \rho_0)\delta(\theta - \theta_0),$$

where $a_1 = \rho_0 \cos\theta_0$ and $a_2 = \rho_0 \sin\theta_0$, or in another, equivalent form

$$\delta(\rho - \rho_0)\delta(\theta - \theta_0) = \sqrt{x_1^2 + x_2^2}\, \delta(x_1 - a_1)\delta(x_2 - a_2).$$ ∎

In addition to the above multidimensional delta functions, whose support consists of a single point in space, delta functions, whose supports are curves or surfaces, are also introduced. For example, if σ is a surface in the space $\mathbf{R}^3$, the corresponding *surface delta function* δ_σ is defined by the equality

$$\delta_\sigma[\varphi(\mathbf{x})] = \int_\sigma \varphi(\mathbf{x}) d\sigma,$$

where $\varphi(\mathbf{x}) \in \mathscr{D}(\mathbf{R}^3)$, and the integral on the right-hand side of the equality is a surface integral of the first kind[3]. Similarly, a *curvelinear delta function* is defined, which corresponds to a certain curve ℓ in the three-dimensional space $\mathbf{R}^3$:

$$\delta_\ell[\varphi(\mathbf{x})] = \int_\ell \varphi(\mathbf{x}) d\ell,$$

where, a curvelinear integral of the first kind appears on the right.

In many cases, the notation for the curvelinear and surface integrals is not explicitly used, since it is possible to express such delta functions through certain combinations of "ordinary," one-dimensional delta functions. For instance, the surface delta function, corresponding to the plane $x_1 = 0$, is more naturally interpreted as the one-dimensional delta function $\delta_1(x_1)$. Similarly, the curvelinear delta function, concentrated on the x_3-axis, may be written as the product of one-dimensional delta functions $\delta_1(x_1)\delta_1(x_2)$. In a similar way, the field of a spherical wave, radiated by an instantaneous point source located at the origin, and propagating at a speed c, is expressed through the one-dimensional delta function

---

[3] Naturally, it is also possible to define the surface delta function of the second kind, which is equal to a surface integral of the second kind of a test function.

$$U(\mathbf{x},t) = \frac{A}{|\mathbf{x}|}\delta_1(|\mathbf{x}| - ct),$$

where the amplitude A depends on the energy of the source.

There are also other, useful for solving applied problems, formulas expressing surface and curvelinear delta functions through one-dimensional delta functions. Let us give several such formulas, while omitting bulky derivations.

Let σ be an isolevel surface of the scalar field

$$\sigma : g(\mathbf{x}) = a. \tag{A.54}$$

Here $g(\mathbf{x})$ is some smooth scalar function of a vector argument. By using reasoning similar to that which have led to Eq. (A.42), it is not difficult to prove the validity of the following relationship:

$$\delta_\sigma = |\nabla g(\mathbf{x})|\delta_1(g(\mathbf{x}) - a). \tag{A.55}$$

Here $\nabla g(\mathbf{x})$ denotes the *gradient* of the scalar field $g(\mathbf{x})$, which, in the Cartesian coordinate system $\mathbf{x} = (x_1, x_2, x_3)$, has the following form:

$$\nabla g(\mathbf{x}) = \mathbf{j}_1\frac{\partial g(\mathbf{x})}{\partial x_1} + \mathbf{j}_2\frac{\partial g(\mathbf{x})}{\partial x_2} + \mathbf{j}_3\frac{\partial g(\mathbf{x})}{\partial x_3}, \tag{A.56}$$

and $(\mathbf{j}_1, \mathbf{j}_2, \mathbf{j}_3)$ are the basis vectors of the Cartesian coordinate system.

It is possible to verify the validity of the relation (A.55) by using geometric considerations, *viz.* by noting that the factor $|\nabla g|$ on the right-hand side of (A.55) accounts for the effect of compression (if $|\nabla g| > 1$), which changes the volume under the delta function $\delta_1(g(\mathbf{x}) - a)$.

Similarly, it is possible to explain the origin of the following expression:

$$\delta_\ell = |[\nabla g_1(\mathbf{x}) \times \nabla g_2(\mathbf{x})]|\ \delta_1(g_1(\mathbf{x}) - a_1)\delta(g_2(\mathbf{x}) - a_2) \tag{A.57}$$

for the curvelinear delta function δ_ℓ concentrated on the intersection of the isolevel sufaces

$$\ell : \quad g_1(\mathbf{x}) = a_1, \quad g_2(\mathbf{x}) = a_2. \tag{A.58}$$

In (A.57), $[\mathbf{c} \times \mathbf{d}]$ denotes the *vector product* of the vectors $\mathbf{c}$ and $\mathbf{d}$.

Example 2. Until now we have been discussing *scalar* multidimensional generalized functions, whose arguments were *scalar test functions* $\varphi(\mathbf{x})$ of a vector argument $\mathbf{x}$. In physical applications, one often deals with generalized functions of a vector functional argument $\varphi(\mathbf{x})$. Therefore let us discuss a typical example of such vector three-dimensional generalized functions

$$\mathbf{P} = \delta(\psi(\mathbf{x}) - c)\,\nabla\psi(\mathbf{x}), \tag{A.59}$$

acting on an arbitrary vector test function $\varphi(\mathbf{x})$ in the following way:

$$\mathbf{P}[\varphi(\mathbf{x})] = \int \delta(\psi(\mathbf{x}) - c)\,(\nabla\psi(\mathbf{x}) \cdot \varphi(\mathbf{x}))\,d^3x. \tag{A.60}$$

Here $(\mathbf{a} \cdot \mathbf{b})$ denotes the *dot (scalar) product* of the vectors $\mathbf{a}$ and $\mathbf{b}$.

It is easy to uncover the geometric meaning of the generalized function of a vector argument introduced above, by noting that

$$(\nabla\psi(\mathbf{x}) \cdot \varphi(\mathbf{x})) = |\nabla\psi|\,(\mathbf{n} \cdot \varphi),$$

where

$$\mathbf{n}(\mathbf{x}) = \frac{\nabla\psi(\mathbf{x})}{|\nabla\psi(\mathbf{x})|}$$

is a vector orthogonal to the isolevel surfaces of the function $\psi(\mathbf{x})$. Thus, according to the relation (A.55),

$$\mathbf{P}[\varphi(\mathbf{x})] = \int_\sigma (\mathbf{n} \cdot \varphi)\,d\sigma,$$

where σ is the isolevel surface $\psi(\mathbf{x}) = c$. In other words, from the physical point of view, $\mathbf{P}[\varphi(\mathbf{x})]$ is nothing else, but the flux of the vector field $\psi(\mathbf{x})$ into the domain, where $\psi(\mathbf{x}) > c$. ∎

A.8 Continuity equation

A.8.1 Singular solution

Let us discuss an, at first sight, unexpected, but important for physical applications, example of the use of the delta function for solving partial differential equations.

Let us consider a one-dimensional gas of moving particles. Let the velocity of a particle located at the point x at the current moment of time t be equal $v(x,t)$. If the velocity field $v(x,t)$ of the particles is known, the law of motion of the particles can be found by solving the nonlinear differential equation

$$\frac{db(t)}{dt} = v(b(t),t), \tag{A.61}$$

where $b(t)$ is the coordinate of the particle at the moment of time t. By ignoring the inner structure of the particle, we assume that the size of the particle is negligibly small, so that it may be considered as a mass point having the singular density

$$\rho(x,t) = m\delta(x - b(t))\,, \tag{A.62}$$

where m is the mass of the particle. Let us derive the equation, which is obeyed by the singular density of the particle. For that, we differentiate both sides of Eq. (A.62) with respect to t. As a result, we have

$$\frac{\partial\rho}{\partial t} = m\frac{\partial}{\partial t}\delta(x - b(t)).$$

According to the chain rule of differentiation of a function of a composite argument, we have

$$m\frac{\partial}{\partial t}\delta(x - b(t)) = -m\frac{db(t)}{dt}\frac{\partial}{\partial x}\delta(x - b(t)).$$

By taking then the equation of motion of the particle (A.61) into account, we arrive at the following equality:

$$\frac{\partial\rho}{\partial t} + m\, v(b(t),t)\frac{\partial}{\partial x}\delta(x - b(t)) = 0. \tag{A.63}$$

Since the factor $v(b(t),t)$ in the last term does not depend on x, it can be moved under the sign of the derivative

$$v(b(t),t)\frac{\partial}{\partial x}\delta(x - b(t)) = \frac{\partial}{\partial x}v(b(t),t)\delta(x - b(t)).$$

Next, by taking into account the sifting property of a factor of the delta function, we can write

$$v(b(t),t)\delta(x - b(t)) = v(x,t)\delta(x - b(t)).$$

As a result, Eq. (A.63) is transformed into the following form:

$$\frac{\partial\rho}{\partial t} + \frac{\partial v(x,t)\rho}{\partial x} = 0, \tag{A.64}$$

where ρ is the singular density (A.62) of the mass point.

Recall that Eq. (A.64) is well known as the (one-dimensional, in this case) *continuity equation*. It occupies the central stage in physics of continuous media and deserves an additional comment. The derivation of the continuity equation given above shocks many physicists, since this equation is traditionally derived from the law of conservation of mass of a continuous medium, while ignoring its atomistic structure. Our derivation, however, shows that the continuity equation remains valid also for the singular density of each separate atom of a gas.

A.8.2 Green's function

Apart from the physical significance of the singular "microscopic" solution (A.62) of the continuity equation (A.64), this solution plays an important part also from the mathematical standpoint. Let us demonstrate this by discussing the solution of Eq. (A.64) supplemented by the "classical" initial condition

$$\rho(x,t = 0) = \rho_0(x), \tag{A.65}$$

where $\rho_0(x)$ is a smooth function, which we represent in the following form:

$$\rho(x,t=0) = \int \rho_0(y)\delta(x-y)dy. \tag{A.66}$$

Let us go back to the singular solution (A.62) of the continuity equation, while omitting the mass of the particle, but writing the solution itself in a more detailed form

$$g(x,t,y) = \delta(x-b(y,t)), \tag{A.67}$$

which explicitly depends on the initial coordinate of the particle:

$$b(y,t=0) = y. \tag{A.68}$$

As it follows from the previous discussion, the function $g(x,t,y)$ satisfies the Cauchy problem

$$\frac{\partial g}{\partial t} + \frac{\partial vg}{\partial x} = 0, \quad g(x,t=0,y) = \delta(x-y). \tag{A.69}$$

From here, in view of the relation (A.66) and linearity of the continuity equation, it is possible to write the solution of Eq. (A.64) with the smooth initial condition (A.65) as

$$\rho(x,t) = \int \rho_0(y)g(x,t,y)dy. \tag{A.70}$$

Thus the singular density $g(x,t,y)$ (A.67) is nothing else, but *Green's function* of the continuity equation.

Keeping in mind the specific singular form (A.67) of Green's function of the continuity equation, it is possible considerable to progress in understanding the properties of the solution to the continuity equation. To this end, let us substitute (A.67) into (A.70). As a result, we obtain

$$\rho(x,t) = \int \rho_0(y)\delta(x-b(y,t))dy. \tag{A.71}$$

Let us transform this expression by means of Eq. (A.42) for the delta function of a composite argument, according to which

$$\delta(x-b(y,t)) = j(x,t)\delta(y-a(x,t)). \tag{A.72}$$

Here $y = a(x,t)$ is the function inverse to the function $x = b(y,t)$, and

$$j(x,t) = \frac{\partial a(x,t)}{\partial x} \tag{A.73}$$

is the (one-dimensional) Jacobian of the mapping $y = a(x,t)$ of the x-axis onto the y-axis. By substituting (A.72) into the right-hand side of Eq. (A.71), we obtain

$$\rho(x,t) = j(x,t)\int \rho_0(y)\delta(y-a(x,t))dy.$$

By using the sifting property of the delta function on the right-hand side of last equality, we finally obtain

$$\rho(x,t) = \rho_0(a(x,t))\, j(x,t). \tag{A.74}$$

A.8.3 Lagrangian and Eulerian coordinates

Recall the traditional hydrodynamic terminology. According to it, the coordinate x of a particle in a certain stationary coordinate system, is called the *Eulerian coordinate* of the particle. Thereby the initial coordinate y of the same particle is called its *Lagrangian coordinate*. Both Lagrangian and Eulerian coordinates define the spatial position of the particle. Thereby, if a stationary observer prefers to characterize the position of the particle by its Eulerian coordinate, another observer, who moves along with the particle, it inclined to indicate its Lagrangian coordinate. Such an observer is like a person, who prefers to tell his place of birth, but not his last address.

In this terms, the function $j(x,t)$ (A.73), appearing in Eqs. (A.72), (A.74), represents the Jacobian of the Eulerian-to-Lagrangian coordinate transformation.

We are now ready to comprehend the geometric meaning of the expression (A.74). It means that the density $\rho(x,t)$ of a certain continuous medium is proportional to its initial density $\rho_0(y)$ in a neighborhood of that particle, which, at the current moment of time t, finds itself at the point with the Eulerian coordinate x. Accordingly, the Jacobian $j(x,t)$ of the Eulerian-to-Lagrangian coordinate transformation accounts for variations of the density of the medium, caused by deformations of an infinitesimal domain, "frozen into" the medium and containing this particle.

A.9 Method of characteristics

In this section, by the example of the continuity equation, we discuss the basic ideas of the *method of characteristics*, effective in solving partial differential equations of the first order. In the case of the continuity equation, this method is especially illustrative, since the trajectories of particles of a medium serve here as characteristics.

A fruitful approach to solving a mathematical problem consists in trying to reduce it to a simpler, well-studied problem. Figuratively speaking, one retreats in order to leap forward and gain new results. A typical example here is the method of characteristics, consisting in replacing partial differential equation with more familiar ordinary differential equations. In order to achieve this in relation to the continuity equation, we rewrite it as

$$\frac{\partial \rho}{\partial t} + v\frac{\partial \rho}{\partial x} = -u\rho, \tag{A.75}$$

where

$$u(x,t) = \frac{\partial v(x,t)}{\partial x}. \tag{A.76}$$

We solve Eq. (A.75) along with the initial condition

$$\rho(x,t=0) = \rho_0(x).$$

Recall that a solution of any partial differential equation represents a function of several independent variables. In the case of the density field $\rho(x,t)$, these are the spatial coordinate x and time t. In the method of characteristics, it is assumed that all these variables depend on one common parameter, chosen so that the original partial differential equation would turn into an ordinary differential equation. For the continuity equation, it is convenient to choose time t for such a parameter assuming that the spatial coordinate x is a function of time $x = b(t)$. Indeed, as it follows from the chain rule, if $b(t)$ satisfies the equation

$$\frac{db}{dt} = v(b,t), \tag{A.77}$$

the left-hand side of Eq. (A.75) turns into an ordinary derivative with respect to time, and the continuity equation it transformed into the ordinary differential equation

$$\frac{dR}{dt} = -uR \tag{A.78}$$

for the function of a single argument $R(t) = \rho(b(t),t)$.

The system (A.77)–(A.78) of ordinary differential equations is called *characteristic equations*. In our case, each of these equations plays a qualitatively distinct role. Solutions of the first of them (A.77) define the *characteristics*, i.e. the trajectories, $x = b(t)$ in the plane (x,t), of particles constituting the medium. And the second equation (A.78) describes density variations along the characteristics (trajectories of particles).

By supplementing Eq. (A.77) with the initial condition

$$b(t=0) = y, \tag{A.79}$$

we fix the point on the x-axis, from which a characteristic departs, i.e. the point where the particle starts its motion. Accordingly, the initial condition of Eq. (A.78) must be the value of the initial density $\rho_0(x)$ at the same initial point y, so that

$$R(t=0) = \rho_0(y). \tag{A.80}$$

From the standpoint of hydrodynamics, the initial condition (A.79) fixes the Lagrangian characteristic of the particle. Whereas the equation (A.78) determines the evolution of the density in the vicinity of the particle with a given Lagrangian coordinate y, and represents the *continuity equation in the Lagrangian coordinate system*. Hence the solution

$$R = R(y,t), \quad x = b(y,t) \tag{A.81}$$

of the Cauchy problem (A.77)–(A.80) describes the behavior of the density field in the Lagrangian coordinate system.

However, for solving many applied problems, it is more important to know the density field $\rho(x,t)$ in the Eulerian coordinate system. The problem is that, at a fixed y, the field $R(y,t)$ determines the density of the medium at the points with the Eulerian coordinates $b(y,t)$, which might not coincide with the Eulerian coordinate x of the observation point. A typical such situation is depicted in Fig. A.12.

The situation is saved by the fact that by varying the Lagrangian coordinate y, we obtain a *family of characteristics*, one of which ends up at the point x at the current moment of time t. Mathematically speaking, knowing the mapping $y \in \mathbf{R} \mapsto x \in \mathbf{R}$, given by the formula $x = b(y,t)$, one needs to find the inverse mapping $y = a(x,t)$, determining the Lagrangian coordinate of the particle, which finds itself at the point x at the moment of time t. By substituting the inverse mapping into the expression for $R(y,t)$, we obtain the sought-for density field

$$\rho(x,t) = R(a(x,t),t)$$

in the Eulerian coordinate system.

Evidently, the solution of the continuity equation (A.78) in the Lagrangian coordinate system has the following form:

$$R(y,t) = \rho_0(y)\exp\left[-\int_0^t u(b(y,\tau),\tau)d\tau\right]. \tag{A.82}$$

Accordingly, the Eulerian density field is given by the expression (A.74), where, according to (A.82), the Jacobian (A.73) of the Lagrangian-to-Eulerian coordinate transformation is equal to

$$j(x,t) = \exp\left[-\int_0^t u(b(y,\tau),\tau)d\tau\right]\Bigg|_{y=a(x,t)}. \tag{A.83}$$

In conclusion, let us discuss another, simpler than (A.78), equation in the Lagrangian coordinate system

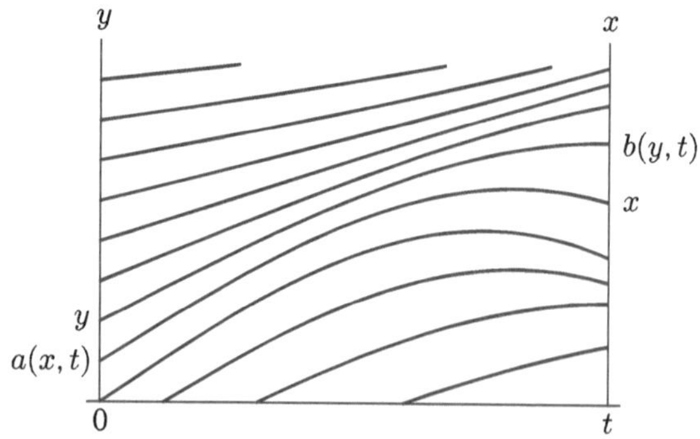

Fig. A.12 A set of characteristics of the continuity equation mapping the Lagrangian coordinates into the Eulerian ones, and vice versa.

$$\frac{dC}{dt} = 0, \tag{A.84}$$

supplemented by the initial condition

$$C(y, t = 0) = c_0(y). \tag{A.85}$$

The solution of this equation in the Lagrangian coordinate system

$$C(y, t) = c_0(y)$$

is independent of time. Nevertheless, the field corresponding to it in the Eulerian coordinate system

$$c(x, t) = c_0(a(x, t)),$$

which describes, e.g., the behavior of an *impurity concentration* of a continuous medium, is not so trivial. The corresponding equation in the Eulerian coordinate system has the following form:

$$\frac{\partial c}{\partial t} + v\frac{\partial c}{\partial x} = 0. \tag{A.86}$$

Obviously, the solution of the last equation with the initial condition $c(x, t = 0) = c_0(x)$ can be represented in the "integral" form

$$c(x, t) = \int c_0(y)\delta(y - a(x, t))dy \tag{A.87}$$

similar to (A.71)

Let us also note that Eq. (A.84) is an obvious corollary of the mathematically more important Cauchy problem

$$\frac{\partial y}{\partial t} + v\frac{\partial y}{\partial x} = 0, \quad y(x, t = 0) = x \tag{A.88}$$

with respect to the Eulerian-to-Lagrangian coordinate transformation $y = a(x, t)$.

Example 1. Let us find the fields of density and passive impurity concentration of a medium, whose velocity depends on the distance to the origin of the coordinate system according to the linear law $v = \gamma x$, while assuming that the initial density and impurity concentration are equal to $\rho_0(x)$ and $c_0(x)$, respectively.

Note, first of all, that the corresponding Lagrangian-to-Eulerian coordinate transformation and its inverse are equal to

$$x = b(y, t) = ye^{\gamma t}, \quad y = a(x, t) = xe^{-\gamma t}.$$

By substituting them into Eqs. (A.71), (A.87), we obtain

$$\rho(x, t) = \int \rho_0(y)\delta(x - ye^{\gamma t})dy = e^{-\gamma t}\rho_0(xe^{-\gamma t}),$$

$$c(x,t) = \int c_0(y)\delta(y - xe^{-\gamma t})dy = c_0(xe^{-\gamma t}).$$

At $\gamma > 0$, the density field, with time, decreases to zero; whereas the concentration becomes everywhere constant and equal to $c_0(0)$. If the total mass of the impurity is bounded and equal to m; then, at $\gamma < 0$, the density weakly converges to the delta function $m\delta(x)$, and the concentration converges to the so-called "needle-shaped distribution," which is equal to zero at all $x \neq 0$ and to a value of $c_0(0)$ at the origin $x = 0$. ∎

Index

N-wave, 120
U-wave, 120

absolute maximum principle, 196
absorption rule, 64
acoustic time, 109
acoustic wind, 360

Burgers equation, 153

Cauchy distribution, 444
characteristic equations, 5, 467
characteristics, 467
coherence length, 358
compact function, 441
conditions of physical realizability, 64
conjugate space, 441
continuity equation, 8, 464
continuity equation in the Lagrangian coordinate system, 467
continuous functional, 442
convex hull, 55, 76
critical parabolas, 54, 125
curvelinear delta function, 461

del operator, 189
derivative of a generalized function, 449
detonation wave, 77
diffusion, linear, 134
dissipation-density field, 112
divergence of a flow, 7
dot product, 463

E-Rykov-Sinai principle, 60
envelope, 75
Eulerian coordinate, 4, 466

family of characteristics, 468
forces, gravitation, 21
functional space, 441

Galilean invariance, 86
general Leibniz formula, 451
generalized function, 441, 442
generalized function of a composite argument, 456
generalized solutions, 39
ghost field, 80
global principle, 60
gradient catastrophe, 44
gradient of a scalar field, 462
Green's function, 465
groups, 257

Heaviside function, 446
Hopf-Cole substitution, 102
Hubble expansion, 90

impurity concentration, 469
infinitely differentiable compact functions, 441
integral equations, 39
irreversible physical processes, 77
isoclinic line (trajectory), 18
isotropy of the delta function, 459

Kardar–Parisi–Zhang (KPZ) equation, 84
kernel of a functional, 441
KPZ equation, 101

Lagrangian coordinate, 4, 466
Lagrangian coordinate, averaged, 104
Lax-Oleinik absolute minimum principle, 53
Leibniz formula, 451
length scale, 89
Lie groups, 257

linear continuous functional, 441
linear functional, 441, 442
lithotripsy, 332
lithotripter, 369
local connection with the properties of a flow, 22

Mach number, 109
maximum principle, absolute, 196
method of characteristics, 466
momentum, conservation of, 107
mother function, 445
multiscale signal, 136
multistream motion, 42
multistream solutions, 42

noise, 160
nonlinearity, types of, 271
normalization condition of the delta function, 443

peculiar velocity, 90
plane wave, 335
point of overturning, 45
polytropic gas, 106
potential field, 202
potential, localized, 119
product of a generalized function and an ordinary smooth function, 450

ray, fire line, 14
reflection symmetry, odd, 86
regular generalized function, 442
regularization of equations, 83
resonance, 389
Reynolds number, 88
Reynolds number, acoustic, 88
Reynolds number, current, 94
Reynolds number, self-similar solution, 99
Reynolds number, singular initial condition, 97
Riemann equation, 3
right-sided functions, 446

sawtooth wave, 123, 124, 309
scalar multidimensional generalized function, 462
scale invariance, 88
scale-invariant function, 443
self-action, 357
self-focusing, 357
self-similar solutions, 95
sifting property, 442
sifting property of a factor of the delta function, 451
sign function, 455
simple wave equation, 3
single-valued solution, 46
singular generalized function, 442
smooth function, 450
sound-speed field, local, 106
space of test functions, 441
stationary waves, 92
support of a function, 441
support of a generalized function, 443
surface delta function, 461

tangent line, 56
test function, 441
thermal smoothing, 48
tilt-angle field, 16
triangular solution, 100

unit step function, 446

vector product, 462

wave-overturning time, 42
weak convergence, 444
weak dispersion, 358
weak solutions, 50

FSC
www.fsc.org
MIX
Papier | Fördert gute Waldnutzung
FSC® C083411

Kolibri 360 GmbH
Ferdinand-Jühlke-Straße 7
99095 Erfurt, Deutschland
produktsicherheit@kolibri360.de